THE STAR-GAZER

ZSOLT DE HARSANYI

The Star-Gazer

TRANSLATED FROM THE HUNGARIAN

by

PAUL TABOR

G · P · PUTNAM'S SONS

NEW YORK · MCMXXXIX

I

I

UNDER the Ponte Vecchio stood a young man absent-mindedly tearing a sheet of paper into strips, which fluttered away, borne on the waters of the Arno—a young man who meant to kill himself.

For a long time he had thought of suicide. At first a stale weariness had come over him; gradually the thought had taken shape. Then he had made up his mind: he was going to kill himself. His life seemed finished at twenty-three. He could so clearly see himself already a corpse that it did not seem to him to matter much exactly when he drew the noose of the rope he kept hidden at home. A few days more or less! He felt as though mere indolence had prevented him from dying, either yesterday or the day before.

But this very slackness, this weary idleness which loathed the thought of having to live, had prolonged his life again and again. He was so used to his own incapacity for action that he felt curious to observe: would his will ever gather enough strength to make the decisive effort and do this thing which his mind had considered in all its bearings? Yet not even this curiosity was alive in him. Even that made him shrug his shoulders. What use was anything!

The clear green river was now muddied into yellow by the autumn rain; it flowed with the heartless indifference of the infinite, bearing the tiny paper scraps to destruction. He was going to die the day after tomorrow, or maybe in the next half-hour. The flowing river made him remember his life, from its baby memories: A yard in a house in Pisa where he had played in the sand with the neighbors' children. Sometimes a grain of sand looked very beautiful, sparkling, catching the sun like a great diamond. Deeply entranced, he watched the miracle, waiting till the invisible grain of sand began to glitter again, and then lost its glory. The other children could not understand what he was looking at; they jeered at him and pushed him about.

His father's shop, a draper's shop, with strange musty-smelling bales of cloth, with brocades and silks; an empty shop, and his father sitting in the corner playing some old tune on his lute. The little boy stopped

3

in the doorway to listen. He could not tell why the music filled his heart with such peaceful sweetness . . . and then, in the yard outside, the raucous, vehement, complaining voice of his mother. . . .

Later they had moved from Pisa to Florence. His parents had seemed never to stop quarreling; sometimes they had quarreled all night long. It still brought a little boy's terror into his eyes to think of those two quarreling grownups: his mother, with wildly rumpled hair, shouting and stamping about the room, quite out of control; his father, with a deathly pale face and eyes moist from helpless rage, standing there motionless. He had grown up to the tune of such scenes, and often the neighbors had crowded in on them to protest against the fiendish din. . . . He and the younger children had run away to hide in the corner, as though they were frightened of being trampled on. . . .

His thoughts moved to the friendly village of Vallombrosa: The pealing of an organ in the monastery, with its stone flags and whitewashed walls—a fairy-tale world of music and incense, ruled by the fat, eternally smiling abbot, Don Orazio Morandi, whose favorite pupil he was. Hours of exciting and happy study, of discoveries in geometry and arithmetic, of the Greek verb, the Latin *accusativus cum infinitivo*.

It had been a time whose magic could never return. In his young mind the unutterable delight of learning had fused with the mysterious ecstasy of confession and holy communion. He had made up his mind to be a monk and had already entered the novitiate, when his father had come and taken him back to Florence, saying curtly that he should never be a priest. Long days of grief and pining for the happiness of monks, hours of secret weeping in the dark, while the healthy snores of his sisters and his one brother filled the night around him.

Then Pisa again: The university, where his father had sent him to study medicine. The noisy japes of wretched student lodgings; the pride of the student's gown; the pillared university courtyard, crowded with students; the numbered doors of the lecture rooms on the open corridor. . . . Lectures on Galen which wearied and sickened him, and dead bodies whose stink pursued him even in his dreams. Then suddenly another world of magic, opened to him by Ostilio Ricci, tutor to the little Medici prince—the amazing world of algebra and geometry. . . . Even the young man about to die smiled at the memory like a dreamer, sitting, just awake, on the edge of his bed. That had been a time worth living, eager and exuberant in its demands and joys! When the ducal tutor saw the quick wit of the draper's son, he began to give him private lessons. Not that it was necessary to teach, as he soon perceived. He had only to show his pupil this or that, and then lend him Euclid's book. The lad could not tear himself away from it, his pleasure in it was so keen. From a Sunday night to a Tuesday morning he could not manage to put it down. "One hour more," he kept on saying to himself, "and then another, and then a last one," till, half-asleep, he slid off his chair, pulling the candle along with him, and only by sheer luck not setting the house on fire. He questioned everyone who might tell him something about Euclid. Had this amazing Greek worn a beard? Had he lived to be old? Had he any family? Was he a cheerful fellow? Or not? But Galileo found out very little. Even Ostilio Ricci knew scarcely anything about Euclid's life, and there was nobody else at the university to whom he could turn. His professors of medicine, whose lectures he shamefully neglected, frowned upon him. So he wandered about the streets of Pisa, with his head full of delightful geometrical shapes, sitting to rest by the Arno and scribbling with a twig in the dust the Pythagorean theorem of the rectangular triangle, which obsessed him. All his thoughts were haunted by Euclid, the unseen hero of his dreams.

And then—the miracles of algebra! One could use letters instead of quantities. What a triumph of the human mind! The ancients said: "Add any two numbers, and multiply the sum by two, the result will be the product of twice the first number added to the product of twice the second." This was true. Multiply the sum of three and five by two; the result is the sum of six and ten. Or multiply four and six by two; the result is the sum of eight and twelve. One could demonstrate with a million examples. But these Arabs simply used letters which could be made to stand for any quantity; and what other people put into so many words, their algebra expressed like this: $2(a + b) = 2a + 2b$. This was immensely clever, witty, and practical. No *commedia dell'arte* was so enthralling; he had not read the most fascinating of Boccaccio's tales with half such eager curiosity as the heroic tale of how the cubic equation had been solved. For a long time no one could solve the cubic equation. The great scientist, Luca Paccioli, announced that mankind would never solve it. But Scipione dal Ferro did! Dal Ferro would not share the secret with anyone but his favorite pupil, who had to take a solemn oath to tell nobody. He guarded the mystery faithfully, just as a famous painter keeps to himself the mixtures of powdered stones and plants and different oils which compose his coloring. All over the world armies of scientists were struggling with letters, formulae, complicated processes. And thirty years later the stuttering Niccolò Tartaglia found out for himself; he could put into writing a formula which reduced cubic equations to child's play. And then, like a thief attacking a man who has found a diamond, the jealous, covetous Cardano stole Tartaglia's treasure, robbed him of his solution. His pupil, Ferrari, could solve even equations of the fourth degree!

The imagination of other students was fired by the deeds of arms of ancient heroes. They admired Alexander the Great, Leonidas, or Julius Caesar. But this young man dreamed of the learned, of those scientists and mathematicians who battled with the mysteries of theorems, pushed on into the undiscovered territory of a new potential with desperate adventurous content, sometimes doing battle to the death for the Golden Fleece of an unknown formula. His whole being revolted against the trade his father had chosen for him. He loathed Galen, Hippocrates, and all the rest, was sickened with weariness by the jumbled and chaotic science of the human body's "humours." In this teaching all was uncertain and contradictory. In his own beloved study all was clear, certain, radiantly exact.

But then a new ideal came into his mind. He became a disciple of Aristotle. Even medical students were made to study that ancient sage, but at first the young man had scarcely troubled about him. Only later had he been impelled by the magic of algebra and geometry to want to know something about physics. And so at last he made up his mind —he would die sooner than be a doctor! He had not the least wish to learn the secrets of human beings; but he longed to know the secret of all else—of the whole universe. "Space and time are eternally divisible." The sheer greatness of this conception brought tears to his eyes. The man who dared write such a thought was greater than any pope or king; a man whose mind had power to raise him from off the earth, from the central point of the whole cosmos, into blue infinity, thence to proclaim the truth which shall solve everything, past, present, and future. Such a man is almost equal to God.

He pored over the eight books of Aristotelian physics. He wanted to know about matter, movement, weight, water, sound, heat, and—to see it all. He would stand in the middle of his room letting a stone drop to the floor a hundred times, and a hundred times he would pick it up again. He raised his arm; the stone fell with a loud clatter; he watched it entranced and dropped it again. His eyes were wide as though he were seeing God. Wherever he could find two vessels he poured water from one into the other, using all conceivable variants of height and speed. He filled his pitcher with water, placed it in a basin, and let stones fall into it. He pushed and knocked, measured and dropped, piled up or stood in water—everything. In fact, he behaved like a lunatic; and every night, after praying to the Saviour and the saints of Holy Church, he prayed to Aristotle. Yet, being a godless youth, he did not waste much time on prayers.

Aristotle was the fundamental truth, the Alpha and Omega of knowledge. All that the human mind could ever conceive had been born in the cool alley of the Temple of Apollo at Athens where the sage walked among his pupils. Every argument began with and returned to him. The faith of men was given to the Holy Trinity, but their minds could belong only to Aristotle. Wherever in the world there was disputation, whatever language the arguers used, it sufficed to throw into the argument the authority of the Peripatetic genius: αὐτὸς ἔφη. He said it. No need to name him; that settled the matter.

Till then he had accepted Aristotle as a being second only to God, because his teachers had so instructed him. But in Pisa he realized it consciously. He was like a nun seeing the Virgin Mary. And it was then he began to watch the stars. . . .

He also arrived at a double turning point in his life. A deep cleft opened between him and his father—and the same cleft separated him from Aristotle. Both had been terrible experiences.

The father was firm in insisting that he should become a doctor. But when the elderly draper came over to Pisa to see his son, Galileo blurted out his decision. The older man laughed at first, then, seeing the strength of his son's resolve, became afraid and tried to use his authority. They were sitting drinking in a tavern. The Chianti had loosened his father's tongue.

"You're almost a man now; I can talk to you about such things. But no . . . what I wanted to say . . ."

"Say it, sir. You want to talk about my mother."

His father nodded, a little confused and red in the face:

"Perhaps it's wrong, but I'd better say it. Your mother is a very good woman, only—it was the devil gave her his temper. You may not realize."

"Of course I realize. At home we children used all to discuss it among ourselves. When I came to Pisa the thing I liked most was being away from home, our horrible home. I hope you aren't angry, father; but that was how we were always talking among ourselves . . ."

"A nice thing to have to listen to!"

"You mustn't mind it, father. You're so kind and gentle we'd follow you to the end of the world. But she . . ."

His father, a poor and careworn man, the last of an old Florentine family but now a struggling draper, nodded and took a deep draught of the red wine:

"Poor thing, she can't help it! If you're born with yellow hair, who can blame you for that? Nobody! She was born with her temper. . . . But sometimes I can't bear it any longer. Tell me, where am I to find joy? Apart from music, which I love, only in my children. You are my first-born, my greatest hope. Your sisters will marry and go to live with strangers in strange families. But you two, you and your brother Michelagnolo, carry on my name, which used to be noble, and now is tarnished and humbled by shameful poverty, through no fault of mine! Michelagnolo hasn't many brains; he'll never understand anything except music."

"But, father, perhaps he . . ."

"No, don't interrupt! You know it just as well as I do. He'll grow up to be a musician, and glad enough to snatch a bare living. Whereas you! . . . Ever since I taught you to read and write, all your masters have said they'd never had such a clever pupil. Why don't you use your gifts to help your father?"

He had drunk a good deal—already his tongue was beginning to stumble over the quick Tuscany speech; yet he was still sober, and it was plain that he meant what he said and was opening his heart to his son.

"Listen, father," said Galileo. "I want to ask you something. What made you marry mother?"

"I fell in love with her."

"And you wouldn't have married anyone else?"

"No—though, God knows, they wanted me to make many a rich match. But I only desired the Ammannati girl. I used to follow her like a sleepwalker. You see, Galileo, your mother was a very beautiful girl. . . ."

"I know she was; you can still see it. So you wouldn't have married anyone else, sir, because you loved her. You see, it's just the same with me. I can choose no other career except philosophy, because I'm in love with it. No use to offer me anything else! Riches? Glory? This is the only thing I want. I love it like a woman."

"Like a woman—but how do you mean?"

"Yes. You see, I'm eighteen. Other students, even the poorest, are already thinking about marriage. I never think about it. I've never been in love, and I can't imagine I ever shall be. All the others find a pretty Bianca or Lucia. I have only my science. I blush when they talk of it. My heart quickens whenever I begin to think that soon I'll be sitting at my desk to draw parallaxes."

"Parallaxes? What's that?"

"Listen, father! Have you ever traveled in a fast coach?"

"Indeed I have."

"Well, if you looked out of the side window, you thought that the trees along the road were all moving in the opposite direction. . . ."

"Yes. And then?"

"But did you notice the distant hills, far beyond the trees, almost on the horizon? They don't seem to move against the coach. And yet they don't remain motionless. They look as if they . . ."

"Yes, yes," his father interrupted him. "They look as if they were going the same way as the coach. But why shouldn't they? It's quite natural."

Galileo had not expected such an answer. He glanced with delighted surprise at his father, at this poor little draper who had never said a word to him about science. The old man answered his surprise with a wise, rather melancholy smile:

"I see that surprises you. You ought to have remembered where you get your brains. Not from your mother; she isn't clever, only very strong and violent, like the earth when it quakes. She gave you the strength which I never had. But I gave you your talents, Galileo! Others know that, though you may not. I'm a man of parts, who promised much, but whose wings were clipped. I might have gone far. No need to ask me in what—I'll tell you: in music!"

He fell silent again, and the boy dared not look straight at him. He felt that his father was about to open his heart, but he knew that he would shrink back into himself at a single inquisitive look or word. It was like some rare bird on a branch, and he dared not move for fear of frightening it. So he pulled out his clay pipe and began to fill it with great care. He waited till his father said:

"My son, I've a real gift for music in me. You should know that about your father. I'm not the kind of musician who tinkles pretty tunes for ladies. I know music as a science, as a system, as a complicated wisdom. I know it so well that I've written a long book about it, full of wholly original ideas. With God's help, it may get printed. If you think, you'll see that music and mathematics were born in the same part of the human mind. Mathematics always came to me easily. Do you understand?"

"Perfectly," answered the boy, lighting his pipe and puffing excitedly.

"I look at you, and I see my own talents. I remember how once I wanted to live only for music and philosophy, for the wise and beautiful things in which men delight. I didn't do it, son. I opened a shop, to keep my family, and I can only dream sometimes of what I wanted. It hurt me at first, no use denying it. But there's nothing we can't manage to get accustomed to. You have your mother's strength. If you want to, you can conquer yourself. Be wise, Galileo, be rich and successful! And then you can follow your inclinations and do your work at the same time—just as I wrote my book on music."

The boy shook his head.

"I simply can't become a doctor! All you've done, sir, is to argue against yourself. Father, you have talents but no strength. But I have both! Why shouldn't I try to get what I want? I'll become a great scholar and get a professorship. I can live on that. And I'll live better than anyone else. Because I'll be a more famous scientist than anyone ever has been yet! Listen, that thing we started talking about, the parallaxis . . ."

"No, son, we're long past that! What if I never get to know what a parallaxis is? It's more important to talk about you. How do you mean to become a great scholar? It takes a long time and a lot of money. It's sad to say it, the saddest thing a father can tell his son: I haven't the money for it."

The boy looked up, startled. Something had entered his life which he never had considered before.

"You haven't the money?" he repeated in a puzzled voice.

"No, my son. But, of course, you never thought of that. Your parents have paid for you and said nothing. But now you must hear. We're very poor, the shop is going from bad to worse, and there seems no hope of better times. The weavers are asking more and more, and money is scarcer every day. I have to sell everything below cost. Perhaps I can hold on till you take your degree, but only by stinting your sisters and brother. How can I wait till you're a famous professor of mathematics and physics? It isn't possible."

Silence, till the father repeated, more firmly, though his voice was more calm:

"It isn't possible."

Then they were silent again, till the boy said:

"I'd rather die than be a doctor."

"That's easy said. But how can I keep you, without the money?"

"Father, listen! There are plenty of poor students with bursaries from the university. They get money from the ducal house. Why shouldn't I get a Medici bursary? You have so many friends in Florence who like you and will do what they can. Perhaps you could arrange it at Court. They would only have to ask Ostilio Ricci, the Duke's tutor, who knows who I am and what I can do. . . . "

He gazed imploringly at his father, whose eyes, clouded with wine, lit up:

"Now you're talking sense. That's a good idea."

Galileo snatched his father's hand and shook it hard; persuasively he drew his chair up close:

"I beg you, sir; I implore you to try to do this. Try everything! There's only one way I can show my gratitude. I . . . I promise to become a great scientist . . ."

"You're a good boy," his father answered, made sentimental by the wine.

Galileo embraced his father passionately, clumsily. They kissed each other. They were talking thirteen to the dozen; soon neither of them knew what he was talking about. They scarcely noticed how and when they left the tavern.

Next day the father was ashamed and silent. Yet, somehow they could revive the idea of the bursary, and when the older Galilei left he silently agreed to suspend his decision about his son's career.

About that time a student called Rossi came to the University of Pisa. He came from Padua, where he had been mixed up in some love affair; he was afraid that the brother of the seduced girl would kill him. He studied medicine and could not abide mathematics. Galileo met him in the corridor of the lecture hall. They started to talk about Padua, and Rossi began to complain and bewail the ill fate which had forced him to leave it. He was full of praises of the "Bo."

"Bo? What's that?" Galileo asked.

"That's our name for Padua University. Long ago there was a tavern standing on the site of the university, or close to it, I can't say which, and its sign said: 'Al bove'—'At the Sign of the Ox.' The name stuck. Professors, students, even the townspeople, call Padua University the Bo. The Bo . . . ah, Dio mio!"

He almost wept. He spoke about the Padua customs, the splendid fights with the scholars of the Jesuit school, the miracles of near-by Venice. He dropped some notebooks which he was carrying under his arm. And, when he picked them up indifferently, Galileo saw mathematical formulae on the scattered sheets.

"What's this?" he asked eagerly.

"Notes of Moletti's lectures. But I don't need them now."

"Who is Moletti?"

"Don't you know? The mathematician of Padua. He is famous elsewhere too. But I can't do with mathematics. Give me diseases!"

But Galileo was already reading the notes. Only scattered sentences; yet they held his interest at once.

"Couldn't you lend me these?"

"You can keep them."

He took them, and began to read in the street on his way home. Moletti, the Padua mathematician, said astounding things; he attacked the divine Aristotle! He asserted that, though he had been a great philosopher, not all his statements could be accepted. He had often been wrong! For instance, his axioms on mechanics were full of mistakes.

The boy reading in the street stopped in amazement and consternation. It was just as if he had read that there was no God. At home he sat down at his table and shook his head. A turbulent anger filled his soul at such blasphemy. But some irrepressible urge forced him to continue with his reading. When he had finished, he went for a walk. It wasn't a walk; soon it had become a run. The chaos in his mind drove him on, like a broken-down, clumsily working mechanism.

"Aristotle maintains that the velocity of falling objects differs according to their weight; that is, a piece of lead drops quicker than a piece of wood. This is not true. The velocity of a falling piece of lead and that of a piece of wood are equal."

It was this small detail which made the greatest impression on his mind. He tried to picture the falling lead and the falling wood, and watch them closely. But this was no use; these mental pictures were not precise enough. He could not solve the problem like that. He tried ten times, without success. Angrily he shook his head, as though he wanted to shake his own slow mind. He set the question again. Which fell quickest? There was no answer. Then he looked around and felt his pockets. He drew out the key of his room. He stood still in the midst of his senseless hurry, in the center of the Piazza dei Cavalieri, holding the key; he stared at it helplessly, stupidly, and then looked about for a piece of wood of exactly the same shape. People turned to stare at the gaunt young man who seemed to be crazy, hurrying aimlessly, with a key held out in front of him and a look of madness on his face.

He rushed home. He had a chest at his lodgings full of all kinds of rubbish—iron rings, screws, wooden balls, files, string, a mysterious copper cone, a thimble, a bell jar, nails. He found two apparently equal articles: an iron cylinder and a wooden cube. He took one in each hand and let them fall together. But he couldn't be sure whether they touched the floor at the same time. He had dropped them too close to it. He set a chair on the table, climbed up, and let them fall again from there. Again he could not properly time their fall. They had rolled away. He jumped down and picked them up again, climbed up on the table again, and started afresh. After he had done this five times, he sat down at the table and, resting his head on his arms, began to think.

All that night he scarcely slept. Next day he spent the whole morning slinking around the Palazzo Bottonie, till at last he could filch a stone ball from the wall surrounding it. This he carried to a turner, whom he ordered to make him a wooden ball of exactly the same dimensions. It was ready next day. Galileo went to the university and dropped the two balls from the open gallery onto the marble flags of the yard. But the experiment failed. He couldn't drop them exactly at the same time, nor measure whether the crash of their fall sounded simultaneously. And, if not, which of them touched the flags first? He was soon surrounded by grinning fellow students. Finally one of the proctors came along and shouted at the student Galileo for ruining the pavement of the quad.

But he went on stubbornly experimenting. He read the Moletti notes again and again, was tortured by thoughts, fighting tooth and nail for Aristotle and yet horrified to see how, against his will, his doubts increased.

Since his childish experiments had been useless, he sought the defense of his hero in books. His greatest trust he placed in Cardano, the mathematician. Cardano's references led to other books. After Cardano, Pietro Pomponazzi, then the works of Nizzolio, Patrizio. But when he discovered the books of Telesio he was shocked to find that the godlike Aristotle was besieged by a thousand questions and taken to task by all these authors.

His chief trouble was that he had nobody to ask. He was unpopular, he could never stop arguing—passionately, aggressively, impatiently. He disliked his fellow students because they scoffed at him and were interested in other things. There was no faculty of mathematics or physics in Pisa. Often he sighed for Padua, where Moletti could have answered his questions, or for Bologna, where the famous Cataldi taught mathematics. Here in Pisa, Cesalpino, the professor of medicine, was his teacher. And Cesalpino disliked him. No professor likes a student who cuts his lectures, and the dislike increases when the student does not try to hide his lack of interest in the subject. And, though Galileo sometimes came to lectures, he was apt to ask inconvenient questions, the answers to which seemed never to satisfy him; and he argued impudently.

While this storm of doubt was raging furiously, his father came to see him again. He came with a grim face, bringing bad news—the ducal Court had refused the bursary. There was room enough in the Medici college, where forty students were being maintained; but the professors had not sponsored the petition. In vain had Ostilio Ricci, the ducal tutor, used all his influence. His professors reported that the student Galileo Galilei was idle, argumentative, and impudent, and not fit to receive a ducal stipend. There were many other diligent young men, regularly keeping their lectures, blindly accepting their teachers' opinions. They deserved scholarships, full board, freedom from cares. Not so Galileo.

Father and son were sitting together again. But not in the gay, intimate mood of the night at an inn spent drinking Chianti. This was a rainy winter morning; they shivered and sat grimly facing each other, their tempers frayed.

The father tried not to look at his son:

"I'm not even going to reproach you. It would be no use. I can only tell you the truth. The shop is going from bad to worse; I'm almost broken with the cares of it. How shall I ever find dowries for your sisters? I was earning my bread at your age, and you idle here and rob your brother and sisters of the little I have."

"I don't idle! I study, I torment myself, searching for truth. . . ."

"That sounds very fine! But your family must eat, mustn't they? For the last time I ask you to settle down to medicine. It's your only hope of earning enough while you're still young. You're my eldest child, and I'm ailing already. When I'm dead and you're the head of the family, how are you going to face your duty?"

"By that time I shall be a famous scholar. And, father, I refuse to consider your death. . . ."

"A famous scholar!" His father made a weary gesture. "Never mind about that! Arguments would be wasted on you. This is my last word, and now I'm going back to Florence. Either you come home at the end of this term to tell me you've made up for lost time and will soon be qualified as a doctor, or you'll have to be a draper like me. If you won't do that I'll wash my hands of you! You can go as a soldier or row in the Venetian galleys for all I care!"

Galileo began to plead:

"Father, I might have been a monk—but you prevented it! And now you want to prevent this too. . . ."

The older Galilei became impatient. "I can't see what it is you're after! What do you want? What *is* a scientist?"

"Well, I want to be a university professor. I know that doesn't bring in much, but it'll be enough for me because it will bring me fame and glory. And I want to be famous. I want to make our family famous . . . our name, which I'm so proud of, father . . . What is it? Why do you look at me so strangely?"

His father crossed himself and said:

"God forgive me, but sometimes your poor mother has just such a look in her eyes, as though she were mad. And now I see the same look in yours. . . ."

Galileo snatched his father's hand. He would have liked to tell him how much he loved him, get close to his heart. He turned to this haggard, weary man with the warm sweetness of a child. But the old man snatched his hand away and stared at the wall.

"Let's leave all that." He sounded like a stranger, almost an enemy. "We'll say no more. You're causing me too much sorrow."

They parted thus in morose estrangement, both nursing a defiant grudge. Had his father gone from him warmly and tenderly, Galileo might have done his best to conquer his inclination—though not for long. That would have been quite impossible. As it was, he did not even try. Not one medical lecture did he attend. He amused himself by making fantastic drawings of strange contraptions, cranes, and weighing machines. He was lost in the pleasures of thought; and, if he remembered sometimes that he was on a short reprieve, he forced himself to think of something else.

Once in the course of an aimless walk he happened to enter the Campo Santo. He looked vaguely at the three buildings on the square—he knew them so well that he could have drawn them with his eyes closed. On the left the Baptistery, a round building with carved white semicolumns, and above them a row of smaller pillars; the huge white marble Cathedral with all its galleries and arcades; and on the right the surprising Leaning Tower of white carved marble, like the others, but daringly, almost crazily, beautiful, with the fantastic beauty of sugar-ice. It was as though someone had dreamed that a tower was bending in the wind. Suddenly this idle student felt an urge to enter the Cathedral.

Inside the organ was being played; yet a gang of workmen were going about their business undisturbed. Buckets of lime, rafters, and ladders were stacked beside the west door. They were setting up a monument to Archbishop Rinuccini, who had died last year. People were standing about in the center nave staring upwards; they were watching the builders, who had just finished fixing the great lamp, clinging to the walls of the dome. Either they had renewed its chain or strengthened its rivets in the ceiling. Anyhow, it was still swinging in a calm, slow arc.

The good-for-nothing student became alert. His mind, which had for years been trained in such exercises, began to ask questions.

Why did the lamp swing? Because it had been moved from its original position. This, Aristotle had explained in his work *De Motu*. But suppose he had not dealt with the matter; suppose there had never been an Aristotle; suppose that . . . Galileo Galilei, student of Pisa, had never read him? What would he say? For believers, a motionless lamp was one among many; for a young scientist, it was a weight suspended on a chain. This weight longed to fall. It was the personification of stubborn and ceaseless longing to fall, never quiet for a moment, forever tugging at its chain, hoping it would break—but not having the strength to break it. It hung there struggling with the chain, demanding silently day and night to be allowed to fall down. This stubborn urge had probably worn out the former chain; possibly they had changed it for a new one to prevent the threatening wish of the lamp from being fulfilled.

What had happened then? The workmen had set the lamp in motion.

They had tilted it from its motionless vertical tugging. But they could not change its ambition. The lamp was still determined to fall. But the chain held it up with the same obstinacy; it never allowed the lamp to increase its distance from the ceiling beyond the chain's length. Two opposing desires. Their strength and stubbornness were equal. Which would win? Neither; they struck a bargain. And now the lamp, which had been set swinging and so had had its distance from the earth increased, longed to be back in the perpendicular because that was the nearest it could get to what it desired. The chain was protesting that the lamp must not be allowed to get nearer the earth than its length permitted. At present they were fighting it out; the swaying lamp swung an equal distance beyond the lowest point and began again its downward striving. The swing of the pendulum was getting shorter and shorter; the two enemies were beginning to come to terms. In the end they settled their dispute with a precision possible only in nature, and perfect only in natural law; the lamp had come as near to the earth as it could, persisting in the effort to reach it by its sheer weight; while the chain attained its end of not letting the lamp fall any lower.

A numbing amazement caught at the heart of the staring young man— that strange excitement with which we perceive truth; the birth-pangs of a new idea. He wanted to shout his joy, to cry "eureka" to the whole world. With the discipline of a trained mind he tried to formulate what he had seen: "The swing of a pendulum is the relationship between freedom to fall and a restraining force." Let someone take away the restraint, cut the chain—there would be freedom to fall, and the lamp would crash to the stone floor. But, if this was so, those truths for which one searched in two freely falling bodies could also be studied in the pendulum; only its restraining force must be deducted. So that, if Galileo Galilei, who ought to have been attending a medical lecture, wanted to find out whether lead and wood took the same time to reach the ground, or fell unequally—all he had to do was to make two pendulums of the same length, fasten lead to the first and wood to the second—and then watch whether their swinging was done in equal time. Watch, that is to say, whether Aristotle was right or Moletti.

He ran out of the Cathedral all the way home. He found the wooden ball and the stone, which would do for lead. But he needed a tall

wooden frame and enough string to make two long pendulums. He had
no money to buy anything. So back again into the street, either to borrow a little money or somehow get hold of what was required. He must
get these things even if it meant killing someone.

Next day the two pendulums were hanging in the yard of his house.
He had climbed an olive-tree to fix the horizontal board. On this board
he hung the two long pendulums; one of them carried the wooden ball,
the other the stone one, close together. He paused and took a deep breath
—and waited, like a jealous lover hesitant on the doorstep, not daring to
move, afraid of what he will see inside. Then with both hands he grasped
the two balls hanging down almost to the ground and ran back as far as
the strings permitted. Carefully, slowly he let them go at the same time.
They started on their swinging paths, and he watched them with shining
eyes. The two balls touched the lowest point at exactly the same second;
they swung equally to the other side, stopped at the same height in the
air, and returned like twins. It was a long time before their diminished
swinging came to rest and they hung motionless. But now there was a
tiny difference in their settling into complete stillness. Yet Galileo did not
mind. He threw up his hands; there must have been a slight difference in
the suspension—one string was rubbing against the board more than the
other. . . .

The squint-eyed maid sang in the kitchen. The steps of people in the
street, the distant rumble of wheels, drifted through the silence. Spring
sunlight flooded the yard. There stood the young man watching these
balls. He almost wept, he felt so shaken. He had proved Moletti, refuted
Aristotle! His heart beat wildly.

After that he gave much of his time to pendulums. His eyes saw pendulums in everything which hung and swayed. The hanging tassel of a
curtain, a pretty woman's golden earrings, swinging as she went to church,
a child sitting on a swing—for others they were tassels, jewels, or swings;
for him only pendulums. The wavy, swinging line of the pendulum's
movement was inscribed deeply in his soul. When he saw in a book the
picture of a hanged man, this too was a pendulum, a weight dangling
from a rope, swinging when the wind moved the corpse. Others might be
horrified at the sight and avert it with the sign of the cross; he saw in it
only another proof that Aristotle had been mistaken.

This absurd young man who never came to lectures got a bad name in the university. His professors saw in him a godless ne'er-do-well.

And then the future, whose disturbing thought he tried to exclude, became the present. Time passed with fatal speed, in reading, in disputes, and experiments, till suddenly there came a day when reality met him face to face. He would have to leave Pisa. His father had stopped sending him money. His student days had come to an end. He had no excuse for staying on there. It was long since he had attended a medical lecture. He showed no progress in philosophy. He had not been promoted, had attained no academic rank; his family had every reason to consider the money spent on his training as completely wasted. Had his father asked what he had been doing all this time, he could only have answered: I read, I argued, and I experimented.

But Vincenzo did not even ask. At home nobody spoke of his career; it went without saying that this failure must earn his keep behind the counter. He went home, found a place in the overcrowded house, was glad to see his brother and sisters again; bowed his head to fate. But, even if he did not speak to anyone, his heart rebelled against being a draper. At first he made up his mind to work hard and willingly and yet continue to read, explore, and study . . . till one fine day he would jump out of this draper's shop like a cherry stone through the fingers of a playful child.

He started work on the day after his return. His father explained to him at length where everything was and what the prices were. At first he even enjoyed his work. The different fabrics amused him; he gazed at the patterns of the brocades as though they were pages of a picture book, stroked the velvet and silk, fingered the pleasantly thick cloth. He could still remember many things from his childhood, and was quick to learn how to handle the scales and use a yardstick. He remained gay and alert. In the first days he even brought customers, since gossip spread that the son of Vincenzo the draper had come back from Pisa University, and many inquisitive people wanted to look at him.

But he realized at the end of the first week that it would be difficult to go on living like this. He could not adapt himself to his family. From morning to night the house was full of noisy strife. His mother was more wildly shrewish than ever. Terrible furies dwelt in this heavy woman. All day long she railed at one or another of her children, even when things were going well. And when she had had her fill at home she would go off to visit one of the neighbors and come back with the proud boast of having "spoken her mind" to her wretched hostess. But sometimes she would wake in a fit of spleen, and then there was no staying under one roof with her. Any trifle would provoke her to wild rage, to shouting, throwing things about, rushing up and down like a woman possessed, with her graying hair hanging over her forehead, the glint of hell in her restless eyes, on her pale lips. Her family looked on helplessly. The storm passed; mother had eased her mind, was suddenly gay. Now she adored them all, almost throttled in a fierce embrace the daughter whom a moment ago she had chased with the carving knife. The maid whom she had beaten five minutes before was kissed, caressed, and helped to sweep up the mess of the broken crockery. And then her mistress would snatch up a garment, a book, or a piece of Venetian glass, and rush to take the gift to the neighbor whom she had mortally wounded the day before.

The return of Galileo brought new fuel to her flame. For the first two days she welcomed him with exaggerated love. She kept kissing him, stroking his hand, complaining about everyone else. But on the third day she picked a terrible quarrel with him. He was an idle hog, she bellowed, standing in the doorway, pouring out epithets on his head. After that he became her favorite target. When her fit was on her she rushed to the shop to storm and rave at the useless wastrel, or the weak father who could not rule his son—and all this in front of customers.

This thundery air was equally trying to all the others; they all lived in an atmosphere of gathering storm. And soon there was strife between his father and Galileo. Every night the student locked himself in the shop and read his books there in peace and solitude. But this brought their quarrel. The father stayed out late one evening with friends. He came back long after midnight, to see light through a chink in the shutters. Fearing a thief, he entered and found his son, who had constructed a model of a water-carrying machine out of small wheels and stray bits of wood. He had needed some water for his experiment, and had spilled it over two lengths of cloth. This began their first serious quarrel. It was only the first.

He had not been four weeks at home before his father turned him out of the shop, saying he would never be any use in it. Galileo remained an idling wastrel; at meals either eloquent silence or the broadest hints made it all too plain that he had not earned his daily bread. His sisters tittered and whispered about him; little Michelagnolo fidgeted and grinned at his end of the table, staring with all an urchin's unholy joy at his big brother being humbled. Galileo sought refuge in his books from shame, poverty, loneliness, and the family bickerings. He went to Ricci, the ducal tutor, and borrowed books from him. Even this proved humiliating. His mother would snatch up one of these volumes whenever she needed something to put under a pot or pitcher. And so Galileo had to take back stained leather tomes, and try to placate an indignant scholar. His mind was always full of experiments, but he had no room to carry them out. There was no cupboard in which he could lock his implements; his sisters and brother were always pilfering and wrecking his screws, handles, and wheels. He had to go out if he wanted to read in peace.

Just then his mind was full of Archimedes. Archimedes' life had been so interesting! He tried to imagine him in the flesh, and the story of the golden crown unfolded like some thrilling play. He could see King Hiero sending for his learned kinsman, Archimedes, and putting the golden crown into his hand: "Can you find out whether the rascally goldsmith has mixed any base alloy with pure gold? But you must tell me without spoiling my crown with a single scratch!" The sage asked for time to think it over and went home. He pondered the task day and night. Then, when he was having a bath, suddenly the thought had come to him: every object submerged in water loses as much of its weight as is equal to the weight of water supplanted. Overjoyed, he ran stark naked into the streets calling wildly to the citizens of Syracuse: "Eureka! Eureka!" He had found a method to discover the secret of alloys by calculating their weight, using water scales. He was able to answer the king's question. Then he invented the screw propeller of ships, and later the laws of the balance of levers. He calculated the circle's circumference by its diameter; he constructed catapults; when the Roman soldier broke into his house, trampling out a complicated geometrical pattern drawn in the sand, Archimedes shouted at him, "Don't disturb my circles!" And died on a sword.

But strength of soul was not enough. Galileo's position became more and more impossible. He crept home like a beaten puppy, slinking in by the back door. Meals had become so difficult that he preferred to miss them altogether and stay out on the hills. Better go hungry than feel they grudged him his food. His mother railed at him every day; his father simply would not speak to him. His hopes for the future slowly faded. He began to drink, because wine was a ready way to numb his grief. But, since he had no money for drinking, he was forced to cadge small loans from old acquaintances or steal from the till of the draper's shop. When he was drunk his hopes flowered suddenly; but next day, with a bitter taste on his tongue and an aching head, he found all far worse again. He grew frayed spiritually; his physical condition was no better. His eyes became sunken, his skin thick. He was shabby now, and he had no money to buy himself clothes. He was too ashamed to ask his father.

And so at last he had decided to kill himself. Here he stood at the foot of the Ponte Vecchio, watching the river as it flowed. As the ripples passed him he said good-by to them . . . and to his life.

"What a pity!" he thought.

He stared into the water. After all, why shouldn't he drown himself? He would jump in, and then what would happen? His imagination, which he wanted to force to see his death struggle, would not obey; his thoughts at once became scientific. He thought how much lighter his body would become in the water, losing as much of its weight as that of the supplanted mass. Man was scarcely denser than water, so you had to subtract a great deal from the weight of a submerged human body. Therefore, if someone filled himself up with air, he could float on the water like a bagpipe. Archimedes could have measured the exact quantity of air and matter in such a drifting man. Only it would have been a little complicated. . . .

The youth about to die suddenly started. A tremor ran through him. A spark struck in his mind, but was gone instantly. He strove to recapture it.

"What was it?"

He said it aloud. And tried to start all over again on the trail he had already blazed. Oh, yes: I was thinking that one could construct scales which would measure the proportion of the weight of double alloys without harming them. Suppose you prepare a cube of gold and copper . . . this cube could be measured on ordinary scales and then under water. After that you could take an equal cube, but of pure copper, measuring it above and under water . . .

In the next moment the young man was running across the bridge. People meeting him in the row of goldsmiths' booths might have called: "Stop, thief!" He crossed the bridge, passed the house of Machiavelli, and turned off toward the Palazzo Pitti. He was out of breath. Gasping, he told the two halberdiers at the gate that he must see the Honorable Ostilio Ricci at once. It was an urgent matter of life or death!

He was lucky; the ducal tutor happened to emerge from the Boboli gardens alone, with a book in his hand.

"What is it, Galileo?"

"Your Honor, I . . . I've invented a . . . a . . ."

"Take your time, my son. Get your breath first. What have you invented?"

"Hydrostatic scales. I can measure exactly the proportion of different metals in an alloy. . . ."

Before Ricci could reply, Galileo had seized his hand and shaken it. Sobs of released tension racked him.

"Your Honor . . . I don't know . . . Your Honor . . ."

He stuttered and wept with burning excitement, staring at the dignified, bearded old gentleman. Ricci tried to soothe him.

"Well, well, pull yourself together! Come to my room. You'll be calmer by the time we get there."

They climbed the stairs. A few minutes later Galileo sat down at the table and made a quick, jumbled sketch of the new scales.

"I'm sorry if the drawing is untidy, but it's the first time I've put it to paper. I thought of the whole thing, just now . . . on the bridge. . . ."

Ricci looked at the drawing, deep in thought.

"Amazing. You've invented a magnificent thing, my son. I wasn't disappointed in you, after all. Now you'll have to prepare a model of this and . . ."

"How, Your Honor, how? I'm a beggar; even my boots have holes in them."

"Here you'll find everything you need. We'll call someone who can help you. I'll expect you tomorrow at the same time, but bring me a neat and precise plan."

"I've no paper left, Your Honor. And even my compasses are smashed."

"Oh . . . I see. Well, prepare the drawing here. But you can't go on like this. I must speak to your father. Now go, I'm busy. Can you leave the drawing?"

"Oh, yes, I have it in my head."

He ran all the way home. His younger brother, Michelagnolo, was out playing in the yard.

"Where have you sprung from, Galileo?"

"The grave; but I've come back, Michelagnolo," he laughed, and ran on into the house.

II

The young scientist without a job did not die. The hydrostatic scales were made according to his plans. A neat, pretty instrument, it worked without a hitch. The ne'er-do-well rose at once in his family's esteem. Ostilio Ricci had a long talk with the draper, and encouraged him warmly to have a little patience with the boy; his was an exceptional talent, and sooner or later would be a great one. Vincenzo grumbled and complained. Times were so bad! But at last he capitulated. He would go on waiting a little longer. Let the boy study and read; things would work out somehow in the end. The new scales were set up in his shop. All Florence had heard of this strange new contraption invented by the draper's son. Customers all wanted to see it, and the father exhibited and explained it with a certain pride. He ordered a new doublet for his son and even bought him a pair of boots.

There was another pair of these scales in the rooms of Ricci, the ducal tutor. He, too, displayed them, but not to commoners. Galileo now had free entry to the Palazzo Pitti; the halberdiers let him pass unquestioned. He knew the way up to Ricci's apartments, and on the stairs, as he joyously hurried to his patron, had often to make way for such grand personages as hitherto he had seen only in public—remote and almost supernatural beings. Often he found courtiers with Ricci, all of whom were kind to him.

Ricci impressed it upon him how important were these new acquaintances. He knew the extent of everyone's influence, what connections this or that man possessed. One day he told Galileo excitedly:

"Now, my son, show us your best! Do you know who I'm expecting? Vittorio Cappello."

Galileo blushed. He, too, was aware how much a personal meeting with Vittorio Cappello could mean; all Florence knew the immense power of this proud, handsome, ostentatiously pleasure-loving man.

The Cappellos were Venetian nobles. Old Cappello had a daughter, Bianca, so beautiful that when Titian saw her he instantly longed to paint her portrait. Bianca was not yet seventeen when she fell deeply in love with a young Florentine, Bonaventuri, a poor nobleman, working as an underpaid clerk in the Venice bank of the Salviati. The windows of the Palazzo Cappello faced the bank. When old Cappello perceived that his daughter's head had been turned by this miserable bank clerk, he told her plainly that he would kill her rather than see her married to such a man. But the young lovers were not so easily restrained; they became secretly engaged. There was no hope for their love in Venice, so they fled one day and came to Florence, where the boy's parents were living in poverty. It was a terrible scandal. The nobles of Venice swore revenge and death to the Florentine adventurer. The Cappellos offered a reward of two thousand gold ducats to whoever killed Piero Bonaventuri. But they only managed to catch his uncle, and even him they imprisoned in the famous Piombi. Bianca lived obscurely in Florence with her husband, in a mean house. Piero's mother was bedridden; they were too poor to keep a servant. Bianca, the dreamy beauty, did all the housework. But gradually everything was forgotten. Venice had apparently forgiven the whole thing. Three years passed. And then one day it happened that Prince Francesco de' Medici, the eldest son of the Grand Duke, a young man of twenty-two, glanced up at a window as he walked across a Florence square. There stood Bianca, and her loveliness dazzled the young prince. A few days later he managed to meet her, declared his love, fervently besieged her heart; but Bianca would not even hear him. Piero was the man to whom she had given herself. Nothing would have availed Francesco de' Medici if he had not found a very useful ally in Piero himself. This husband was sick of poverty and even a little tired of his lovely wife. So he tried to persuade Bianca not to be too hard on the prince. Bianca began to hate the man to whom she had sacrificed her youth. And now the Prince found her less obdurate. She became his mistress, and remained faithful to him. For dynastic reasons Francesco had to marry Joan of Austria; but all the time he loved only Bianca. His neglected wife soon died, and the Prince, who meanwhile had become Grand Duke, decided that his second marriage should be according to his heart. So he married Bianca. The despised heroine of a scandal was now the Grand Duchess of Tuscany; and Venice, which had abused and slandered her, hurried now to fête her with solemn pomp.

Bianca's brother, Vittorio Cappello, settled down in Florence, where he soon became hated by the whole town; he warmed himself haughtily and daringly in the sun of the love between husband and wife. But, though hated, he was also feared, because he understood revenge. He counted as the most powerful man at Court.

"Be careful," Ricci said. "If you gain his favor you've made your fortune."

They waited nervously and soon heard the approaching steps of the favorite. Vittorio Cappello entered Ricci's room. They welcomed him with deep bows, and when they straightened it excited them even more to see that he was not alone. Beside him stood Bianca Cappello.

"Good morning, Ricci," said the Grand Duchess. "My brother tells me you've something interesting to show us."

"Yes, Your Highness . . . and by a coincidence the young inventor is here as well. May I most humbly present . . . Galileo Galilei."

Young Galileo flushed to the ears, and muttered something half-inaudible. He tried to make a deep obeisance, but was clumsy enough to upset a glass bowl from the table. What ought he to do? He was paralyzed with nervous fear. He bent down to pick up the shattered pieces, and when he rose he saw the others smiling at him, but not in scorn.

"Well, let's see it," Vittorio drawled. "What *is* this invention?"

"With your kind permission, the young man will explain it himself."

Ricci signed to Galileo, who took a deep breath . . . and then two more; some heaviness seemed to choke him and prevent his speaking. He coughed and began:

"I ought to begin with the story of Hiero, King of Syracuse, and Archimedes. . . ."

He told this story. With the first words his numbing embarrassment fell away. He was a natural speaker, and liked explaining things. From time to time he glanced from the Grand Duchess to the favorite. But he soon saw that only Bianca was really interested. Vittorio only nodded absent-mindedly from time to time. He drummed on the table. But Bianca's attention never wavered. And this deeply moved young Galileo.

Bianca was then forty-four. But the fire in Galileo's eyes brought back an answering look of youth into the eyes of this mature woman. Bianca's beauty was no legend. Many people said that she was loveliest now that she had almost begun to fade. Above her perfect white forehead her hair, dressed in the cunning fashion of the age, looked auburn and chestnut brown at the same time; her eyes were very blue, and her full sensitive lips a living red. But her snow-white skin was her chief beauty—skin as alive and delicate as a breath, as soft as velvet, which maddened the eyes straying upon its surface down to her breasts, where the gown hid them— and dreaming the rest. While Galileo talked on vividly to this beauty, he suddenly knew that his hand was shaking as it touched the scales, that his mind was empty; he did not know what he was saying or what he had said a moment ago. He could only stare at this crowned perfection, silent like a man seized by sudden dizziness. But Ricci noted his confusion. He came quickly to the rescue, and finished the improvised lecture. Bianca laughed:

"I didn't understand it all, but I can see that it's all extremely interesting, especially . . ."

Galileo swallowed hard and waited in agony. But now Vittorio interrupted, touching the sleeve of his sister's pearl-embroidered gown.

"Bianca, we're already late."

"Yes, we must go," she answered quickly. "Thanks to you for your charming lecture, Maestro."

The tutor and Galileo again bowed low. They looked up to find the vision gone. The light sound of her steps outside . . . or did they only think they heard . . . ?

For several days Galileo's thoughts were in confusion. Then he knew that he was in love with the wife of the ruling Prince of Florence. He had never known what loving meant. While other boys ran after wenches, he had read and hankered for new machines and played with geometrical designs. Now he longed for a friend to talk to. He had no such friend; his whole childhood had been lonely, and his boyhood too. He was so much cleverer than his fellows that he found their stupidity a torment; he could argue with them, but never talk. His elders disliked him at the first glance; they considered him impudent, swollen-headed, and disrespectful. Ricci was perhaps closest to him; but he was a courtier; he would have been the first to laugh at this ridiculous love. So he bore the sweet torment in his heart and spoke to nobody. The only outward sign of this secret madness was the eagerness with which he led the talk to the subject of the Grand Duchess Bianca. But he gave that up because soon he noticed that most Florentines hated and cursed the woman of Venice. They blamed her for Vittorio, whom she allowed to meddle with politics so that he had his fingers in every pie, leading the Prince, who cared for nothing except his chemical experiments, into all kinds of foolish policy. He was the curse of Florence.

"But wait till Cardinal Fernando returns from Rome," his father said one night at supper. "He'll show them! That'll be the end of the witch! And that brother of hers who loads us with taxes."

Fernando was the younger brother of the Grand Duke. Being a younger son, he had no hope of succeeding to the throne and had chosen to be a priest. He might still possibly become Pope, like the other Medici, Leo X. And the "witch" was Bianca. The people of Florence were convinced that she was a *jettatrice,* a sorceress, the Devil's leman, who deserved to burn in front of the Signoria, where Savonarola had died in flames.

Galileo did not try to defend her. He was terrified of letting them see his love. Slowly he ceased even to speak of her. He locked away his crazy thoughts, this love which was like faith, with no other object save the joy of worship.

His dreams did not make him idle. He found a new field for his exploits in the works of Archimedes. The epitaph of the Syracusan caught his fancy at the first reading—it was drawn up by the great scientist himself long before his death. Three geometrical figures had to be carved on the stone, all three of them of equal height: a cone, a hemisphere, and a cylinder—and below them only the figures: 1 : 2 : 3. This meant that the volumes of these three geometrical bodies were in this relation to each other. Galileo considered the discovery itself a stroke of genius; he was enraptured by the thought that a scientist should construct such an epitaph for himself. He was delighted by the fact that Cicero had recognized the nameless gravestone of the Greek from this inscription among the ruins.

All this led him to geometrical bodies. Other parts of Archimedes' writings awoke his interest in the problem of the center of gravity. The sphere's center of gravity was inside it, like the seeds in a fruit . . . there was no problem about that. The cube's center of gravity was given in a natural way by its diagonals; where the lines connecting the corners crosswise meet, there rested the cube's center of gravity. It was just as easy with the cylinder. But where was the cone's, the hemisphere's, the pyramid's center of gravity? A whole continent of problems opened in front of him, all to be conquered; different geometrical bodies were standing in this continent like castles to be besieged. He started eagerly, and his victories carried him on like a successful general.

He reported faithfully on all his results to Ricci. The tutor watched with ever-increasing amazement the razor-sharp intellect and ingenuity of the young man. They discussed again and again the possibilities of the future. And Ricci talked to the elder Galilei almost every month. Vincenzo praised the youth and smiled with the proud humbleness of parents; but, when he heard that it would cost more money, his face fell.

"It's impossible, Your Honor. Impossible."

"You must get some money somehow, Messer Vincenzo."

"Impossible. More than ever now. My eldest daughter has a suitor. Whatever I can spare must go to her dowry."

"Oh, so your daughter has been bethrothed. But Galileo didn't tell me. . . ."

The tutor glanced at his protégé, who looked at his father.

"Virginia engaged? But I didn't know. You never mentioned it, sir."

"What if I didn't? Have you no eyes? Haven't you noticed young Landucci always hanging around the house?"

"Benedetto? Of course! But I didn't think that . . ."

"You never do think of such things. You don't care what happens to your family. Sometimes you don't speak to us for weeks. Whatever we may be talking about at meals, you're always thinking of Archimedes; and I wonder you don't try to eat the tablecloth instead of bread. . . . But all this doesn't interest His Excellency. Benedetto Landucci has proposed to Virginia, and by God's grace this marriage will put us back where we ought to be. I suppose you know that Benedetto is the son of our Ambassador to Rome, a very distinguished young man. He has no fortune, of course; so we shall have to provide a dowry. He's entitled to that! But, until we have it, they can't get married. What kind of a father should I be, to spend the money on a grown-up son who can't even earn the price of a pair of boots—and rob my daughter of her happiness?"

Galileo blushed for shame. His father continued:

"I don't know what more I could do for you. You live in my house, I give you food and shelter, I even have to buy your clothes. You're no use to me in the shop, I don't want you there. You can read and learn to your heart's content. What else do you want the money for?"

Ostilio Ricci shrugged.

"Of course, all this has nothing to do with me. But I must tell you, Messer Vincenzo, this boy ought to travel."

"Travel? Where to? What for?"

"He ought to go to Siena, where mathematics are highly esteemed, even more than in Padua or Bologna. He could work there, and make a name for himself. And he ought to go to Rome. I'd provide him with letters of introduction. Perhaps he could even get a professorship somewhere. If once he was properly established all the rest would come of itself."

The draper listened rather sourly and shook his head. His son left the talk to the others, drew apart and began to scribble. While Ricci sang his fervent praises he went on with the long deduction which at home he had had to give up in despair. It concerned the pyramid's center of gravity. At first he still caught a word or two of their talk, but soon he became engrossed in thought, forgot the time, the place, the whole outside world. When somebody touched his shoulder, he cried out happily:

"I have it now!"

"What is it this time?" Ricci asked, looking over his shoulder at the closely scribbled pages.

"I know the center of gravity of the truncated pyramid!"

"What do you mean? Be careful, my son. Nobody has managed to find that out yet."

"Well, I have!"

He hugged his father like a young bear. But Ricci caught his arm and pulled him away.

"Hey, you! Stop that! You'd better explain."

The young man turned back obediently to his papers. After a few sentences Ricci understood everything.

"My dear boy. You must be bewitched! It's amazing! It's so beautifully clear! Messer Vincenzo, listen. I'll give you a parable. You're a musician, the whole of Florence knows how well you play the lute. Well, this boy of yours is a lute which has few equals in the world . . . only there are no strings on this lute. You'll have to provide them. Where will you get them? I don't know. But unless you get them, you'll commit a sin against yourself, against your son, your family, and . . . science."

Vincenzo Galilei knew nothing at all about the problem of the truncated pyramid's center of gravity. But he was forced to see that while he had been talking to Ricci his son had made an important discovery.

"Your Excellency"—he shook his head mournfully—"life is always giving me hard nuts to crack. How am I to find money both for a son and daughter when I haven't really enough for either of them? Well, Moses struck water from the rock! I'll lose my sleep for a few nights, that's all. I shall have to think what's best to do."

Father and son left the Palazzo Pitti together. They said not a word on their way home. When they had almost reached the house, Galileo spoke:

"Father, I'm going away."

"How?"

"On foot. Without money. I trust myself enough to risk it."

"I see. And what do you expect? How are you likely to return?"

"Hungry and ragged, no doubt. But I'll have more knowledge."

"And when will you start?"

"At once . . . only I'm rather hungry. But I could set out tomorrow morning."

"No. Wait a week."

Galileo waited. He worked diligently, putting his problems of the center of gravity into shape. The bulky manuscript was entitled *I baricentri dei solidi,* and he had almost finished a week later when his father called him aside.

He put a purse into his hand.

"Ten gold pieces. Don't ask anything, and don't tell your mother. Now you can start whenever you like."

Next morning the boy paid a last visit to Ricci. He spent a long time with his patron. Then he went home to dinner, packed his wallet, said good-by to everyone as casually as though he were going to the other end of the town—and began his journey. It was a spring evening gathering into dusk. He never turned to look behind him.

III

He left in spring and returned in autumn, bringing back the memories of a few months; but they were worth long years. He had seen Siena, attended the mathematical lessons in the Senesis lecture hall, argued all day, made friends with the learned of that ancient city of the Piccolominis, astounded them all with his daringly presented doubts of Aristotle; then, wearied of them, repacked his bundle and set out for Rome through the grilling heat. He had presented himself at the Collegio Romano, with Ricci's letters of introduction, had been asked into many houses, where he was bored, disrespectful, and disputatious, and had again drifted on. There was a single memory which he treasured and carried deep in his heart: the memory of the Jesuit Father, Clavius.

If he tried to think what Clavius was, he saw a short, stocky man walking beside him along the shadowy paths of the Pincio. This little man was very fat; he panted in his tight black gown and fanned his bald head with a great plantain leaf. But, even so, he never stopped talking either in broken Italian or barbarous Latin to the young stranger. For Clavius was a German, born in the city of Bamberg. He had become a Jesuit, had been sent by his Order to Portugal to study in Coimbra University. The Provincial General of the Jesuits had discovered outstanding mathematical talents in this young barbarian, and Coimbra was the best place to develop them. He had become a professor, been transferred to Rome to teach mathematics and, even more important, geometry, at the Jesuit College. The young Florentine who shocked all his new acquaintances with his stubborn, contradictory temper, his disrespect for Aristotle, had become Father Clavius' friend in the first fifteen minutes of their meeting. Galileo had sketched for him the hydrostatic scales, had explained his formula for timing the falling of bodies by the swing of a pendulum, had described his researches in the field of the center of gravity. Clavius was a man of fifty and Galileo twenty-three, but in a week they had ceased to notice it. They forgot the racial difference of Italian and German, the difference be-

34

tween the strict life of a Jesuit and the worldly life of a vagrant boy. They argued and talked like two deeply interested equals.

The returning wanderer brought home a book in his bundle. It had been written by "Clavio Cristoforo": the Latin translation of Euclid for those who did not know any Greek, or not enough to be able to read him.

They were friends as well as fellow students. The elderly Jesuit, who had no family, was fond of the tall, handsome young man, as lively as a puppy. Clavius was calm and quiet, at peace with all the ways of the world; he found pleasure in violent, rebellious, argumentative, and restless youth. On his part, Galileo felt deeply grateful for the steady kindness of this Jesuit, so tolerant toward his firebrand restlessness. And he loved in him the man he hoped to become. The younger Jesuits told him that Father Clavius was often called the Euclid of the sixteenth century. Pope Gregory had commissioned Clavius to work out the scheme of his new calendar.

Sometimes, as they walked together, he glanced at the bald, fat little priest, and thought with enthusiastic respect: This man decided that for the whole world October 15 should follow October 4 in the year 1582.

He would have stayed in Rome in order to be with him. But Ricci had written that it might be possible to get him a professorship in Bologna. And Father Clavius had been taken ill; he had to visit the sulphur springs in the Campagna. They had parted affectionately. The priest had blessed his young fellow scientist. On a late summer morning Galileo had set out to tramp back to Florence.

And now he was home again. His family received him without enthusiasm. A new mouth to feed! Instead of getting some glorious job and sending home money to contribute to Virginia's dowry, he had idled as usual! His father was the least unfriendly—but only because he had heard from Ricci about the chances in Bologna. On the first day he had a long talk with this prodigal son, mostly on the subject of Virginia: the suitor was being difficult about the dowry, and had demanded not only his, the father's, but even Galileo's warranty. He knew that the young man had no work at present; but sooner or later he must earn. Galileo lightly answered that he was willing to go bail for any sum. No doubt he would soon begin his career. Clavius had encouraged him in Rome.

The first time he visited Ricci he found a great bustle at the palace. Something important had happened in the ducal family: Cardinal Fernando, the Grand Duke's brother, had come home. Up to this time he had been on very bad terms with the Grand Duke, whose second marriage he strongly opposed. But Bianca had done all she could to reconcile them, and Fernando de' Medici had decided to visit Florence. His must have been one of those glittering cavalcades which had clattered past the young vagrant on the road from Rome. Now banquets and pageants followed in rapid succession; the ducal Court staged one splendid hunting expedition after the other.

"Wait and see," said Vincenzo Galileo, when his son reported all this at meals. "I don't trust all this talk of reconciliation. Fernando has come home to restore order."

"What do you mean? And how should he restore order?"

"I can't say exactly. He'll send this Venetian rascal, this Vittorio Cappello, packing. And I think that witch had better be careful."

Galileo hid a piteous smile. He was still in love, and did not answer. Absence had done nothing to change his heart. Whether you pray out of the depths or on the highest peak of a mountain—you believe equally in your prayer.

"You must have heard some interesting things in Rome," his father continued. "Tell me, aren't they talking about our Cardinal?"

"Of course they are! Cardinal Fernando de' Medici has restored the lost authority of the Vatican as the patron of arts. Whenever they dig up an old statue or coin or gem, they take it straight to him. He buys everything worth while."

"He certainly has the money for it!" growled Vincenzo.

"And the knowledge as well! They say that four years ago they dug up a marble group of Niobe and her children near the Porta San Paolo. They took it from the earth practically without a scratch. I didn't see it, but Clavius did, and he told me how beautiful it was."

Vincenzo nodded and, as usual, quoted Dante:

> O Niobe, con che occhi dolenti
> Vedeva io te, segnata in su la strada,
> Tra sette e sette tuoi figliuoli spenti.[1]

---

[1] "O Niobe! in what a trance of woe
Thee I behold, upon that highway drown
Seven sons on either side thee slain."

(*Purgatorio*, canto 12, v. 37, Cary's transl.)

"What else did he buy?"

"A Venus which they called, in his honor, the Medici Venus. They dug her up somewhere in Tivoli. They talk about a famous statue of a faun, but I don't know anything about it. I don't believe, father, that Cardinal Fernando will stay in Florence. He likes Rome so much better, and all his work to strengthen the Church. There is much talk about the 'propaganda college' he has just organized."

"What's that? A 'propaganda college'?"

"To propagate the faith among heretics and unbelievers. They say it's working very diligently. It trains missionaries to spread our holy faith all over the world. Cardinal Fernando is very much interested in this. Why should he come home, where he can only play second fiddle? And why should he trouble about Florence when he can attend to the affairs of the whole world in Rome?"

"You're only arguing! Cosimo was his father, and therefore Florence is his life, even if he has been made a cardinal. We old people have lived to see many things here on the banks of the Arno. And so will you. Now that Fernando has returned, the rule of the witch will soon be over."

Galileo was silent. He could even restrain his love of argument if they talked of Bianca. But he thought deeply of all he saw and heard. The town was filled with a nervous and feverish excitement. People woke every day with the feeling that they would hear extraordinary news. Idlers lounged outside the Palazzo Pitti, staring up at the windows of that proud building and waiting, they could not tell for what. They waited in vain. Nothing could happen behind those windows! The Court had left Florence. Cardinal Fernando had gone to Bianca's favorite summer pleasaunce, to their villa at Poggio a Caiano.

Galileo's patron joined the Court. But before he left he had some exciting news for his pupil:

"There are great things in store for you, my son: you'll receive a letter of recommendation to the City of Bologna, written by Princess Bianca's own hand. And after that, your professorship is more than probable."

Galileo blushed and paled for joy.

"Bianca's . . . letter of recommendation . . . by her own hand . . ."

"Yes, my friend. Her chamberlain was in Florence yesterday; he had to settle a few things for the Court. I'd asked him some time ago to procure this letter for you. He promised, and now one-half of his promise is fulfilled: he has mentioned the matter to the Grand Duchess. And . . . would you believe it? . . . she hadn't forgotten you!"

Galileo gaped, but could not speak; he was far too happy.

"But they discussed all this out hunting," continued Ricci, "and the chamberlain couldn't get you a letter in the forest. Now I'm going myself to Poggio a Caiano, so you can leave all the rest to me. I'll bring you the recommendation. When you get it you must go straight off to Bologna. Till then—trust me and go on working."

Ricci left Florence, and Galileo studied diligently. Every day he worked at his essay on the center of gravity in different bodies. He got on fairly well with his father. Whenever his mother was seized with a fit of shrewishness, he fled from home. There was always a book in his pocket. Either Dante or Ariosto. He read the *Divine Comedy* for the fifth time, and amused himself by working out scientifically the probable dimensions of Dante's Heaven, Purgatory, and Hell. He even made notes, a whole structural plan, with possible cubic calculations and details of areas. When this ceased to amuse him, he buried himself in *Orlando Furioso,* relishing its waves of sonorous rhyme and its host of characters. When he was sure of being alone in the misty by-ways of Giullari he read it aloud. The sweet rhymes were lost in air, but he closed his eyes with childish pleasure: his mind caught the rise and fall of the verse which seemed to carry him back to the glowing beauty of Bianca Cappello. He waited for Ricci and the letter. It would be almost a sacrilege to use it, when *her* hands had touched the page. He could never give it to anyone else. But if he got his professorship, by delivering it, he would be Bianca's lifelong slave even in science; all he discovered, invented, elaborated, should be for her, a tribute to her glory.

October came, it was still like summer; a dim light played over the waves of the Arno, the whole world was soft, full of sweet music. The horrible news reached Florence on a drowsy golden afternoon.

Galileo was crossing the Piazza della Signoria, thinking out a difficult problem. He started at the sight of a running figure which passed him on the corner of the Uffizi, calling out some news. The people in the street began to follow.

"What was that?" he asked a little girl.

"I didn't catch it, sir," she answered; "but it sounded as if someone were dead."

The young man shrugged and tried to control himself. But a dull hammering in his temple warned him that some strange terror was in the air, something which concerned him closely. He ran on and met Signora Maccanti, Benvenuto Cellini's daughter.

"What is it, Signora Maddalena?" he called out.

"Haven't you heard, Signor Galilei? Prince Francesco and his wife died last night."

He stood as though his feet were nailed to the stones. He had more questions to ask, but Signora Maccanti was almost running; her veils trailed after her like chimney smoke in the wind. Bianca dead? It was impossible!

Three fiercely gesticulating men were standing beside him; he knew them; they were the ushers of the Bargello. He could not speak, he could only stare.

"Do you think," one of them asked, "that Fernando did it?"

"Yes, I do," cried the other violently. "And I think he was right. Now we'll have peace and order at last."

"Yes, but how? Poison?"

"I don't know. Come on, let's go to the Bargello. They may know more there."

The town had become like Dante's hell, a place of uneasy crowds. People bumped into one another and gabbled questions, but all the answers were equally vague.

Galileo went on toward the bridge. The goldsmiths' row was jammed with people. One could scarcely move. Some were on their way for news to the Signoria, others in the opposite direction to ask at the Palazzo Pitti. Galileo walked with no more thought in him than a dead man, surrendering to the moving crowd which thrust him to and fro in its blind jostling. Children cried and screamed, terrified by the excitement of the grownups. A group of young men howled soldiers' songs with all the fervor of a riot, although whether the news was true or not the songs had nothing to do with the situation. An old man with a white beard kept shouting:

"Let's find Vittorio! Kill him! Let's find Vittorio!"

Galileo got pushed into a corner and stood leaning against a wall. The bells began ringing all over the town. People from the Pitti confirmed the event. The Grand Duke and Duchess were lying dead in their summer palace; the guards at the Pitti had officially received the news. The husband and wife had died together, some said in the same moment; but there was still no knowledge of who or what had killed them.

Galileo slowly came to himself. He reached home out of breath. Acquaintances and even strangers had stopped him many times on the way. The shop was closed, but a crowd of neighbors sat in the living room with bottles of Chianti before them. They pressed him for news, but he only drank thirstily. The wine numbed him. He went into the yard, out of the tobacco smoke and excitement, and looked at the stars. Sobs shook him, tears blinded his eyes. He stammered out his drunken grief alone.

"Bianca . . . Bianca . . ."

He did not remember how or when he got to bed. He slept late next day and awoke to hear the news confirmed. The Grand Duke and his wife were dead. Cardinal Fernando, as next of kin, had taken over the government. Probably he would resign his orders.

"But what did they die of?" he asked his mother.

"There are all kinds of stories. I'm certain Fernando did it. But don't say that to your father, because you'll make him very angry."

"Angry? It was he who prophesied . . ."

"Yes, but if you say so much as a word you may get into trouble."

"Where is father? In the shop?"

"No, he hasn't opened the shop at all; he has gone to the Signoria. He left a message for you: you can find him in front of the Palazzo Uguccioni."

But Galileo wanted to talk to Ricci. He crossed the Ponte Vecchio, but beyond the bridge were halberdiers closing the street against all comers. It was late afternoon when he met the tutor by chance at the Loggia dei Lanzi.

"That letter is lost forever," was Ricci's greeting.

They hurried to the nearest tavern, sat in the farthest corner, and talked in whispers. The innkeeper recognized the courtier and began to hover round the table, but Ricci was prudent enough not to raise his voice.

"What happened in Poggio?" asked the boy.

Ricci shrugged. He told the story of the Poggio days in detail. The Court had been exceptionally gay. To all appearances the Cardinal was completely reconciled with his brother and his brother's wife. On the eighth day there was a hunt. The Prince had become very hot while hunting, and sat down in the park to rest near a little lake. The ground was damp, and soon Francesco rose, saying he felt suddenly chilled. That night he was feverish. Bianca wanted to call a doctor, but the Prince insisted on trying to cure himself with medicines he had taught himself how to brew. He had a great faith in his own mixture called Bezoar. This was a very costly remedy; its ingredients were the gallstones of a crocodile, a hedgehog, a Peruvian goat, and an Indian antelope. So he took Bezoar and would see no physicians. His wife and brother sat with him day and night. But four days later Bianca also fell ill with a high fever; she became too weak to nurse her husband. They were lying in adjacent rooms of the Villa.

They sent messages to each other every hour, detailed accounts of how they were feeling. But the messengers lied, both hers and his. Both were told that the other was recovering, although in truth they were both getting worse. Duke Francesco had a terrible cramp which tortured him cruelly. He died after forty-eight hours of agony. Bianca knew nothing of this. They kept telling her that her husband was getting well.

"On the sixth day," Ricci whispered, "I was in her room. She knew that she was going to die. She said to me: 'Tell my lord, Duke Francesco de' Medici, that I take my leave of him. Tell him that I was always faithful to him and have loved him to the very end. If I have ever offended him, I humbly beg his pardon, because I'm dying.'

"I . . . I confess she brought the tears to my eyes. She lay there listening. We had told her how much better her husband was, but we couldn't lull her uneasiness. She knew that something had happened. The Prince's body was being carried out of the next room, and although they did it very quietly, you could hear the steps coming and going. As soon as his brother died, Prince Fernando ordered out his coach and drove into town with the Archbishop of Florence. This happened at night; nobody knew about it here. The Grand Duchess heard the sound of jingling harness and horses at that unusual hour. I saw from her face that she knew the truth. And she said: 'It is as I wish it; I am dying together with my lord.' That was the last word she spoke."

Galileo sat staring at Ricci.

"Was she beautiful when she was dead?" he said at last.

"Yes. Very beautiful."

Another long silence. Galileo had ready a new question, but the old courtier was before him:

"I've heard all the nonsense they're talking here. Someone told me that Princess Bianca had made a poisoned cake for Cardinal Fernando, but that Francesco had eaten some of it by accident, and when she saw she had killed her husband she ate some more in order to die with him. I can only say that our new gracious sovereign, Duke Fernando, sent doctors out to Poggio immediately to hold an autopsy on the bodies, and find if any trace of poison was in them. They've done their work, and haven't found anything. The Court thinks that poor Prince Francesco killed himself by using his own medicines without enough knowledge."

"Then why did the doctors find no trace of those?" the young man interrupted violently.

"My son, it's a very bad habit of yours to argue, and it's growing on you. Don't try to contradict the official opinion of the doctors. You should do as the Court does, and consider it an unlucky coincidence that they both died at the same time. I most strongly advise it."

Galileo fell silent. He asked again:

"Did she look beautiful when she died?"

"I've already said so. But we mustn't talk of this now. For the next few days I shall be very busy, but as soon as I'm free I'm going to send for you. Instead of the Grand Duchess' letter we'll get you some other recommendation. And now I must leave you."

They parted, and did not meet again for a fortnight. When Ricci sent for him, Galileo went to the Palazzo Pitti. It was full of new faces. Prince Fernando had placed new men in every post. There was no trace of Abbioso, Dovara, Serguidi, and other Court potentates who had been basking in the favors of the Cappello party and directing the affairs of Florence. Vittorio himself, it was rumored, had fled as soon as his sister was taken ill. New people appeared, who seemed to have been long preparing for the posts they held.

"I shall soon be dismissed," said Ricci. "This world isn't mine. But I'd like to see you set on the right path first. I don't know Usimbardi, the new Minister of State, well enough to present you to him. But there's Belisario Vinta, a good friend of mine, a man of the future. You shall meet him tomorrow. Today he's too busy. And there's something else . . ."

Ricci produced a list, with the names of influential gentlemen all interested in mathematics, physics, geometry. He commented on every name, telling how its bearer could be approached, where he could help. Galileo listened attentively, and made notes. Baron Ricasoli, Count Vernio, Piero Alamanni . . .

"You'll see, my son, you'll prosper yet even if I'm not here any longer."

"I owe gratitude to two: God and Your Honor."

"Don't thank me. It's not for you I'm doing it, but for science, which I prize above all! And it's to the interest of science that you should be given a professorship. Then you can marry and . . . what? You shake your head?"

"I shall never marry."

"Nonsense! Why not? That's the order of things."

"No. I shan't marry."

"Why not?"

"Because," Galileo hesitated, "because I'm . . . I'm in love and she . . . I can't even think of her. . . ."

"You can't marry her? Has she been given to someone else?"

"Oh, no! To me, now! Only to me!"

Old Ricci looked curiously at his pupil. There was possessive, almost triumphant, happiness in Galileo's face. The old man shook his head.

"My son, you're a little mad. I always told you so. But I won't ask you any questions. I don't want to pry into your secrets."

IV

The heavily sealed letter of recommendation which the young scientist sent to Bologna was addressed to Signor Dall'Armi, senator of that city, and a very influential gentleman in the university. It was written by no less a dignitary than the Archbishop of Tarso himself, Ascanio Piccolomini, whose father had been a valued member of the Medici court. Galileo's protectors and friends increased daily.

At first only the neighbors had known his face; he was the draper's son who had been sent back in disgrace from Pisa without taking his degree. Then he got to know some friends of his father, a few of whom had even a little learning. Ostilio Ricci had presented him to a few courtiers. Many knew his hydrostatic scales; with several he had disputed on Aristotle, and shocked them by expressing audacious doubts on some statements of the wise Greek demigod. Someone had read his short essay on the plan of Dante's *Divine Comedy;* he was asked to lecture on it. Slowly he was becoming known; it was half fame, half notoriety.

Archbishop Ascanio was ready to help this extraordinary youth in whom he was interested. Galileo had made a strange remark which the Archbishop especially liked.

"You're a clever young man," he told the draper's son.

"Yes," Galileo said indifferently. "I was born very clever. Sometimes I surprise myself with my own sharp wits."

"Aren't you afraid they'll think you a braggart when you talk like that?"

"Afraid? Oh, no. I don't say things like that to anybody—only to a man who will understand. A stupid man can't know that I'm clever. His mind has no standards to measure mine. If someone has only got an ell, how can he measure five pints of wine? You can't discuss wit with stupid people. If ever I mention it to anyone, it's a sign that I consider him clever too."

"So I'm up to your standard?" smiled the Archbishop.

"Oh, yes—you!" The young man smiled back at him.

44

"I like you, boy. And now, since we're both so clever, let's draft this letter of recommendation as craftily as ever we can."

They started work gaily, cunningly considering the different points. The letter duly went to Senator Dall'Armi in Bologna. Ascanio was not the only one who suggested Galileo for the professorship; but letters from several other influential friends carried glowing recommendations. Ignazio Danti, the mathematician of Bologna, died. Bologna really needed a mathematician to fill the *cathedra pomeridiana,* the afternoon lectureship. And so far there had been no other candidate. The Galilei house was full of babble about the time when the boy would become a professor. Vincenzo himself, his mother, and his brothers and sisters began every other sentence with the words: "If the Lord helps us" or "unless anything unexpected happens"—but, given these pious reservations, they planned his future on opulent lines.

The candidate waited and worked hard. He was quite sure of the originality and importance of his work. He wrote a long letter to Clavius about the truncated pyramid's center of gravity, and received a reply worthy of an equally learned man. This answer encouraged him so much that he even ventured to write to Moletti, famous at Padua University, in whose works he had found the first traces of his revolt. It began a regular correspondence, and then another professor of Padua, Riccoboni, who lectured there on rhetoric, joined them after a time. One learned correspondent brought another. And suddenly the draper's son, by now a bearded youth of twenty-four, discovered that he was writing to many scientists and distinguished patrons. On one and the same day came a letter from Antwerp written by the Abbé Michel Coignet, court mathematician to Duke Albert and Isabella of Austria; from Count Antonio Bissaro at Vicenza, whose favorite pastime consisted in corresponding with the learned. Galileo had become almost famous in the international world of mathematics and physics. Yet he still had to live on his father's money, and could not earn a single gold piece. At home the only "useful" thing he had ever done was to mend the scales used in weighing the cloth bales; but any tinker could have done that. Something would have to happen soon; both he and his family felt his idleness a disgrace and a burden.

And his fine hopes received their first check at just this time. News of a dangerous rival came from Bologna. There was another candidate for the professorship, a man called Giovantonio Magini. This Magini was a Paduan, but he had studied at Bologna University, taking his degree in due course like a diligent student. His real subject was astronomy, on which he had published several books; his whole reputation was that of a learned, solid, and respectable man. The unruly, argumentative draper's son would have to pit his strength against this worthy; this Galilei just twenty-four, who had no degree, had never printed a book!

This news disheartened him. He had been so certain of his success. He longed for good old Ricci to comfort him. But Ricci had left the Palazzo Pitti. He had gone back to his native village, and soon there came news that he was dead.

Galileo would have found so many things to discuss with him. Moletti had just died at Padua. He had been very old and ailing for a long time. So old, in fact, that nobody had expected him to die; they were all too used to seeing him still alive. Now he was gone, and there was a vacancy for the chair of mathematics at that famous Venetian university, although out of respect for Moletti's memory the Republic of Venice had decreed that they would not fill his seat for a time. This professorship was a new possibility. There was also a new ruler in Florence. Cardinal Fernando had become Grand Duke by his brother's strange death. This Cardinal had no intention of returning to Rome to train missionaries; he had already resigned his Cardinal's hat, and would soon become a layman again with the Pope's permission, and begin his reign with all the reforming zeal of a new prince. Plans for reshaping the government were fermenting in every department of state—many of them concerned Pisa University, which Florence controlled. It now seemed possible that Pisa would reconsider its decision and add a mathematical faculty. Finally someone discovered that there had once been a chair for mathematics in Florence itself, without the university bounds—a chair at one time held by Ostilio Ricci, then young and a favored Court mathematician. Perhaps the prince could be induced to re-establish this professorship and, in his zeal for reform, entrust the teaching to this clever young Florentine.

The fact that there had been such a chair in Florence had been unearthed by Cardinal Francesco del Monte; or rather, by his brother, the Marchese Guidubaldo del Monte, a rich landowner of Pesaro, and an amateur engineer. In the ever-widening circle of his patrons Galileo had obtained the friendship of the Cardinal, who sent for him one day. His brother, the Marchese, had come from Pesaro, and was curious to see this new mathematician.

Galileo found a tiny old man at the Cardinal's palace. This ancient had the look of a fairy-tale troll: his long thick beard hung down to his belly, his head was completely bald, and between the beard and the shining pink ball of his cranium there was a network of a thousand wrinkles. Two surprisingly young bright eyes were set among the labyrinth of folds. He looked as old as Methuselah, but his eyes were as young as a twenty-year-old boy's. He was always smiling, a gentle smile, as though of perpetual wise forgiveness; though what and whom he was forgiving, nobody knew. He stood up to welcome the young man, bowing punctiliously; his politeness was excessively formal.

"I've heard of you, my most excellent sir," he began, as though reciting a poem.

"From whom, Excellency?" Galileo asked, surprised.

"Partly, my lord, my brother, partly my dear old friend, Moletti, whom death by some unaccountable error has taken before it has taken me."

"Moletti mentioned me to Your Excellency?"

"He did, and showed me some of your letters, most learned sir, which filled me also with feelings of respect and admiration. The wittiness and ingenuity of your calculations in the matter of the centers of gravity have filled me with a rare delight . . . But was Aristotle, the great Peripatetic, really so wrong to maintain that falling bodies—"

Galileo hotly interrupted:

"Aristotle was an idiot to write that . . . Forgive me, Your Excellency, my temper . . ."

This only brought an added indulgence into the old man's smile.

"Not at all, most excellent sir. It is the order of the world that youth should be fiery. I dislike both violent old men and prudent young ones. Will you make me so happy as to acquaint me with those experiments of yours with pendulums, which prove that the time of falling bodies is equal and independent of their weight?"

Galileo shifted on his chair, began to set forth his theory, his reasons for contesting Aristotle. The old man listened, leaning forward politely. Sometimes he nodded. When the young man had finished his long lecture, the Marchese asked leave to present his counter-arguments. An unequal conversation began. The old aristocrat talked in polite, calm, and involved sentences, interrupted by wild gesticulations again and again from Galileo. Indeed, Galileo got so fired by his own eloquence that at last any mention of Aristotle caused him to breathe out fiery abuse. But Marchese Guidubaldo only nodded and smiled. They both immensely enjoyed their talk. Soon they had strayed to a different subject, were asking their host for paper and ink, drawing circles and scribbling equations. When the servants brought in lighted candles, they were still talking.

The Cardinal invited them in to supper in the next room. Their host said scarcely a word, but these two never ceased their argument; they scarcely noticed the exquisite food. After supper they returned, still talking, to their pens and paper.

When most of the problems were settled, they were surprised to see that the red gilt candles were almost burned out, and the Cardinal gone.

But they stayed for a while. The Marchese inquired about the young man's position and future. Galileo told him everything. He talked of his Bologna hopes and the danger represented by this new rival.

"I have the honor of knowing poor Magini," the Marchese said; "and I'm extremely sorry to have to tell you that he's impossible. He isn't stupid, he's worse: he's mediocre. He has the kind of stubborn diligence which distinguishes all beasts of burden; he has an instinctive horror of everything new. If they give him this chair, he'll only do good to the university and harm science. He'll be so careful to tell his students of what is, and keep them from trying to think what will be."

"Your Excellency," Galileo answered, "pardon me if your figure of rhetoric tempts me to turn it upside down for myself. I feel that I should be even more useful to science than to the university. In me there is an abundance of what will be. And if all this brings to Bologna University fame which will endure for centuries, I shall certainly have been of use to Bologna."

The Marchese bowed, but did not rise.

"An answer worthy of a student of the classic past, and himself a classic of the future."

In the next two days they spent long hours together. The old Marchese Guidubaldo left Florence with the promise to do everything in his power. He invited Galileo to stay in his villa at Pesaro, and asked him to write as often as possible.

But the young pauper had no money to go to Pesaro: he could only remain a diligent correspondent. Whenever he had a special reason for despair, he found consolation in letters to Clavius and the Marchese Guidubaldo. And this was often. His hopes of Bologna began to fade. As months slipped by they became extinct. And in August came the shattering news: Giovantonio Magini had been appointed to the chair of mathematics at Bologna.

Now there were only two possibilities: either to wait, perhaps for years, till Venice should replace Moletti, offering the chair to a young man without even an academic degree; or to hope that the government of Florence would restore a mathematics faculty to the University of Pisa, inviting to teach there a former student who had cut his lectures, argued with all the professors, and expressed the most ridiculous views. Both hopes were slender indeed. Yet Galileo pursued them eagerly. He visited all his patrons, waited in anterooms for letters of recommendation, corresponded, tramped many weary miles. His documents became frayed in his pockets, his courage frayed in his soul. He was again on the verge of suicide. During sleepless nights he pondered a hundred times whether he could continue the terrible fight, whether it wouldn't be better to cease to live. But always when things were at the worst some apparently serious encouragement came to hearten him. His mother's rage, always itching to vent itself, broke out again one winter's day. This time it was Galileo who bore the brunt of her seething anger, with all the strength in it of Vesuvius. She abused the ne'er-do-well with terrible words. That day her son felt rather worse than usual. He answered back. Mother and son stood face to face, she almost beside herself with rage, and he unbalanced by his despondency. They shouted at each other like two mad people. His mother struck him twice full in the face with all her strength. It happened in the moment when the father came out of the shop to try to quiet them. And then Signora Giulia began to sob and kiss and caress her son without rhyme or reason, the son whom she had struck a moment ago. His sisters led her out of the room. Father and son were left together.

"This can't go on," said Vincenzo softly. "I've had enough of it."

Galileo could only hang his head. "Father, I know! I'm terribly sorry for you. Tomorrow I shall leave home."

"Where will you go?"

"To Pisa. Either I get a position at the university or . . ."

He ended his sentence with a shrug. Then he went off to pack his wallet. That day he visited his patrons, waited for hours at the office of Belisario Vinta, whom Ricci had advised him to cultivate. Vinta was always very good-natured, and for a long time he had been promising to support his petition with the Grand Duke. He promised again.

Galileo rose early next morning. They were all asleep, and he wanted to spare himself and them the pain of burdensome farewells. He left behind him a short letter, and went out into the freezing dawn. Shivering, with his bundle slung over his shoulder, he almost ran to the edge of the town, to the shop of a wheelwright who had promised him a lift to Pisa.

The Rector of Pisa University received him frigidly.

"Yes, we have had several letters from distinguished persons on your behalf. But the Board of Professors considers it entirely inadvisable to establish any new professorship. Our next meeting will be on Monday, and then I'll raise the question again. But I'm afraid I can't hold out much hope."

Galileo listened, numb with weariness. He visited a few other notables of Pisa, begged their support and showed his letters. He was glad when he had done this unpleasant duty, and need do no more for several days. He lodged at a dirty inn fit only for vagabonds; what little money he had left was scarcely enough to buy him food. He tramped the streets, huddled in his shabby cloak, and longed to die.

Early on Monday afternoon he went back to the university. All the professors were still in conference. He went into the janitor's room to warm himself and avoid old acquaintances. To his glad surprise he found a letter there "*Al Molto Magnifico Signor onorando Il. Sig. Galileo Galilei, Pisa.*" He broke the seal with his fingers stiff from the cold. It read as follows:

Most Honored and Esteemed Messer Galileo:

You, Sir, have missed no opportunity of distinguishing me far beyond my merits by telling My Lord Brother, the Cardinal, how much you rejoice that I should appreciate you. For all of which I thank you and kiss your hand, most Honored Sir. I was in some trouble to know whether you, Messer Galileo, had allowed the scientific objections raised by me, and to speak truly, I delayed in answering your letter because I secretly feared you had misunderstood them. Now with delight I learn that you have sent your reckonings on the forces of gravity into foreign lands, and that there they are like to bring you much honor. But let me be brief. If, Sir, you know me truly, you will not scruple to tell me precisely in what manner I can serve you best. And I kiss your hands.

I sign myself Your Worship's brother by inclination,

GUIDOBALDO DEL MONTE, Marchese.

Pesaro, 30th December, 1588.

The young man heaved a deep sigh, as he came to the end of this courteous missive. No news, no hope.

A gowned student opened the door.

"The conference is finished," he told the janitor. "You can give me the cloak of His Magnificence."

Galileo got up and left the room. The Rector was just coming down the stairs. He bowed and waited.

"We've settled the matter, Messer Galileo," said the Rector coldly. "The professorship is to be established. But we can only begin the lectures next summer. However, it is settled. I must tell you that in our opinion a chair of mathematics is still unnecessary. But we don't wish to set ourselves up against the clearly expressed desire of the government. We can discuss the details later, when I have more time. I wish you a very good day, Messer."

He continued his majestic way. Other professors were already crowding down the stairs. Galileo did not want to meet them now. All of them had been enemies. Now they had become his colleagues. He hurried out into the street.

"So I'm a university professor!" The thought amazed him.

Then he remembered that in six weeks he would be twenty-five, that he was very hungry and had little money to buy food. He tried to recall Bianca's face. When it came to him he knew he was happy. He stood in the drizzling rain, stared around him and laughed. Folk in the street looked askance at this foolish young man.

V

His mother was in her blackest mood when the prodigal brought back news of his appointment.

"That's all very fine," she snarled. "What's your wage?"

"Sixty gold pieces," Galileo modestly replied.

"Sixty gold pieces a month? You're lying."

"No, not a month. For a whole year. Five gold pieces a month."

"Five! You ought to be ashamed! Any artisan earning five gold pieces a month would be ashamed. So this is your famous professorship! Have you idled about all this time at home . . . for that?"

The father interrupted.

"Let him be, Giulia. Why dishearten him?"

"Hold your tongue, you! It's really you who are to blame that he's what he is. At twenty-five most men have their own home and children, are earning their own living and helping their families. What's to become of the children if we two die?"

She sobbed noisily. No one else said anything. They knew only too well that whatever they said, whether they agreed or disagreed, their mother would be roused to still greater fury. They only wanted to get away from her. Galileo beckoned furtively to his father; they ought to go to a less dangerous place to talk in peace. One by one the children crept away from their glowering mother, whose sobs rose furiously. The shop was closed; Galileo and his father went into the street. It had happened so often. If they wanted quiet, they must be out of doors.

So they paced up and down the cold street, surrounded by a blue shimmer of snow, under old houses whose pent roofs gave them the look of having pulled their hats down over their eyes.

"I didn't want to excite mother," Galileo said, "so I didn't argue with her. I'm certain I can make my way. Other professors live by what they earn. I'll give private lessons. Why shouldn't I?"

"It isn't the question merely of *living*, my son. I have to tell you some-

52

thing which I've never mentioned before: I feel that I'm going to die soon."

The young man tried to interrupt.

"No, no," his father anticipated him. "I'm quite sure. I'm over seventy. That wouldn't matter, but I'm ill. I may live three years, perhaps, or die tomorrow. What's to become of you all! Your mother must live. How are you going to help her do it on five gold pieces a month?"

"But, I tell you, I'll give private lessons. And . . ."

"And?"

"I'm sure to invent some things. There's so much money in inventions." His father sighed.

"I wish you hadn't said that, son."

"Why not?"

"Just try to imagine what I'm going to feel on my deathbed. What shall I be thinking then when you're all standing around me to watch me die? That everything is going to be all right, because my son will be an inventor? Am I to leave my wife and children at the mercy of . . . an idle dreamer? Can I rest in peace when I know you're like the other fools who invent flying machines or *perpetuum mobiles* and spend their lives in the anterooms of rich patrons?"

"Forgive me, sir, but perhaps I'm not so mad as all that. At twenty-five I've become a university professor in Pisa. Were those hydrostatic scales I invented . . . idle dreams?"

"Yes, you invented them. And how much money did they bring in?"

"Listen, father, there are many things about which we don't agree. There's one thing you ought to know about me: I'm an honest man. I hope you won't deny me that."

"No. I admit that. Honesty is very strong in you. And I know you're kindhearted. That's true."

"Well, you see, it's like this. You've fed and sheltered, clothed and kept me for twenty-five years. Consider all that as a loan. If your other children need it, I'll repay them honestly. But how I do it is my own business. Don't trouble with that. Maybe I'll kill a man in a dark alley and snatch his purse. If God should call you from this earth, I'll be the father of the younger ones. I promise. Don't think about the rest."

Vincenzo stood still, so did his son. Their eyes met.

"Listen, Galileo. You're going to Pisa now, and nobody knows when you'll return. Perhaps you'll be away when I die, and I won't be able to talk to you on my deathbed. Will you swear a solemn oath to keep the promise you've just given? Because if you do, I can die in peace."

"Of course I will. I swear it by God and the Holy Virgin and all the saints."

"Thanks, Galileo. And now we'll never speak of it again. But one thing more: you'll find it harder than most other men to keep this oath. You've no notion of money-making and no notion of how to deal with it. Tell me, don't you even like money?"

Galileo shrugged. They began to walk again.

"I can't really say I don't like it, because I'm so glad whenever I have some. But again I can't say I like it, because if I did I should feel I wanted it. And I've never felt that."

"Then you'll never have any! Money goes to those who really want it. It won't go to you."

"No," agreed Galileo eagerly. "Not money, perhaps. But knowledge, science, and ideas . . . the whole universe will pour them into me. Because these are the only things I love. More than women, or children, or money, a hundred thousand times! I may be poor all my life because I don't care; but it's going to be a happy poverty because I can work."

"What do you mean by work?"

It was some time before his son could answer.

"Two different things," he said at last. "And I don't know which of them tempts me most. One: to solve problems which my mind brings to me for solution. I've a hungry mind which can never be satisfied. It devours thoughts. It gnaws and nibbles at them incessantly. Have you ever seen a hare in a wooden cage? It must bite and bite; its teeth are made that way. The second thing I mean by work is bringing light into other minds. Instinct forces me to teach people all that I find out for myself. I don't mind people's ignorance, but their half-knowledge maddens me with rage. Sometimes I feel that if old Aristotle were living today, and I met him somewhere, I'd take hold of him and give him a good shaking."

"He's your favorite hate. What harm has Aristotle ever done you?"

"What harm has he not! He taught sheer rubbish."

"How can you talk like that of a great genius?"

"But he did, father, he did, he did! He did teach rubbish! He said there were heavy bodies and light. That the former wanted to sink by every means, the latter always wanted to rise! What idiocy! Each body has a certain weight; they all want to fall—on and on until something stops them. And then he said that a projected body was carried by the moving air. What folly! He had no idea about the essence of movement. I'll work out the whole thing and put an end to this whole stupidity."

"Why must you shout so loudly in the street?"

"Forgive me, father. I can't help it. I always lose my temper when I think of the Peripatetics and Aristotle."

"So Aristotle's errors in which the world has been believing for two thousand years will be set right . . . by you?"

"Yes, father. Why not?"

"And it never seems strange to you to hear yourself saying a thing like that?"

"No. I'm only glad. And I'm never surprised at my own intelligence. I've never met anyone whose wits were as sharp as mine."

The old man shook his head.

"You're like a man possessed by fiends. If you don't keep a guard over your tongue, people will either say you're a fool or else they'll burn you at the stake. I can't alter you! At least you're honest and kind, with all your craziness; and that's something. Now let's go home. I'm very cold. Your mother may have quieted down."

VI

Before he left for Pisa he received a mark of the highest favor, an audience with the ruling Prince. It had been arranged by Belisario Vinta, the all-powerful courtier.

The Grand Duke of Florence received him at the Palazzo Pitti. Galileo entered with many bows according to the Court etiquette, till at last he stood before his sovereign and clumsily attempted the final low bow which had been taught him. He saw a man of forty, a little shorter than himself, a man with a sparse beard covering his chin like a thin moss, a man with red, inflamed-looking eyelids, and a head stuck like a cake on the white starched frills of his ruff. Otherwise the Grand Duke wore sober black from head to foot: his aunt Catherine de' Medici, Queen of France, was recently dead. She had been the most successful member of this family of Florentine bankers.

"Galileo Galilei," he read aloud from the memorandum in front of him, "professor of mathematics at Pisa."

"Yes, Your Highness."

"Hm!"

The Prince fidgeted uneasily. There was a kind of benevolence in his face, but also weariness, infinite boredom.

"The study of mathematics is most important, and we want to promote it according to our capacity in the interest of the commonwealth. Mathematics and the related sciences have done much for strategy. Have you ever studied strategy?"

"Not so far, Your Highness."

"It would be desirable to do so. The perfection of guns and other machines of war is a highly commendable task. Men of learning should study deeply the theories of fortification. We have decided to develop Leghorn as a strongly fortified port, and your science can help us there."

"Yes, Your Highness."

Here the conversation flagged. The Prince stared absent-mindedly into space, probably wondering whether to say anything more. He decided

56

not to. Again he turned his weary eyes on the scientist and nodded his head. This signified the end of the audience, and Galileo obeyed, with more deep bows. The Prince showed him a special favor by giving him his hand to kiss.

Galileo sat down outside to have a talk with Belisario Vinta.

"Was our Prince gracious?"

"Yes, he gave me his hand to kiss."

"And what did he say?"

"Frankly, I didn't listen very carefully. Or rather, I watched him and not his words. I wanted to find out what sort of a man he was. I was surprised to feel the gentleness and kindness emanating from him. It's impossible that he should ever have . . ." Galileo's tongue had run away with him; he felt himself blush.

Vinta smiled.

"Ever have killed his brother and sister-in-law. You needn't hesitate to say it. It certainly is impossible."

"But then . . ."

"Did Francesco and his wife die a natural death? I don't know. Perhaps not. Heirs to thrones always have their followers willing to assist the fates, provided they have nothing to fear. But whatever happened, it was without the previous knowledge of the Grand Duke. He is a gentle, wise, and kindly prince. We can be thankful to have him for our ruler. God grant he'll marry and rule us as long as possible, now that he has left the Church. Do you know one man who wants Bianca again?"

Galileo did not answer that.

"When do you leave for Pisa?"

"I've packed most of my things. But I shall visit Your Excellency to thank you for your great kindness."

"No, caro mio, you can't do that. I'm going away. His Highness is sending me on an official errand to Rome. But there's no need to thank me. I'm delighted to do all I can. And I shall be able to do even more in future."

"Even more?"

"Yes. Only, please, keep that to yourself. But if you've any trouble at Pisa, write at once to me and to Guidubaldo del Monte. The Prince knows him very well and esteems him highly. And now come with me. I want to present you to another very important patron."

Galileo followed the courtier, wondering. Vinta opened the door of one of the offices. There sat a man taking notes from a multitude of books. Galileo recognized him at once. Everybody in Florence knew him, Giovanni de' Medici, Prince Cosimo's illegitimate son.

Vinta presented him.

"I've heard about you already," Giovanni said in a high, eager voice. "I'm glad that we work in the same field. I, too, am in love with the technical science. As you see, you've even found me at work! These books are all on fortification. I'm preparing a lexicon of them."

Vinta left them together, taking cordial leave of Galileo. Giovanni de' Medici didn't seem to be a very clever man, though he seemed to have read a great many books.

"Do you know," he said, with the eagerness of a man discussing his hobby, "that strategy knows over five hundred systems of fortification?"

"Really?" Galileo politely inquired.

"Over five hundred! What progress since the days of the Greeks, who considered that 'the breasts of their warriors' were their strongest defense! The Romans showed more common sense. Only the other day I was reading how the legions dug a trench all round their camp, even if it was only for one night!"

"How interesting. I didn't know that."

Giovanni de' Medici delivered a long lecture on strategy. He greatly admired Machiavelli, who had drawn up plans to fortify the city of Verona. Galileo listened carefully, quietly. While half his mind took in the words of the Medici bastard, the other weighed the mind of the lecturer.

"A gullible imagination," he told himself. "He can't see essentials, only the curious. He delights in detail and can form no true picture of the whole."

But he nodded and tried to be engaging. Suddenly an idea formed in his mind. Giovanni de' Medici remarked casually that the Italian universities were guilty of gross neglect in not giving a special faculty to the science of fortification. The sons of all the princes in Europe would come flocking to attend such lectures. Galileo interrupted him:

"I'll do it in Pisa."

"How?" Giovanni asked. "Who can give the lectures?"

"I."

"You? But how? You haven't studied it yet."

"That doesn't matter. I'll give it a few days and know all about it."

"All? Enough to give instruction in it?"

"Of course. I can easily master the subject."

Giovanni looked puzzled. But when they parted he patted Galileo on the shoulder with condescending good will.

"If you want to serve His Highness well, study the science of fortification. Especially the problems of Leghorn, which is very important for us. God guide you."

Galileo described this interview to his father. Old Vincenzo became very excited.

"That's splendid," he said. "When are you going to start it?"

"Start what?"

"The study of fortification, of course!"

"I don't know. I have so many other things to consider. I'm not quite ready with my thesis on the centers of gravity. Then I have to work out my theory of movement to prove the gross errors of Aristotle. I shall have to show the absurdity of his statement that the velocity of different falling bodies depends on their weight. And after that . . ."

"In a word, all your idle fancies mean more to you than the Prince's favor."

Galileo drew a deep breath. He had a hundred answers ready. But he did not speak. They talked no more about the matter. Better to avoid disputes!

The Galilei house had become more peaceful as the time drew near for him to leave it. They avoided quarrels, were ostentatiously eager to admit one another in the right, during these last few evenings. But the last evening of all shattered this laborious peace with a single incident.

Early next morning Galileo was to leave for Pisa. They sat down to sup in oppressive July heat. Galileo's bundle was packed already. His mother had become extremely emotional; now instead of noisy abuse she covered him with excessive affection. She kissed his hair again and again, brushing nonexistent dust off his doublet, as though she were playing a part in a comedy—the part of a tenderly grieving mother. This got on the nerves of all the others. Some kinsmen had come in to supper, members of the Ammannati family, who had always been ashamed of the Galileis. But now, when Galileo was setting out to be a university professor, they felt they must honor him with their presence. They all sat down in the courtyard to sup off a leg of mutton with gnocchi, drinking deeply from the straw-covered Chianti flasks which had been cooled in the well.

At supper Galileo said:

"This is almost a miracle. Today God vouchsafed me the wonderful gift of perceiving a new curve."

He spoke to his father, the only one of them who, he felt, might possibly understand. The others listened politely, but Vincenzo turned with interest to his son.

"What kind of a curve?"

"I shall call it the cycloid. How can I explain in a few words? If I presume that a circle is rolling on a given straight line and I take at random a point on the surface of this circle, this point describes a certain line as the circle moves. This I call a cycloid. Euclid didn't know this curve. He didn't think of it. I did! And I can tell you, sir, in hundreds of years people are going to say all over the world: the son of Vincenzo Galilei, the Florentine draper, was the first man to think of the cycloid."

"Wait a moment. I don't quite understand. What's all this about the circle and the point?"

"How am I to make it clear? Well, father, try to imagine a cartwheel. Try to make yourself see it! Close your eyes."

"Well?" his father asked, a little impatiently.

"Try to imagine the spokes of this wheel. Mud has splashed one of the spokes, let us say in the middle, a little nearer to the hub. A spot has remained there, hasn't it?"

"Well? What of it?"

"Till now the cart has been standing still. Now it starts. The wheel turns. Try to imagine what trace this dot would leave. A sloping, wavy one. It can be drawn precisely. This is the cycloid. The Galilei cycloid. *My* cycloid. Can you imagine it?"

The father shook his head.

"I still don't see it clearly."

"Michelagnolo," Galileo told his brother, "run and bring me pen and ink."

The boy growled at having to leave his supper. But this was his brother's last evening at home. He obeyed, and came back sulkily to his food. Galileo pushed the paper under the light of the torch in the wall bracket, and started to draw with quick, expert strokes. He had an excellent eye and a skillful hand: the drawing might have been made with compasses. He drew a row of circles noting in each the place of the imaginary point. The diagram was quickly made: the connected points had formed a cycloid. His father nodded with pompous gravity, as though this discovery had been his. After all, it was made by his son, the fruit of his loins, who had him to thank for his existence. The others were silent and bored.

"But this isn't all," Galileo explained triumphantly. "There is no necessity to fix that point *inside* the circle. I can determine its position outside the circle with the stipulation that it should be connected somehow with the original circle. Look, sir: this kind of cycloid has even loops. Isn't it interesting! I haven't quite finished with it yet; this new curve has innumerable possibilities in its variations, nature, qualities. It'll take me weeks or even months to study it. As soon as I'm in Pisa, I'll start. I'll give up my whole time to it."

"Your whole time?" Vincenzo growled. "What'll you live on, if you don't do anything else? On your five gold pieces a month?"

"But, father, how can I care about anything else now? Oh, can't you realize: a new curve! Do you know what that means? A brother has been born for the ellipsis and the parabola! Or a cousin, since this isn't a cone segment. It's as much of a historic event as the loss of the Spanish Armada last year, or the execution of Queen Mary of Scots, two years ago. Even if I didn't do another stroke of work all my life after that, I should still be famous."

This annoyed Vincenzo.

"Famous, famous! And you'll starve to death with all your fame. What use will your cycloid be then to anyone?"

"Use? But, father, this is a new curve! Oh, for heaven's sake! Don't you see what that means?"

"No, I don't. And I don't want to see. I only know that after so long a time of poverty and idleness you'll be starting work in earnest tomorrow. But your mind is still full of all kinds of rubbish when you ought to be thinking seriously about life."

"Rubbish?" The discoverer of the cycloid was amazed.

"Yes, rubbish! I've never wanted to say this before, but since we're on the subject you may as well know it. You play with these problems, as you call them, like a child playing with its top. The things on which you squander your time are like some game of riddles after supper to pass the evening. Why, you simply *amuse* yourself! You draw lines and circles like a scribbling child, and call it science. It's easy enough to be a scientist if your father has to fill your belly!"

Galileo swallowed hard.

"Yes, you've fed me, sir, till I'm twenty-five and have grown a beard. But surely there's no need to bring that up again when it's the last time I'm eating at your table. And why do you hate me for taking pleasure in my work as well as in other things? Do you envy me?"

The mother rose noisily from her place.

"Vincenzo, stop hurting my son! Don't you dare to hurt my treasure on his last night!"

She bustled over to him, caught him in her arms and kissed him. She began to cry. She upset a glass. Virginia and Anna screamed and jumped up, bewailing the wine spilled on their gowns.

"Oh, mother, leave me alone!" cried Galileo.

Signora Galilei's mood changed instantly.

"Leave you alone? What do you mean by pushing me off when I kiss and try to shield you on your last evening. You wicked brat! You ungrateful—!"

Now she was scolding him like a fishwife. The more they tried to appease her, the worse she became. Then old Vincenzo lost patience and also turned against his son. What did he mean by provoking his mother in this way? They abused him together. One of the Ammannati cousins, an honest stonemason, stepped in between. Now they were all three shouting at once. The evening quiet became a brawl with furious sobs and thumping of tables. The neighbors began complaining of the noise, yelling for peace. The girls shouted back; the farewell supper ended in tumult.

Galileo fled before the hurricane. He sprang up and rushed into the street without his doublet, in his shirt sleeves; he hurried on till he reached the Arno. But even there he could find no peace; the river banks were crowded with people trying to get cool after a sweltering day. He avoided all those who knew him, and hurried on, past the houses, to the outskirts of the town. Here the dark river banks were deserted; from the distance came the sounds of belated roisterers.

He sat down by the river and let the quiet and darkness soothe his mind. It took long to calm his jangled nerves to the point where he could think of any future. He realized with a painful shock how lonely he was, how few people knew him. It was true that he had burdened his family, even as a grown-up man. But what did they know of the many important questions he had solved during his long time of idleness? What did they know of the glorious world which was slowly forming in his mind, different from all the worlds that had ever been, built on a new perception of reality? While he felt the pain of his desolation and the lack of comfort in human beings, he was unable to defy and confront his loneliness with the courage of unique genius. He longed for friends, for the love of his own kin. For he really loved his father, his mother, his brother and sisters, but he strove vainly to get nearer them; they drifted away from him like ghosts.

He sat alone on the river bank till midnight. Then he went home. He listened and waited a long time at the house door. There was no sound or light inside. He opened the door carefully, and cursed its creaking hinges under his breath. He crept through the eerie moonlit yard, found his doublet, and went into the shop, where he had left his bundle. He shouldered it and stole out of the house. The door creaked again. He waited to see if anyone woke. But nothing stirred. He pressed his forehead to the doorpost and began to sob. He felt as helpless as a child driven from his father's house. In thought he embraced them. But he would not take a real farewell.

Through the dark streets he went to the Cathedral. Here at four o'clock he was to meet the wagon which would take him to Pisa. He sat down in front of the west door, below the iron figures of Ghiberti. The square was empty. His eyes were still full of tears. But soon he felt better. He began to think about the cycloid, drawing its variations in his mind with increasing interest. And soon sweet peace had consoled his heart.

The dawn came at three. He waited impatiently for the cart. At last he heard its rattling over the cobbles.

"Good morning!"

"Good morning, Messer!" the wagoner's fresh strong voice was like the sun. Voices sound strangely clear in this early twilight. Galileo slung his bundle into the cart and climbed up beside the driver. It was nearly day now. The houses in this morning twilight seemed to have sharp outlines and queer bright colors as they slipped away past the rattling wagon. When he turned back to look at Florence, it shone—a glittering golden town.

VII

Professor Galilei stood facing the Rector.

"I've sent for you," said that worthy portentously, "because I find myself compelled, by the statutes of our university, to reprimand you with full severity. This reprimand—"

"Good! Good! I understand! Aristotle," the young professor interrupted violently. "I've heard it all! Continue, Messer!"

"My friend, this reprimand is no mere formality. The traditions of our ancient university have a deep significance of their own. If I reprimand you, it is not mere conversation—which you take leave to interrupt even before I finish my sentence. The matter does not end there by any means! My official duty is to see that such a reprimand bears fruit."

"And how does Your Magnificence hope it will do so?"

"There is only one way: in future you must curb your unruly tongue and avoid giving scandal to your students, especially those preparing for holy orders, by abusing Aristotle. Such talk as yours is in contradiction to the principles of all sound teaching since it shakes the confidence of youth in our greatest and holiest authorities. It is a terrible thing to undermine a young man's faith in principles which have endured for two thousand years, principles first laid down by the ancient sages and then divinely re-established by the new wisdom of Christianity. If a single pillar of this edifice is shaken in a young mind, the whole building begins to totter. We create skeptics who cannot be useful sons of the State or Church. Anyone who shakes the general belief in sacred authorities sins against both. And you, Messer, are such a sinner. It is my duty to rebuke you sternly. I hope that you will lay my words to your heart and in future try to show yourself worthy of the trust of His Holiness the Pope and His Highness the Grand Duke. In which hope I dismiss you now."

But the young professor did not budge. The Rector, about to nod his august dismissal, frowned angrily at this stubborn young man.

"I cannot accept your reprimand, Magnificence."

"What do you mean? There is no question of your acceptance. You

65

have no right to do anything else. Our rules do not admit of argument."

"Because your rules did not provide against an *unjust* rebuke. Your Magnificence has reprimanded me for a sin I have never committed. I never have abused Aristotle. All I have done is to point out some of the errors of that great sage. Surely that's a very different thing."

"I can see no difference. It seems to me unparalleled insolence for an insignificant young man, himself scarcely more than a student, to criticize in such a manner as you do the axioms of eternal genius."

"Excuse me, but—Leonardo da Vinci? Was he insignificant? In the course of his study of Lucretius he clearly perceived the gaps in Aristotle's teaching. Be so kind as to look up da Vinci's treatise on the movement of slanting planes and the fall of bodies. . . . And was Giambattista Benedetti a dunce? Benedetti criticized Aristotle for forgetting to notice a number of things. I refer Your Magnificence to what Benedetti says about centrifugal forces and the gold piece spun on a table, which doesn't fall; and to his contradictions of Aristotle on the velocity of the fall of different weights. And to Tartaglia! And to Michele Varrone! And to Moletti of Padua, my patron of venerable memory! All these have contradicted Aristotle. And Giambattista Bellaso says just the same. Recently I've discovered to my great joy that his teaching on the velocity of falling bodies is exactly the same as mine, in plain contradiction to Aristotle. Were these all fools or enemies of State and Church?"

"You've named six skeptics. I could give you the names of six thousand learned men who taught and believed."

"Truth doesn't depend on the number of its believers. How many believed that Jesus was the Son of God at the time they crucified Him? Yet now we all know that He was. My theory of the velocity of falling bodies is the true one. It is time that the whole world should know it."

"It is not in very good taste, Messer, to draw the Son of God into your arguments. I must call your attention to the fact that the Protestant heresy, which has done such terrible harm to our Holy Church, was the result of just such mischievous questioning. I don't care if this sounds insulting; at heart you're a Protestant!"

"I can't allow you to say that! I'm a true and faithful son of the Church. I must protest against all such allegations."

"You see, instead of bowing your callow head to my age and official authority, you answer me with an insolent protest. I repeat that you are a Protestant at heart. And unless you can speak in a proper manner, I have other methods to bring you to reason. You have two more years to spend in this university. After that our agreement terminates. You must know that in face of the decisive opposition of the majority of the professors, not even your influential friends at Court could have it prolonged. I shall protest against you in any case."

"Others will be on my side. Jacopo Mazzoni—"

"Yes, I can well believe that. He is a personal and intimate friend of your worthy father, whom I pity from the bottom of my heart. . . . But name me another! You cannot. You're exceedingly unpopular here. All your colleagues have told me again and again how much they object to your overbearing, argumentative manner. Your opinions on the Peripatetic wisdom, that great treasure of human culture, are mere insolence. Therefore I reprimand you again, most severely. And I call your behavior base ingratitude toward our ancient university which gives you a livelihood."

"A livelihood? Five gold pieces a month! And even from those you make deductions! Was it my fault that last year the whole country was flooded and impassable when I visited my sick father in Florence? And I lost my salary from the third to the fourteenth of November."

"If you knew more about academic usage, you would realize that this is a general custom at all Italian universities. In Bologna just as much as Padua. No honest man takes money for work he hasn't done. . . . Please keep your temper; I haven't questioned your honesty. But now my patience is at an end. Why should I trouble to argue with you, sir? Unless you can accept my authority as Rector of this university—you'd better leave us, once and for all!"

For an instant Galileo stood quite still, then be bowed and turned to the door. But he stopped and came back.

"Your Magnificence, Aristotle asserts that heavy bodies fall faster than light ones. Tomorrow afternoon I intend to prove that he was wrong. I shall invite Your Magnificence and all the other professors to be present at my demonstration."

"I'm afraid I shall have no time," said the Rector.

But the angry young man did not stop to hear him. He slammed the door of the Rector's *aula*. He instantly regretted his bad manners. Ought he to go back and say it had been an accident? But then he shrugged. What was the use? He went with long, impatient strides toward the staircase, through the yellow arcades. A few students were lounging about; some of them doffed their square hats to the new professor, but a number did not even touch the brim. Galileo was not popular with the students. It would have been a wonder had they respected him; the other professors were always crying him down, holding him up to public ridicule. They treated him with critical disdain. Old Mercuriali, who had been his professor of medicine, would not even speak to him. And soon this coolness changed to open hostility. He was treated as if he had some contagious disease. Nobody wanted to sit beside him at the conferences; if he happened to speak he was ignored. Soon he gave up going to meetings. And since his colleagues did not trouble to hide their contempt, the university servants were just as insolent. Once he slapped a janitor's face; after that they respected him a little. But he could not slap the students' faces. They were wildly impudent to him, inventing all sorts of practical jokes, pinning mocking rhymes to his gown, hiding beetles in his cap, putting nutshells under the legs of his chair, shouting mockery after him in the street and, if he turned back, jumping into the shelter of a doorway. There were only five or six among them who really wanted to learn. These liked him and he won their love. They accompanied him often on his field walks. There was a boy called Valerio Luca, who had the sharpest wits. An ugly youth with a crooked shoulder and a face like an owl's; but his mind devoured mathematics as flames eat faggots. It was a joy to teach him. Few of the rest showed much intelligence.

He had only one friend among the professors, old Jacopo Mazzoni, lecturer in philosophy. Galileo was going to him now. Mazzoni, who was still kindly disposed toward his old friend, the Florentine draper, gave a free private lesson every day to his new colleague. He possessed great knowledge in matters which Galileo had never learned. And the lesson often lasted several hours. Galileo found a home in Mazzoni's house, which was on the other bank of the Arno, beside the fortress. When he reached it now, Signora Mazzoni, a white-haired, black-shawled matron, sat sewing in the small courtyard; her pets, ten or twelve cats, lay somnolent, sunning and purring at her side.

"I kiss your gracious hands, Signora."

"Welcome, my son. Go straight in; Jacopo is expecting you."

The old astronomer was always afraid of catching cold and wore a cap even in the greatest heat to protect his bald head against drafts. He was sitting among his books, spheres, and globes, not even braving the mild air of the yard.

"How are you, Messer?"

"I don't know, I'm sure. Feel my pulse; I'm certain I have a fever."

"Oh, no, sir, no fever today. Why, you're looking the picture of health."

"Do you think so? Well, sit down. I've prepared the books. We'll continue with the orbits of the planets. Name the seven planets, my son. But . . . is anything wrong? You look so strange."

Galileo told of the reprimand. Mazzoni shook his head.

"If only you didn't argue so violently. But you always give them the rough side of your tongue! You're always cursing. Well, what was the end of your talk with the Rector?"

"He refused to attend my experiment tomorrow."

"That's just like him. An obstinate, narrow-minded man. He isn't interested in truth. What else did he say?"

"He said if my professorship was over, he would prevent the agreement's being renewed."

"That's bad. But it doesn't seem to worry you. Though it isn't so easy . . ."

"I've long been resigned to the possibility. And I wouldn't stay here even if I could. I know how much I'm disliked in Pisa. I have still two years; time enough to find another post, by the grace of God. My great dream, although I dare not say it, is to be given Moletti's chair at Padua. It's still vacant, and as far as I know Venice doesn't intend to fill it immediately. Perhaps they'll wait another two years. The Marchese Guidubaldo del Monte, who has influence both in Venice and Padua, may do something for me then. But I'm gossiping when I ought to be learning. What was that question you just asked me, sir? To name the seven planets. . . ."

Soon they were deep in astronomy. Before them the celestial globe in handsome brass engraved with the signs of the Zodiac, the Milky Way, and all the constellations. This subject attracted Galileo. It pleased him to draw the different phases of the moon, the seasons of the day and year caused by the sun's movement around the earth, gaps of darkness caused by the movement of the stars. His master was delighted by his quick progress. Only one thing worried him: Galileo kept questioning Aristotle. The book of books, the astronomer's Bible of the sky, lay at their elbow. Its Latin translation was named *De Caelo*.

"But wait a moment," Galileo sometimes said. "Let me think that over. Can it be true?"

"Don't talk like a fool. This is an axiom. You must learn it by heart."

"Even so, I want to think it over. I found several errors of Aristotle's in mechanics; I may find some here. This *primum mobile,* for instance, seems an unnatural and confused theory. The sun moves . . . and yet he doesn't move! That can't be true!"

Old Mazzoni shook his head and smiled. He liked this restless young man who examined everything, like a dinner guest of the Borgias examining his plate, lest he eat poison. And even when he accepted Aristotle, it was with reservations.

"You're a foolish boy," said old Mazzoni. "I'm sure even your dreams are all about Aristotle."

"I admit I'm foolish. I've found something out."

"And what may that be?"

"I've found out what it means to be a fool."

"Well? What does it mean?"

"In this world everyone shows wisdom who accepts whatever he is told. The fools are those who use their minds. There are millions and millions of clever people who follow Aristotle. But not many fools! And I'm among them. And you, too, sir, are a fool, because when I explained to you my theory of motion you followed your own understanding mind and not the old rules. But after tomorrow there'll be a few more fools. Experiments should convince everybody who cares to watch them."

"I'm curious myself. Have you finished your preparations?"

"More or less. I must go now, it's very late. Valerio Luca and a few others are waiting for me at the bridge. We're going up into the Tower. Many thanks for today's lesson, Messer."

He bowed to the white-haired old lady still in the courtyard among her cats, to which he nodded. He hurried to the bridge, where a group awaited him. His students were standing there together; the two boxes they had put down on the stone parapet.

"Careful, gentlemen," he said as he joined them. "Don't drop these boxes into the water, or I'll jump in after them."

The boys laughed and started to cross the bridge. There were four of them: Luca, a Polish student called Casimiro, Carlo from Pistoia, and Giuseppe from Vallombrosa. Two of them carried the boxes under their arms.

"Suppose," said Galileo gaily, "we do as the Peripatetics did. We need only follow them in their customs, not in their thoughts. Luca, imagine yourself a lecturer and tell us the object of our experiment. Explain what I shall have to explain tomorrow . . . Oh, by the way, Casimiro, have you taken round the invitations?"

"All of them, sir."

"That's a good boy. . . . Well, Luca, let's hear."

Valerio Luca began his lecture.

"The aim of our experiment is to prove that bodies of different weight dropped from an equal height reach the ground at exactly the same moment—thereby proving that the velocity of unhampered fall is equal for all kinds of bodies. Therefore we are going to drop bodies of different weights but equal form from the parapets of the Leaning Tower, and time them as they reach the ground. This we shall do by means of hourglasses. At the moment when the two objects fall, we shall open the hourglasses, to close them again as the objects touch earth. These experiments have a dual aim. In the first place: to prove that any two objects fall simultaneously. In the second: to measure the time of fall from different heights. Our experiments are intended to prove that the velocity of falling bodies increases evenly."

"Correct. What previous experiments were necessary to reach this result?"

"We started with the supposition that the rules which govern bodies moving on slopes are identical with those which govern bodies falling unhampered. We prepared a long run of planks which had a very slight slope but stretched the whole length of the courtyard we used. We carved a smooth trough into the planks and provided a very smooth ball of bronze. We started the ball at the beginning of the run and took our places at equal distances along it, with hourglasses in our hands. Each of us noted precisely the time of the ball's rolling down. By this means we were able to determine that the velocity of these falls was increasing evenly."

"Did we succeed in measuring the acceleration?"

"We did. Our master and professor, Galileo Galilei, of Florence, fixed by these experiments the law that the distance covered by a falling body is equal to the distance covered during the first second multiplied by the square of the number of seconds. If the rolling object has covered on the slope one inch in a second, it would cover four inches in two seconds, nine inches in three, sixteen inches in four seconds, and so on. The same applied to falling bodies."

The young professor nodded. It warmed his heart to hear a pupil define the law he had discovered; it was like listening to a sentence of his own biography.

"What did all the Peripatetics of the world know about this?"

"All the Peripatetics of the world," answered Valerio Luca in the voice of a little boy saying his lessons, "knew nothing at all."

They reached the open square where three buildings stood side by side, the first memories of Galileo's spiritual life. Behind them the Campo Santo with his mother's pride, the Ammannati Chapel. And in the foreground the Baptistery, the Cathedral, and the Leaning Tower.

"What a strange notion—to build a leaning tower. How did anyone ever come to do it?" the Polish boy asked.

"Heaven knows," answered Galileo. "As a child I heard all kinds of stories. They say in Pisa that Guglielmo and Bonnano, who started building it four hundred years ago, planned it as a normal, straight tower, a campanile like so many others. It took two hundred years to finish, and then it began suddenly to lean. The town of Pisa became frightened; first they strengthened the soil underneath, then the center of stress was cleverly shifted on the floors. Now it has stopped leaning farther. Luca, you'll go up on the roof; you three, choose one floor each; and I'll stay here. Open the boxes."

There were hourglasses and smaller boxes in the two cases. Into the wooden bottom of the boxes, holes and troughs had been carved for two balls, one of them metal, the other wood. Both boxes had been constructed in such a way that their bottoms could be tipped with a single touch, the two balls starting at exactly the same second in the trough and so beginning their fall simultaneously.

The students vanished into the tower. In a few minutes Carlo, the Pistoian, appeared in one of the broad spaces between the columns of the second story and lay down on the stones between them. He had two small boxes. Only these and his head showed through the parapet. A little later Giuseppe, the student from Vallombrosa, appeared on the floor above, just over his head. He, too, lay down with his boxes. He shouted down:

"Casimiro and Luca are out of breath!"

"All right," Galileo shouted back. "Be careful not to lean too far out."

Casimiro soon reached the fifth floor, and finally Luca's head appeared on the sixth. The four young faces were now exactly above each other, as though a vertical line connected them. A few days ago they had measured the exact spots from which they would have to drop the balls. It was decided where these should reach the ground: in increasing distance from the base of the tower, according to height. The balls dropping from the sixth floor had to touch the earth fourteen feet from the tower's wall.

"Ready?" Carlo shouted from the second floor.

Galileo took up the hourglass.

"Yes, ready! One . . . two . . . three!"

In the next moment he moved the pin of the hourglass; and, when his eyes saw the two balls and his ears heard their simultaneous drop, he moved the pin again. Then he took another hourglass and cried:

"Once more, Carlo! Ready? One . . . two . . . three!"

The hourglass . . . the impact of falling balls . . . the hourglass. He looked at the sand in the glass, nodded, put it aside. He took a new one and called up to the fourth floor. The balls were falling, one after the other, till Luca had dropped his. By that time the three others had joined their master. They helped him to handle the hourglass, find the balls which had rolled away. Then they examined the hourglasses carefully. They consulted well-prepared schedules. Everything fitted exactly. The hourglasses had proved beyond question the Galilei thesis of acceleration in unhampered falls.

"If this doesn't convince them," Galiieo said, "then nothing will. We've dropped the balls a hundred times at least, calculated the time of the falls in every case. That's enough, gentlemen. I have to give some private lessons and write some letters."

On his way home he called at the university to find out whether anyone had damaged the notice he himself had written and pinned on the board. No, nothing had happened to it! It was an invitation to all stu-.

dents to assemble next day at noon in front of the Leaning Tower, where Galileo Galilei would demonstrate his latest thesis in physics.

That night he could scarcely sleep for excitement, though he had to get up early next day. First two private lessons, and then at eleven a summons to appear at the palace. The Prince and his Court were spending the summer in Pisa and he had been notified to report at eleven sharp in Belisario Vinta's office where his expert opinion was required.

"Greetings, my friend," the courtier smiled when Galileo came before him clad in his shabby Sunday best. "We haven't met since I came to Pisa. Are you well? Good. Well, let's come to the point. Giovanni de' Medici has invented a dredging machine. It is very important for us to clear the mouth of the river at Leghorn where we are building a new harbor. Signor Giovanni says that his machine is excellent for this purpose. He has made a small model and presented it to the Grand Duke, but it's hard to judge such a miniature toy. To prepare a full-sized copy would be expensive and so our Prince is a little afraid of ordering it. He commands that an expert should see the model."

"I see. Where is it?"

"In Signor Giovanni's rooms. We're expected at a quarter past eleven. The Princess will also be there. Then you'll have to examine the machine. Be very careful what you say about it."

"Why should I be so careful? I'll tell the truth."

The courtier smiled.

"Truth is only healthy at Court in very small doses, *amico mio*. If the invention is useless, and I'm rather afraid it may be, you'll make an enemy of Signor Giovanni. But if you judge it to be good, the Grand Duke will spend a lot of money on it, and it won't work; who'll be made responsible? The expert."

Galileo frowned.

"Certainly not an easy position to be in."

"Well, *amico,* life isn't easy at Court. Shall I tell you what duties I had to fulfil in my official capacity seven years ago? I was entrusted by Prince Francesco to negotiate the marriage of Eleonora de' Medici and Vincenzio Gonzaga. Gonzaga's first wife had been a Farnese girl; but, as their marriage was childless, Gonzaga had their union dissolved by the Holy See. But that didn't satisfy the Farnese family. They spread the rumor that it was the husband's fault, not the wife's. When it became known that we intended to marry Gonzaga to Eleonora they swamped us with messages: we should only make Eleonora unhappy. Not only would she never become a mother, she wouldn't even become a wife. At Gonzaga's side she would be a virgin till the end of her days. We were rather worried, because the marriage seemed very useful politically. When I reported the matter to our blessed master, Francesco, Bianca Cappello was also present . . . er, excuse me."

For Galileo was blushing. The sound of Bianca's name had caused him to start.

"Well, Bianca had the strange notion of demanding a proof of Gonzaga's manhood. We were to find a pretty, healthy peasant girl who had known no man, and Gonzaga must prove before witnesses that he could turn a virgin into a woman. Duke Francesco didn't much like the idea, but he always did what Bianca wanted. . . . We informed the bridegroom. At first he refused most emphatically, but when he saw that our chance depended on the test, he had to accept. They found a girl and asked Duke d'Este to act as witness. At the first test Gonzaga failed. The virgin was a virgin still. But Gonzaga made all sorts of excuses; he insisted that if we gave him another chance he would prove his worth. Our Prince discussed the matter with Bianca and they decided that he could try again. This time they chose me to be the witness, and you can imagine my fury! I'm naturally shy. I consider the purity of the home of supreme importance. I hated the thought of this shameless mission! And besides, there was something rather ridiculous in it. I tried to get excused, but Bianca insisted. Finally, so as not to hurt my chances of Court advancement, I accepted. Venice was chosen as the place of the "trial of strength." Everything happened as we had stipulated. And this time it was a success. I had to deliver a full report to Francesco and Bianca, who were spending the summer at Serravezzo. You ought to have heard it! I wanted not to have to go into details but simply announce that everything was all right, but Bianca wasn't content with that! She questioned me for a full thirty minutes. I was terribly embarrassed, and Francesco laughed at me till tears rolled down his cheeks. Well, you see, that's what happens to courtiers. . . . Now we can start. Be careful what you say. . . . Have you any questions?"

"Yes," Galileo stammered when they were walking side by side. "Do you think, Your Excellency . . . did Bianca ever deceive her husband?"

"Never. She was a bitch and I disliked her very much indeed, but her worst enemy could not accuse her of infidelity. Poor woman, she was always a faithful wife."

Galileo walked as if in a dream. The story he had just heard had hurt him more than he realized. Bianca, his visionary Bianca, rose up suddenly from the grave with a tempting smile, shameless eyes, a wooing voice.

But he had to collect his wits. They were passing halberdiers and rich-liveried lackeys on their way to the anteroom of the ducal apartments. A Court official with a wide ruff and a short rapier announced them at once. They entered. Prince Fernando, his young wife, and Signor Giovanni were all sitting round the table, on which stood a small, toylike contraption. The Grand Duchess Cristina, a granddaughter of Catherine de' Medici, embarrassed the scientist by having red hair just like Bianca's. But she was rather plain. And her dress showed that she was soon to present an heir to the Grand Duchy of Tuscany.

Signor Giovanni greeted Galileo most cordially. He had asked the Grand Duke's leave to explain his invention. He discoursed at length about its principles. It was a sort of complicated pulley system with transmissions of cogwheels. He placed a box full of sand under the small model and then began to turn a handle. Its tiny buckets really scooped up the sand to pour it down the other side. Giovanni finished his demonstration and looked triumphantly at the expert, preparing his features for words of praise. But Galileo, looking intently at the model, shook his head.

"Well?" the Prince asked.

"This invention is useless," said Galileo.

"Useless?" Signor Giovanni was appalled. "Didn't you see how it scooped up the sand?"

"Yes, on the ground. But it won't work under water. The position of the buckets is such that the water would wash out the sand before it came to the surface. This thing is no use."

The Prince looked with a sneer at Giovanni, then glanced at his wife. "What do you say to that, Giovanni?"

"I can only say," Giovanni's wrath was almost choking him, "that this man knows nothing at all of technical matters. His argument is ridiculous. This invention will work excellently; I'm prepared to swear it in church."

"Galilei?" The Prince turned to the expert.

"This machine is useless."

The Prince nodded. He motioned to Vinta, who touched Galilei's arm. They retired backward with low bows. The Medici bastard, who stayed behind, called after them with an outburst of fury:

"Idiot!"

Galileo turned again in the doorway.

"The invention is useless," he repeated.

He would have spoken longer, but Vinta caught him by the arm and drew him away. The doors closed after them.

"I hope you realize that you've made a very dangerous enemy?"

Galileo stopped, with an angry face.

"Devil take it, I never thought of that! I forgot everything else. When I looked at the model I only thought of the invention and told the truth. I can't help it. If I find any mistake in scientific work, I have to point it out."

"Is the dredger really no use?"

"Perfectly useless. They couldn't get out a handful of sand with it. It would be a sinful waste of money. God bless Signor Giovanni, but why didn't he invent something better? I'd have been happy to praise him. Now he, too, has turned against me. As if I hadn't enemies enough. . . ."

"I know. But friends too."

Smiling, he scrutinized Galileo.

"I like you, *amico*," said he suddenly. "I've liked you before, but now even more. Don't lose heart; you can always count on me. Signor Giovanni is powerful at Court, but I, too, have a certain influence. And I've told you, I may have even more—within a year. I'm busy now, so I must leave you. Where are you going?"

"My pupils and colleagues are waiting at the Leaning Tower. I've to conduct an experiment. There, too, I shall prove myself in the right, and enrage everyone, just like here. The devil has bewitched my life."

He said good-by, pulled his hat well down over his eyes, left the palace gloomily. But as he hurried off to the Cathedral, his annoyance vanished. He wanted to fight.

It was almost noon when he reached the square. A huge crowd of students, more than he had ever expected, was jostling around the Leaning

Tower. And old Mazzoni was also there; he had even brought his wife. He was the only professor. Valerio Luca and the three others hurried toward him. They had everything ready; the boxes with the balls and hourglasses were all at hand. Galileo greeted his old colleague.

"None of the other professors coming?"

"I don't know. I haven't spoken to any of them today."

"Well, perhaps they'll try and behave decently for once. It isn't noon yet."

They waited. When the bells rang, the boys ran up to their appointed places in the tower. The others crowded around the base. Galileo explained to them how much free space he needed. But all the time he kept on looking toward the town. Nobody came.

It was long past noon. Galileo shrugged.

"Let us begin."

He clapped his hands, and the hubbub died around him. He began his lecture, explained the essence of the experiment. Then he called up to Carlo.

"Ready? Start!"

A packed ring surrounded him; the students had become excited and curious. The balls fell, touching the ground at the same instant. Then came the balls, from the stories above. The experiment was finished.

It had absolutely no effect. The students stared; the balls fell. Galileo fidgeted with the hourglasses. The gowned youths gaped at him in silence. Every face showed that they had no idea what he was after. When Luca dropped the last pair of balls, Galileo cried:

"*Quod erat demonstrandum.*"

But he did not await the effect of this. A disappointed student cried:

"What? Is this all?"

No answer came from Galileo. The students drifted away when they saw there was going to be no miracle. But Mazzoni clapped him on the shoulder.

"Admirable! And these louts have no inkling of what's happened. But I have seen and understood. This has been the most important half-hour in the whole history of learning. These balls were aimed at the body of the Peripatetic school. From this moment it has ceased to rule the world."

Galileo thanked him but no longer wanted to talk to anybody. Not even Mazzoni; not even his four favorite pupils, who had come running down from the tower and collected the balls. Luca reported in a flurry:

"They've stolen two hourglasses."

Galileo shrugged. He ought to have been prepared for that. It was an old tradition of Pisa University that the property of professors was there to be stolen, but the thief had to report next day to receive a ransom for it. They would be sure to bring it to his room. He said good-by to the Mazzonis, dismissed the students, and entered the Cathedral, ostensibly to pray but really because he wanted to be alone. He stayed about fifteen minutes in the cool, incense-laden dusk. When he came out the square was empty.

He entered a tavern, but only to drink. He gulped down glass after glass of the red wine, determined to numb with drink the pain of his mind. In the late afternoon he remembered a private lesson. What did it matter? he thought, and changed his tavern. Again he drank. At last he was beginning to feel drunk, his mind was dark, only lit by sudden flashes of consciousness which showed him himself and his position. Suddenly in one of these lucid instants he realized that he sat in a third inn; the lamps were alight, and a singing girl was sitting beside him.

He grabbed her hand and began to stammer:

"You've fooled me, Bianca. You aren't an angel. . . ."

The girl laughed.

"Why do you call me Bianca?"

He took her into his arms, and was very surprised to feel her yield. He kissed her lips. The darkness of drink swept over his mind in their swooning kiss. Next day he could not remember how he got home.

VIII

His father died.

He had been expecting it. For a long time Vincenzo Galilei had been saying that he would not live long. His letters to his son had all been melancholy and resigned to death. But gradually this very melancholy had taken from them the terror of reality. The expected news came with a horrible suddenness of its own.

He asked for leave, and went home for the funeral. He walked with his mother beside the coffin; after them came the girls and his brother. Livia, the youngest, had just turned thirteen. Michelagnolo was sixteen now, a tall youngster whose upper lip showed a faint moustache. Anna, who was seventeen, was not there, since she lay ill at a convent. Virginia stood with her husband beside the grave; after a long engagement she had recently married her old suitor, Benedetto di Luca-Landucci. This Benedetto was not sentimental. On their way home after the funeral, he took his brother-in-law aside to discuss money matters.

"I want your support, Benedetto," said Galileo, when they sat down at home. "You've seen how the family is left, and I'm scarcely making two ends meet myself."

Benedetto showed an abundance of good will.

"I see everything," he said expansively. "And I'm glad to help. I don't want to meddle in the way you provide for your mother and the children; you're the one to decide that. I'll help you by not insisting on the new instalments of Virginia's dowry. I didn't worry your father during his illness, but now if we sell the shop, the price will just about cover his debt to me. You can have a few months to pay me the amount you've guaranteed."

Galileo felt his gorge rise.

"Thank you. Although I hoped that you wouldn't touch the estate at present. There are many debts, and I must do everything to help my mother and the children to start their new life."

"You admit that there are debts which will have to be paid! But I'm one of your creditors. I've told you I can wait for your share. If all your other creditors are as lenient, you won't do so badly. I've already found someone who might be willing to buy the shop. We took an inventory immediately after your father's death. Here it is; you can run through it."

He spread out many parchments on the table. The inventory, the list of debts, carefully drawn up by Vincenzo during his last days. Galileo glanced down the columns of figures, and was appalled. He had no idea how to pay all this. He tried weakly to persuade his brother-in-law. Perhaps he would wait for the rest of the dowry? But Benedetto would not be moved. He turned to Virginia: maybe she could make her husband relent? The young wife only answered coldly:

"Poor father's death has been such a grief to me. . . . You shouldn't trouble me with such things. In any case, Benedetto looks after all the money. I never interfere. You try to persuade him!"

A very difficult week followed. From morning to night Galileo haggled with the creditors. His pockets were full of lists, closely scribbled, covered with figures and notes of ways and means. Where could he get a little respite? Every night he fell into bed, worn out, and started next morning all over again; every day he found Landucci in the shop counting the bales of cloth and watching everything with lynx eyes to see that nothing was being taken. Not that he suspected anyone; only it seemed the right thing to do. And naturally scarcely a day passed without his having a terrible quarrel with Signora Giulia. Vincenzo had scarcely been buried, when his house was full of the din of strife.

In a week Galileo could go back to Pisa. They found a purchaser for the shop and decided to start something else. They had to sell a good deal of furniture. Landucci received an instalment of his dowry, and then demanded his wife's part of the estate. But the new shopkeeper only took one room. At least the mother with her three children could stay on in the old home. They were secure for some time to come, even if they had to pinch and scrape.

Galileo himself got a few gold pieces. He could not spare these; his experiments in Pisa were expensive and he had pressing debts of his own to settle. He refused even to consider the problem how he should pay Landucci his guarantee. It would be paid somehow. . . .

Before leaving he went back to the grave to say good-by. His father's name and coat of arms were cut in sharp, clear strokes on the white tombstone; the arms, a ladder with four rungs. This ladder, their family crest, somehow symbolized the dreams of the kneeling son; he would climb these rungs to knowledge and fame, always one rung higher. . . .

He returned to Pisa—to contemptuous students, hostile professors, financial cares, enraged Aristotelians, and the intrigues of Giovanni de' Medici. This Medici bastard did everything in his power to injure him. He had managed to get enough money to build his dredging machine, which was taken to Leghorn, set up there, and put to work. But it all happened exactly as Galileo foretold: the water washed the sand out of the buckets before they reached the surface. It disturbed the mouth of the river but did not dredge it. The Grand Duke had not minced words with Giovanni, who, with the strange perverted sensibility of the human soul, grew angrier than ever with Galileo. He slandered him everywhere, spread foul rumors about him, even went so far as to write all the notables of Pisa, members of the University Board who had any say in prolonging the new professor's contract. Giovanni's intrigues even had an effect in Florence. And Vinta, who could have circumvented all this, had gone to Rome in his Prince's service, to watch the conclave. He had been sent there as a skillful diplomat to guard the foreign interests of Tuscany. No Spaniard or favorite of Spain must be allowed to become Pope. Pope Sixtus had died in the previous summer. Vinta was successful in his intrigue; Cardinal Castagna was elected. But soon after beginning his holy reign, as Urban VII, he also died. Another conclave had to be summoned. It selected Cardinal Sfondrato, who took the name of Gregory XIV. But he, too, did not reign long. Vinta had to go back to Rome. And then the Cardinals chose Aldobrandini, who ascended the throne as Clement VIII. Vinta was very busy in the Vatican. Signor Giovanni could slander Galileo as much as he pleased. And yet just now Vinta might have helped him more than ever. The courtier's prophecy was fulfilled: the Prince appointed Usimbardi, his clerical Prime Minister, to the See of Arezzo, and Vinta was made Prime Minister in his place.

But when Galileo considered his future, he did not even desire this help. Even if they prolonged his agreement, he did not want to stay in Pisa. He longed to be out of this hostile atmosphere. He had only enraged these "Peripatetics" instead of winning their admiration by proving his thesis against Aristotle. Most of his colleagues would not even bow to him in the street. And when the new Dean, Matteo d'Arexa, was elected, Galileo heard they were doing everything against keeping him on.

He had ceased to care. He staked his all on a single card. Either he would achieve his greatest ambition, the still-vacant chair in Padua, or relinquish it all. He would go back to Florence, become a tinker, a smith —anything! This he wrote to the old Marchese Guidubaldo, whose letters were his only comfort. He added that he would like to spy out the land in Venice, but had no hopes at all.

"It is very distasteful to me," replied the Marchese, "to think that you, Most Esteemed Sir, are not being treated in accordance with your great merit. Still more distasteful is the thought that you yourself, Sir, have given up hope. If you come to Venice this summer, let it be through Pesaro. I shall not hestitate to serve you in any way that lies in my power, since I cannot endure the sight of your present state. My powers are but weak; yet, such as they are, they are at your service, Sir, to their fullest extent."

Mazzoni also promised him a letter to his former classmate at Padua, Count Antonio Querenghi, a man of influence in Venice. Galileo himself had some connections through his scientific correspondence. He was in touch with the famous Count Bissaro at Vicenza, with Riccoboni, who at Padua lectured on rhetoric, a man without very much influence, but who at least could give information and advice.

He did not even apply for a renewal of his professorship. When summer came and the term ended, he did not even take leave of Pisa. He had intended to deliver a final lecture, summing up all his arguments against Aristotle; but that morning he sprained his ankle and could not go out. The students dispersed. Only his four faithful pupils visited him. He embraced them, and they promised to keep in touch with him through diligent letters. He said good-by to the Mazzonis. They were really sorry to see him go. And when he closed the door behind him, the thought of the old lady in the yard with her purring cats in the sun around her brought tears to his eyes. These people had loved him.

He packed his few belongings and paid his landlord, saying that he would leave in two days. But that same night he rose before dawn; when the porter came early to take his luggage, he stole from the house and walked to the Signoria in the morning quiet. A cart awaited him.

He longed to be gone. When they reached the edge of the town, he buried his nose in *Ariosto* and did not look back at this hateful place. He only stayed long enough in Florence to visit his family and was appalled to find out that his mother had been spending wildly since her husband's death. Signora Giulia had no notion of thrift. They all consulted with Landucci about the best way to make her economize. There was the usual storm, but in the end they found the solution more easily than they ever hoped. They persuaded Signora Giulia that it was only prudent to spare herself; she would get very ill if she persisted in carrying the burden of the household. Let Anna relieve her of it. This was Landucci's idea, and it proved an excellent one. Since her husband's death Signora Giulia had been obsessed with the fear of illness, and they managed to scare her. She was glad to leave all cares to her grown-up daughter. She only stipulated a little pocket money for herself, and they let her have it after long haggling. Landucci, who feared lest her wild extravagance would end by burdening him with the care of the children, was so relieved at the new arrangement that he even consented not to press his claim for the remainder of his wife's dowry. He only asked that Michelagnolo, too, should guarantee it. So now everyone was satisfied, and Galileo could leave Tuscany with a lighter heart.

The last night of his journey to Pesaro was spent at Urbino. Next day he started early and arrived in Pesaro about noon. Not so long ago, from the Leaning Tower, he had seen the Ligurian Sea; now the glittering blue of the Adriatic lay before his eyes. The cobbler's cart which had brought him here put him down at the Foglia bridge. From there he had to go on foot with his scanty bundle.

"Per favore," he addressed the first passer-by, "could you tell me where the Marchese Guidubaldo del Monte lives?"

"I'm his gardener, sir, and I'm going home. Are you the learned man from Pisa?"

"I think I am. My name is Galileo Galilei."

The old gardener bowed deeply.

"Welcome to Pesaro, noble sir. Our master has given orders to all his servants, should the learned man from Pisa arrive we are to pay him all the respect due to his rank. Will you follow me, please?"

"Father," Galileo said, "put on your hat; the sun's very strong."

"A thousand pardons, but I should feel that I was being discourteous.

Should our master see me with my head covered, he would be very angry. . . ."

They went on together. When they came to the villa gates the old gardener whispered to a lackey. In a moment, the shabby, dusty traveler was surrounded by obsequious servants. And he had not even reached the marble colonnade outside the villa, when he saw the old Marchese approach. The old gentleman also walked bareheaded, with elaborate ceremony, solemnly welcoming his guest, not carelessly pleased to see him again. When they were face to face, he bowed:

"Welcome to my humble house! Dispose of it, Messer!"

He stepped to Galileo's side, touched the fingers of his left hand, raised it, and conducted the newcomer as though he were leading out a lady in waiting at some royal ball. Servants in coats embroidered with the Del Monte arms were posted between the statues on the staircase leading up from the hall. When they came to the foot of the stairs the Marchese turned and faced Galileo.

"It is an old tradition of my house that whoever crosses its threshold for the first time should receive some trifling gift. My gift is neither gold nor silver, but a promise. I promise that even if I die in the attempt, I will obtain for you the professorship at Padua, most esteemed sir."

He bowed again, then pointed to the staircase with a gesture of elaborate ceremony. Galileo went on up the stairs. He longed to embrace this strange old man, but feared it might be a breach of ceremony.

So he kept his stormy gratitude to himself, and loved the old Marchese only in thought.

"I hope you may not despise what poor entertainment my house can offer. My dear cousin, the Marchese Giambattista del Monte, commander of the Venetian infantry, always uses these humble apartments when he does me the honor to pay me a visit."

They passed on through many winding passages hung with Gobelins, with white statues in their alcoves, till they reached the guest chambers. The Marchese ushered in the scholar, entered himself, and bowed again.

"We dine in an hour. Till then nobody shall disturb you. You must rest. This fellow here is your body servant. His name is Ippolito. *Arivederci.*"

The solemn, punctilious old gentleman took his leave.

"I should like to wash," said Galileo.

Ippolito bowed, like everyone in this princely villa, and led on the guest. There were three rooms, a bedroom, a parlor, and a dressing room. In the dressing room a silver washbowl was already prepared with two silver ewers filled with hot and cold water. Ippolito stood like a graven image. Galileo felt a little ashamed. He grew conscious of his frayed and sweaty shirt. He waited, fingering this and that, till the man should leave him. But still Ippolito stood motionless. At last Galileo ventured to say:

"Thank you, I don't need anything just now."

The man bowed again.

"Very good, Messer. Will you please ring for me to dress you?"

He vanished. Galileo pulled off his clothes. He stood naked, and began to wash. The perfumed soap and the soft towel delighted him. Set out on an antique chest above which hung a Venice mirror, stood a whole row of essences and powders. He had no notion what they were for. He opened and sniffed, but still dared not use them. Exploring further, he discovered to his surprise that fresh linen and a new doublet and hose had been laid out for him. Also a pair of light summer shoes. This rejoiced his heart. But was all this for him? Or for some other guest, using this room? At last he tugged the red bell rope beside the door.

The valet came back. At once he took the snowy gossamer shirt and drew it over the guest's head; he helped him into the other garments. Everything fitted. Galileo felt fresh and light of heart. The fine soft clothes caressed his body, filling him with a sense of ease. Ippolito flung open the door. Galileo entered his parlor.

His books and small possessions were all laid out. He wanted to light his pipe, but the servant offered a much finer tobacco than his own. A tray with fruits, a long-necked flagon of yellow wine, and a glass were standing at his elbow. Ippolito filled the glass and departed silently.

Galileo stood up again. He preened himself. Then he looked out of the window and saw a very beautiful garden; among the green gleamed marble statues and seats. He turned back into the room.

"Father," he thought, "you died without sharing any of this. I feel I ought to ask your forgiveness. All your life you toiled, and died in drudgery. But even work comes to me as pleasure. Forgive me. Life is very unjust!"

IX

Galileo spent a week in this noble house. There was time to swim in the sea, ride about the estate, see the sights in the town; but chiefly to sit and talk with his host. The Marchese lived all alone in his palace. His wife had died a long time ago; his grown-up sons were traveling in foreign lands. Nobody disturbed them as they sat discussing mathematics or concocting schemes for obtaining the Padua professorship.

The Marquis knew the organization of the University of Padua very well. In his youth he had been a student in Padua and prided himself on holding a Padua degree. He minutely described the life in Padua—different from all other universities. There were universities—so-called—at Pisa, Bologna, Siena, all over the world. But there was only one Bo, and though it was the greatest privilege for any young man to be a student there, it was a still greater honor to be a professor.

"In the first place," said the old gentleman, "the Bo is close to the Serenissima. . . ."

"To whom?"

"Not to whom but to *what*. In these parts we call Venice the Serenissima because her old title was 'Res Publica Serenissima'—the Most Serene Republic of Venice. Well, the Bo is close to the Serenissima. It is easier to get books in Padua than it is in any other Italian city. Venice is in touch with the whole world."

"Excuse me, but Florence . . ."

"Most worthy sir, please don't imagine that I want to wound your feelings as a Tuscan; but it can't be denied that Venice, with the sea open to her, has more possibilities for the learned than any other Italian state. And in Venice the printing of books is highly developed, the books are good, and cheaper than elsewhere."

"We, too, in Florence . . ."

"No doubt! No doubt! I know that for a long time Florence was the real city of sciences. But now she has forfeited that distinction. And chiefly as the result of printing. It is well known that after the invention

87

of printing, presses were brought from Germany to Italy. But not to
Florence. The first printing press was set up in the little town of Subiaco.
The two Germans from Mainz who gave us the art of printing settled
there. But they were soon tempted to move to Rome, into the famous
house of the Massimi. And the third printing press was not set up in
Florence, but in Venice. Only much later were the commentaries to
Virgil's *Bucolics* printed in your native town. This is rather surprising,
since at that time Lorenzo the Magnificent, who certainly had an instinct
for such things, ruled over Florence. And yet, in this matter he let
Venice take the lead."

Galileo was silent, and decided not to defend his Tuscany. He was
no match for this erudite Marchese.

"So the tradition of books," Guidubaldo continued, "is older in Venice
than in other parts. Professors and pupils can get them more easily.
Padua has more scholarships to offer than any other university; many
young priests and other young men can study there free. Living is
cheaper in Padua than in any other Italian town. But, above that, there
is something else which gives outstanding value to the Bo: the intellectual
freedom of Venice. There are many opinions about politics; one can
argue forever on forms of government. There are Machiavellians and
Republicans. I am not wise enough to decide these issues. I don't know
whether a constitutional republic or a gifted tyrant is the better. But this
I know—it was so in my time and it has been ever since—the Serenissima
has always given full intellectual freedom both to her students and professors, at the University of Padua. Everyone can teach whatever he
likes, and everyone can study whatever he pleases. Sometimes strange
things happen. In the city of Venice there is a censorship: the publisher
can only print books which the Serenissima passes for publication. But
in Padua anything can be taught. So a professor of Padua may be forbidden to print his book in Venice, but he can lecture on the same subject
to an audience of several thousand students. The freedom of scientific
thought is a very, very important thing; it is like the sunshine ripening
fruit, which otherwise would perish for lack of it. Don't forget that the
influence of the Church is smaller in Venice than in other states. And
usually, though no doubt for the best of reasons, it is the Church, with all
the rigidity of her dogma, which oppresses certain faculties of the mind."

"By God, you're right!" exclaimed his guest. "How much I suffered from that in Pisa! It was always the priests who turned against me most violently. And I still can't understand why! Aristotle didn't belong to the Church. And yet they defend him with rabid zeal as though he were canonized."

"But, Messer, you ought to understand! Would you care to listen to my opinion? I must tell you that I'm a faithful son of the Church. But the Church believes, perhaps not althogether unreasonably, that she has the duty of swaying souls. Therefore she must always be on the alert to see what thoughts science implants in them. In old times only monks could read. Priests cultivated not only theology but all knowledge. The saints, the Church Fathers, were learned men who also studied the scientific lore of the ancient world, Euclid as well as Aristotle. In this way the teachings of the Greeks received almost dogmatic confirmation. Aristotle is almost as much an authority as any Father of the Church. Whoever attacks Aristotle may easily find himself attacking the authority of the Holy See. Do you think, Messer, that the Vatican would be pleased at a discovery which disproved a thesis that has been accepted and maintained for centuries by the Holy Fathers of the Church? Can the Pope admit without further question that a man who for centuries has been honored almost as a saint was simply mistaken?"

"I see your point; but surely there's a deeper error! It's surely admitted that science progresses and advances. Its results sometimes show us entirely new truths which supplant the old ones. These truths become so apparent that no one can doubt them. Why does the Church run such a risk? Why doesn't she hasten to proclaim these new truths to the world, so that the faithful may be strengthened in their belief in the holy fount of all truths?"

"That you must ask the Church, not me. Take, for instance, the case of Giordano Bruno. Do you know about him?"

"No, I've never heard of him."

"This Bruno was born in Nola. He became a Dominican friar, but he behaved so immoderately at Naples that the authorities began to watch him. From Spanish Naples he fled to Rome. But he didn't stay there. Some inner fire was burning in him, forcing him to eternal dispute and vagrancy. He traveled all over the world, arguing at Geneva with the Calvinists, in London with the Puritans, and here in Italy with the Church. And he was a Dominican! Two years ago he came to Padua and delivered some lectures. I went to hear him, I even made his acquaintance. A strange, violent, passionate man; but there's a kernel of truth in what he says."

"What does he say, then?"

"He sees the whole world in terms of the spirit. He denies reality to matter. He told me something to the effect that the whole world should be conceived as an entity, just as we see a human body. And this Giordano Bruno was also learned in astronomy. Have you ever heard, sir, of Copernicus?"

"I have, but I haven't read any of his writings."

"Well, Giordano Bruno wrote a book in which he speaks of Copernicus' teachings. In this book he asserts that the fixed stars are not mere tiny points of light, but that each is a sun. Upon which the Church had him arrested."

"For saying this?"

"It isn't known exactly why. But they say the Church dislikes a scientist who asserts the existence of so many suns. There's only one sun mentioned in Holy Writ—the sun which stood still at God's command, by the prayer of Joshua. Giordano Bruno is now in prison. I hear that the Inquisition is taking up his case. The theologians are probably considering whether it is heresy to teach the existence of several suns."

"There we have it!" said Galileo eagerly. "That's just the point. Why should the Church pronounce on a question of astronomy? What if such a theory should prove true, after a few Torquemadas have damned it, and the whole Church turns out to have been shamefully mistaken?"

The old Marchese shook his head.

"It would not be the shame of the Church, Messer; only of a few narrow-minded priests. It isn't the Church, it's her theologians who feel called upon to give their opinions on matters which really don't concern them. And that's the fine thing about Padua! There the learned man can talk in peace on his own subject, with no theologians behind his back. That very Torquemada you've just mentioned drove the Jews out of Spain. But a hundred years ago Venice received them magnanimously, and settled them on an island now called the Giudecca, where they live very well. They trade, pay taxes, serve the community. The Serenissima leaves them free. But look at Bologna! There foreign students are forbidden to follow their national customs; the university wants to force them to be Italians! And where is Bologna's scientific status now? You ought to be glad that you didn't succeed in getting a professorship there, Messer. In Padua you can lecture freely in a rich, well-equipped university. What buildings, what institutions! Only the money of Venice can do that. There's no other place for you except Padua. What a wonderful system of classes! Enough to rejoice the heart of a learned man!"

"What system?"

"Well . . . about two hundred years ago the Bo was divided into two faculties. One is called the Giurista, the other the Artista. The former teaches jurisprudence; the latter, philosophy, medicine, and theology. Both faculties have their own rules. The students are divided into groups according to their nationalities. In my time the law faculty had twenty-three groups. There were Bohemians, Poles, Hungarians, Provençals, Burgundians, Genoese, Tuscans, Scotch, Venetians, Dalmatians, Spanish, and heaven knows what! These groups are all autonomous. The Scotch, equally with the Hungarians, elected their own governing body, their own attorney, librarian, and so on. And the whole body of professors votes for its own Rector in both faculties and for what are known as its 'wise men,' and for its quaestor and its chief proctors. The university dignitaries are in constant touch with the leaders of the different national groups. There's a rule for everything; the constitution of the university has a law to provide for any event. There's no such student life anywhere else! Most of them live around San Biagio, as I did in my time. *Dio Mio!* What a life that was! I still remember what wonderful fights we had with the *sbirri.*"

"With whom, Your Excellency?"

"The *sbirri,* the police spies sent out by Venice. They tried to spy on us."

"Forgive me, but I don't understand. Why did they spy if political freedom is so unlimited there?"

"I didn't say *political* freedom. I said a learned man is free to teach whatever he likes in his own subject. That's different. On the whole this is such a complicated question in Venice and the territory of the Republic, that only those can understand it who live there. Venice is a republic, but the most tyrannical. Its fundamental principle is that anything which benefits the State is lawful. It is honest and praiseworthy to hire an assassin to murder any man who harms the State. But the Council of Ten decides who *is* harmful and who isn't. The Ten are elected by the people; therefore the citizens of Venice assassinate those who are a danger to them. You've never been in Venice, I think?"

"No, never."

"I envy you the moment when you see it for the first time. And the years of youth you're about to spend there. Because whoever lives at Padua is always going over to Venice. There's always something interesting happening there: illuminations, serenades, *bucintoros,* the election of a doge, a *festa.* . . . You'll see what a splendid life it will be!"

"Forgive me, but I dare not look forward to it. Have I any hope?"

"*Ecco,*" the Marchese nodded, "that's just the point. You must know that the University of Padua belongs to Venice. The Republic controls it through the medium of three gentlemen. They're called the *riformatori,* and they're re-elected every year. These three gentlemen dispose of the professorships. Four years ago, when my poor friend Moletti died, the three *riformatori* decided that they would leave his chair empty in token of the Republic's gratitude. Now that the three *riformatori* have decided that they have fulfilled this obligation, they must be made to give the professorship to you and to no other candidate."

Galileo looked up with a start.

"So there is another candidate! Who is he?"

"Didn't you know? Magini. His time at Bologna is finished, and now he wants to get to Padua."

Galileo sprang to his feet, forgetting his host, but apologized instantly.

"Don't, please, be angry with my ill manners. I have an excuse. When I lived in the most painful and humiliating circumstances in my father's house I had every hope of receiving a professorship at Bologna. This Magini was appointed instead. Only because he was older than I. Now I'm again without maintenance, but my cares have increased. Hope is held out to me again, and again it's Magini who comes to blight it. I'm accursed. I was born under an evil star."

"Sit down, Messer, and compose yourself. There's no serious danger. Magini has no reputation at all. Anything may happen without prudence, but you and I are prudent men. Let us return to our three *riformatori.* I know them all very well. Signor Michiel is a rich nobleman; he loves science, collects weapons and antiques, and doesn't know much about mathematics. But he's a man of sense. With him the only danger is that his stomach is uncertain, and so he is apt to be choleric. Much depends on the mood in which we find him. The second, Aloise Zorzi, is the son of a great patrician family, a gay, likable, very shrewd fellow indeed, and a good mathematician. He has a son of about your age. The third, Zaccario Contarini, is a member of the famous Contarini family. Unluckily he is not very trustworthy; he is self-righteous, vain, and a little sly. He'll promise anything, but don't count on him. However, there's one way to approach him. He has a kinsman, Giacomo Contarini, a most learned man, an excellent historian and politician. Zaccario can deny him nothing, and we'll find a way to win over Giacomo. We can ask for Giovan Vincenzo Pinelli's help. Do you know his name?"

"No, I've never heard of him."

"Well, you'll often hear of him in future—the most influential citizen in Padua, and only on account of his great learning, no mean feat in such a university town. He comes from Naples. By now he must be nearly sixty, but nobody thinks he's more than forty-five. He came of a rich house: they expected him to study law and fill some high office of state. He was fifteen when he enrolled as a student in Padua, and there he has stayed ever since. That shows you what a city Padua is. Pinelli is still very rich; he has the finest library in the whole Republic; he keeps open house for all the learned and has no greater joy than to talk with scholars. He's my very good friend; my recommendation is decisive with him. And that means much because, once he has made up his mind to help somebody, he never stops till he succeeds. Pinelli is a close friend of Giacomo Contarini and also of Michiel, the other *riformatore*. But he is on equally good footing with Zorzi. Recently I was so fortunate as to be able to help my friend Pinelli to some rare old books; and he tells me he will do anything I ask, in return for them! I shall ask him to help you, most honored sir, with the same tenacity and zeal as he would help me. But first you must go to Padua, then to Venice. I'll give you a letter to Pinelli."

"Thank you with all my heart, Your Excellency."

"I'm glad to do so. But that isn't all. The commander, my cousin, is an intimate friend of the Doge himself. He will visit the Doge at my request. And I have here a list of eighteen names, some my kinsmen, the rest my friends, all interested in science, all in some way connected with the *riformatori*. When you leave this humble house—to my great sorrow —you shall have these letters. And now allow me to take you to your rooms."

A lackey with candles went in front of them. At Galilei's side walked the Marchese, and two servants with torches closed the procession. They parted ceremoniously at the door. Galileo entered his apartments. Sweet wine, cakes, and fruit had been placed in his room. He tasted everything like a child. Though he felt very sleepy, he wanted to put off going to bed, it was so sweet to be alive here and enjoy everything. For a long while he listened to the murmur of the sea just beyond his open window, until as last he fell asleep.

Every day was equally delightful. When they were not discussing the wonders of Padua and their plans to win over the three *riformatori,* they sat at the great drawing table debating the problems of geometry. The Marchese had a surprising gift for finding new problems to solve, and often he pondered them for months in his country solitude. He had alway something to say; and Galileo, who listened eagerly, praised his host and felt himself in the seventh heaven.

But the last day clouded his happiness. A new guest arrived, a day earlier than he was expected. His name was Scipione Chiaromonti, a mathematician like Galileo, but a year younger. He lived with his father, a physician in Cesena, and had exchanged letters with the Marchese. A tall, gaunt, thin-necked, tow-headed young man, very proud of his knowledge and fine manners. It seemed to annoy him to find a rival at the villa. Not only because of scientific jealousy. Every word he said, his drawling arrogance with the servants, his frequent mention of other aristocratic friends—all this proclaimed that he was suffering from the ugly disease of wanting to curry favor with the great. Had he been the only guest in the villa, he could have said: "I and the Marchese." But the presence of another commoner spoiled his pleasure in these aristocratic surroundings. Anything which anyone else could get became less valuable in his eyes.

The young men disliked each other instinctively. They exchanged pinpricks, but tried to restrain themselves. Chiaromonti arrived in the afternoon, and somehow they managed it till supper time. But at supper they quarreled. Chiaromonti, with a supercilious smile, informed the

Marchese that he was engaged in some absorbing work. He was writing a commentary on Aristotle! Galileo's eyes glittered with rage.

"Do you mention his theory of movement?"

"I shall, of course. But I'm not so far yet."

"Well, Messer Scipione, when you get so far take care what you say, because it's full of the most arrant nonsense."

The son of the Cesena physician stopped eating and stared:

"Perhaps I didn't quite catch your meaning. Full of what, did you say?"

"Full of all kinds of fallacies, Messer. If you heard that, you heard what I said."

Chiaromonti shook his outraged head.

"I could have imagined many things, but I wasn't prepared to meet such sacrilege in this shrine of learning, or such boorishness in this noble house."

"Listen, *amico*," cried Galileo, "you needn't criticize my boorishness; that's my business. Let's stick to the argument. If you're willing to discuss it, so am I. I say again—and His Excellency will bear me out—that Aristotle made statements about mechanics which I have been able to prove are complete fallacies."

Chiaromonti turned to their host, to say in a confidential voice which subtly expressed their superiority to this upstart from Pisa:

"It seems to me, Signor Marchese, that our pleasant if outspoken guest has drunk a little too much of this glorious wine. He'll probably come to his senses tomorrow morning."

Galileo sprang up, pushed aside his chair, and seized the neck of a crystal flagon; but a lackey was already grasping his elbow. He drew a deep breath.

"Forgive me, Signor Marchese! If I stay here, I might take this fellow by the throat."

He rushed away into the garden. There he walked up and down, with bull-like fury, till all the lights in the house went out. Then he returned to his room and wrote a long apology to his host. He was overwhelmed with contrite shame. He had risked the good will of his greatest and most generous protector. But next morning the Marchese came to his room and greeted him with all his usual courtesy.

"Most learned sir, I have your letter, and I consider the whole question as closed. Let us forget it, if you please. I come now to take my leave of you and give you the letters."

Galileo departed from the villa, accompanied by his host and all the servants. He entered the waiting coach, which took him to the head of the bridge.

So ended the fairy tale of Pesaro. He left the coach and climbed into a cart which rumbled away through the heat of the afternoon—carrying him to fresh uncertainty.

He was sitting in Pinelli's library in Padua. He had never seen so many books. It was hard to believe that this was a private collection. The shelves almost touched the ceiling, thousands of books arranged on them in a double system: the manuscripts laid in heaps on the shelves and attached to them by thin chains; the modern, printed books standing side by side. Their tall gilded backs melted into a deep, rich glow. High ladders stood here and there against the shelves; dictionaries and books of reference were laid out on tables; globes and spheres had specially constructed stands. This sight filled Galileo with all the rapture which a true Moslem might experience as he gazed into the paradise of houris. He and Pinelli had met already to discuss the plan of campaign for the professorship. The chances had improved. Magini, who had swept him aside in the matter of the Bologna chair, seemed no longer to be a serious rival. Galileo realized with delight that his name was already known in Padua and that if he succeeded he would owe it as much to his reputation as to any letters of recommendation and visits.

"But the position," Pinelli told him, "isn't quite what our dear Marchese supposes. Certainly the influence of the Church is smaller here than at other universities. But the old Marchese hasn't been here for a long time, and things have changed. You must know, Messer Galileo, that we've been waging a fierce war against the Jesuits. I think you ought to hear how it all began, since if you get elected to this professorship—and it seems very likely that you will be—you must fully realize what it means if it breaks out again. So light your pipe and make yourself comfortable, because the story isn't short."

Pinelli went on to relate the history of the Jesuit campaign in Padua. Its antecedents went back for many decades to the time when Protestants first began to appear among the students of the Bo. The ancient liberality of Padua did not concern itself with their religion, only with their knowledge. But in Venice there was always a Church dignitary who bitterly reproached the Council of Ten for allowing French Huguenots and

German Lutherans to infect Padua with their heresy. Cardinals were continually protesting. They succeeded in so far that the Council of Ten brought up the matter of religion at a meeting of the university council. But the professors stanchly defended their ancient tradition of intellectual liberty. The religious strife became more acute. The clergy began to get impatient; the Protestant students became provocative. It went so far that the German students' corporation complained in Venice that the Bishop of Padua had insulted them, because he had preached a sturdy denunciation of heresy. But still the university authorities refused to interfere with the customs of their foreign students. Thereupon the Church sent a congregation of Jesuits to Padua. They began their work in abject poverty, but very soon they opened a school and developed it from year to year. Suddenly they had all the money they needed, although nobody knew whence it came. At first they only taught grammar to schoolboys; but soon they were lecturing on philosophy, metaphysics, mathematics, and theology. Suddenly the Bo became aware that another university had sprung up within sight of its very walls. Where formerly only the announcements of Padua University were posted, the counter-announcements of the Gymnasium Patavinum Societatis Jesu appeared on the walls, and a few days later the Jesuit school even hung up a bell to summon its scholars. For centuries only the Bo in Padua had rung its students in to lectures. At the same time news came in from all parts of Europe that slanderous rumors were being spread against Padua's reputation for learning. In Frankfort, at Buda, or in Amsterdam it was said that Padua had degenerated. It was now no more than a nest of heretics, a sinful town of orgies and disreputable fights. The pupils of the Jesuit university slowly increased. The Bo lost more and more of its students.

All this had gone on till the previous year, when Pietro Alzano, Dean of the Law Faculty, decided that something must be done. He delivered a stirring speech to the university council asserting that the Jesuits were doing grievous harm to the spirit of humanistic education by introducing dictatorial methods. Their professors did not lecture, they dogmatized; their students were given lessons to learn by heart for the following day. But the ancient laws of Padua University had all been framed to prevent such dictatorship. The fundamental principle of the whole humanistic educational system was to make the pupils listen, repeat what they had heard in their own words, exercise their powers of expression in constant debate. The Dean appealed to his professors and the students to defy this Jesuit system, which might fatally obstruct the progress of science. The results of his speech were soon apparent, especially among the students. The pupils of the two universities formed two hostile camps and began to fight in the streets, at first only with bare fists, but they soon armed themselves. Civil war of the universities broke out in Padua between the Jesuits and the Bovists. It happened often that an armed Jesuit group invaded a university lecture room, starting a bloody fight there and in the streets; and Padua students quickly retaliated by forcing their way into the Jesuit college. Abusive cries and scurrilous drawings appeared on the walls; every day the professors of both universities found in their pockets or on their desks insulting pamphlets and caricatures. Finally the Bovists began to organize. Their ringleaders were sons of the most distinguished Venetian families: Quirini, Contarini, Giustinian, Dolfin, Trevisan, Correr, Valier. These lads concocted a strange plan. They walked in procession at midday through the streets of Padua disguised as ghosts, in white sheets, followed by crowds of gaping people. It was a huge mob by the time they reached the Jesuit school. These students entered one of the lecture halls where a Jesuit priest was just beginning his dictation and threw off their sheets. They were all stark naked. They abused the Jesuit professor and mocked him cruelly; then wrapped themselves in their sheets again and departed.

A strong protest was sent at once to the Council of Ten. Though these students were mostly their own kinsmen, the Council punished them severely, hoping to restore peace by this means. But now the professors themselves entered the fray. Da Fuligna, Dean of the Faculty of Arts, joined Alzano in an appeal for protest to the whole university. The Bo decided to delegate a committee of three, which should inform the Venetian Senate of the true state of affairs. Its members were Cremonini, the famous philosopher, Sassonia, the equally renowned metaphysician, and Francesco Piccolomini, whose noble descent especially fitted him to voice the grievances of Padua. But even before the committee departed for Venice, the mathematician of the Jesuit university visited the dean with a Papal Bull, signed by Gregory XII, empowering the Jesuits to lecture and confer degrees at Padua, with the same right as the university. He added that if Padua made difficulties, he had the power in the Pope's name to excommunicate all its professors. He departed in triumph.

The two deans of the university agreed to brave excommunication rather than surrender their freedom to teach. The Bo had some clerical professors: Matteazzi and Descalzo lectured on civil, and Montecchi on canon law. These presented themselves *in corpore* before the Governor of Venice to demand the preservation of their ancient academic freedom. The question was relegated to the Senate. After a lengthy debate it was decided that the Jesuits could continue their work but must not assail the ancient prerogatives of the Bo. Thus Padua triumphed. And there the matter might have ended, but for sudden tragedy. Dean Alzano was attacked in the street by masked assassins. They stabbed him to death. His murderers could not be found.

"Did the Jesuits kill him?" Galileo asked.

"Nobody knows," replied the cautious Pinelli. "The inquiries were useless."

"And what's the situation now?"

"Well, now there are two schools in Padua: the university of the Bo and this inferior school controlled by Jesuits. The Bo is allowed to teach all subjects, as she did for the last three hundred years; whereas the Jesuits must content themselves with teaching Greek and Latin grammar. Seemingly they've resigned themselves to it. But you probably know that Jesuits can't be judged by the standards of other people. Why do you shake your head, Messer Galileo? Isn't that the truth?"

"I don't know. I met one exception, anyhow."

"And who was that?"

"A German Jesuit called Clavius, a professor at the Collegio Romano. He's as honest as anyone I know."

Pinelli raised his eyebrows and shrugged.

"Clavius? Yes. I've heard of him. They say he's very learned in geometry. But may I give you some advice? While you are working for your election, don't show too much liking for anyone even remotely connected with the Jesuits. The three *riformatori* don't like them."

"I don't like them either. But I'm not their enemy."

"Good. But what will you say if the question is raised and you have to take sides?"

"I don't know enough about the question, Messer. If they ask me about the Jesuits, I'll say that it was a piece of arrogance to try and start a second university in Padua. But if they contend that every Jesuit is a devil, I shall be forced to say that I know a German Jesuit in Rome, a good and honest man who never showed me anything but kindness."

"But don't you think that by saying that you'll weaken the position of Padua?"

"I don't know. When I begin an argument I never quite know where it will lead, whether it will harm or help me. I don't care. I only know that all the angles of a triangle make a sum of 180 degrees. Neither 181 nor 179, but precisely 180. Some people may argue that one degree more or less is of no importance—that it's a hardly noticeable concession. They're probably right. They're politicians, not mathematicians. I who was born a mathematician shall never be able to say that 179 is equal to 180."

Pinelli eyed his young guest reflectively. At last he said:

"Listen, Messer Galileo. If your Padua professorship should depend on your saying 179 instead of 180, what would you do?"

"Probably I should say 180, Your Excellency. But it wouldn't be easy. First I should call myself a fool for sacrificing life and future to my stupid obstinacy. I should call myself a stubborn ass for sacrificing my needy family for the sake of a few trivial words. I could lie so easily by making a mental reservation. I should think myself vain, stupid, and narrow-minded. But I shouldn't be able to give the false answer."

"Because your character wouldn't let you?"

"No, only the frame of my mind. It was shaped by Nature so that it could never forget what comes after the decimal point. My thinking is not righteous; it's only precise. I might commit robbery if my family were starving, but I could never extract a false square root. Even now my conscience tortures me, Your Excellency. I'm a petitioner, a poor devil at the mercy of others. I must seek the favors of powerful men. I possess the rhetorical gift to defend Padua University eloquently against the Jesuits. It would be so simple not to mention this Clavius, who's a Jesuit but a great man. But, Your Excellency, I'm a mathematician. If a man who isn't that is asked whether three dozen grains of dust are equal to thirty-seven grains, he can answer honestly and calmly that in fact they are. I can't, because then the binomial equation wouldn't be right. I should have to shout and thump on the table so that the whole world should listen, so that carts should stop in the street and ships on the sea—because it was wrong. One grain of dust wasn't accounted for."

Pinelli fell silent again; his face looked serious.

"I'm sorry not to be able to contradict you, Messer. Well, perhaps now I'd better show you the university."

They walked to the university buildings. Galileo felt slightly apprehensive. It always embarrassed him a little if the instruments he worked with were being discussed. The sculptor's heart quickens at the sight of a block of marble; the poet is thrilled at the sight of a goose quill, at that of a finely bound book. . . . Galileo was by nature a scholar; the sight of a university building meant more to him than to anyone else—as much as his monastery means to a monk. He stopped as they were crossing a little bridge.

"I like this stream flowing through the middle of the town. What's its name?"

"The Bacchiglione. Its tributaries meander all over Padua. Some people turn up their noses at it and call it a weak imitation of Venice. But I like it very much."

"Is Venice more beautiful?"

"Venice is incomparable, Messer. But I'm like a man who admires a very beautiful courtesan and yet loves his wife. And my wife is Padua. But we turn off here toward the Santo."

They walked along strange and beautiful streets, sometimes bordered on both sides by long arcades. These low, shady colonnades gave its special character to the city. People went up and down in the cool; the little shops were dim and mysterious; only the middle of the road glowed in the sunlight; the pavements on either side seemed part of the interior of the houses. At last they reached an open square. The domes of St. Anthony's Cathedral rose in front of them.

"Whose statue is that?" asked Galileo.

"Erasmo da Narni's, by Donatello. But the people call him Gatta-melata. A hundred years ago that man on the horse commanded the armies of the Republic. You see that house, Messer, the two-storied one on the corner of the narrow street, with a balcony and two windows on the second floor? Donatello lived there when he was working in the Cathedral. We have had many famous men in Padua. I'll show you the house in the Via San Francesco where Dante lived. And thirty years ago Torquato Tasso was a student here. He visited me often; I knew him well."

"What kind of a man is he?"

"Well, at that time he was a very gawky, tall, thin, fair-haired boy. Everybody laughed at him for his awkwardness; and he spoke a very strong Bergamo dialect and even stammered. People had to turn away their heads so that he shouldn't see them laugh. I always thought him a little mad, and I wouldn't be surprised if he ended in a madhouse. He was very ambitious, and always wanted to live with great people. Now he's got what he was after. They tell me he has gone to Rome because he wants them to make his nephew a cardinal. But just look at this pleasant little square. This is the vegetable market. That building is the Palazzo del Municipio. Next to it are the law courts. Isn't it beautiful?"

Galileo nodded.

"Is the university far from here?"

"*Ecco il Bo*," answered Pinelli.

It was a yellow, two-storied building, its doors proportionately low. Over them a formal shield carved in high relief with the mystical beast of the Republic, the winged lion of Mark the Evangelist, its head looking to the right, its right paw on an open Book of Holy Writ. The fabulous blunt-snouted beast was there to proclaim that this house of learning owed allegiance to the State of Venice, the Most Serene—Venice, the city of craftsmen and merchants, grown great by war against the Turks, fighting even her fiercest battles for gold with which to foster learning.

"This will be a great moment," Galileo said.

His guide turned with a look of inquiry.

"I mean the moment when I enter. When my head passes under these arches and everything else remains behind."

Pinelli stared in some surprise at the eccentric black-bearded young man.

"You like to say strange things, Messer. What do you mean?"

Galileo only laughed and shrugged. There was a certain lack of deference in his silence. There was even foolishness, since he ought to have paid the most scrupulous deference to this old gentleman whose influence in Padua was so great. By the everyday rules of social usage he should have entered these doors as a humble supplicant, on the left hand of this rich and distinguished man—yet they passed through them like the young pretender to a throne with beside him his far-sighted prime minister.

Galileo asked, looking up at the ceiling, "What are these?"

"The coats of arms of distinguished students. It is a custom here to preserve the memory of our best graduates by painting their coats of arms on the ceiling. As you see, all the nations are treated alike. Anyone who has earned the distinction, no matter what his nation may be, may have his arms here. There are many Protestants, and at least their colors are decorative. The motley figures on the shields, the red, blue, green, and yellow bars look well against the white grounds . . . But, forgive me, something unusual seems to be happening. Look, the whole university council is coming down the steps. . . ."

From above them, down the staircase on their right, came a dignified company. All in broad black gowns like togas reaching down to their ankles, flat academic caps on their heads. They were silent, but full of excitement like men who have just decided something important after long debate: their resolute faces showed that they had no more words to waste. Pinelli advanced and addressed the old man in their midst:

"Greetings, Magnificence. Is there any news? Have you decided anything? I didn't know that the faculties were in conference."

The white-bearded old man greeted Pinelli with great cordiality.

"Yes, we've been holding a general conference, but we none of us expected to have to summon it. As usual because of the Jesuits. I'm glad to say we were unanimous. We intend to go as a body to Venice, together with a representative of the City, and demand to be heard there by the Senate. I shall head the *giuristas,* and Riccoboni the *artistas.*"

Pinelli was just beginning to answer this with a courteous speech when a cry interrupted him. It came from the young petitioner at his side.

"Riccoboni!" cried out Galileo. "Which of you is Riccoboni? I'm Galileo!"

These dignified men had paused on the staircase. They all turned to a slight ascetic-looking scholar who spread out his arms.

"Are you he of Pisa?" he cried out.

In the next moment they were embracing. They looked into each other's eyes. Round them the noble council of the learned, while the two young scientists rejoiced to be face to face. Pinelli clapped his guest's shoulder proudly.

"Messer Galileo, let me present you to your future colleagues. First His Magnificence, Niccolo Borlizza, Dean of the Giurista. I see you already know Signor Riccoboni, head of the Artista."

A movement in the group on the staircase. The scholars exchanged whispers and glances. Riccoboni, the young professor of rhetoric, put his arm round the stranger's shoulder and turned to the rest:

"This is that Galilei of whom I have said so much. He hopes to join us. Will you welcome him?"

A general introduction began. But Galileo could not keep track of so many names. Only two of them stuck in his mind because he had heard them so often before. The first was Cortusio—the well-known botanist in Pisa. Galileo had never imagined him as he was—a short old man, with a silver beard, as bald as an egg, as though hair had never grown on his skull. His thin lips and jutting chin betokened a short-tempered little old man, with an argumentative disposition, not the type of a peaceful lover of plants. The other was more famous still: Fabrizio, the renowned physician, broad-shouldered and middle-aged, who at the first glance looked calm and full of kindness. His whole being inspired —commanded—respect. Under the wide brow, two wise and penetrating eyes.

"Even if I had not known that this was the renowned Fabrizio d'Aquapendente," Galileo thought, "I should still feel I had met a man."

They began talking. They told Pinelli first that the city council would act in accordance with the university against the Jesuits, to save Padua's ancient reputation by protesting to the Council of Ten. But soon they turned their attention to Galileo. He had to answer five questions at once. He stood in a cross-fire of celebrity, grasping the hand of enthusiastic Riccoboni, who did all he could to increase his fame.

"Excuse me," Galileo said, looking round with unconcealed curiosity. "Is Messer Cremonini among you, gentlemen?"

A gentle, middle-aged man stepped forward.

"I'm Cremonini; I told you my name a moment ago, but I saw that you hadn't caught it."

His voice was that of a gently protesting scholar whose fame seems to have been ignored, yet at the same time it was conciliatory. Galileo stared with the clumsy happiness of a spaniel surrounded by hounds. Cremonini continued:

"I know your fame, and wonder whether you come here as my enemy. You may know—I'm called Aristotle Redivivus in the world of science."

"Are you so great a Peripatetic, sir?"

"Yes. Or, to be more explicit, I can explain Aristotle fully in the light of Neoplatonic ideas, and I can reconcile him with the new knowledge of Averroes and the psychology of Alessandro d'Afrodisia. If you are of a different opinion in these matters, I'm very much interested in it, and I promise to listen to you patiently."

The others were exchanging covert looks which betrayed a certain weariness with this colleague who paraded his learning in so many words. Borlizza, Dean of the Law Faculty, interrupted:

"It interests all of us, but not on the staircase of the Bo. When do we meet again, Messer Galileo?"

Pinelli interposed:

"Perhaps my house would be a suitable place. My friends, I should be honored if you would dine with me. Messer Galileo would have the chance of getting to know his future colleagues."

This caused a great hubbub. They talked together. One had a lesson to give after dinner; the other wondered whether or not he could postpone a very urgent trip to Venice; the third, fourth, and fifth had doubts of their wives. But finally some of them accepted, while the rest promised to visit Pinelli early in the afternoon. They divided into two groups, from one of which Galileo took leave in all the glory of a petted and celebrated stranger. With the rest he went back to Pinelli's house. He, a young man of twenty-eight, dressed like a commoner among the university professors in their gowns, was the center of the company.

Everyone seemed eager to talk to him; they were all trying to catch his eye; and he saw with amazement and delight that his fame was much greater than he had thought it.

There was nothing unusual in the arrival of all these guests at the Palazzo Pinelli. This house was the constant meeting place of the learned, as Marchese Guidubaldo had said it was. A long table awaited them in the dining room; the servants seemed to have standing orders to be ready at the last moment for any number of new guests.

During the meal they discussed Aristotle. It amazed Galileo to find how much this conversation differed from those in Florence, Pisa, or Siena. There, learned disputes soon turned into passionate arguments with bursts of rage which threw to the winds every law of debate—brawls, if not with fists, then at least with words. Here it was otherwise. No one interrupted another speaker; they all listened with grave attention.

Sometimes their views were entirely opposed, but this only served to increase their courtesy, their praises of each other's authority, till they almost seemed to apologize for their thoughts. They never altered an opinion. It rejoiced Galileo to hear their debates. Everything the Marchese had told him of the learned freedom of the Bo was now an audible reality.

Cremonini interested him the most. This was his man, a professor of natural sciences and, even if not a skilled mathematician, a master in his own field. Cremonini had gone home to dine with his wife, but he arrived immediately after dinner. He entered and greeted the company a little shyly, and at once the conversation ceased to be general. Apparently everybody expected an interesting duel between the two scientists. Galileo himself was well prepared for it. While he answered politely all that was said to him, the other half of his mind was drawing up plans for his argument against Aristotle. He took stock of all the pros and cons, as he had a hundred times in Pisa.

But to his great surprise he had no chance to use all this. Cremonini sat down, fingered some of the objects on the table with the uncertainty of a near-sighted man, and then said:

"Everybody is expecting a dispute on Aristotle from us, Galileo. I'm not afraid of it. I should be happy to entertain this learned company with a pretty display of sparks from our mental rapiers. But instead of sparks which do not warm, I would rather choose the fires of affection and understanding."

He paused, the effective little pause of a skillful speaker. Their host raised his cup:

"Bravo, Cremonini."

Cremonini warmed to his discourse, and continued with the formal perfection of oratory:

"If the heartfelt wish of us all should be fulfilled and you are chosen by our mistress, the Serenissima, as a not unworthy successor to the unforgettable Moletti, it will be highly important to us both, whose fields of thought are so closely related, how nearly we can manage to agree upon basic principles. You who have won all our hearts from the first moment have come here like Samson; a Samson who intends to scatter us, Peripatetic Philistines, with the jawbone of Aristotle, the ass."

He paused again to get the effect at which he aimed—good-natured laughter. His colleagues smiled and some applauded. Cremonini continued:

"But, dear Benjamin, though you come with Samson's intent, you come in error. For you do not know the city of Padua. Wherever else you might have gone in Italy you would have had occasion to whet your steel. But here, on our beloved soil of ancient Patavium, you must sheathe your sword, for you will not need it. Believe me, our teachings and beliefs are not preserved by clinging to the axioms of Aristotle, but by something quite different, Galileo. I, as the official if unworthy spokesman of natural sciences, can tell you in a single word what forms the foundation of our lives. Freedom!"

The orator fell silent again, and glanced with experienced modesty at the tablecloth. A roaring applause:

"Stand up, Cesare!" Pinelli shouted proudly.

Cremonini rose, greeted by a renewed applause, and ran his fingers along the rim of the cup in front of him.

"You've no doubt heard of the evil strife which has been raised in our ancient and free city by the confusion of two things: religion and science. I hope I shall not be called a braggart if I say that the main purpose of my life's work is to demonstrate to all and sundry that religion and science walk different paths. The man who tried, by means of the natural sciences, to question the sacred truths of our holy religion would be guilty of sacrilege. We should be the first to condemn such an axiom, since faith and knowledge are things apart. But at the same time we would risk our lives to prevent science's being attacked with religious weapons—and some of us indeed have given our lives—to shield the integrity of learning. Let me refer only to Giordano Bruno, who was recently with us, who has been imprisoned by theologians for making a statement about astronomy. We respect theology as a holy science which has its representative among us. But we have never permitted theology to decide for us our physical, historical, medical, or mathematical problems; and we never will!"

A burst of applause. Cremonini waited till it had died down, and turned again to Galileo.

"Thus, if the future fulfills our hopes and we greet you, most learned and excellent sir, as one of our colleagues, do not seek the real strength of your achievements in disproving this or that philosophical school, in some of its details, but rather in the certain knowledge that here your work will never be hampered by meddling influences. Once you are convinced of any truth, you can proclaim it freely. Some perhaps will disagree with your statements. Then we shall fight, but only with the weapons of thought. In the name of us all I welcome you most affectionately to the free soil of the Republic; and I wish to beg you to imprint our motto on your heart: Render unto Caesar the things that are Caesar's, unto God the things that are God's, and give to learning its full due!"

He sat down: all the guests applauded him. Cremonini sat bowing his acknowledgments. But they were clamoring already for Galileo. They demanded an answer. After some hesitation he rose. Silence fell.

"Your Excellencies, masters of learning," he began, "I cannot tell you how much these good words mean to me. They are too kind to permit me to do them justice. I feel that if I tried to answer them seriously my halting Tuscan would make you laugh."

They smiled with pleasant nods, encouraging him.

"I won't presume on the patience of my gracious hosts. I can only say that I value from the bottom of my heart the wisdom of Messer Cremonini, and that his wisdom fills me with infinite peace. For, indeed, during my short career all that I have considered untenable and tried to disprove, because it seemed false to me, has sought refuge behind the authority of the Church. There is darkness behind the clerical cloak. I have no greater longing than to be with those who try to light up that darkness. But that does not depend on me. Your Excellencies, I like plain speech. I tell you that my heart's desire is to hold a professorship in Padua. Help me to get it, and I promise you shall never regret. Will you help me, please?"

Looking around with a pleading smile on his face, there was something of the trust of a little boy in him. The company laughed, cheered him, came crowding around him. Then everybody returned to his place, and they began to talk. Pinelli drew him aside.

"I've asked nearly everyone, my friend. And I must congratulate you on winning everyone here. They're all enthusiastic about you. The support of the university council is assured. Now we have to gain the support of Venice."

"Shall we succeed?"

Pinelli nodded, smiling.

"Now that I know you, I'm certain we shall. Your proper place is here with us. You seem surprised—"

"Because in Pisa everybody considered me unbearable. The feeling that anyone could like me is so strange that I'm confused by it." Pinelli laughed:

"All right. Sit down, drink, and get used to it."

Two guests cried out from either side of his empty chair:

"We can't allow this. The host is monopolizing our friend!"

Galileo went back to his place, radiant with happiness.

XI

His lodgings in Venice were poor, but all he needed was a bed. And every morning when he opened his eyes he smiled at the first stirring of consciousness. He was young and healthy, he was a genius, his affairs were progressing well, and the magic city had enchanted him.

"The *marangona*," he thought happily, as he washed himself.

He knew already that the morning bells were called thus in Venice. Their tremulous music filled his room through the open window. And he heard the silence of Venice: the eternal murmur of her waters. This strange, continuous noise, heard still while he slept, adding a background of the infinite to every moment of his life. Sometimes the musical, drawling cry of the gondoliers:

—*A-oel!*

This was their warning when the gondola turned out of a narrow canal.

—*Sia stali!*

Keep right!

—*Sia premi!*

Keep left!

—*Sia di lungo!*

Keep straight ahead!

At first no foreigner understands this; he has to learn it as he learns the Venetian speech; it is something different. It is softly pronounced; the vowels drop from the end of words and the words themselves are soft and full of color and of varying taste.

While he dressed, he suddenly closed his eyes. He wanted to think of the Grand Canal, since he could not wait till he was ready, and could see it with his bodily sight. It came back to him with its dark green water, bordered by white and golden and rose-colored palaces, and then the black, slowly gliding gondolas. The gondolier stood at the stern, a red cap on his head, leaning on his long pole, with short thrusts impelling his black swan. How could he drive it on so quickly with such effortless strokes? The gondola swung, the rower dipped his oar.

"*A-oel!*" came the cry through the open window as though his dream-gondolier were answering. Galileo put on his hose and doublet. He drank the orange juice which he had prepared for breakfast overnight, so as not to light his pipe with his stomach empty. Then he ran down the narrow wooden stairs, stepped into the alley where two people could not pass, and hurried on under the washing strung between the windows. At last he reached the waterside. Here he stopped and looked around. He was never tired of it. He still found Venice a little unreal, a city which was unbelievable.

Having stood for a while, he set out again. If you have no money for a gondola, you can walk all over Venice, provided that you know the way and are willing to go the long way round. He had learned how to get to the Rialto, the latest wonder of the town, which was still unfinished but open already to traffic. There were shops on its marble body, just as on the Ponte Vecchio in Florence. A great many people were standing at the head of the bridge, arguing in their whirlwind dialect, bargaining or telling of bargains they had made.

It was easy to get from here to the Merceria and to make his way along the labyrinth of crowded shops to the corner of the Procurazio. There, wonder of unbelievable wonders, St. Mark's Square lay before his eyes. To his left in its Byzantine pomp the Cathedral, opposite the tall square, its white campanile fluted with coral lines, and on either side of the marble-flagged Piazza the palaces with their row of arcades. The square was open only on its third side, where showed the irregular group of smaller houses. But, if he turned his glance again to the left across the hovering flock of pigeons, he was spellbound by the Doge's Palace in white and rose-colored marble, its lovely columns rising tier on tier. Two columns stood at the water's edge, one with the older, now faithlessly abandoned, patron of Venice, St. Theodore, with his crocodile; the other crowned by the winged lion of St. Mark. Between them the sea, glittering in majestic caprice, a radiant blue flecked with dazzling gold. Under the Rialto the water had been warm and green, but here it was different again.

This was the usual beginning of the day for Galileo. Here he came every morning before he started his round of petitions. He had managed to see all three *riformatori*. And he found them all exactly as the Marchese had described them. Michiel was a sour, sick, nervous man; Zorzi jovial and loud, gay and honest; Contarini pedantic, vain, and slow-witted. After his first visit he had called several times on each of them. He was surprised to see how differently things went here. There were officials in Pisa who settled the affairs of the university, but they considered this business a mere formality, a showy tribute to their position, and asked for no say in matters of learning. But these Venetian patricians were very scholarly, well versed in the affairs of the Bo. At first all three had seemed uncertain whether Moletti's chair should be filled at once. But perhaps they had done enough to respect his memory, and the university curriculum was certainly not complete without mathematics. It seemed far harder to decide whether or not the young aspirant was worthy to fill the place of so great a scholar. The three *riformatori* made searching inquiries. They cross-examined, talked about different, unrelated subjects, with the secret, or at least half-hidden, intention of making sure that his general knowledge was up to standard. They invited him to dinner and watched his table manners, his gestures, his general behavior.

And Galileo had to pay many other visits with letters from the Marchese, Pinelli, and others: mostly to people who could put in a word for him with the three. He made the acquaintance of a number of influential men. In the end he lost count of many of them, and had to make notes of all their promises.

All these calls brought success. Only Contarini, the third *riformatore,* still held aloof, and mentioned that the excellent Magini of Bologna was also a candidate. But he was the only one to bring that up. Even here the Marchese's advice was useful. Galileo visited Giacomo Contarini, who received him with a great show of sympathy, promised everything, and succeeded in winning his cousin, Zaccario Contarini, on his behalf.

And the supplicant was given other help beside this for his professorship. Michiel, the morose *riformatore* from whom he had expected the least, questioned him so long about his financial status that at last Galileo confessed his poverty. Whereupon the tetchy, nervous Michiel muttered that something would have to be done, that he would see Pinelli about it, as he had to visit Padua soon. Three days later came a message from Pinelli that Michiel offered the candidate a loan. And next day he received a letter:

> To-day I have spoken to His Excellency the *Riformatore* Michiel, who tells me that he will lend Your Honor two hundred gold florins without security.

And Michiel, the grumbling, the morose, sent two hundred gold pieces! Galileo had never seen so much money. It came in the nick of time, when he had to settle some pressing debts and send home a substantial sum to Landucci, who was dunning him for his share of the dowry. He could even keep something for himself, and know for the first time in his life how it feels to finger a little gold.

Sometimes he felt inclined to amuse himself, and found a new friend to share his pleasure. This friend, Benedetto Zorzi, was the son of the *riformatore*, a very gay and pleasant young man. Their friendship began at his father's house, and they went on meeting. Benedetto showed the city to Galileo, explaining its sights; he knew the secrets of every palace along the Grand Canal, which family owned it, and all its scandals, all the gossip and rumors of Venice, the Most Serene. They drank together, and Benedetto had always paid. Now it was Galileo's turn. So they made a night of it, and walked at dawn, still dazed with wine, under the deserted arcades of St. Mark's Square, arguing about God. Galileo was naturally religious; he had no doubts in any matter of faith. Zorzi argued that you could be sure of nothing, not even of the existence of God; that it was foolish to go to confession, to pray and fast without really knowing why. They were still drunk, and almost began to quarrel; two *sbirri* appeared between the dark columns and began to question them; but, when one of these two noisy young men proved that his father was a senator, they soon disappeared. Next day they were sober. Their friendship was as strong and pleasant as ever.

Two weeks of the lovely Venice autumn had slipped away—the day came for the three *riformatori* to hold a conference on university affairs, among them the mathematical professorship. Galileo was told that they were to meet at eight o'clock in the morning in the Doge's Palace. It was not certain how long the conference would take. But if he wanted to hear their decision at once, he must wait at the Scala dei Giganti, where the *riformatori* would pass on their way home.

So he lounged in front of the Doge's Palace, although it was not yet eight o'clock. He went to the water's edge and looked out to sea, at ships passing or riding at anchor. There were small *mestieretti* and *bragozzi,* little fishing vessels coming from Chioggia. Then the *colli,* the great merchant ships. He saw some *carracca*-sailing boats, *fusti,* and huge armed galleys which he still could not distinguish from each other, although Benedetto Zorzi had once spent the whole afternoon explaining the difference between *galeri, galeazzi,* and *galeoni,* all of which were "galleys." He idled on the stone quay, watching the crowded, bustling harbor, bemused by the red and brown sails, the rich gilding of the galleys, the radiant blue of the water between. The sun was burning; this shimmering heat was almost visible in the vibrant air.

Then he began to watch the people. Petitioners approached the Doge's Palace, sweating in their holiday clothes, their heels clattering on the flags. Half-naked urchins played with a small black dog. Six men strained their naked backs to lift a chest out of a gondola. It must have contained some metal or marble piece, to judge by its weight. Galleymen got out of small boats, stripped to the waist, spots of pitch on their linen trousers, their chests and backs almost black from the sun. Ushers were coming and going with parchment rolls. Liveried *gondolieri* were standing about awaiting their masters. A company of pikemen marched stiffly from the Merceria; on the corner they turned toward the Riva dei Schiavoni, probably on their way to barracks. There were few women in the crowd. Wives stayed at home; servants did not visit this part of the city where there were no markets.

This was Venice, in the forenoon heat of a September weekday. The young Florentine watched it, tense with anxiety. Would Venice avail herself of his mind and knowledge, give him a livelihood and, what mattered even more, his chance to work, to explore, to experiment? If she did, his life would really begin. If not, then let the devil take Galileo!

It was almost eleven when he saw the three *riformatori* coming out of the Palace. He had left his place at the foot of the Scala dei Giganti. He rushed back with scarcely voice enough to greet them. Zorzi was the first to tell him the news.

"Your business is settled, my friend. We've decided to fill the chair, and employ you. You will receive an official notification, but you may already consider yourself a professor. Your commission is not for the usual short time, but for four years, with a prolongation of two. We've decided this so that no insecurity may hamper you in your scientific work."

The young professor could only stand smiling in his embarrassment, forgetting even to speak his thanks.

"Don't you want to know about your salary?" Michiel asked.

"Oh, Your Excellency . . . yes, I'd like to know. . . ."

"We've decided to increase by half what they gave you at Pisa. So you'll get a hundred and eighty gold florins a year."

"A hundred and eighty? But I had only sixty at Pisa. This is three times as much."

"You're wrong, *caro mio*. A gold florin is equal to five Venetian lire here; that is, two and half Italian lire. If you reckon the difference in currency, you had three hundred lire a year at Pisa, while here you'll get four hundred and fifty."

Galileo Galilei stared blankly at the three *riformatori*. Zorzi laughed.

"A nice mathematician, I must say! Can't you even do this simple sum in your head? For shame, signor! Aristotle would have seen that instantly. Well, reckon it out at home on paper, and you'll find that you have to resign yourself to getting thirty-seven and a half lire a month instead of the twenty-five they gave you at Pisa."

Contarini added, with almost malicious glee:

"But you won't get it all, because by the rules of the university we deduct two and a half per cent. That's twenty-five Venetian lire and twelve soldi. And you'll have to pay three and a half lire for the document containing your appointment."

"Yes, sir," said Galileo obediently.

They were still standing in the sun. Zorzi patted him on the shoulder:

"Well, young man, be more careful in your lectures, and try to multiply a little more accurately. And let me welcome you most affectionately in the name of the Most Serene Republic among the professors of the Bo. The term begins on St. Luke's Day, October 18th. What are your plans till then?"

"I thought, Your Excellencies, I'd go to Padua at once, try to find lodgings, introduce myself to those whom I haven't yet met. Then I must return to Florence to settle my family affairs. I must be quick about it, because today is September 20th. I've scarcely a month in which to do everything and move my things."

"And you'll have to come back here in the meantime."

"Here? Why?"

"Naturally. You've to report for your documents; this you must do in person. Then there are other formalities. Your documents will be ready in three or four days. Go to Padua now and return in a week. Then you can leave for Florence. Well, a week from today, you understand? How much is the sum of twenty and seven, professor?"

"Twenty and seven?" said Aristotle's happily radiant enemy. "Twenty and seven make twenty-six. Because I shall be here by then."

The *riformatori* nodded, then went on their stately way toward the Piazzetta. Their liveried gondoliers sprang up to meet them. Galileo waited an instant before he turned.

He walked in the opposite direction, and went straight into the Cathedral. He passed under the Zuccaro mosaic and then stood still. He did not search for altar or image, but stood in the middle of the church. He prayed. With a leaping heart, overflowing with happiness. There were no words to his prayer; he stammered even in his thoughts. He thought only of God and knew the deepest gratitude he had ever felt. He did not even join his hands, but what he felt brought tears to his eyes.

These few minutes refreshed him, as a bath refreshes a tired man. He left the Cathedral, and went in search of Benedetto Zorzi. He knew that his friend spent this time of the day in a small inn on the other side of the clock tower where they met every day before they dined. He looked up at the gold and blue face of the clock, out of which two toy negroes with hammers suddenly came; they began beating out the chime.

Benedetto sat in the cool of his tavern.

"I can't join you," Galileo said. "I must hurry to my lodgings. I'm going to Padua. I've got the professorship."

"I know! My father told me so this morning. Whatever Contarini might say, he and Michiel had decided for you. What shall we do now? Wait, I'll come with you, and we can talk on our way."

He paid his host, and they set out along the Merceria. There was a strong smell of fish around them. The terrible heat kept everybody indoors; there were few people even in front of the shops.

"There's something I've wanted to ask you for a long time," Galileo began. "The wife of our former Prince was a girl from Venice. . . ."

"Bianca Cappello. I know. What of her?"

"I'd be interested to see where she lived. Do you know, by any chance?"

"Of course I do. The Palazzo Cappello is still standing, opposite the Salviati bank. Piero Bonaventuri, who eloped with her, used to work there. Shall we go that way?"

"Not now. Next week, when I'm back."

He packed his bundle, sent for a gondola, and was rowed to the pier. He took leave of Benedetto, who went home to dine. He got into the large rowboat, was rowed to the mainland, and was delighted to find the stagecoach already waiting. There were some passengers in it, also on their way to Padua. Galileo booked his place and climbed into the coach. His neighbor glanced at him and said:

"Pardon me, but aren't you Messer Galileo, the mathematician?"

"Yes. Oh, I know you, Messer! Your Excellency, Signor Uguccioni, our Ambassador to Venice. Pardon me for not having recognized you."

They began an amiable talk. Galileo told the Ambassador of his triumph. Uguccioni congratulated him politely, and then said:

"So now you'll have to request the Grand Duke to give you leave to change your citizenship."

"I beg your pardon? I don't understand . . ."

"Didn't you know? You can't take office under a foreign republic and still remain a subject of Tuscany. You must ask His Highness Fernando to release you from your oath of fealty. Of course, it's only a formality; I've no doubt they won't raise any difficulties."

Galileo was startled.

"I can no longer be a citizen of Florence?"

"Not if you intend to serve the Republic in Venetian territory. That goes without saying."

"Oh, yes, I see," Galileo quietly answered.

This was bitter news. His joy was suddenly extinguished. He was lost in his thoughts, and scarcely spoke all the rest of the way.

XII

The term began with the usual ceremonies on St. Luke's Day, but the new professor had to wait for his first lecture. When the syllabus was being prepared, he had been asked to teach astronomy and geometry, and he had to prepare his material carefully. Then again, it was hard to fit in his lessons among the rest. For years every professor had had his schedule, which must not be disturbed.

It took two months before the new professor could appear in front of his students. By an ancient Paduan tradition, he had first to deliver a Latin oration instead of a lesson; to sketch the importance of his subject, the basic principles of his work and general philosophy.

The room which Messer Antonio Rosato, the Chief Proctor of the Artista faculty, had chosen for him, was crowded to the last seat. But there was nothing unusual in that, since it was one of the smallest halls available. In accordance with the usual custom, the Dean led in the new professor, followed by all the professors of the faculty. Galileo looked inquisitively at his hearers. Some of them he had often seen in the street or precincts of the university. His heart lit up with a strange new joy. He felt like a newly married lover alone with his bride. He longed to embrace these young souls and say: "You are mine; you were given to me to teach and guide."

But now he had first to make a speech. He had written his long oration in choicest Latin some days before and was well prepared. When the Dean had formally introduced him he began to deliver it, with grave dignity, pronouncing the sonorous chiseled sentences with a seriousness befitting the occasion. He did not feel in the least nervous, since his fiery thoughts burned down all barriers between him and his hearers. Had he talked to one across a table, he would have felt ashamed to speak so formally; suddenly he caught sight of a face, to which he addressed himself; he forgot to be solemn. Really, this occasion was just as intimate. For a few minutes he kept to the text of his Latin speech, and then perceived that he had wandered away from it. He spoke of the delights of knowledge, the pleasure and glory of the mind, of how beautiful and attractive was geometry.

"Just think, without geometry there could be no craftsmanship or architecture! It is true that when you see some hideous building or a glass which has an ugly shape you begin to wish that there had been no geometry. But think of the Doge's Palace; think of a Murano vase with glass roses. Without geometry these beauties would be absent from human life. The slate on which you scribbled the first geometrical diagrams was a philosopher's stone. Geometry gives you magic wings to fly into the infinite heaven, glance around among the shining multitude of planets and fixed stars, like the angels themselves. Whoever understands geometry understands everything in the world. Anyone who knows nothing of geometry should close his books, he can never know any other science! Geometry teaches us real learning because this science explains itself. Whoever contradicts geometry, denies self-evident truth. . . . And let me tell you something else . . . a secret. . . ."

His voice changed to the sly, joking tone of the gossip; he almost winked:

"By geometry you can tell an ass when you see him. In other sciences anyone can defend stupidities; the most you can do with him is to argue. But there's no arguing here; only one truth exists. And whoever doesn't see it is an ass. Respect geometry, the alert watchdog of the house of wisdom. Geometry is the only sure test of fools."

He continued at random, passing from one thing to the next, selecting odds and ends from his vast subject. He enjoyed himself thoroughly; there was something in the atmosphere of the room which made him feel how well they were listening. He was sorry to notice the Dean making covert signals; his time was up. So, by a cunning twist of speech, he jumped back to the peroration of his rehearsed speech. His voice became solemn again, his manner dignified. And he rounded off with a perfect sentence in ornately classical Latin the gay patter which had taken the place of his written speech.

The students applauded madly. Wherever he looked, he saw interest and affection. As if every face was saying: This is our man. And he remembered dimly, for a moment, his lectures at Pisa, which always dragged and seemed to take eternities. Why was this? What was the difference between Pisa and Padua? He retired in an outburst of applause; his smiling colleagues came to congratulate him, though a few could scarcely hide their envy. In the passage he was accosted by Messer Rosato, the Chief Proctor.

"Your honor, we're going to change your lecture room."

"But why?"

"I have served the Bo for a long time. If we keep you in this room, there will be a quarrel at your next lecture, perhaps even fighting among those who want to get to it but can't. You shall deliver it in the great lecture hall of the Artista faculty, which is our largest."

He knew that this was the highest compliment. But there were other tokens of success. The same day a host of people visited Pinelli's house, among them many leading men of the town. Count Querengo, the provost, came, and many others whom he had never seen before. A few days later letters began to arrive. The news of his great triumph sped to Vicenza. Bissaro wrote to him. Giacomo Contarini sent him warm congratulations from Venice.

His name appeared at last on the curriculum of the university. *"Galileo Galilei: Sfera e Euclide,"* which proclaimed that the new professor was lecturing on the astronomy of the spheres and Euclid's geometry.

It was winter now, the thirteenth of December, and very cold. He was glad of this; he always liked the number thirteen. Through a cold drizzle he hurried to the university. All around him students trudged in the same direction, blowing into their hands. When he passed under the winged lion at the entrance, the Chief Proctor was awaiting him.

"What did I tell you, Your Honor? The hall is packed. Some are even standing."

He walked gaily upstairs. In front of the lecture hall a dense crowd stood, jostling and quarreling in Latin. He could hardly make his way through them, and it was just as hard to get to his desk. The Proctor helped him. Already he was on the rostrum but could not begin with the door still open. Late-comers were refusing to be locked out, demanding that the door should not be closed. Rosato had to fight his way there and use his full authority to get order.

"In the Name of the Father, the Son, and the Holy Ghost!"

Galileo paused and smiled.

"My sons, listen to me. Don't take down my lectures. Let everyone put into writing at home whatever he remembers and, if he has doubts, let him ask his fellow students. There shan't be any dictating here. Anyone who wants to study that way had better go to the Jesuit school; then we shall be less of a crowd. Well? Nobody leaving? Speak out freely, let me hear you! Well?"

"We are staying!" cried the first daring voice.

Galileo laughed. So did all the others. It was a gay and noisy beginning. Then unexpected applause. The students applauded their own gaiety. Galileo nodded.

"*Bene.* Listen to me then. First of all, I'll teach you something very stupid. It is a single word: *Almagest.* You must remember it, yet I may as well tell you at once that it makes no sense at all. But everything has some origin, even nonsense. This, for instance, comes from the fact that fifteen hundred years ago there lived in Egypt an astronomer named Ptolemy who wrote a book entitled: *Megale syntaxis tes astronomias.* Who knows Greek? Translate it for me. Don't all talk at the same time. Or I'll say to you what a colleague of mine said at Pisa some years ago. His name doesn't matter. This professor was continually interrupted, especially by one of his pupils who was always whispering to his neighbor. At last the professor became furious and burst out: 'It's unbearable to think that my lecture should be worth so little that an ox has to bellow every time I begin to speak.' "

Stormy laughter. The students were delighted. What a man!

"So only one of you should speak up. Here you, you with the red hair, answer me. You seem to be a clever chap. Well?"

" 'The Great Summary of Astronomy.' "

"Right. What is your name?"

"Gellio Jasceride, at your service."

"Excellent. Well, the work of the Egyptian Ptolemy was translated at the command of a Baghdad Caliph into Arabian. You know that the article of the Arabs is '*al.*' You've all heard about the Spanish-Arabian words like *Al*cazar, *Al*hambra, or *al*gebra. The Arabians called this astronomical work which became very famous among them '*al megale,*' 'The great.' Or '*al megiste,*' 'the greatest.' This Spanish-Greek mixture was twisted during the centuries, and became Almagest. I must tell you again that it scarcely makes any sense, but it belongs to general knowledge. You'll be taught a lot of nonsense anyhow before you're educated."

The students roared, enjoyed themselves, and listened entranced.

"But now we ought to talk some sense. For a long time science knew only the Arab translation of this Almagest; but in the last century, when humanism made the study of ancient manuscripts fashionable in Italy, they found somehow the original Greek text; and a humanist, called Giorgio di Trebisondo, translated it into Latin. It was published at Venice, and this is the book I'm going to explain to you. In the first place, I must tell you about the theory of epicycles. Are you listening?"

"We are!" they called out in unison.

"Before that you must know about the so-called eccentric circles, which were discovered before Ptolemy wrote his book. But, to understand that, you must get acquainted with a still earlier astronomer, called Hipparchus. This man explained the irregularity of the planets' movement by these eccentric circles. But what are the planets? Well, here we are. Listen carefully: As you know, the center of the universe is the earth. . . ."

He continued, stopping sometimes to tell a joke, address his words to a single member of the audience, and ask his name at the same time. They listened to him with deep enjoyment. When he finished, there was an almost audible sigh of relief. The Chief Proctor told him afterward:

"I don't know, Your Honor," he laughed, "what will happen. We need a still larger hall. I'll ask the Giurista for theirs. But we can't go into the Cathedral."

The next lesson he delivered in the *aula* of the law faculty. The success of the new professor was something unique. It found its echoes in many cities. The first two who congratulated him were Guidubaldo del Monte from Pesaro and Mazzoni from Pisa. And Mazzoni's letter contained very interesting news. He told Galileo how surprised the professors at Pisa were at the triumph of their despised colleague. Some denied it fervently; others contemptuously shrugged and tried to belittle the standards of Padua; but there were some who took Galileo's part. Mercuriali, the old professor of medicine, was telling everyone what a very talented young man he had always considered him. Mazzoni said something to the effect that the old man who had been a professor of Padua would be glad to receive a few friendly lines from his former colleague.

Galileo wondered and smiled. Mercuriali had really been the least spiteful of his detractors in Pisa. So he wrote to him a few polite lines with the magnanimity of a happy man, telling Mercuriali that they still remembered him in Padua, and addressing him as "The Palace Count" because this title had been conferred on him after curing the Emperor Maximilian. And the answer amused him very much:

Most Gracious Sir,

Till now I did not believe that mathematicians, who only like sober realities, could find their pleasure in surpassing the masters of eloquence. But your letter, which I received yesterday, changed this belief of mine, and I see that even mathematicians strive to win us by their readiness to please. Your words are more honeyed than I deserve; but perhaps you wrote them in the belief that some idle rumors had reached my ears, and you wished to console me. Let it be thus, if you would have it so! I am certain that at least I possess the affection of your most esteemed self, whom I tried to praise with my humble words. Your Excellency may remember how once I expressed the opinion that only the University of Padua would be a fitting home for your talents. . . .

Galileo smiled and shook his head. He recalled what a useless idler he had been in the eyes of this Pisa sage.

. . . No doubt they still remember me at Padua, since I lectured there for eighteen years, and sincerely respected most of my colleagues, to whom I send my humblest greetings, remaining at the same time with all my family your Honor's most sincere and humble and obedient servant,

HIERONIMO MERCURIALI.

Galileo dropped the letter and began to think. He would be twenty-nine in a few days; Mercuriali was sixty-two. He had a salary of twenty-seven and a half lire a month, Mercuriali was the best paid of all the Italian university professors, with a salary of six hundred and ten.

But then he shrugged. He would not exchange his knowledge with this old man. He handed the letter to Pinelli, then returned to his studies. He was deep in the problems of fortification, to get as many well-paying private pupils as possible. The young noblemen who came to study at Padua took more interest in that than in other subjects, because it was necessary to the defense of their castles and estates. They would come to him, he was sure of that. Padua was a pleasant city; and, when one is twenty-nine and healthy, life can be very good indeed.

XIII

It was a glorious spring; one could sit in the open air at noon. Galileo carried a table to the garden porch and wrote a letter. It had to be carefully composed: it dealt with a scientific problem in which he himself was very much interested, and was addressed to Giacomo Contarini, who had helped to win over the third *riformatore*.

Most Excellent Sir!
Through Messer Giovan Vincenzo Pinelli I was instructed about the question raised by Your Excellency. I will try to give the answer which seems to me most truthful. The question was whether smaller or greater power was needed for the progress of a galley according to the position of the oarsmen inside the ship or on deck. In my opinion there is no difference in this, because the conditions of physical power are the same in both cases. An oar should be considered as a lever. If the relation of power, resistance, and action is the same, the resulting power of the lever is also equal. This thesis is of general inference and unchangeable. . . .

The sound of a lute came from the house. Galileo looked up from his letter. This sound still worried him. His younger brother, Michelagnolo, had been living with him for quite a long time now. In Florence things had gone from bad to worse. His family were forever quarreling. Landucci could not abide the hot-tempered Signora Giulia; her own children, even, were wearying of her shrewishness. In the meantime Anna, the second girl, whom they called Lena, had also married; and Livia, the youngest, had entered the San Giuliano nunnery to study in peace. Michelagnolo had been left alone with his mother, with whom he quarreled from morning to night. Galileo could find no other remedy except to have his younger brother to live with him; let the two girls look after their mother and decide with which of them she should live.

Michelagnolo was now eighteen. Galileo had seldom seen him in the past few years; he was almost a stranger. The boy differed strangely from all his family. He had only one Galilei characteristic: his father's love and talent for music. Otherwise he was utterly different from his brother and sisters. Shorter than Galileo, with fair hair, a thin fragile body, he did not like to talk, remained always reserved and shy. He neither showed affection nor seemed to desire it. Nobody could discover what was in him. When his brother told him that among the many foreigners in Padua he might hope to find some who would want to learn music, and so help to contribute to their expenses, he showed no enthusiasm. Galileo got him a few pupils, and Michelagnolo taught them diligently, but did nothing to get new ones for himself. On his first payment for the lessons, he kept back more than he admitted. He cheated his brother, who saw it instantly.

But Galileo never mentioned it; for, though he liked to argue and win his argument, this was a triumph which did not tempt him. Like so many men who have never known the glow of passionate love, he clung to his kindred like a child. Such men are apt to turn to their own, in search of human warmth which the world denies them. So he shut his eyes and carefully avoided embarrassing questions, so as not to have to rebuke his brother.

Michelagnolo was a good musician. To him, all instruments were the same; he handled the lute, the viola da gamba, the pipes, with equal skill. Now that they were living together, Galileo took great pleasure in music. When he tired of work, of private lessons and much reading, he would sit down to make music with his brother. He loved the old tunes they had heard as boys, especially catches and formal part-songs, with their gay, slyly sensual words. But the boy cared for none of this; he preferred to chase pretty girls in the city streets. But he could not refuse the request of his brother. He took his viol and began to tune it carelessly, using with trained skill the hand which held the bow. Then he asked indifferently:

"What shall we play?"

Galileo liked the old songs of their childhood. He tinkled the lute and hummed the air. He played very well himself and, though he lacked practice, his inborn musical instinct and perfect hearing helped him out. Sometimes the people in the street stood outside and enjoyed the concert from beginning to end.

But often, when the brother was strumming, Galileo had more important cares. Good music would not have disturbed him, but the wretched stammering tinkle of the lessons was a sore annoyance. He could not say anything. Michelagnolo would have been only too glad to stop giving lessons and let his brother make up the lost fees. At such times Galileo would leave his work and try to find another task which did not need such concentration. Now, while he sat writing his letter to Contarini, the strumming began. He sighed, stood up, and walked a few restless steps, then he took his hat and told the maid that he would take a short walk.

It was only a few yards to the botanical garden, the empire of his colleague Cortusio. The garden had been created fifty years previously by the bounty of the Serenissima, and its saplings had become full grown and leafy. There was a bench in the botanical garden, under a jutting bastion of the ancient battlement. This was Galileo's favorite seat. If he was tired of walking, he sat down, leaned back and, closing his eyes, turned his face to the sun. He looked like an idler, but his brain was busy all the time: he was planning a treatise on mechanics. Its scope would be small, but it would be just the kind of book he wanted, for he planned this year to finish the lectures on the spheres and Euclid and start on mechanics next year. But he would not slavishly annotate Euclid and Ptolemy; this theory of mechanics would be—Galileo's!

He had already finished the introduction. He thought of it here in the sun on the quiet bench: "Before we begin to discuss the mechanical instruments, I find it extremely important to explain their advantages and drawbacks. This is worth scrutinizing; the more so because I see the whole world of the learned disappointed at getting no results, because they want to use machines for tasks which are impossible in themselves. They are deceived in thinking that they can lift the most gigantic weights with a small power.

"Really what they want is to cheat Nature, although it is her unalterable law that no resistance can be overcome by a power less than its equal. I hope to prove in my further comments how false this supposition is."

Because not only Aristotle had been wrong . . . but Archimedes too. Archimedes discovered the purchase. What was a purchase? Imagine a stonemason standing on the scaffolding of the half-built house and shouting. A huge block of marble has to be pulled up. The wheel of the pulley is on the scaffolding, a rope is made fast along its edge. One end of the rope is slung around the marble block, the other is pulled by the workmen. They pull the rope downward, while on the other side the block of marble is rising. Now, Archimedes invented a pulley where the marble block was not right at the end of the rope. He fastened the rope to the scaffolding, adjusted another pulley to it and so on, creating a system of pulleys, called a purchase, where the pulleys, lifting each other, finally lifted the block of marble. Plutarch said that after inventing it, Archimedes cried out in his pride: "δός μοι ποῦ στῶ, καὶ τὴν γῆν κινήσω."

"Give me one fixed point, I'll move the earth!" He thought that if he could fasten his purchase outside the earth and hang the earth on the pulleys, he could lift this weight by the use of many thousand pulleys with his little finger. Up to now everybody was convinced of the truth of this statement. "Archimedes said it." Therefore it was impossible to doubt. But to lift something was to triumph over the resistance of a weight. The weight represented a certain power: it was common sense to suppose that to vanquish this power, equal strength was necessary.

The trouble was that ideas were still confused. "Weight," "power," "movement," were used by science indiscriminately. Galileo had examined these words again and again to find something new, not among, but above them; there it hovered unnamed. And then he found it, and called it *"momentum."*

What was momentum? "I call *momentum* the longing of every object," he would say in the second chapter of his work, "to fall to earth." It has been said that this desire, this inclination, can simply be defined as the weight of the object. But no, says the inventor of new mechanics; for what happens when a small child sits on one end of a seesaw with his fat, heavy nurse on the other? Suppose one end much longer than the other. The nurse would be sitting on the shorter end, the child on the longer. And yet the nurse would be up in the air, while the child swung down. The nurse was much heavier than the child. But her *momentum* was smaller.

He was going to write a very clear and witty little treatise refuting Archimedes. He stood up and stretched himself. Under exotic palms brought from distant lands he made his way homeward. He felt gay and content. At the gate he met Cortusio, the professor of botany.

"What news, *amico?*"

"I've been doing a little thinking in the garden. In fact, I've managed to do a good deal."

"Indeed?"

"First I threw the earth from its orbit, and then I invented the *perpetuum mobile*."

Cortusio smiled. This young professor was always joking. He behaved like one of his older students. That was why they liked him so much. He nodded, and passed on to the delights of his flowers.

At home Galileo found the table laid for dinner.

"Any news?" he asked, ladling out the steaming minestrone.

"Yes," Michelagnolo said. "Great news. The wheelwright who was our neighbor in Florence has been here."

"Oh, why didn't you send for me? What did he say?"

"Virginia has had a baby."

"What? Already? Is it a boy or a girl?"

"Boy. They've christened him Vincenzo."

"After poor father. He didn't live to see his first grandchild. Didn't they send a letter with the wheelwright?"

"No, only another message. Lena is also expecting a baby. Her husband has gone to Spain on business, and she's alone with mother. She can't live with her. All the scenes may harm the child. And she can't move to Virginia's when there's a child there too. And you know how mean Benedetto is. So Lena wants to come to Padua, because she'd like to see you and rest a little from all the din."

"I see. She's welcome, but how are we going to live here? There's no room. . . ."

"Don't worry about that; there's some other news too."

"Well, yes? Go on."

"Well, I had a long talk again with the Pole to whom I've been giving lessons. He tells me that musicians live royally in his country. Dukes and counts have huge estates. Every day they entertain hundreds of guests; and, of course, they all have orchestras of their own. And they also keep palaces at Cracow or some other big city, where they give banquets in winter. They love music, and when they're drunk they fling their full purses to the musicians."

"Do you think," Galileo hesitated, "that you ought perhaps . . ."

"I think," Michelagnolo said, himself rather hesitant, "that I might beg a few letters of recommendation from the Polish students here; there are many of them at the Bo, and all of them noblemen. I'd only need . . ."

some money for my journey . . . and if you could . . . I mean . . ."

"Naturally," Galileo sighed. "You can't start penniless. . . . Well, I must think it over and write to Lena that you're leaving me, and she can have your room."

"That would be splendid. And you know, the Pole told me that their King, Sigismund, adores music; and if I have any luck I shall get a place in the royal orchestra. . . . And he told me too . . ."

"I didn't mention it before," Galileo interrupted him, "but I think we ought to talk about it since we're talking of money. You really must try to earn your living. Lena's marriage gave no trouble, but Virginia's has saddled us with a great burden. You yourself signed the guarantee for the rest of her dowry. I can't deal with all this; you see yourself how I scrape and starve. Yes, yes, you ought to go to Poland. May the good Lord guide you and let you send me money as soon as possible. Livia is fifteen now; we shall soon have to be finding her a husband. And mother is always asking for money. It would be a blessing for us all if you managed to find some well-paid work."

"Oh, yes, of course . . . Poland is a very cold country, they travel on sledges . . . and just think, there are bells on the horses and . . ."

"Yes, yes, I know. Well, I'll see what money I can find. . . ."

He made a few shy attempts to borrow, but without success. The Polish students were all eager to give his brother letters, but money was more than they could manage. He was still in debt to Michiel and Pinelli. He valued the Marchese Guidubaldo's good will too highly to ask him for a loan. In the end it was Cremonini, the kindly professor of philosophy and a strictly orthodox Aristotelian, who came to his aid. He had been saving for years to buy a vineyard, but now he broke into his savings and lent Galileo fifty scudi.

Michelagnolo departed the next day. He could scarcely stop to take leave of his brother; his mind was already in distant lands where drunken princes threw purses to their musicians.

At the same time Lena arrived. Her husband was a draper, just as old as Vincenzo had been. Poor Lena had lost her beauty and was very thin. Galileo welcomed her with delight. At supper on the first night he asked her, stroking her hand:

"Are you happy with your husband, Lenuccia?"

"Of course I am. Very happy."

But she said it in so half-hearted a voice, so nervously, that he asked no more. He drew back like a snail into its shell. He tried another method of winning her love. He explained his professorship, the organization of Padua University, the fight with the Jesuits, and proudly showed her his diploma, which stated that the Venice Signoria appointed Signor Galileo Galilei "as the worthiest representative of his subject" to the vacant chair of the great Moletti. Lena listened politely, but her face plainly showed that her thoughts were wandering. She remained so distant and unapproachable that after a few more attempts he gave it up. Brother and sister remained strangers. Lena did not even manage the household—she spared herself because of her pregnancy. She came and went like a strange guest, sometimes taking her meals in her own room, saying that she was feeling ill.

The term ended. Galileo began to long for his mother. Although he had suffered so much from her rage, memories of it had not killed his love. He wrote to her that he wanted to spend his vacation in Florence, and asked whether she could receive him.

Signora Giulia took a long time to answer. She mentioned Galileo's suggested visit only at the end of her letter. "I cannot hide from you how things are going here, because you must be prepared if you come home. If you come I shall be overjoyed to see you. But Benedetto is clamoring for his due, which you guaranteed, and says that if ever you set foot in Tuscany he will have you arrested as a debtor. I think he has the legal right to do it, and certainly he would have no scruples. I only tell you because I would not like anything to happen which might cause me fresh sorrow."

Galileo felt a lump in his throat. So Landucci would like to have him arrested. Of course, he could not do it here in free Venice; but at home he need only summon a bailiff.

"Curses on that grasping swine!" he shouted to Lena. "So I can't go home, then!"

And yet he did. He wanted so much to see his mother. At the last moment he borrowed seven hundred scudi at exorbitant interest from the Corsi brothers, paid his debt to Cremonini, kept only a trifle for himself, and gave all the rest to his brother-in-law. Soon he had forgotten the whole thing, and was relieved that he had so long a respite from this wretched business. He was happy and gay. His first year had been a brilliant success, and he had finished his treatise on mechanics. He read it again from beginning to end, and was entranced by his own book.

"I've never read anything half so clever."

XIV

Their reunion was voluble, warm, and emphatic. It was a great delight to play with his small nephew, whom they called Vincenzo Landucci, the latest addition to the family. But the first joy had soon evaporated; quarrels followed and the usual noisy scenes. Even the last day was marked by a maternal thunderstorm provoked by some trifle. It was long before Galileo could free his mind of his mother's curses and abuse. He still heard her angry voice, even when he was back in Padua in his house near the Santa Giustina church. He had sought refuge in his veranda from the heat of the September sun and began to ask himself the real meaning of the pain he had brought back from Florence. It was not merely his mother's rage, he was used to that, as a part of his home. Something worse troubled his soul, but he could not say what. He had to discover it among the events of his holiday. At last he found it: a chance remark. One day he had gone to the Palazzo Pitti to visit Vinta, the Prime Minister. But the whole Court was away for the summer. The young clerk who gave him the information asked:

"How do you live in Padua, Messer Galileo? How does it feel to be a Venetian?"

He evaded the question, but its thorn stuck in his flesh. Now he knew how deeply he loved Tuscany. The suggestion that he was no longer a Tuscan citizen was a kind of insult. He was proud to think himself a Florentine and often boasted to himself that his ancestors had been *gonfalonieri* more than three hundred years ago and had sat in the civil council of Santa Maria Maggiore with the rank of *"eccelsi signori priori."* They were distinguished noblemen, rich merchants, and only became drapers in the later centuries; and even their poorest descendants had kept the family honor unstained. The last, whose full name was Galileo Buonaiuti Galilei, felt himself the pride of his whole race. All the ancient beauty and dignity of Florence, the town of the Medicis, the town of blood and pomp, in some way belonged to him. How could anyone call him a Venetian? It was a mere accident that he had to earn his living in Padua.

Science might hire its soldiers under foreign flags; they owed to the alien flag only their lives, but not their origins. Of course, it would be fine to live at home and follow his calling in a distinguished position like Ostilio Ricci. But that was a dream. In reality he must be happy and grateful to God, who had made of him the youngest professor of so famous and learned a university.

And he was happy. When he entered the *aula* of the *giuristas* for the first time in the new term and looked at the crowded rows of students, his soul rejoiced. He began his lectures on mechanics, prepared for so many months with care and study and incessant thought. His pupils took in every word. It entranced him to think that he was planting a completely new scientific system in hundreds of retentive young minds. These minds would scatter all over Europe like the Olympian torchbearers to carry his light.

It was his custom to branch out into new fields. Without preparation he began to talk at one of his lessons about Tartaglia. He told what witty inventions were known as Tartaglia's, to whom the Venetians had once complained that shipping accidents were frequent on the Malamacco. Several galleys had gone down there, and the wrecks, containing precious freights, were obstructing the sea traffic. Tartaglia, after many scientists had tried in vain to cope with the problem, took two galleys and emptied their holds completely. He placed them on either side of the wreck. Some divers descended with strong ropes and fastened the wreck to the two galleys. And now the galleys were pumped full of sea water, till they were almost wholly submerged. The divers descended again and pulled the ropes tighter. Then Tartaglia began to pump the water out of his galleys. As they became lighter, they came up again; and they lifted the wreck at the same time. By the time all water was pumped out of them, the wreck appeared on the surface and could be salvaged. Tartaglia also invented the wonderful diving bell in which divers could work in perfect safety.

After that Galileo analyzed the words "water" and "invention" and began to talk about hydraulic machines. He spoke of the famous Giuseppe Ceredi, who had invented three different machines for raising water. He had explained them in his treatise entitled *Tre discorsi sopra il modo d'alzar acque da'luoghi bassi* and published twenty-odd years ago in Parma.

"You do well to remember the name of Ceredi," said the lecturer, "because his was a rare intellect. In connection with his own inventions he described a number of devices used for carrying water in Italy and Germany, and called the attention of his readers to their unnecessary complication and clumsiness. 'Inventors without scientific training,' as Ceredi said, 'can find out useful things only by chance; while scientists draw their conclusions consciously, from general principles.' Never forget this! The best of science is not to be acquired from professors and books. The greatest scientist is Nature. Yes, Nature, the greatest mathematician and physicist of all. Do not learn from me, but from her. I am only helping you: opening your eyes to show you her laws better. But to return to our subject. I wanted to tell you about the three inventions of Ceredi. Listen."

He described the first two. He had begun to tell them about the third:

"I've forgotten it. But it doesn't matter. These two are enough. Now I want to tell you about Vitruvius, who was a Roman and gave much time to this problem, although he was often mistaken . . ."

He continued his lecture, but it annoyed him not to be able to remember the third Ceredi machine. When he got home the first thing he did was to look it up among his notes. He had a huge batch of manuscript notes, because he always made a summary of the books he borrowed. He did not find it, so he began to think about the problem. He sketched, pondered, calculated. An idea came, and he sat for hours at his table. He discovered an excellent machine, but still wasn't sure whether it was the invention of Ceredi. He went over his notes again. Now he was really furious and rushed off to Pinelli. His patron was out, so he went into the library alone. He found the Ceredi book and began to read eagerly. Suddenly he shouted and thumped the table. Pinelli found him in this mood.

"What are you so excited about?" he asked.

"An amazing thing, Your Excellency. I wanted to recall someone's invention; and, without knowing I was doing it, I invented a water-carrying machine which must be just the thing for irrigation. And it's completely original."

"I don't understand you. What did you want to find out? What have you invented?"

Galileo told him. He asked for a quill and ink and sketched his machine. Its fundamental principle was simpler and more interesting than Ceredi's. It was so simple that Pinelli too became excited.

"Go home at once, make a drawing, and apply for a patent!"

"Yes, you're quite right! Then . . . I must go. . . ."

He rushed off without taking proper leave. At home he began to pre-pare the detailed drawing. He thought to have done it in a few hours, and then it need only be sent to Venice together with the application, when he could wait in peace for the result. But it happened differently. Because in the drawing the machine developed and became even more in-teresting under his fingers. It could not be so easily drawn. A special knowledge would be necessary to make it perfect. Either he had to find an expert who would make the plan according to his instructions or a craftsman who would prepare a model.

He chose the latter. It took six weeks to make the little toy machine. It was very pretty indeed. If he put it on a table and placed a vessel with water at its side, the little contraption sucked the water and irrigated the tabletop—it was a joy to see; the whole room became soaked. As soon as it was finished, he drew up his application for a patent, addressed to Cicogna, the Doge, himself.

Next day he went with the model and the petition to Venice. He called on his old friend, Benedetto Zorzi, to ask his advice. Benedetto greeted him with affection, and took him at once to the Signoria. The son of the senator knew his way in the labyrinth of the Doge's Palace; they soon found out where they had to file the application. The clerk explained that it had to be signed by six *provveditori* and then submitted to the Doge. The Doge would refer it to the expert committee of law, who would put their opinion into writing and make a proposal. Then the act would return to the Doge and be introduced at a meeting of the council called *Pregadi*. There they would discuss it, vote on it, and announce their decision to the applicant.

"How long does it take to do all this?" Galileo asked anxiously.

"If there is any obstruction, about two years. But if you have influential friends it could be done in six months."

Galileo felt as though someone had stunned him with a blow. It was the beginning of December, and he had dreamed of making a fortune by Christmas, since the Serene Republic would be sure to commission scores of his model, and he would be certain to find a patron to exploit the high profit on these.

"It would be better not to leave the model," Zorzi said. "It might get lost here in all that time."

"What shall I do with it?"

"Give it to me. I'll show it to my father, then he can do his best for your invention, having seen it with his own eyes."

He nodded. Zorzi took the little model. His friend looked downcast.

"*Caro mio,* don't look so upset. We've settled your official business; now let's amuse ourselves. Do you remember those two lads, Magagnati and Boccalini, with whom we drank at the Tre Rose?"

"Dimly."

"Well, I'm going to meet them. We'll find them and then try to discover some really good wine."

In an hour they were sitting together. The two other young men were really old acquaintances. Now he remembered that they had made a night of it the last time when he had been in Venice; he had come then to present himself to the new *riformatori,* Their Excellencies Barbaro and Grimani. The two young dandies knew all about the famous mathematician. They were in high spirits, their credit unlimited, their ages less than twenty-five; so that Galileo, approaching thirty, counted as a wise old man among them.

When he stood up in the late afternoon—fuddled with wine, with a loosened tongue, and told them that he had to go back to Padua, the three young men protested violently.

"Are you lecturing tomorrow?"

"No, but . . ."

"Why don't you stay, then? Any of us can give you a bed for the night."

"It isn't that . . . but, to tell you frankly: I have no money . . ."

They began to laugh.

"Do you think we have? But we can get credit anywhere in Venice."

"But . . . I . . . I can't accept that. . . ."

"What nonsense!" Zorzi cried. "This model is worth a fortune! You'll repay us from the fortune it's going to earn you!"

Galileo was persuaded to stay. Traiano Boccalini proposed another inn, and they took a gondola to the Giudecca, where they drank sweet Cyprian wine in a Jewish *bodega.* Then Girolamo Magagnati took them to the inn behind the Riva dei Schiavoni where the one-eyed Greek patron could always provide gay and pretty girls. They made a long night of it, and it was late on the following afternoon when Galileo started for Padua. In the stagecoach he fell asleep. He woke with a start:

"Where's my model?"

He sat up and shook himself. He tried to remember the night before. In the first inn he had had his model. But was it with them on the Giudecca? The memories of the evening and night were lost in a haze. There was only one thing he remembered clearly: the girl with the black hair and very red lips and loud laughter who rumpled his hair, looking deep into his eyes while he caught her waist. But the model was gone.

He wrote to Zorzi, but heard three days later that Benedetto could not find it either, although he had been the round of all the taverns. Galileo had to resign himself to the fact: his model was lost and he could not afford to have a new one made.

A few weeks later he was called urgently to Provveditore Hieronimo Malipiero about his invention. He went to Venice at once, in pouring rain and chattering cold. He had to wait for almost two hours in the anteroom, before Malipiero received him. The *provveditore* was a gray-haired, stooping, rather deaf patrician.

"I've your application at hand, Messer Galileo."

"Yes, Your Excellency."

"What? Talk louder, I'm hard of hearing!"

"I only said 'Yes, Your Excellency.'"

"Well. Our Most Excellent Doge has commanded us, Provveditori Correr, Soranzo, and myself, to render him expert opinion whether your required patents did not infringe on the rights of any former invention. Could you show us the machine?"

"I'm sorry, Your Excellency, but I can't. I had a small model, but it was lost. I could prepare a new one, if necessary."

"I see. Could you explain it at least by word?"

Galileo started to explain the fundamental principles of his invention at the top of his voice. But when he was halfway, Malipiero, who apparently didn't understand a word of it, interrupted him:

"Thank you. I see everything. A new idea; no infringement of any old one. Thank you, my friend, that was all."

This was at the beginning of February. Some weeks later the three experts prepared their report and advised the grant of a patent for twenty years. Then spring came and nothing happened. It was September when Galileo received the official notification that he would be granted a patent if he would present a new model within a year. Those who infringed on his patent should pay a fine of three hundred ducats.

On the evening when he received the letter, he was supping with Pinelli. There were many other guests, among them Tommaso Morosini, the Mayor of Padua. After supper the young professor showed his patent to the company.

"Of course, you'll have the model made at once?" the Mayor said.

Galileo shrugged.

"I don't know. Frankly, I'm rather tired of the whole thing. It interests me only as long as I'm working on it. If the machine, which serves irrigation, is useful, the Republic will have it made. They have my drawings."

"But listen, there's money in it! It would be worth while to take it up."

"Yes, that's true. Well, I'll order a model."

He began to talk of something else. The supper finished well after midnight. When he got home he saw light in his room . . . At first he thought it was a thief, but when he opened the door, he found Michelagnolo sitting there in miserable plight, his clothes ragged, his face thin, his eyes sunken and feverish.

"What's happened to you?"

"I couldn't stand it any longer, Galileo. I starved. I almost froze to death. Now I'm going home to Florence."

"Home? Why don't you stay here? I'll get you pupils."

"But I don't want to give lessons. I'm so tired, I want to rest."

"And what about Landucci's money? Must I pay it all? He's always pestering me."

Michelagnolo answered this with a sulky shrug. Galileo felt suddenly very sorry for him.

"Well, never mind. We'll manage somehow. Tell me now about Poland."

He fetched glasses and wine, and sat down at his brother's side. The boy cheered up and began boasting of his adventures.

XV

The four friends—Zorzi, Boccalini, Magagnati, and the mathematician of Padua—set off on a walking trip. This was the summer vacation, but Galileo stayed on in Padua; he was afraid of Landucci, to whom he still owed a considerable sum, and did not dare to visit Florence.

The three young patricians were amused at the thought of having to walk. It was natural for Galileo; he had tramped the roads before, and knew them well. When they felt that they had walked far enough, they put up at a wayside inn or simply slept in the shady woods. It was all amusing, they were young, healthy, and very gay.

"I think," Benedetto said, "that Messer Galileo is the one of us who can enjoy life most. . . ."

"I think that's true," the young scientist hastened to agree. "I can often be happy. I have moments when I'm perfectly contented. Quite often. You need a special gift for happiness, just as for music or mathematics. And I've got an especially large share of this talent. Sometimes I'd like to dance and sing or shout for joy, for no special reason—just because I'm alive."

"I envy you that," Magagnati said. "I've had no real happiness in my life, although I'm rich and come of a good family."

"It's the same with me," Boccalini added, chewing absent-mindedly at a grass stalk.

"Yes, and with me, too," said Zorzi. "Although I've got everything from life. But when great joys came my way and everything was just as I wanted it, I never *knew* myself to be happy. Some little thing was always there to spoil it. Some small wrong done to me which I hadn't repaid. I envy Messer Galileo's disposition. What can be his secret?"

Galileo answered gaily: "Light-mindedness."

The rest looked puzzled, so he explained:

"The greatest gift God gave me was a light mind. Call it frivolity, thoughtlessness, or even foolishness. I mean by that the fact that my heart is unable to dwell on cares. Of course, I'm terribly worried by money. I'm gloomy then, torturing myself. But in an hour it's all forgotten. I simply throw it out of my mind. Life itself is my joy. Nothing can equal it. I understand those birds up there singing for sheer joy of life. It is the same with me. Sometimes I want to stop strangers in the street, buttonhole them, and tell them with delight: I'm alive! I'm alive!"

Magagnati, who was the soberest among them, shook his head.

"Don't take it amiss, Messer Galileo, even if you *are* a famous scientist. Sometimes you sound very much like a child."

"Well put, Messer. That isn't an insult, it is rather a compliment. It's my conviction that nobody can be a talented man if he hasn't got something of the child in him. Our talents are divine, and they must be of the same sex as the angels of God. And the angels are children. I know that there is a child of ten hidden in my soul. That's why I shall remain young forever, no matter how old I live to be. God created me to be wise and happy. . . . Look, even now . . . how blue the sky is, how interesting the world, what a joy to live!"

He sighed with such delight that the others laughed. They began to wrestle on the grass. Galileo found it easy to beat them; there was huge strength in his big frame. He lifted them one after the other and dropped them, laughing. He immensely enjoyed the trip, the company, the world, the sky, the entire universe.

At night they slept in tiny inns, choosing the most primitive ones on purpose. They often slept out. They tramped aimlessly from village to village and went round the sights of every town. They visited Verona and stood in the classic amphitheater which had been half destroyed by an earthquake. They talked to the ghosts of Dante and Catullus hovering in this ancient ruin. It was mostly Galileo who talked, especially to Dante. As a Florentine, he had grown up knowing the smallest details of the *Divine Comedy;* wherever he started a *terza rima* he could continue for minutes on end. His friends were amazed.

"It's no special talent of mine," Galileo said. "In the first place, I am a Florentine, and, in the second, I once wrote an essay on the topography of hell."

"The topography of hell?" asked the puzzled Zorzi.

"It's an old problem. Science has considered it for the last hundred years. I succeeded the best. I went through all the cantos, and wherever I found some little reference to the proportions of hell, I noted it carefully. Then I put the whole thing into a probable geometrical system by long and complicated reckonings, the employment of conic sections, the use of the stonemason's static experiences, and Dürer's observations."

"Dürer? Who was Dürer?"

"As Venetians, you ought to know, because he spent many years in Venice. He was a famous German painter and scientist, of Hungarian origin. He lived at Nuremberg. He belonged to the very few whom I'd be willing to accept for wise men."

"Do the Germans know anything at all?" Zorzi asked.

"Of course they do. Didn't they invent the printing press? My friends, you must get used to the fact that people across the mountains have minds as well. There are stupid masses and intelligent exceptions everywhere."

"Have they got any great mathematicians?"

"I know a German Jesuit father at Rome, Clavius is his name, an excellent man. And I heard something about a former German astronomer, called Copernicus, only I haven't read his works yet. But I must read him, because some fools have been abusing him to me, so he must have said interesting things. The last was a German pupil of mine who came to me and asked me to explain Copernicus to him. He had read him out of curiosity, but couldn't understand his book. But *I* haven't so much as read it. I always keep putting it off. . . ."

At Vicenza they visited Bissaro, a correspondent of Galileo, but found him away. So they soon left and came to Costozza, a small village where lived Count Trento. Camillo Trento was well known, an honored guest among Venetian patricians, a famous student of law, and a great patron of literature. These rich young men knew him well, and were looking forward to presenting their famous friend. But the Count was also away; he had taken his family to Lake Garda. The *maggiordomo,* however, recognizing the distinguished Venetian names, knew his duty even in the absence of his master. He prepared them a magnificent repast. It was a very hot day, and after they had eaten and drunk, they longed to be cool. The *maggiordomo* pointed proudly to a door on the right of the dining room.

"No one in Italy can offer his guests so cool a resting place as my master, the Count. If you will follow me, *signori* . . ."

In the second room a gust of cold air met them. They were amazed. The *maggiordomo* pointed to a pipe whose mouth led into a round black hole in the wall.

"Not far from our palace," he explained, "are the famous caves of Costozza. An ice-cold spring is in them. This pipe leads through its walls and underground to the spring. That is where this cold air comes from."

"This coolness is divine," Zorzi said. "Couldn't we sleep here a little?"

"I can prepare some daybeds for you, Your Excellencies," said the *maggiordomo*. "But please, close the mouth of the pipe. This cold is dangerous for a sleeping man. Several of our guests have caught chills in here."

"Never mind, my friend, bring us your daybeds."

In a few minutes they stretched themselves luxuriously on the cushions, even taking off most of their clothes. The cold air caressed their perspiring bodies. Galileo pulled off his shirt. The *maggiordomo* again said something about closing the pipe, but they drove him off gaily. Soon they were fast asleep behind lowered blinds.

Galileo awoke chilled to the bone. He began to rub his shivery chest and shoulders, pulled on his clothes and woke the others. They, too, felt chilled. Hurrying out into the heat, they said good-by to the *maggiordomo,* and left a grateful note for their absent host. Night found them in a distant village. Next day Galileo woke with a bad chill. He felt an unpleasant pressure on his temples and he coughed. But he went on with the others. At nightfall he was feverish. On the third day he was so ill that they had to hire a cart to take him to Padua. There they put him to bed. The physician, whom they called at once, diagnosed acute tonsillitis, and told him that he must not get up. The three Venetian youths were extremely sorry, and regretted that their pleasant trip had ended so badly.

Galileo felt very ill. He could hardly talk, his throat was so swollen; he could not even welcome his many visitors. Professor Fabrizio prescribed a cordial and ordered him to salve his throat with a mixture of lard and the gall of calves. High fever tormented him; once or twice it brought an almost pleasant, half-dazed consciousness. On the fourth day he recovered a little, and wanted something to read. Pinelli brought him a few books. He also brought news.

"Yesterday," he said, "a German scientist lectured in Venice. I had to repeat his name three times before I could remember it: Cristiano Wursteisen. He spoke on astronomy. They tell me that it was all incredible nonsense, mostly about the system of Copernicus, a compatriot of his. Part of his audience was so annoyed that they left in the middle of the lecture; others stayed, just for amusement."

The sick man was thinking.

"Has Your Excellency got the book of Copernicus?"

"I don't know, I must look it up in my library catalogue."

"Would you lend it to me if you have a copy?"

"With pleasure. But why do you spend your time with such nonsense, when you can read so many serious books? It happens so rarely that one has the good fortune to stay in bed. I always use my time to catch up with my reading. . . ."

"I know . . . but still, if you could lend it to me. . . ."

Pinelli promised. And an hour later Galileo had the book, entitled *De revolutionibus orbium caelestium*. He skimmed through it, reading a few sentences at random, then he began again right from the preface.

Osiander, the pupil of Copernicus, was strangely noncommittal about the book in his introduction. He tried to present it as a fantasy, the curiosity of a strange theory. This caught the reader's attention at once. What was this strained preface for, humbly and servilely apologizing, almost saying: *"Please don't take all this too seriously!"* Was this Osiander entitled to do it? Was it done with the knowledge of the author? Now Galileo was really interested to find out what this curious man might have to say, and how much he meant it. He drew the lamp closer on the small table littered with glasses, books, and clay pipes. And so began to read Copernicus.

He began to read at eight o'clock and was still reading at five next morning. Often he put down the book and looked at the wall, lost in his thoughts. He frowned and strained his eyes as though trying to see something very clearly. Then he read on. He could scarcely curb his curiosity, but he was forced to read carefully and slowly so as not to lose the thread of this astronomer's thoughts. At five o'clock in the morning he put down the book. But he took it up again, and again read the preface. It filled him with a sudden rage; he wanted to tear out these pages, and would have done it, only he had an inborn respect for books. This Osiander was a weak coward. Copernicus was daring, almost heroic; while the preface seemed to be timid and hypocritical. He had finished reading. Outside the sun was shining brightly.

The sun. The Sun!

He blew out the lamp. A cock was crowing, the birds in the garden were making a great to-do. But otherwise there was deep silence. The world was just stirring. The earth and the sun turned toward each other. The sun was shining on the parts of the earth beyond Asia, to rise in the evening above the Atlantic and at night greet America with her radiance. But which of them was moving, and how? Because this astonishing German, this Copernicus, stated his calm, firm, well-founded theory according to which the earth was not the center of the universe, but the sun. The earth was simply a planet, like Mercury, Venus, Mars, Jupiter, Saturn! And his way of proving it was decisive, startlingly so.

Of course the ancients had said similar things. Pythagoras and Aristarchus maintained that the earth was moving. But this had been forgotten. The system of Ptolemy, which Galileo himself had explained so diligently in his Almagest lectures, had stood firm for thirteen hundred years. And now this German returned to the forgotten theories. Yes, the earth moved. The sun stood still and the earth spun round it like all the other planets. Their orbits, if drawn in our imaginations, are like silver hoops one inside the other; and in the innermost center of these hoops an immense sphere of golden fire as the focal point of the blue universe.

The sick man was lying exhausted, but still could not sleep. His temples throbbed, his deep-set eyes were points of light. He tried to turn over on his side and slide into oblivion with closed eyes. He fell half asleep, but in the next moment he started up again. Must someone be condemned as a fantasist because he had said the most daring thing for centuries? The theory of Copernicus clashed in the first place with those of Ptolemy, but beyond that with the theories of that final authority, Aristotle. . . .

It was Aristotle again. . . . Copernicus' book had informed him that its author was a Roman Catholic canon, not even a Protestant. So this priest of the true faith was found opposing the Peripatetics! Suddenly a fervent feeling of comradeship filled him for the unknown German scientist.

Again he tried to get to sleep; but in vain. Life was stirring outside. Fresh, gay voices sounded in the virginal silence of dawn; they were clearer and more resonant than by daylight. And the sun. . . . Suddenly he felt he must look at the sun. He did not even wait to find his slippers; he sprang out of bed and ran into the courtyard. There he looked skyward full of excitement. Even if it should blind him he must see whether the sun moved or the earth. But the sun forced him to close his eyes. He stood there, blinded, barefoot, in his nightgown.

At this moment Professor Fabrizio opened the gate. Aghast at the sight of his patient, he said: "Are you mad, *caro mio?* What are you doing?"

"Nothing," stammered a guilty child. "I . . . I had to look at something. I'm going back now."

He ran back to his bedroom.

"How did you sleep, you hopeless creature?"

"Thank you . . . to be frank, I didn't. I read the whole night."

He pointed at the book.

"Oh! This? I've read it. A lot of nonsense. I am no expert, but I know enough to realize that the sun is moving around the earth. She rises in the morning and sets in the evening. I can't imagine how a sane man can dispute the testimony of his eyes. It's a fine thing for such a madman to find a reader willing to catch pneumonia for his sake. If you do that again, I shall stop calling. I'm going out to my vineyard, to spend the whole day there; that's why I've come so early. Tell me, Galilei, have you really gone mad? What do you believe?"

The sick man was absent-minded. He smiled.

"If I knew what to believe!"

His physician departed and he was alone again with his thoughts. It was almost eleven before he slept. When he awoke, he had an ague. But his thoughts turned again toward Copernicus. The print was dancing before his feverish eyes, but he read through the book again.

In the next days the sickness attacked his joints. His left knee and wrist hurt terribly. But he had decided that Copernicus was right. He must be, although he could not prove it. Yet a scientist must never believe anything for which there is no absolute proof. But where should he find one? Copernicus was convincing enough on paper. But this was no general proof. While he could give no proof, he would have to go on teaching the Almagest, although he felt certain that it was false, and that the universe was wholly different. But he was going with all his talents and might to try and find a proof for Copernicus. . . .

Zorzi came from Venice to visit him. Galileo was in great pain, perspiration glistened on his forehead, he had bitten his lips till they bled.

"Well!" said Zorzi, gently stroking his right hand. "Is life still so good?"

The sick man groaned, and began to smile:

"Yes! Life is wonderful."

XVI

When he left the house for the first time after his long illness, he felt as if the whole world had been changed. If he looked at the sky he searched out the sun, hiding behind clouds, and tried to train his imagination to feel her as stationary and the earth as moving. In idle hours as a student at Pisa he had often amused himself with a fantasy, lounging over a bridge, looking into the Arno. Always he had had the feeling that really the water was standing still, that the bridge was moving steadily forward in an opposite direction to the river, that both banks, and with these banks the whole town of Pisa, the whole of Tuscany, the whole world, were rushing along. All that was moving on and on, and only the Arno streaked with ripples remained there motionless. Now he played the same game with the sun. Or rather he became convinced that this game which he forced his mind to play with him was the truth, not fancy, though it contradicted the belief of millions of people through hundreds, thousands, of years. As he walked in the streets with bent head, he realized that the ground he trod was the surface of a huge sphere rushing through space, with him and millions of others, with countries, mountains, and seas, though the streets of Padua stood motionless in the breathless heat.

Could this be true? Why did not all men, all objects, fall off this sphere in its rushing flight? He smiled; these were questions worthy of the priests who accused Giordano Bruno. The earth was rushing in a vacuum; therefore nothing could fall from its surface. Not even its atmosphere, its circle of air, surrounding it as the skin round an apple. The theory of Copernicus completely satisfied the imagination. Only, for the time being, it could not be demonstrated. Aristotle had surveyed the stars of the sky, and named them; and Peripatetic science considered the subject closed, the description sacred and inviolable. If you looked at the sky you really *saw* it according to Aristotle's description. There was no visible point from which to refute that. So Galileo could no nothing but believe in Copernicus and teach the Almagest.

He lectured, but without enthusiasm. During his lectures he was always searching for loopholes and fallacies in his own words. But he did not find them. Yet he was glad when the lecture came to an end. He hurried home to read Copernicus and followed out his own calculations, by which he checked the deductions of the German astronomer.

One day he received a package from Pisa. Old Mazzoni, who had taught him astronomy, had written a book, a *Comparison of Aristotle and Plato*. He found it a clear, diligent little work; but one paragraph in it roused his attention. Mazzoni mentioned Pythagoras and Copernicus, condemning them both. He brought up an argument against their theory which seemed completely new, and his own.

He started with the supposition that the earth was not flat, but spherical. He did not accept this theory; he only premised it. Then he referred to the fact that at sunset a mountaintop was still in daylight, while the valley was already dark. If one stood on the peak of a mountain, he saw the sun below the usual horizon. Thus, if one were to stand on a mountaintop a thousand times higher, he would see still further below the usual horizon and no doubt discover many new stars. So if the earth was really a ball, the person standing at the highest point of our hemisphere was in truth looking down from an immensely high mountain and ought to see a vast expanse of sky. This should be so, if the earth were spherical. But it was not so, because wherever you traveled, you saw the same chart of the sky. Therefore the earth cannot be spherical.

This argument startled Galileo. It was so simple and clear, almost childish. It nearly shook him in his conviction. But he was too far advanced in rebellious doctrines. His imagination was trained to find arguments for the new theory, and not against it. He put away Mazzoni's book and pondered, although in vain. But when he had wrestled three days with the problem, one night, on his way home from Pinelli, he stopped at the Santa Giustina and glanced up at the silvery blue sky. He tried with the whole force of his mind to imagine the order of the universe as set forth by Copernicus. He saw infinite space, placing the radiant kernel of the sun into it, and around it the planets. Like a second God he placed them within it, some nearer, some farther off. Now let them begin their whirling course around this nucleus. And suddenly he began to realize the true proportion of such distances. How far could the earth be from the sun, and how big were they both? Suppose that where Florence lay, a huge and radiant diamond had been set down, the largest diamond in the world. And, about as far away from it as Padua, a tiny shining particle would be spinning—like a diamond splinter fallen out of the pocket of an Amsterdam diamond cutter. This splinter would be the earth, a tiny grain compared with the huge diamond of the sun. Did it make any difference in perspective, from which point on this tiny grain you chose to view the secrets of the horizon? No difference at all! All the difference was lost from such a minute observation point when these vast distances were in question.

This reassured him. When he wrote to Mazzoni, he praised his book warmly, but mentioned his new conviction in the matter of Copernicus and Aristotle. Mazzoni had first shown him the secrets of space, but now he parted from his instructor and followed new roads of the mind. He had respected and liked Mazzoni before: he still liked him, but no longer accepted his authority. Copernicus engrossed him more than ever. He went into Venice, ransacking all the libraries to learn more of him. He asked the German students of the Bo to write home and find out all they could about a canon called Copernicus and what his fellow countrymen thought of his teachings.

In a few weeks he had a good deal of information. Copernicus or, as he was called in Germany, Nikolaus Koppernigk, had been the son of a poor coppersmith and was born more than a hundred years previously in a town called Thorn. His uncle, a bishop, paid for his education and put him into the Church. It was this bishop who made him enroll at the University of Cracow where Orudzewski, the famous mathematician, was a lecturer. The young priest began to love mathematics; and, when he had finished his studies at Cracow, he came to Bologna, where Novara, the clever Italian, was his teacher. Here he acquired his astronomical knowledge. Then he went back to Germany, became a canon, but only to return to Italy, still studying. And—strange coincidence—he had been a student of the Bo.

The young mathematician was very much excited by this discovery. He began to search through the old registers and found Copernicus' name among former students of medicine. Galileo felt himself put to shame. Copernicus, this great astronomer, to enlarge his scope had studied medicine, while he had rejected this science with disdain. This wonderful German whetted his curiosity even more. From Padua, Copernicus went to

Rome, where he became a professor of mathematics at the university. After a few years he returned to his country, where he faithfully discharged his duties as a canon of the chapter-house, but still devoted time to his astronomical theories. He knew that he had chanced upon something utterly new. He only confided his thoughts to a few learned friends. He did not want to publish yet. He even made his colleagues promise never to mention his daring theories till he had finished working out his proofs. It took him almost forty years to elaborate a far-reaching system. At last his disciples became impatient. Two of them wrote what he had taught them. One of them signed Rheticus, remaining anonymous, choosing the form of a letter for his essay. The other, Osiander, gave all the details; but, scared by the incredible boldness of this new teaching, he wrote a preface, cloaking it as a playful fantasy, to avoid conflict with the Church. Copernicus could not protest: fifty-four years ago he had received the first copy of Osiander's book, as he lay dying. He had worked out the greatest thought on the universe; but it was only as a parting message which he left behind, not awaiting the answer.

This was all that was known about Copernicus. But in connection with his theory the German students brought news of an interesting scientist. Galileo had heard his name, like those of many other foreign colleagues; but had not found him worth any special attention. Now, this Kepler, as they called him, counted as a stubborn eccentric, almost a madman, in German scientific life, because he defiantly upheld the Copernican system. Galileo was very much interested in him. He got a few details about the man, but he had to wait till he met a Moravian student to find out all about Kepler.

This Moravian knew Kepler personally. He described him as a thin, frail young man of twenty-six, the son of a poverty-stricken German innkeeper. After finishing his studies with great difficulty, he had been appointed to the mathematical chair at Graz. This was no mean achievement, since he was a Protestant.

"I went to Graz, Your Excellency," the Moravian said, "because I had been strongly advised to study under Kepler. But I was disappointed: for a long time he did not lecture at all. He fell in love with a certain Frau Lorenz, who was only twenty-two at that time, but already twice a widow. A very proud woman, though very beautiful. Kepler proposed to her, but she would only marry a man of noble family. He assured her that his family were really impoverished nobility. She demanded proofs, and so he was compelled to leave everything, to go back home and get the documents. His students had to wait and kick their heels. I got tired of it and decided to leave. I thought that the gossip was true; Kepler could not prove his noble descent and was feeling too ashamed to return. I had already prepared my journey to Padua when he came back. He had probably succeeded in getting his proofs because Barbara, Frau Lorenz, married him. I left on the day of the wedding because I did not want to change my plans."

"What sort of a professor is he? What is his manner of lecturing?"

"Very gentle and serious. He speaks softly, nervously, starting at every noise."

"And what did he say?"

"I attended only one or two lessons of his, Your Excellency, when he spoke about general matters. And, to be frank, I didn't understand them wholly. Your Excellency explains everything much more clearly. I'm very glad that I came here. I also learn that Herr Kepler's teachings are contrary to the classical scientists and Your Excellency's own opinions."

Galileo smiled strangely and nodded.

"Yes, of course. But all that may change. Thank you for the information."

He tried to picture the German. It hurt him a little that Kepler was only twenty-six, while he was over thirty-three. And yet the German had taken a firm stand for this shattering revolutionary theory. But . . . would not the real glory go to the man who not only said he believed in Copernicus, but proved his theory beyond all doubt? If Kepler could do it, he probably would have given his proofs to the world. Or perhaps he had the solution already, but wanted to perfect it. And while Galileo meditated in Padua, the young German might come out one day with some astonishing work. Galileo began to fear this possibility. Yet Kepler was a spiritual comrade, a clear, fearless intellect like his own, a thinker who did not dread authority and did not try to curry favor. There were moments when he almost resented Kepler's existence, and then again he longed to embrace him.

But it was Kepler who made the first step toward a personal acquaintance. One day a package arrived from Graz: Kepler had sent him his new book. Galileo opened it with a storm of conflicting emotions—jealousy and fear that Kepler had got ahead of him but also pride that this German had heard of his Padua colleague and considered him important enough to send him a copy of his work.

The book was entitled: *Prodromus dissertationum cosmographicarum*— "Introduction to a Description of the Universe." This reassured Galileo. If this was only an introduction, the description itself was incomplete. And, reading the preface, he knew that Kepler only believed in Copernicus but could not advance a proof of his theory. Yet he liked the book; it was simple, clear, and witty. He wrote to Kepler at once, thanking him warmly and expressing his joy "to have found such a companion in the search for truth." He told him that he had read only the preface but intended to study every word.

The letter was long, not the message of a stranger to a stranger, but written by one comrade to another. In his spare time Galileo went carefully through the *Prodromus*. It was just what he had expected: a clear and sensible summing up of the Copernican system, with a few quite important additions. It was so simple, so clear and convincing that he conceived a deep affection for its author. He felt that he was not alone, that far away, beyond high mountains, there was someone, in the silence of the night, who was bending over books and calculations just as he did—a spiritual brother. Even scientific jealousy was forgotten. He loved this young professor of Graz in much the same way that he loved his kindred; it was as though Copernicus had been their spiritual begetter.

Padua had again become a hornets' nest. The professors could not leave for their vacations—because of the Jesuits. The Fathers had been breaking all the rules again; there was a fight over every point of education. Their latest move had been to send a petition to Venice in the summer heat when no professor remained at home. They had tried to force this petition through the Padua town council and present it to the Council of Ten before the board of professors could meet again. But the Bo discovered this furtive trick. All the professors stayed on in the city, and stormy conferences began. The petition demanded a wide extension of the Jesuit curriculum. The town council supported it. All Padua had taken sides. The Bo was led by Cremonini and Riccoboni, while the Jesuits were helped by such personages as Cornado, Bishop of Padua, Gualdo, his Vicar General, and the Mayor himself.

Committee meetings followed one after the other. The situation became critical; some shrank from any open resistance, fearing another such mysterious assassination as had cost the life of the former Dean, a few years back. But fortunately the students were all away. The more sober professors wanted to arrive at some decision before they returned and riots began.

Galileo neglected these meetings. Even when he attended them he sat among the others absent-mindedly scribbling astronomical equations. This attitude annoyed Cremonini.

"I really don't understand you, Galilei. Aren't you interested in the fate of the Bo?"

"Of course I am. Why?"

"You just sit here, never saying a word, as if you were a stranger indifferent to our cause, to our struggle."

"What struggle?"

"For the liberty of the university! To defend ourselves against compulsion. The Jesuits want to get us under. We mustn't let them. While we try to find out what to do, you . . . you sit and scribble!"

"Yes. Equations. And perhaps one of these equations is going to give Padua more authority than all your meetings and debates."

Cremonini turned away, shrugging impatiently, and glanced at Riccoboni. "The Florentine," both of them thought. They both considered him an eccentric, a man who knew all about his particular subject, but was useless outside the lecture hall. The debate continued, and Galileo went on scribbling. When they parted, he had no idea what resolution he had accepted unanimously with the others.

As he walked home, he ran into a priest. He glanced up, apologizing, and was surprised to see Girolamo Barison, the Dean of the Jesuit school. They eyed one another. There was something sinister and alert, determined and strong, in the Jesuit. Galileo took home this impression. His conscience began to prick him. He had caught a glimpse of the terrible conquering force against which Padua had to fight. He ought to join the others, discuss the plans of the campaign, plead with vicar generals, take trips to Venice, draw up petitions. The authority of Padua and his own livelihood were threatened. But at home he saw Kepler's book on the table. He found the page he had been pondering during the conference and promptly forgot all about the Jesuits.

His whole being was absorbed by the world of Copernicus. While his fellow men were living on the flat earth of the ancients, under the blue hemisphere hung with stars, with the sun and the moon, he began to exist in another universe: on the surface of a tiny ball revolving round the primal nucleus. He not only believed in the new teaching: he *knew* it was true. Although it was never out of his mind, he trained himself to deliver lectures which belied this knowledge. He felt humble and out of love with himself and became much quieter than usual. Sometimes he paused in the midst of a lecture and was horrified by the smooth fluency with which he explained Ptolemy's system. He blushed for his scientific integrity. But then he collected his wits and went on teaching, like the faithless priest of a false and foolish creed. Often he pondered, walking in the botanical garden or lying in his darkened room. When he had smoked too many pipes or could not go to sleep, he sometimes excited himself to the point of hating himself for this cowardice. He abused and cursed himself as a traitor, a besmircher of the virginal truth. He recalled his years at Pisa when he had defied the whole world and professed his faith. Now he instructed hundreds of young minds in this falsehood. The thought made him decide to be heroic, to go to the university next day and confess humbly to his students that he had been misleading them, but from now on would teach the truth, even if the world collapsed about him. But next day he saw how childish all this was. What at night was simple, noble, and heroic, seemed foolish in the sober morning. After all, he had no proof of what he knew.

So he resigned himself to his "double life." He was busy nowadays with private lessons. Several distinguished young men came to learn with him the science of fortification, among them a Prince d'Este and a Swedish duke named Gustavus. They were proud, handsome young men whose retinue waited in front of his shabby house while they spent an hour or so with the young professor.

Galileo invented a new measuring rod. It was composed of two diagonal copper rulers with a movable cross-circle. A radiating system of apportionments showed the figures of different scales. It was a fundamentally simple idea, but its use and principle were more intricate. First he made a cardboard model; and the Swedish duke, who was very intelligent, at once offered a good price. Whereupon Prince d'Este also wanted one. But cardboard soon wears out, so Galileo called in a carpenter, made an exact drawing of the "geometrical and military compass," as he had named it, and ordered two models. Finally he had some made of copper. He could sell any number of them. His aristocratic pupils thought it quite a fashion to possess one. Often they paid him fifty lire for what had cost him less than fifteen.

When orders increased, he decided to embellish his invention with some embossed sign and to have the copies made in Venice instead of in the small shop in Padua.

He was just preparing to go to Venice when he received Kepler's answer. Eagerly he broke the seal. A cordial, almost fraternal letter. His new friend began with an affectionate greeting, expressing his hope that Galileo had finished his book and would give him his sincere opinion.

"Believe me, I prefer the objections of a single understanding man to the applause of the ignorant mass."

But he urged him to put off his reserve in the matter of the Copernican system, even if till now it had been justified. Silence would be of little use to their common master; masses are never won by arguments, but by the authoritative words of famous scholars. And if these scientists kept silence, it was equal to treachery. It would be easy to cope with the great crowd of the illiterate and the half-educated, as they did not understand mathematical problems and would accept new theories more easily. The mathematicians, who would demand exact proof for every new statement, were more to be feared.

"Be trustful, Galileo! Stand forth for truth! I do not think that many of Europe's famous mathematicians would oppose us; the power of truth must be all-convincing. If Italy is not the place for you to confess your faith publicly, perhaps Germany would offer us the necessary freedom. But at least let me know personally if you have found proofs for the Copernican system. . . . Farewell and give me the honor of a detailed answer."

Galileo brooded for a long time. He felt himself a traitor, but a helpless one. Kepler himself admitted that all their statements must be proved. But how? Anyone could point at the sky and call all mankind his witnesses: it was evident that the earth was stationary, that the sun rose at daybreak and moved on all day across the sky till it set at evening. Whoever tried to maintain the opposite would harm his own cause —unless he could prove it.

He put the letter aside and left for Venice.

XVII

He had two new acquaintances there who especially interested him. One was a rich and distinguished young man, Gianfrancesco Sagredo; the other a monk, Fra Paolo Sarpi.

Fra Paolo belonged to the Order of Servites and, although he was still in his forties, had attained the rank of a Provincial. His theological knowledge was famous in the whole of Italy, and the Serenissima employed him as its official adviser in juridical questions. Everyone in Venice knew him; his thin fragile form, almost lost in the brown habit, could be seen daily in the Piazza at the narrow Merceria. The people called him the "handsome priest," because everybody noticed his finely molded features and his small beard. He was always accompanied by some friend; having quarreled bitterly with the Papal Nuncio, he feared an attack by hired assassins. The Nuncio had ample reason to hate Fra Paolo Sarpi, because the monk in whose hands lay the defense of Venetian rights whenever these clashed with those of the Holy See, had proved himself a fanatical Venetian patriot. Some called him the Machiavelli of Venice; some accused him of serving the Doge instead of the Saviour.

He liked to have scientists for his friends. Fabrizio, the old professor of medicine, was especially close to him. Galileo had met him once; but, when Sarpi heard of his new "compass," he sent a message that he would like to learn its use. Galileo hastened to fulfil the request of the distinguished priest. He went to Venice and tried to explain to him the complicated use of his invention. He did not succeed very well; Fra Paolo had little sense for mathematics; but at least it made them very good friends. There was something rebellious and daring in the priest which attracted the scholar. He could feel a comrade in Fra Paolo, whose hands seemed equally to be tied in the struggle for freedom against the Church. Fra Paolo used his knowledge of the law to limit Papal power in the civil affairs of the Serenissima to the finest point. Galileo contended against Aristotle, this middle-aged monk against the Vatican.

They interested and liked each other. There was a bookshop at the
foot of the Clock Tower, a fashionable meeting place around noon. Sometimes one bought a few books, but mostly one gossiped. If interesting
news arrived, it was told here; information came in from the whole of
Italy, not only scientific but also political. Here it was said that Henry
IV, the French Huguenot king, had returned into the fold of the Church
for the sake of the throne. As he was riding to church at the Pope's
request, he had said: "Paris is worth a mass!" Here they talked of the
death of Orlando Lasso at Munich; of a recent conquest of the Spanish,
who had claimed some new islands, calling them Philippines. Here one
could learn that there had been a revolt in Japan against Christian missionaries and that the priests who had been trained by Fernando, Prince
of Florence, during his cardinalate, had all been massacred. Men of
science, priests, patrician book-lovers, collectors of antiques or simple
scandal-mongers, met here every day before they dined. Then they walked
along the Merceria to the foot of the Rialto, where on a huge blackboard
under the arcades the positions and itineraries of the Venetian ships were
affixed, wherever they sailed on the Seven Seas.

Galileo always visited this bookshop. And it was here that he made the
acquaintance of his other new friend, young Sagredo.

This young patrician had scarcely passed twenty, but he viewed the
world with as bitter a wisdom as if he were threescore and ten. He had
begun his grown-up life very early; his rich father had let him give a free
rein to all his passions, hoping that he would quickly sow his wild oats
and settle down. For years he had been spending money like water; a
train of servants followed his every step; he kept his own fork and wine-
glass at the houses of the loveliest courtesans; he gambled wildly; his
duels followed in quick succession, and already he had killed a number
of men. Since he always kept strictly to the rules of the duel, he never
had any trouble with the law. Now, at twenty, he had ceased to care for
luxury, cards, and wine. His riotous life had become a weariness; he
turned to science; but even here only curiosities interested him. Yet his
sharp wits would have justified a thorough training. At their first talk he
surprised Galileo; not even a professional mathematician could have shown
more sense of the problems they discussed.

"Why don't you devote your life to mathematics?"

Sagredo shrugged.

"Why, indeed! Or why not to law, or Greek, or history? But I don't need any of them; they merely amuse me."

"Every man must have some aim in life!"

"Of course. Mine is to get through this excessively dull world as pleasantly as possible. Or rather, to be bored as little as possible. I sometimes succeed. For instance, I'm very grateful to you, Messer, because our talk has been so interesting. I'm sorry to see that you want to leave me. Where are you going? My gondola is waiting at the Piazzetta; perhaps I could take you somewhere."

"Many thanks. I'm going to the Arsenal, to find a coppersmith."

"Excellent. I've nothing to do. Let's go together."

They crossed the square, and soon the yellow and blue oars of the Sagredo family were cutting the water along the Riva dei Schiavoni. Galileo explained that he wanted to have copies of his invention made regularly.

"How enthusiastic you seem about everything," Sagredo smiled.

"Are you never enthusiastic?"

"No. As far as enthusiasm goes, my family has already supplied all that. According to a family legend, Sagredo is only a corruption of the name San Gherardo. One of my ancestors was the brother of Saint Gerard, an enthusiastic missionary to Hungary, where they killed him in a very original way—they put him into a spiked barrel and rolled him down a high mountain into the Danube. I've heard that the mountain has been named after him. It ought to be called Monte Sagredo, since that's our name. So our family has shown enough enthusiasm. . . . But here we are . . . the Arsenal. . . ."

They picked their way through the labyrinth of the Arsenal to the workshops of the smiths and coppersmiths. Their business, or rather Galileo's, was soon arranged; Mazzoleni, the clever locksmith, was willing to undertake the manufacture of his measuring rod, which seemed a profitable speculation.

They returned to the gondola. Sagredo asked Galileo to explain his measuring rod. Galileo took out some drawings, and did his best to make it clear. By this time he had plenty of practice. But he soon perceived that he had never had so quick-witted a listener. He became so absorbed in what he was saying that he was startled to see that they had reached the Palazzo Sagredo.

"Would you care to dine with me, Messer? I'm alone, so we can talk in peace."

"Thanks, Your Excellency. With the greatest pleasure."

The Palazzo Sagredo was situated between the lovely Cà d' Oro and the parish church of the Santi Apostoli, opposite the fish market. He had often seen it from a gondola, but never hoped to go inside. They landed near the Cà d' Oro, and walked up the narrow side alley which revealed the truth behind this splendor: the façade of the palace was marble and gold; its structure only plain red brick. Lackeys were waiting on the steps. The corridors of the Palazzo Sagredo were covered with thick Persian rugs, there were pictures and marble statues everywhere. A tall marble chimney piece inlaid with gold. In the corners of the rooms through which they passed, great banks of flowers and sweet-smelling herbs. Windows of stained Venetian glass with red-brown sunblinds, which the wind swelled as though they were sails. The floors were of marble; they shone like mirrors wherever they were not hidden by costly rugs.

"You could use this floor for a looking-glass," said Galileo.

"Oh, they did that in the Palazzo Priuli. The floor of one big room is a single mirror, its ceiling of white coffered marble, with frescoes by Titian. Sometimes the master of the house asks his guests to put on slippers before they enter. It's quite amusing to walk on, especially with ladies, because they scream and pull their skirts together round their legs. But here is a more modern world. This room is the beginning of my apartments."

Galileo stood entranced: "Lucca della Robbia!"

"Yes, I bought it in Florence. It cost a good deal. That annoyed my father. He hates modern painting. His painter is Giotto. He's especially angry with Della Robbia, because he says one should either be a sculptor or a potter; to mix the two is unworthy of an artist. He may be right. But I like this plaque with the yellow fruit. . . ."

There was a silent lackey bowing them on at every five steps. Before they dined they smoked a pipe of tobacco. It was light yellow, and finely cut. Galileo had never seen its like.

"I have it sent from Turkey," Sagredo said. "I like this kind best."

They drank Spanish wine, thick and black like oil, to whet their appetites. Dinner began with minestrone, the fish course was mackerel in oil, then a whole pheasant. The cook had skillfully replaced the feathers on the roasted bird; its beak and claws were gilded. The repast was rounded off by a cake of burnt sugar and almonds, in the form of a cage. When Sagredo broke it open, three canaries flew out of it.

"Barbaro, my cook," said the young man indifferently, "cannot manage to give up these jokes. He does it more to amuse himself than me. I told him this morning to prepare quite a simple meal, since I didn't know that I should have such a distinguished guest . . . what are you thinking about, Messer?"

"May I speak frankly?"

"Please!"

"I was thinking about luxury and display. And about money."

"You're quite right," Sagredo nodded. "We Venetians are mad to live as we do. The Senate is always making new sumptuary laws about a yard long, but all in vain. My father is in charge of some of them. Do you know how many things a rich man is forbidden to do in Venice? We're forbidden, for instance, to have a door knocker made of solid gold. We mayn't wear swords or rapiers of pure silver or gold. In the name of the Republic it is forbidden to stud a horse's harness with diamonds. In case of bereavement it is forbidden to drape a whole palace with black velvet. And so on. One begins to pity the poor rich. . . . Why are you looking at me so strangely? Because I'm mocking them? Yes, I loathe the rich. I loathe myself. But naturally I don't intend to give all my substance to the poor; it's so much more convenient not to. But in my heart I detest money. It's already caused my worst grief."

"How?"

Sagredo hesitated a little. He decided to speak:

"I was sixteen and I fell in love. She was a young widow and I wanted to marry her. I even mistook her for a goddess, I even prayed to her. Every night I had myself rowed to her palace, had my gondola moored at the lowest step, and kissed the marble, because she had touched it with her foot. She forbade me even to touch her hand. 'Not till after we're married,' she said. I wanted her madly. One night I went to a gambling den. There, to my great surprise, I discovered her. She had come on from some feast. She began to play, and lost. She took off her jewels, and lost them. Then she turned to me, asking for a loan. I told her she could have it on one condition; that she instantly become my mistress. . . . That gambling den was the Eliseo. Do you know it? No? Well, you know Venice. The Eliseo is well equipped for lovers. This woman granted my request . . . without hesitation! Soon she was gambling again. She was winning. But I haven't spoken to her since. And I shall never marry. Of course, the whole thing looks quite different now. I know that it happens every day. After all, as I said, this is Venice. But at that age I took it to heart. The week after that, I fought three men —and killed them."

"Three? How many have you killed in your life?"

"Altogether? Wait a moment . . . eight."

Galileo recoiled a little. He looked curiously at this pleasant, delicate, fair young man.

"So you've killed eight men?"

"Yes. Do you think that's too many? Of course, you're a Florentine; duels are much rarer there. Eight . . . why, here that's nothing! Do you know how many killings Alfonso Piccolomini was absolved from? He was twenty-five when he confessed to the murder of 370 men. . . . But he'll go to heaven when he dies! He received his absolution in a special Papal Bull. There are three fellows like that in Venice; be careful if ever you meet them. One of them is called Leonardo Pesaro; he is always out for trouble. He comes up to any stranger he meets: 'Why are you staring at me?' They quarrel, he challenges the poor devil, and runs him through. He can't be punished; he always keeps strictly to the rules of the Longiano dueling code. And there are two others, Gabriele Morosini and Annibale Perone. Avoid them like venomous snakes. Can you fence?"

"I'm ashamed, but I can't."

"Well, if you mean to be much in Venice—and I hope you do—you must learn at once."

"I'm afraid," Galileo smiled, "I shall have no time. And I don't often come to Venice. Why should I?"

"One never knows. Perhaps you'll find a pretty wench here."

Galileo laughed: "Everywhere there are pretty wenches—and I'm not so particular as all that."

"Oh, but Venetian women are different. Travelers all say that the women of Venice can stir your senses better than any others in the world. You know, *amico,* I often feel that life has sated me; but sometimes at a feast one stirs my blood, and I snap my fingers and have to say to myself: 'Be careful!'—especially since the latest fashion which shows their breasts. And how cunningly they know how to paint them, the breasts snow-white and the nipples crimson! One really has to be on one's guard. I can only say they make me hate them. Just walk down the street behind the Grand Canal, and look up at the balconies. You can see them sitting there in rows. . . ."

"I have," said Galileo eagerly; "but what queer masks they all seem to wear."

"You see, red hair has been the fashion since Titian painted it. He drove the whole Republic crazy. And now every woman dyes her hair! But the dye they use can only be fixed by sunshine. To finish the dyeing they have to sit in the sun. On the other hand, they don't want to spoil their fine white skins, so they tie a piece of raw beef over their faces. Whenever I see them I want to throttle them! Because I know they only do it to torment honest men and make them suffer. But, after all, what does it matter! Life is like that, and I can't alter it."

None of this meant much to Galileo. At thirty-four, looking back on his life, he remembered no deep sorrow caused by a woman. There had been one real love in his life, and that was the love for dead and buried Bianca Cappello. No other woman had entered his soul. His love life was mere healthy appetite; he appeased this hunger and waited till it came again.

"It would be a miserable shame to take them seriously," Sagredo continued, as though answering his guest's thoughts. "In this world nothing is really serious. Thank God I can laugh. If I couldn't I'd probably kill myself. Then there's always something in books. And sometimes I succeed with a practical joke."

"With a practical joke? How do you mean?"

"Well, sometimes. Look. . . . I'll show you how I amuse myself sometimes. Come over to the window."

They went to the window which opened on the back of the palace. A quiet little street, with steps clattering through the silence. Sagredo took out some copper money, waited till an old woman with a sour, ill-tempered face passed under the window, and then dropped a soldo just behind her. The old woman stood still. She looked around. She searched for her knitted purse, hidden under petticoats, counted her money care-

fully, shook her head, and started to go. Sagredo dropped another coin.
The startled old woman stopped again. A workman passed at the same
moment.

"I dropped that," he said.

The old woman began to shout at him. "You liar! It's the second I've
dropped. Don't you dare to take it; if you find it, it's mine."

"You talk like a fool!" the man said and began to look everywhere for
the farthing.

The crone raised her voice. In a few minutes they were quarreling furiously, and a crowd had begun to gather round.

"It's rather funny," Sagredo laughed. "Sometimes I lower a purse on a
thread, and when someone bends down I jerk it up, like an angler."

Galileo wanted to say that certainly it was very funny indeed if so intelligent a man could find no better sport for himself. He would even have
said it, but suddenly his heart missed a beat, and he stood there tongue-
tied. From the opposite house the noise in the street had drawn a
woman . . . and this woman was Bianca Cappello, come back to life!

"That . . . that woman," he stammered. "Who. . . ? Impossible!"

"That pretty red-haired girl? Her name is Marina Gamba. Why?"

"Impossible," Galileo repeated. "As though Bianca Cappello could
come from the dead. . . ."

"But is she really so like her? Perhaps a little. I've seen the famous
Bianca's portrait. Yes, perhaps, if one looks hard for a likeness . . . why
are you so excited about that?"

"I want to get to know that girl . . . at once. Oh, she's gone back!
Who is she? Tell me, for God's sake!"

"A seedy nobleman called Gamba lives in that house; she's his only
daughter. Quite pretty, too."

"Pretty? She's beauty itself!"

"Ah! The Venetian women! Didn't I warn you?"

"I don't know; but I know that I must meet this girl. Can't you help
me, Messer? I'd be your grateful slave all my life. . . ."

"Well, it's easy enough to get to know a girl in Venice. But Gamba is
a friend of mine. He is a strange, eccentric old man, interested only in
Venetian history. . . . Listen, I know what I'd better do! I'll write to
him that I have a very learned friend who needs certain historical data.
He'll be very flattered. I'll write today. . . ."

"Couldn't you . . . send a message . . . now?"

Sagredo laughed. He pulled the bell rope.

"Petruccio, go round to Messer Gamba and ask him whether he would see me and Professor Galileo of Padua on a learned matter. Hurry."

Galileo was so impatient that he ran downstairs to meet the returning lackey.

"Messer Gamba would be very much honored by your visit, Excellencies."

As they went up the stairs of the Gamba house, Galileo said: "You don't know what I see in this girl, Messer. It's a long story; I can't explain it now. I've seen a miracle. 'The Word became flesh.' I'm not blaspheming Holy Writ. This is a miraculous event for me."

Sagredo only grinned and eyed him curiously. A limping old man came out to meet them. The girl was nowhere to be seen.

"Our learned and excellent friend," lied Sagredo fluently, "has asked me to find him someone really well-versed in the history of Venice. He's writing a book on the history of mathematics in our city, and needs much information. I do not think I could have brought him to a more polished and excellent man than yourself, Messer Gamba."

This seemed to enliven the old man.

"I'm sure I can help," he said. "I've all kinds of material. Nobody has as much as I have. I have just made a note of the word *liago*. Your Excellencies probably don't know what *liago* is? It used to be a sort of balcony on old Venetian houses, mostly on the southern wall. I'll search my notes for all mathematical references. I know that the Serenissima was the first in the whole of Italy to arrange for public lessons in algebra."

Galileo sat fidgeting on his chair, longing to get up and seek the girl in another room. Sagredo steered the conversation with smooth assurance. And it was he who asked permission to fetch a glass of water for himself; he was very thirsty.

"Oh, please, don't trouble yourself!" said Gamba and called out: "Marina! We have guests! Will you bring us a glass of water?"

"I'll be ready in a minute!" a charming voice called back from somewhere.

Of course, she was changing her dress! Gentlemen had come to the house; it would be unseemly to let them see her in her ordinary clothes. Galileo could almost hear his heart beat. His throat was dry. The other two were talking eagerly, but he could not understand a word they were saying. At last came light steps. He stood up, and there stood the miracle! The maiden curtsied low; he bowed. Sagredo's voice still babbled on. They stood looking into each other's eyes. Marina's were as blue as the sea, blue as the dead Bianca's. These two—that wraith of the past and the live reality—became one being.

"I'll fetch some water," Marina murmured. She hovered . . . was gone. All the longing which had gone to Bianca's image, and then lain dormant in his mind, sprang into life. Galileo followed her movements greedily. He felt that he could commit murder to possess this girl. Eight times like Sagredo or 370 like Alfonso Piccolomini.

Their visit was curtailed by the knowing Sagredo. It was arranged that Galileo should come again in a few days. Gamba was to collect mathematical data. They took their leave.

Down in the street Galileo stood in a dream. He whispered: "What will happen now?"

"Now!" laughed Sagredo. "Every morning old Gamba goes to the archives. Spy out the land, and if the girl is at home, knock at her door . . . you can go tomorrow if you like. Take her for a day at the Lido or in the evening to the *serenata*. . . . The chief thing is you should kiss her at once . . . but why need I explain all this?"

"I've never made love to a girl of good family before. If only I could marry her . . . tonight!"

But these were only words, dismissed with a gesture. He was still in debt to his brother-in-law, he had to keep sending his brother money, and Livia would get married this year or next. He was lucky if his new invention brought in enough money for visits to Venice. . . . Sagredo beckoned to a street urchin.

"Hey, you, here's a soldo; tell this gentleman we can't stand here all day. But you'd better shout into his ear, he's very deaf!"

The boy crept up to Galileo and suddenly yelled with all his might, so suddenly that he almost fell over. Every nerve in his body jumped with agony. He was very angry, and was about to rebuke Sagredo. But his friend, without saying a word, pointed up to the window. Galileo saw the glint of red hair, but the girl had vanished the instant she knew she was being watched . . . like a dream at waking.

XVIII

"Try to imagine Venice, Messer Galileo, with its streets unpaved. Grass grew on empty plots. Around the marble churches cattle grazed. . . ."

Old Gamba would have talked for hours, but his guest had risen. Before he went he exchanged quick glances with Marina. They had arranged to meet in twenty minutes at the Rialto.

It was nearly sunset. The people of Venice, who all day long had sheltered from the sweltering heat in darkened rooms, were out in the street again. A noisy, elbowing crowd was taking the air along the canal banks. Men in shirt sleeves sat with their wives at tables in front of the Battoria; swarms of children clung to the women's skirts. Galileo sat down to wait at one of these tables.

He had known her for two weeks now. During these two weeks he had been four times in Venice. He kept visiting Mazzoleni at the Arsenal to see the progress of the measuring rod, paid a short visit to Sarpi's bookshop, looked up Sagredo and other friends. But he hurried away from them at once, and even during his short visits he was always restless. He hurried to Marina to try to tell her of the storm in his heart. But when they found themselves alone together, his tongue was lamed, and all he had to say unspoken. It was she who chattered, while he sat listening, but not hearing her, loving the fresh music of her voice and covertly watching the young lines of her body. Marina was twenty-one, but when they were together their ages might have been reversed: she was the self-assured and guiding one. Galileo was blushing, shy, confused. He felt that if he told her he loved her he would risk his life. The bravest thing he could do was to hold her hand, and he felt amazed that she permitted it. But she let his hand remain in hers as though it were the most natural thing in the world. Yet he seldom dared to take it when they were alone; all his courting consisted of fervent glances, sighs, stammering protests of love.

"You should take her in your arms," Sagredo advised, "and kiss her hard."

"Yes, but how?"

"How? don't you know how to kiss? You put your lips on the girl's and . . ."

"Don't mock me! What if it makes her very angry?"

"You can always appease her by kissing again. But, no fear, she won't be angry."

Galileo did not answer that. This tone was an insult. He would have liked to hear that Marina was a miracle of purity, the evanescent vision out of a dream. Such was the image he had formed of her. Those full, red lips were surely inviolate; no other lips had ever touched them; if he kissed them, heaven would come to earth, he would be the first man . . . in a shattering instant of celestial joy. When his longings urged him to further thoughts, he shrank back appalled, his dream swallowed by reality. How could he, almost a beggar, ever marry her! And, if he could not marry her, what then? He shook off the agony of that future. But today he decided most heroically that he would kiss her at last. Today. He imagined the scene. He would hold her lovely head with its dark red hair between his hands, press his lips on her mouth. She would resist; he would be strong and master her. He would hold her angrily and kiss . . .

She was soon beside him. He saw her coming through the crowd in her dark blue gown with her white veil, watched her walk, like the gentle swing of a gondola. "I'll kiss her," he told himself again, almost with rage. "I'll kiss her, and with a sly movement I'll touch her breasts. I shall snatch my hand away at once, so that she mayn't be very angry . . . but I'll know the place on my hand which her breast has touched, and when I get home I shall stroke and stroke it."

The girl stood smiling by his side:

"Am I late? I couldn't find my shawl. But here I am at last! Where are we going?"

"Anywhere you like. What did you say to them at home? How long can you stay?"

"I told father I was going to the Cirini's. They're kinsmen of ours. But he wasn't listening. I can stay as long as ever I like."

"Well then, shall we cross to the Giudecca? We can sup in the garden of one of the inns and talk a little."

They chose the way through the Merceria. They had to push through

the jostling crowd, and sometimes take hold of each other's hands; even
so they were forced apart and lost each other. Torches flickered in all
the booths, their dancing light gave the streets the look of a shimmering
cavalcade; but above the torches on the level of the first floors it was
night. They walked fast; it was impossible to talk in this clamorous
bustle. When they came out under the arch of the Orologio, they
breathed again, and slowed their steps. Here there was always something
to look at. Foreigners from all over the world in their strange pied
dresses among the Venetians. Cretans in fringed caps and straw slippers;
tall, thin, fair Germans in velvet doublets with broad-slashed sleeves;
Arabs with golden earrings, in snow-white burnooses; Albanian women
with necklaces of golden coins; Negroes with the red or green fez on their
woolly hair from some far coast of Africa. Sometimes a girl in a white
veil made challenging eyes at Galileo; then pulled a face as she saw the
other girl at his side.

"The *sbirri* will catch her," Marina laughed, "unless she's careful."

"What do you mean?"

"Bad girls are forbidden to wear white veils. There's a law about it.
But they always do it."

"I never notice them," Galileo lied.

"There are ever so many of them," Marina continued. "Someone told
me the other day that the Senate had had a census made. Do you know
how many of them there are in Venice? Eleven thousand. Only for foreigners, of course!"

Galileo glanced at her pure young face. It almost moved his pity that
such an innocent, who could have no idea of physical love, should glibly
repeat what some foolish person had carelessly said. Meantime they had
arrived at the Piazzetta. Marina said, as they passed between the columns:

"I saw a hanging here when I was a child."

"A hanging? Children should never see that."

"I know. I still shiver whenever I think of it. Two men were hanged
for being Sodomites."

"For what?"

"I told you. For being Sodomites."

"But—do you know what Sodomites are?"

Marina laughed.

"Oh, no, of course not! I only know it's some ugly crime for which men get hanged."

Galileo pressed her fingers gratefully.

How could she possibly realize what she was saying? He was about to signal to a gondola when someone touched him on the shoulder. There stood Sagredo!

"Don't hire a gondola; here's mine. Come with me, if you like. I have nothing to do, and I am going out to Murano, into my garden, to get some fresh air."

"Let's go, let's go!" Marina cried gleefully.

Galileo hesitated; he wanted so much to be alone with her. How could he kiss her unless . . . But he felt Sagredo secretly nudging him, in a way that could not be misinterpreted. Perhaps his friend had some notion of helping him.

Plashing oars drove on the gondola in quiet strokes. Lanterns on the invisible boats surrounded them, as though Copernican stars had fallen to earth, to hover on the waters of Venice. The illuminated barge of the *serenata* was riding at anchor somewhere near the Salute. Voices in the distance sang of love. The fitful breeze hushed or brought nearer the sound of the lutes.

Sagredo talked of Paolo Veronese and the trouble he had with the Inquisition when that old maestro painted his "Supper at the house of the Pharisee" for the Church of San Giovanni e Paolo:

"I was talking to a kinsman of his this afternoon, and he told me how Paolo Veronese had been summoned before the Inquisition. The Church of San Giovanni e Paolo had ordered an altarpiece. Veronese painted it and got paid. But several of the priests objected to it. Veronese had painted a fool sitting and playing with a parrot among the apostles. And one apostle, who looked as though he had eaten a very good meal, was picking his teeth with a fork. That riled the severity of these priests, who denounced Veronese. Proceedings were taken against him; he was sent for by the Inquisition. And do you know what the old fellow said? That painters should be just as free as fools. Laws made for normal people don't apply to artists. I like that saying immensely."

"What was the end of the trial?" Galileo asked, keeping tight hold of Marina's hand.

"They bound him over to change his picture. He told them that he would—but he never troubled about it again."

"Excellent," said Galileo. "And I think not only artists are entitled to the liberty of the fool, but scientists too. They call me a lunatic! My colleagues at Padua certainly think me one. It's easy enough to understand: I use my own wits and see things in my own way."

"What things?" Marina asked inquisitively.

"For instance, I see that the sun doesn't move round the earth."

Marina began to laugh sweetly.

"Oh, this Galileo is really a fool!"

She stroked his face with her free hand. Galileo joined in her laughter. Marina's caress was worth the whole universe, Kepler and Copernicus included. It was a long way to the Island of Murano. Their boat swung on past the glass blower's factory, then further on among the isles. They moored at a bridge. Gondoliers with torches lighted them onward through the dark; one ran ahead to warn the servants at the villa to expect their master. The villa became surrounded with torches, flickering here and there in the dark; their light showed little of the dim garden, only quickly vanishing outlines of trim box hedges formally cut, flanked by the sudden gleam of a marble image. The air was heavy with scents of flowers. This villa was really a miniature palace; servants were running here and there, making everything ready. Sagredo led them on to an open terrace.

"Sit down here for a little while. You must excuse me, I must look after our improvised supper. I'm sorry to leave you alone, but I'll be back in twenty minutes."

Galileo was grateful for this feast. A small oil lamp stood burning in a corner of the terrace; otherwise it was pitch-dark. They sat on a wooden seat strewn with pillows. Their hands soon found each other. They were silent. The heavy scent of the flowers was headier than any wine. It gave him courage. Now he would kiss her—but he could not do it! He decided to count ten and then . . . But he got to eight and felt something tickling his ear and the fragrance of her hair in his nostrils. Her head was resting on his shoulder. Slowly he turned his head, prolonging the instant till their lips should meet, feeling her waiting to be kissed. He sighed deeply, caught hold of her shoulder and drew her close.

"You don't know how to kiss," the girl whispered with a deep-throated, sensual laugh in her voice.

She took his head into her hands, holding it as though it were some fruit whose flavor she wanted to taste. She set her lips slowly to his. Moving her head with a tiny, nestling gesture, she drank his love like a cup of wine. But this did not satisfy Galileo. He shook off her arms and began a new kiss, as if he were trying to win a race. And while his blood flamed in swooning happiness, a separate particle of his brain was terrified by the sudden thought: Where did she learn to kiss like this? Could this horror be true? had other lips touched these before him? Now these were angry kisses; they took and gave, as though they would torment one another like fighting beasts. They separated only when they heard Sagredo's approaching steps.

"Smooth out your hair," she whispered quickly.

Galileo instinctively combed his thick locks with his five fingers. Terror again! This corner was completely dark; she could not see him. She, so young, where did she get her experience? Was she so quick-witted? After such kisses, how could she think of his rumpled hair? how could she remain so cool? All this passed dimly through his brain; he did not even put it into words. He followed Sagredo breathlessly, a little dazed. Their host led them into a small room unlike any dining hall. It was a tiny room, darkened at midday, for the master of the house to rest in after dinner.

"I had the table put in here," said Sagredo carelessly. "The other rooms are still in disorder, and we can't have supper out on the terrace. Night insects would swarm into the light, and thousands of mosquitoes would come out of the reeds."

Although the supper was improvised, there was no lack of fish, fruit, and especially strong wines. They ate and drank and their talk faltered.

Sagredo talked again of Veronese, then of Tintoretto and his many versions of the Last Supper.

"They would have more reason to summon him before the Inquisition. His favorite way of painting St. John is asleep with his head on his arm, while all the others are talking hard. I shall really be surprised if Monsignor Ofredi, the Papal Nuncio, takes no objection to it. Just think—St. John the Apostle, Christ's favorite, going to sleep at the Last Supper! But it seems to me a stroke of genius. John was only a child compared to the rest. The Last Supper went on and on, till the boy fell asleep. It's a ravishing thought!"

"You see, you see." Galileo was scarcely listening, his wary foot under the table was seeking the girl's. "Even you are sometimes enthusiastic."

"Of course I am, in my own way. I think how amusing it would be to drop a big book just behind St. John. Poor boy, how the noise would make him jump!"

Marina laughed, while under the table she pressed Galileo's foot.

"Respect sleep, most gracious Lord. And remember what a supper that was. There's never been such a great and tragic supper since the world began."

"Are you such a good Catholic?" Sagredo inquisitively asked.

"Yes. I can't deny that I am. I live a heathenish life, but I'm still a believer. Don't you believe?"

"I don't know. I'm not clever enough to have any opinions about religion. Or perhaps I'm too clever by half for my age."

"It isn't with our minds we believe," said Galileo, "but with our hearts. We can only think with our understanding. And with our hearts we can only believe. In God. And in the people we love."

Afterward they lit their pipes, the table was carried away by the servants, and they stretched themselves on the divans, obedient to the host's proposal. A single lamp burned in the room. Wine stood on the little table at their side. But they did not drink. Galileo took hold of Marina's hand, and she seemed not to mind.

They talked only by fits and starts. Galileo wondered how he could ask Sagredo to leave them alone for a little time. But, marvel of marvels, there was no need! Suddenly they found that he was gone; they had not even noticed his going. And so—they realized that they were alone. Galileo took the girl in his arms; he wooed her. Thirstily, dizzily they kissed till they were out of breath and had to stop for a while. Five minutes had passed . . . or perhaps half an hour? . . . when Marina said:

"Where's that Sagredo? Perhaps you ought to go and look for him."

Galileo obeyed. The next dark room was empty. When he came to the terrace, he found a lackey sitting on the steps.

"Where's your master?"

"My master left a message saying that he didn't want to disturb you, sir. He has returned to Venice."

"To Venice?"

"Yes. But he'll send his gondola back for you."

Marina had also come into the doorway leading on to the terrace.

"Will you call us if the gondola arrives?"

"Yes, these were our master's orders."

"All right. Let us know when it gets back."

They returned to the daybed. They kissed again. Long and insatiably; their thirst could never still itself. And now he asked for the first time:

"Do you love me?"

"Yes," she answered gaily, stroking his hair. "Oh, yes, I love you."

"Why? What is it that you love in me?"

"I don't know. You're so nice and foolish. And childish. I feel as if you were my son."

"When did you notice it first?"

"Oh, quite soon. Because I saw how madly you loved me. Women like to be loved in that way."

They kissed again. And question and answer were repeated.

"So you do love me?"

"Oh, yes—I love you."

Time had died; with their kisses they fell into eternity. The servant's knock drew them apart.

"Your Excellency, the gondola is here."

"Thank you," said Galileo quickly and a little hoarsely. "Go out and wait for us; we'll come at once."

The servant left. Galileo had to kiss her again. They embraced closely, their whole bodies touched. His heart throbbed, he thought he would choke. His blood was on fire . . . with a double sense of rapture and horror he found that he met with no resistance. His happiness rose to a dizzy zenith, his pain became the anguish of terrible disappointment— while their bodies joined.

Then he was sitting beside her on the divan. The girl lay there breathing quietly. He searched for words. How should he tell her his horrible loss—the wreck of all he had longed to love, and believe in utterly—and that he never wanted to see her again. He began to say something, quiet and sad, but the girl caught his hand.

"I . . . I am so grateful," said her warm voice. "You don't know how much you have given me . . . by loving me."

Galileo turned to her, surprised.

"Yes," said her voice in the dusky quiet. "I can see that you know I'm not a virgin. But I was on the edge of something so horrible. You know, the man I loved was forced to marry a rich girl. My father is poor, and I like to be seen out in the world. I need clothes, shoes, hairdressing, all that. If I had loved someone, I would have been glad to put up with cares and debts and pinching and scraping. But I had nobody. And then a woman tried to get round me, a Signora Manetti. . . ."

"Manetti?" Galileo cried. "That bawd by trade?"

"Yes. She tried to cajole me, talked my head off. When I met you I'd begun to listen to her. And yet I couldn't. . . . It's horrible to embrace someone without love: you men can't even imagine it. But I was hesitating. I was close to it. And then you came. You see, you've saved me. I fell in love with you, and, now I'm strong. I know you're poor, but it doesn't matter. We'll live somehow. Only . . . love me. You'll love me, won't you?"

Galileo nodded, but could not speak.

"Kiss me," the girl said.

But he did not kiss her.

"Who was the man who left you and married? Tell me all about him."

She hesitated, but he questioned stubbornly and found out everything. Marina had had her first affair at eighteen with one of her cousins . . . without love, just out of curiosity and because all her friends were doing the same. This lasted a year. Then came the other, a young man called Benedetto Tessuti. She fell in love with him. Meanwhile her cousin got drowned. And this was all.

"Did they give you money? Answer me! I want the truth!"

"But, dear, this Tessuti was just as poor as you are! What can you be thinking I am! And on this night! You've hurt me now, when I felt that I could love you so much. You've made me angry."

She turned away. He watched her lithe beauty move through the dusk. Poor girl, she wasn't to blame. She had nothing to do with a foolish mathematician coming and trying to put a saint on a pedestal in order to worship another image. He had hoped to find the greatest love of his life. And had found a mistress. Any other man would have been delighted to have found such a charming girl. Yet here he sat, sighing for a dream! She had thanked him like a child for making her love him.

He caressed her hand:

"Marina, don't be angry."

"I'm not," she said readily and sweetly. "But promise not to hurt me any more."

"I promise. You don't deserve it, anyhow. You're kind and sweet."

"Kiss me."

They found each other again; but now it felt as though they had been lovers for years.

Outside the day was slowly breaking. When they walked through the garden, its beauty charmed their eyes. These trim paths, the beds of cunningly chosen flowers, tall shady pines. The famous gardens of Murano welcomed these lovers—newly made. Birds rejoiced with them all the way to the landing-stage, where they found the gondola.

The sun rose to the left of them. When they had passed the graveyard they saw the miracle of Venice in the early light. It was like drifting from the secret and perfumed air of love into a city of fairy tales built of glittering gold. They were gilded by the morning sun, two poor mice in this luxurious gondola.

They disembarked at the corner of the Cà d' Oro. Galileo gave all his remaining money to the *gondolieri,* who thanked him sleepily.

"You stay here now," Marina said. "I'll walk up alone. Someone may look out and see you with me. Are you staying in Venice today?"

"I can't; I have a lecture. But I'll be back in the evening. I'll wait for you at the Rialto . . . at nine o'clock."

"I'll be there. Don't kiss me now, it's daylight."

She drifted away down a narrow alley. Galileo watched her with happy sensuality and then thought of her in his arms. He walked slowly on through the bright morning, his steps echoing strangely in the quiet. Suddenly he felt in his pockets:

"I've nothing left," he thought, "except Copernicus."

XIX

He was still corresponding with Kepler. Their letters were always comradely, but they soon found that they disagreed on many points. This made no difference to their friendship, yet it spoiled that feeling of complete harmony, of fighting side by side against ignorance and prejudice. They were still fighting for the same cause, but in different ways and places. Kepler had lost his professorship. The government of Styria was taken over by the fiercely Roman Catholic Archduke Ferdinand. His first step after returning from his pilgrimage to Loreto was to dismiss Protestants from all public posts. Kepler was almost in danger of his life; he left his chair and fled to Hungary.

The theory of Copernicus had lost even that small renown which Kepler was able to give it in Graz. All over the world they were teaching the Almagest. The astronomical sovereignty of Aristotle and Ptolemy, which a Protestant German had attacked violently in Graz and a Catholic Italian had not yet dared to attack in Padua, reigned supreme as it had for 2,000 years.

The professor of Padua had other things to do. Whenever he had a free moment, he hurried to Venice. He silenced his conscience by saying that he had to visit Mazzoleni in the Arsenal. And, since he was in Venice, he took Marina out to sup. The gondola rowed them here and there; there was always a ribbon, a dress, a shoe, or a veil to buy, and he wanted to prove his love by these presents. Then old Gamba fell seriously ill, and soon Galileo was paying for the doctors and medicines.

At other times he would have been crushed by such a burden. But it was God's will that somehow he should manage against all odds. Everyone was buying his measuring rod. Mazzoleni was one of the best coppersmiths, and his work was excellent. Galileo presented the first to Sagredo, the next to Badouère, a French student who caught his attention among the others by his sharp wits and original thoughts. All the rest were ordered in advance. Mazzoleni could not make them fast enough; there was a long waiting list of buyers. The coppersmith now made more money by this than his whole salary at the Arsenal.

But still Galileo was poor. His debt to Landucci was a nightmare. Michelagnolo was idling in Florence, not even trying to find any work but waiting on fortune. His mother had also to be helped.

So one day he went to see the *riformatori*. The six-year term of his professorship was now drawing to an end. Would they re-engage him? And for what salary?

Senator Zane in the name of his two colleagues informed him that the Serenissima counted on the further services of Galileo Galilei.

"You are the most popular among the younger generation of the Bo; there is no denying that, Messer. Your lectures are the most crowded, the students always show their liking for you. And we're glad to see that you don't take any active part in these quarrels with the Jesuit school. After six years it seems only fair that your salary should be increased. But we can't do much for you; the fund at our disposal is too small. We can only propose and let the Senate decide. You have many distinguished friends; try to win as many senators as possible. We, the *riformatori*, won't oppose you."

Galileo thanked him for the advice and began to make the round of his friends and protectors: Sagredo, Magagnati, Zorzi, Boccalini, Fra Paolo Sarpi. He wrote to the Marchese Guidubaldo del Monte and visited his cousin, the commander. He spent much money in hiring gondolas, but in the end his prospects justified the expense. The proposition was drawn up by the *riformatori*. Galileo did his best to influence them too.

Marina's love brought him no respite from all this bustle and anxiety. Her father was sick, she could never leave him, and if at night they managed to be together for a few hours of escape, she kept complaining and hurried back to the sick bed. Galileo had also very little time. Besides his visits in the matter of his new contract, his private lessons took up most of his day. His pupils of the past five years carried his fame all over Europe; and, when some distinguished young man like Philip, the young Earl of Hessen, arrived in Padua, his first visit would be to the famous Galileo to ask for instruction in the science of fortification and to buy a measuring rod.

"I can't teach fortification here in this narrow little house. I've scarcely enough space myself."

But the idea stuck in his mind. Why not take a bigger house so that he could realize it? Of course, it would be a daring thing to shoulder the risk and then have to pay the high rent with the rooms standing empty. He began to inquire among his pupils whether there were enough applicants, and the result surprised even him. He could have taken a whole barracks. And at the same time a student of his brought news about the big, two-storied house near the great church which was to let. Galileo went round at once to look at it.

This was really the finest house in the quarter called Borgo de'Vignali. And it had a garden. He had always longed to live in a house with a garden. The house itself was more like a small-sized palace with many rooms on both floors. There were two additional wings built in the court-yard. On the ground floor he found a suite of rooms which seemed to have been designed especially for him. There was a largish hall and a roomy, light study. The two broad windows looked on the garden; the domes of St. Anthony's church could be seen through the trees. An alcove gave ample space for sleeping quarters and could be divided from the rest of the room by curtains.

He began to bargain at once. . . . The landlord named a figure which made him stagger. But when he started to reckon it out he found that by letting half the rooms he could pay the rent. And, since all his life he had been a bad businessman, he let the man see how much he wanted it; whereupon the landlord kept stubbornly to his original figure. He mentioned another prospective tenant, and Galileo hurried to sign the lease. Then he realized that he could have got it much cheaper—but he did not care. He went out into the garden to enjoy the sight of the trees, the small vineyard; he would have liked to stroke every blade of grass. He hurried to Venice, went straight to Mazzoleni:

"Listen, Messer Mazzoleni. Give up your work at the Arsenal and take up your quarters in my house in Padua. There's plenty of room. You'll make my measuring rods all day. You can earn money enough to save plenty for your old age."

"But I have many children, Your Excellency. What am I going to do with them?"

"I told you, I can give you plenty of room. Both for the workshop and your family. The house is very big. Well, what about it?"

"I'd like nothing better, Your Excellency. But if you don't mind, I must talk it over with the wife."

"All right. But do it today and write to me. I must plan according to your decision."

He hurried on to Marina, so that she too should hear the news. As he hurried into the house he stopped. Something caught his attention. A black flag was hung on the door. He ran on anxiously upstairs and found all the inmates of the house gathered in Gamba's rooms. Strangers were quarreling noisily in the sick-room. The old man had just been moved onto a bier. Marina was walking around with dry eyes, talking to all these strangers and bargaining. She was like the deathly shadow of herself haunting these rooms in open daylight. It was as though some secret had been revealed to her.

Galileo led her into the kitchen; it was the only place for undisturbed talk.

"When did he die?"

"Last evening. He'd been in such horrible pain. I could not send you word. But I thought you'd be sure to come in today."

"Who are the strangers?"

"The men of the Calza. They attend to the funeral. I sent for them last night. They're the cheapest undertakers."

"Poor girl, you must be worn out. I'm so sorry."

He took her gently in his arms, but released her at once, and held her two hands.

"You needn't be afraid of the future. I shall be with you."

"I know, dear, you're always so kind. But there's something I've got to tell you about our future. . . ."

"Don't worry now, sweet; we've plenty of time. First get the funeral over, and then rest a bit. Then we can talk."

"No, I'd better tell you now. God was kind to my father when He took him away. He hasn't lived to see my disgrace . . ."

"What disgrace?"

"I'm going to have a baby, Galileo."

He echoed her words, amazed. For some time now he had left to Marina the whole responsibility of their love. He had never thought of such a thing. Now he did not know whether he was glad or terrified.

"Are you afraid that people will talk?" he asked.

"What do I care?" she shrugged. "I haven't got anybody. My relations are all dead, my friends and acquaintances all indifferent. God sent me this to help me bear this terrible loss. But aren't you glad? I thought you would be."

"Of course I am—if you are. And you're not afraid of anything. I suppose we'd better marry as soon as possible."

"Yes. But there's no hurry about it. Let's go back now. You'd better speak to the undertakers. They'll always listen to a man."

She went before him into the living room. She was wearing black; her beauty did not yet betray its secret, the new life forming in her womb while here life rotted into earth. Galileo talked to one of the Calza men, and asked for details of the expense. But he found out that Marina had settled everything far better than he could ever have done. Then he went up to the bier, knelt and kissed the waxen, yellow hand of the dead nobleman. He felt that he ought to ask his pardon, and made a silent vow to take care of his daughter as long as he lived. In doing this he looked at the dead man's hand. He was surprised to see how like Marina's it was. Would the baby's hand look the same? He told her nothing of his joy over the new house. He waited till she had quieted down after the funeral. Gamba had left many debts; and, except for the furniture of his lodgings, he had died almost penniless. Galileo proposed that Marina should move over to Padua; they would find some rooms for her near the house; for naturally they could not live together. The university authorities would never countenance a liaison, and the Jesuits would have seized the opportunity to raise further strife.

Everything went smoothly. He found rooms for her quite near his house. Marina brought her former maid with her; soon she knew where the vegetable market was and which butcher sold the best and cheapest meat.

So began their new life. Galileo did not visit her during the day, he had a thousand things to do, his lectures and private lessons took up all his time. But he went to see her every evening. They were alone and undisturbed; there was no need for secret assignations. The hours after supper became quiet, peaceful; it was just as though they were married. Galileo thought: Why shouldn't I marry her? It would be easier financially, and from her point of view it would be a good thing. But whenever he found himself asking this, he brushed aside the thought impatiently.

One day at the end of October Venice sent him his new agreement.

The Serenissima would employ him for another six years, paying him three hundred and twenty gold pieces a year instead of one hundred and eighty. This increase would have been substantial without this heavy increase in rent. For the rent had to be paid in a lump sum; the landlord could not wait for settlement till the students—some regularly, others at odd times—made it up in driblets. The rooms were full of students of all nations. Mazzoleni's wife, who became the housekeeper, had now to cook for forty men; and their food had to be bought for cash. The measuring rods were still selling well. Two new servants had to be hired. It worked out evenly in the end, but his financial anxieties had not diminished. He did not keep accounts of his debts and income. He had a small iron chest in which he kept money. If a student paid, he dropped the coins into the chest and dipped into it when Signora Mazzoleni asked for money. He never knew which student was late with his payments; sometimes he was astonished when one of them came to him with long-winded apologies and paid up arrears. Landucci still sent him threatening letters, and when these arrived Galileo always went to the iron chest; but he never found enough money in it to make a substantial payment on his guarantee.

But such cares never lasted long with him. He shook them off and forgot them instantly. And he had more joys than ever before. It was delightful to dine every day with his students. The servant ran upstairs to the top story, sounded the brass gong in the corridor, and descended to do the same below. But by the time he reached the ground floor, the hungry, noisy young crowd was jostling in the long dining room.

"*Buon giorno, Eccellenza!*" they shouted gaily when Galileo appeared at the head of the table.

The plates clattered, the stone jugs of Chianti stood in a row. For a few minutes there was no sound, till their young hunger was appeased, except that of eating. Then they all began talking at once. On the right of the host sat young Count Noailles, son of rich French parents; on his left Count Schweinitz, come from Germany to study at the famous Bo. Then the German Lehrbach, the Polish Stanislas, the Tuscan Beatavilla; and so on to the youngest boy, who had arrived yesterday, and whose name only a few had found out yet. They were talking Latin because Germans, Poles, Italians, Frenchmen did not understand each other's speech. Every meal brought something new and interesting. These students came from all parts of the world and had much to tell and many strange stories of their countries and their strange customs. Or they told of their fights with the Jesuit scholars; of practical jokes played on the *sbirri;* of love affairs and serenades. Galileo laughed with them, had a story for every story told, and advised his young friends on their dealing with wenches.

After a noisy dinner the students formed small groups according to the studies they had begun, and the degree of learning they had reached. Galileo had scarcely an hour to himself till supper time. At seven the gong sounded again, and the students crowded around the table. There was always plenty of wine; for Galileo had given orders that till nine o'clock the jugs had always to be refilled. For after supper they sat together till nine o'clock, musical instruments were produced, and songs filled the room. At nine he rose and went to Marina—since that was his custom—but usually he was late in visiting her, and often he did not go at all, but sent her word of more important business at home. He preferred to drink among his students. Often he would send for his lute and sing Florentine songs, even the bawdiest, to their huge delight. It sometimes ended in his drinking himself into maudlin praise of Florence, his head on the shoulder of Count Noailles. Next day he rebuked himself angrily for so foolishly risking his authority. But the lads respected him just as before. They were far too dazzled by his mind to lose their respect for him. Only Signora Mazzoleni grumbled about the amount of wine, saying that His Excellency was just like the foolish innkeeper who paid the score of all his guests.

Marina never reproached Galileo for not coming to see her. Her kiss of welcome was always tender. She began to grow heavier now, and was often sick. But she never complained. She never seemed to want anything; the small events of the town left her quite indifferent. When Galileo was with her, she would sit in the big armchair and work at her never-ending embroidery, listening politely to his talk. If he said nothing, she sat there humming, like a purring cat. If he came to take her in his arms, she offered him her lips obediently, as gently as a favorite pupil receiving the special attention of her schoolmaster.

"I've some very good news," he told her one night. "I'm going to be elected to the Academy."

"Really? How interesting!" She made it sound very polite, yet a certain indifference in her tone annoyed Galileo.

"Don't you want to know which academy?"

"Of course I do. I'm waiting for you to tell me."

"Well, I told you about young Cornaro, who studied here to become a priest?"

"Yes, I think I know him. I met him in Venice."

"Well, he has a lovely little palazzo near the Ponte di Santa Sofia. And after many efforts he's managed to get together some learned men to form an academy in Padua. He only did it to become a member himself, and to have the meetings at his palace. Today we have founded the academy. We've called it 'I Ricovrati.'"

"Why this name?"

"It was Cornaro who thought of it. It's very difficult to find a new name for an academy. Cremonini told us today how many there have been in Padua. There's always someone who's founding one, keeping it alive during his lifetime, and afterward it just dies. In Padua there have been the Torchbearers, the Persevering, the Enthusiastic, the Renascent, the Powerful, the Ethereal, and God knows what all. Well, this new one is called the Accepted. Or if you like: Those who received a shelter. The whole thing aims at the Palazzo Cornaro being the home of sciences. The president is Querengo. They've elected me."

"That's a great honor for you."

Silence. He began to scrutinize her. At last he asked her in another voice:

"Marina, listen. I want to ask you something. You've listened politely to what I've said, and answered me prettily. But I could swear it interests you no more than the price of beef would interest me. You're a strange woman. I've often noticed that you were listening merely because you wanted to be polite. Tell me frankly: What really interests you?"

Marina took a long time answering. At last her deep blue eyes looked from her work:

"Nothing."

"Nothing really interests you?"

"No—nothing."

"Then why live at all?"

"Because I was born. But I wouldn't mind dying very much. Although I'm not longing for that either."

"You aren't interested even in yourself?"

"No."

"Or in the child you're going to bear?"

Marina shrugged.

"I'm curious to see what it'll be like. I am sure it will be pretty and amusing."

Galileo began to get excited.

"Marina, now that we're talking frankly—do you love me?"

"Of course I love you. You're so kind to me."

"It isn't that. Are you in love with me or not? Well?"

"No, I'm not in love with you. I thought I was once . . . but then I began to see that I wasn't. I can't be really in love with anyone."

"Marina, this is terrible. Surely we love each other? I've been thinking, too, that I'd only fancied myself in love with you. . . ."

"I know," she nodded. "But why is it terrible? We agree together very well."

Galileo looked aghast at his mistress.

"You're mysterious and frightening, Marina. What are you, tell me. What's in your soul?"

"Nothing," she answered calmly. "My soul is empty."

"But you let me kiss you. You answer my kisses! Why, sometimes when we're in bed together you hug me as though you wanted to strangle me."

"Of course. It's so beautiful to kiss. And you're a very handsome, noble man. And besides—you're my man."

He had no more to say, and neither had she. It was long before he broke the silence.

"Listen—we'll never talk about it again."

"Perhaps it would be better not to." She nodded, placidly and indifferently.

They dropped the subject. They lived together like amiable husband and wife. And the sensuous fire of their kisses was just as delightful as before. But Galileo knew that he was alone. He tried one evening to tell her of Kepler and Copernicus, and arouse her sympathy for his thoughts which might startle the universe. All in vain. Nothing but charming words cloaking a complete indifference. He had nothing left of Marina except a beautiful mistress for whom he provided. He gave it up.

Sometimes he still exchanged letters with Kepler, whose fortunes had noticeably changed. Tycho Brahe, the Court astronomer of the Emperor of Austria at Prague, wanted an assistant, and someone called his attention to Kepler. Kepler could have gone back to Graz; the Jesuits who became the masters there under the reign of Archduke Ferdinand liked him, even though he was a Protestant, and called him back, promising him complete religious freedom. But he preferred the position at Prague. He told Galileo that Tycho Brahe was very much interested in his Padua colleague, and desired him to write. But Galileo was too proud to follow such a command. When Pinelli told him that he had heard from Prague with the same request, he answered that he would not be the first in this correspondence. Pinelli smiled and did not argue. And Galileo won. He received a letter from Tycho Brahe, a polite, very appreciative, but slightly condescending letter. But Brahe seemed to believe in Copernicus. Galileo answered at once in detail, with many expressions of friendship. But Kepler's next letter told him that Tycho Brahe was dead. The two followers of Copernicus were alone again.

Marina's child was born: a girl, whom they christened Virginia. Giovanni Viola, the priest at the parish church, did not enter the father's name in the register. The young father was amazed at the happiness his little daughter gave him. He came over to see her six times a day, and found her always enchanting. He painted her future in the rosiest colors: he would earn a great fortune for her, and marry her to some distinguished man.

The birth of the child gave new fire to his ambitions. For days together he went back over his proof of a new cosmology founded on the teachings of Copernicus, wondering whether to give it to the world. After a long struggle he decided that it would have to be done. But first he wanted to speak to Fra Sarpi. He was a churchman; it would be well to ask him what would be the effect on the Church of the new teaching.

He went to Venice and awaited Fra Paolo in the bookshop. They walked together along the Riva dei Schiavoni, and Galileo explained his intentions. Next term he intended to lecture on Copernicus, and then publish his lectures in a book. This book was going to change the whole basis of science!

Sarpi listened in silence. He said nothing till Galileo had finished speaking, then he stood still:

"Tell me, my son, do you remember Giordano Bruno, the philosopher, whom they arrested here in Venice a few years ago?"

"Of course. He delivered a few lectures in Padua just before my time. A Dominican who had quarreled with his Prior. The Marchese del Monte told me about him."

"Yes. He taught that God is the soul of the universe, and we, as souls, are a part of God."

"I know. I know. And that every fixed star is itself a sun. Well, what about him?"

"Well, the Inquisition sent him from here to Rome to prison in the Castel Sant' Angelo. They kept him shut up there seven years. And this morning I heard that after seven years of questioning he was sentenced to be burned alive. He was executed a few days ago. The man who brought the news was present. He told me the poor wretch screamed horribly while he burned. Many people swooned from the reek of burning human flesh. And now let me answer your question: choose for yourself! Would you rather go to the stake as a martyr to learning, or hold your tongue and go home to your little daughter?"

"Let them burn me! What do I care! I mean to speak!"

"No, my dear son, you don't. I know you better than you know yourself. You worship life. Its beauty entrances you. You're not the sort of man who would die by fire! And you're quite right! Because life is sweet and beautiful. Go home now to your little daughter!"

Again Galileo lowered his eyes. He was ashamed to show the priest there were tears of rage in them. But even now he realized that he must be silent still.

II

II

I

The undersigned Galileo Galilei pledges himself together with his younger brother Michelagnolo Galilei to pay Signor Taddeo Galletti the sum of one thousand and eight hundred ducats taking six lire and four soldi per ducat. Payment should be made in the following manner: in cash to the hands of my sister Livia six hundred ducats and clothing worth the amount of two hundred ducats; the rest to be settled in five years, in yearly instalments of two hundred ducats. Should one of the instalments not be paid on the date agreed upon, the whole remainder to fall due at once. Both my brother and myself are responsible in the name of our heirs and descendants for the above sum with all our present and future possessions and should one of us be found amiss in the fulfilment of our obligations, the other would be made liable for them. Any other agreements or juridical sentences contrary to the above contract shall all be null and void.

Now Livia was also married to a young Florentine nobleman, Galletti, who had no fixed position, but good connections in Venice. He planned to settle there, and was full of projects which he could realize with the help of the dowry. The marriage contract had been drawn up by a Venetian notary public. The young couple had come to him because Galileo did not want to go to Florence. He was still afraid of brother-in-law Landucci. Though he had guaranteed Livia's dowry, he still owed a large sum on Virginia's. He did not know where he would get all the money. Something was sure to happen, he kept on telling himself.

Michelagnolo had found work. He was still in touch with his Polish friends, and one day he announced that he had been invited to join the private orchestra of Prince Radziwill, one of the richest Polish nobles who lived in Lithuania. So he packed his belongings and started again on the long journey. He wrote a few lines from Cracow, but after that he gave no sign of life. Later they heard that he had written to a friend of his, to say he was going to Wilna from Lublin. Then no more news. But as he did not return, they thought that he must have been taken on. Michelagnolo had promised his brother to ask Prince Radziwill for an advance to send home in part contribution to Livia's dowry. But no money came. Galileo waited till the payments were long overdue, and then had to go to a usurer for a short loan. Still no Lithuanian money! In his plight he turned to his richest friends, Sagredo and Venier, nephew of a former doge. They helped him to pay the debt. But now he was heavily indebted to them, which was even more painful to him. He wanted Michelagnolo to send at least an acknowledgment of his guarantee and wrote four times to Lithuania, but got no answer.

So he would have to shoulder the whole burden! He did not really mind. The promise he had given his father to take good care of his mother and sisters was deep in his heart. He would have done it even without any pledge. He clung almost morbidly to his kindred, was almost vaingloriously proud that the whole family should depend on him, the renowned scientist, and expect him to provide for everything. Somehow he always got out of his difficulties; and, when he saw that nothing really serious had happened, he pledged himself all over again. Livia was ecstatically grateful, and he could return to his work in peace. Galileo was still awaiting the miracle. He felt that only a miracle could help him to find proof for the theory of Copernicus. But if he ever did manage to find this, not even the huge authority of the Church should prevent his proclaiming it. The Church had her scientists, too, like Clavius, whom a clear demonstration would convince. Yet the theory was without proof. And perhaps Galileo Galilei might die after teaching error his whole life long. This was so heavy a thought that he had to escape from it to the small joys of everyday life.

Behind his house there was a garden with vines in it, which he loved to cultivate. He accustomed himself to getting up much earlier. Every day brought something exciting and interesting in the small vineyard. Every vine became his personal friend and responsibility. Some of them were docile and obedient. Others recalcitrant and stubborn, growing after their own sweet will, defying his meticulous care. The time and love he gave to his vineyard was well repaid by his splendid grapes and deep-red wine.

When he rose in the early dawn, work started at the far end of the courtyard, in Mazzoleni's workshop. Galileo might have called it his own factory. It was a small one, but it turned out his measuring rod, for which they still found hosts of ready buyers. Mazzoleni was working with two assistants, also making sextants, quadrants, and parts of scientific instruments. Their customers were rich dilettante scientists, officers, landowners, well-to-do students from distant lands.

A little later the articled clerk of the house, Messer Silvestro, would arrive. The miniature factory was selling the measuring rod with full instructions. But these were not printed, as this might have robbed Galileo of private pupils. They were all hand-written. As the sun rose, Messer Silvestro began dipping his quill into the inkstand, and copied these instructions till midday. He copied all the afternoon till sunset. Sometimes he shouted for silence through the window, having found himself writing down the cries of the students brawling in the yard.

Students came and went continually. There was scarcely an empty room on the two floors. One was inhabited by a Scot, the next by a Pole, the third by a German.

Some came for only a few days to get ideas of fortification; others remained three years, working hard for their bachelor's degree. At meals the great table was surrounded by vociferous youths. Galileo, sitting at the head of the table, laughed with them.

In the evenings it was always Marina and the little house full of children's cries. Just one year after Virginia's birth came another girl, whom they called Livia. Galileo chose the names of his two sisters for his daughters. He had offered Marina the choice, but she seemed indifferent. She had no one after whom she could name her child. She had only a dim memory of her mother, and had no other kinswomen living or dead. Therefore he could rejoice to have his second baby christened Livia.

Whenever he came to the little house he asked how the children were getting on. Was there any news? Always with the same words. And Marina always said there was no news, and that the children were well. His elder daughter sat on his knee, and he played with her. When they were tired he put her down, lit his pipe, and pulled a book out of his pocket. Marina put the children to bed and came to sit in the other armchair with her embroidery. Sometimes they did not speak for hours.

Days slid by, months and years. The book of Copernicus was buried under a heap of newer works; it would have been a hard task to find it. But he did not look for it. His life was settled in a peaceful rut. He was a professor at Padua, teaching Euclid and the Almagest; nothing else remained of his old rebellious self save occasional sallies against Aristotle, whose mechanics he criticized in his lectures. Sometimes he asked for an advance on his salary or went to Venice to cultivate the good will of the two *riformatori*. Or he made a trip with his old friends Zorzi, Magagnati, and Boccalini. Or Sagredo visited him; sometimes even Fra Paolo Sarpi. They had long talks, and life returned again to the old routine.

A little change was brought in the uniformity of his days by the arrival of two strangers, a fencing master called Capra and his son. Soon they had a large number of pupils. Galileo visited them; some instinct drove him to learn to fence, and he needed exercise. He liked fencing from the first, and would miss no lessons. Afterward he had a splendid appetite, and found that food and drink and Marina's beauty could make life very pleasant indeed.

Thus he reached his fortieth year. But he spent his birthday in bed. In January he was taken ill. Sometimes he had felt a pain in his joints, but had not given any thought to it. Now the pain attacked his left wrist and both knee joints. It was agony. His body was swollen, and the slightest movement made him wince. At first he thought he would soon get over it, but it became worse and worse. In the end he called a doctor—old Fabrizio. The professor examined him and shook his head.

"Have you ever had a swelling in your throat, my friend? Oh, yes, of course, you have; I remember now."

"Well? What has my throat to do with my knee?"

"A good deal. We doctors know that a swollen throat is an illness which may often seem to be cured, but the ailment frequently hides in the joints to appear there years later. It may sound odd, but believe me, you have a swollen throat in your knees and wrists."

"I'll believe you if you believe me when I say that the earth moves around the sun."

The old professor began to laugh. "You're always joking, even if you're on the rack. This will be a very painful illness."

"And how long will it last?"

"To be quite frank, as long as you live. It may pass off in a few weeks or even a few days and come back next year. Sometimes it doesn't crop up for many years; then it starts all over again. But you can live to be a hundred with it."

"A nice thing to look forward to. And how shall we treat it?"

"Put a poultice of hot bran around your joints. I'll send Grosso, the city physician, to have a look at it every day. What's this book you're reading?"

"This? My favorite poet."

"Oh, Ariosto?"

"No, I don't like Ariosto as much as I do this man. He's called Berni."

"Berni, of course. I've heard his name. But I never read anything of his."

"Well, listen to this—he calls it: 'Sonnet to My Wife.' It should be read as I'm going to read it to you, with a Tuscan accent:

SONNET TO MY WIFE

So silver-tousled, rough and wild her hair,
Her ripe full mouth upon a face of gold
Hangs like a plum, and though my wife is old,
Her beauty even death himself can scare
No shower of Cupid's darts surrounds my fair,
Her eyes obey twin masters, and they hold
Allegiance right and left; her glance is cold
But never straight, though tempters may not spare.

A huge fist grows upon her massive arm,
Her wide mouth gapes as black as ebony,
Most fitting sight for wonder and alarm!
But you who gaze on beauty's mystery
And kneel entranced to every woman's charm,
Know this—in pride and love my praises vie!

"What do you say to that, Excellency? That man lived in Florence at a time when the most inflated grandiloquence and pompous rhetoric were triumphant there! And yet he dared write such a sonnet! Let me read you another before Marina comes. It's called:

LINES AGAINST MARRIAGE

To eat dry capons or fat beef alone
With not one cup of wine to wash them down;
Fumble in pockets for a missing crown,
Yet pay and pay, and go on paying! Moan
In muggy January, and gasp for air,
Shiver at midsummer; stand at a fair
With elbows in your ribs to watch a play
And yet see nothing; or to tramp the hills
With a pebble in your shoe, and limp and swear—
Never to catch the dexterous flea that swills
Your life-blood and escapes; to dance all day

Attendance on the pleasure of the great!
To be worn out yet never get to bed;
To have one stocking and two legs—What fate,
Brother, can be called worse than all these ills?
I'll tell you: It is far worse to be wed."

"Could you lend me the book? I'd like to read some of it to my wife."

"I'm sorry, I can't. I've stolen it myself. I could not stand my torture without Berni. I'm not surprised that Michelangelo liked his book the best of all."

"Really?"

"Yes. He called him 'the divine.' But I'll have Messer Silvestro copy out a few of his poems and send them to you—as your doctor's fee."

"Very well. Keep it up, my friend; hot bran should help you. Grosso shall be here tomorrow to start your cure."

While the professor was taking his leave, there came a knock at the door. The sick man was surprised to see the fencing master Aurelio and his son Baldassare Capra. This was the first time they had called at his house. Old Capra inquired solicitously about his health, then he blurted out his great news:

"Your Excellency, I came to win you as a patient. I'm planning to become a physician. I've received instruction from His Excellency Grosso, who was kind enough to teach me, and who said that I have an amazing instinct for medical matters."

"This is really interesting, Messer Capra. I shan't object to your curing me when you've learned everything, because I am in great pain."

"I shall do my very best. But there's something else. I'd like to commend my son for your attention. He is making up now for his poor education; he had no opportunities to do so in Milan. We thought that Baldassare might take some mathematical lessons from you in exchange for fencing lessons. He's especially interested in your famous compass. We've heard that Your Excellency has a special factory for it here in the house."

"Yes, that's true."

"Couldn't we take a look at the workshop . . . just to see how it's done?"

"I'm sorry, Messer Capra; you came at the wrong time. We aren't making any just now. But if I recover I shall be glad to explain its use to your son. Don't worry about the price of the lessons; we'll make some arrangement."

Marina arrived. Capra and his son bowed low to her, and, after a few more polite remarks, took their leave. Marina brought hot bran in a pail and some strips of linen. She had met Fabrizio on her way, and was here to start the prescribed cure.

"Raise your knee," she said. "I'll put on the poultice. Don't be afraid, I'll take care not to hurt you. . . . But, tell me, what did those two knaves want here?"

"I don't know. I was surprised at their coming. They're both fools. The father wants to become a physician, the son an astronomer. If it didn't hurt my legs, I'd laugh at them."

"Don't laugh. Those two are spies."

"Spies? Ridiculous! What should they spy for? Oh, this hot poultice is wonderful. . . ."

"I'll tell you what, do you know Simone Mayr?"

"Simone Mayr von Guntzenhausen is a poor, underpaid mathematician. He graduated here, in Padua. Moletti was his teacher. Although he was a German, he did not go back to his country, but remained here. He's teaching little children arithmetic. He counts for nothing."

"Oh, yes, he does. Do you know this Simone Mayr is abusing you everywhere?"

"So I've heard, but it slipped my mind again. Poor little man! Of course he's abusing me. He can never get a private lesson, while my house is full of rich students. Why shouldn't he abuse me?"

"And do you know who is his best friend? This young Capra. They're always together. I tell you, Galileo, these two are up to no good."

"What can they do? The young man is interested in the compass. I'll show him the use of it when I'm better. How are the children?"

"Very well. Tomorrow's your birthday. I'll bring them to see you. They're very excited about it."

"No news?"

"Oh, yes. A former maid of mine called yesterday and told me about the latest scandal in Venice. Do you remember that Leonardo Pesaro?"

"The dueling fop? Of course. Segredo told me about him. What happened?"

"They've caught him now. There was a great wedding in the Minotto di Barba family and a masque. There he met Paolo Lion, whom he had always hated. But Paolo Lion was talking to his betrothed, Lucrezia Baglioni; and, as he did not want a scandal, he refused to quarrel with Pesaro. Pesaro left the masque and collected his notorious friends, among them Camillo Trevisan . . ."

"Yes, yes, Sagredo mentioned him too . . ."

"Well, they all returned to the feast. He rushed straight at Paolo Lion. Lucrezia tried to save her lover. Pesaro knocked her down and ran his sword through Lion. The guests began to scream, the host tried to send for a doctor to save Lion; but Pesaro's companions wouldn't let anyone out of the palace. Lion bled to death. A terrible fight began; of course the guests had no weapons, so they used chairs to defend themselves. Someone knocked down Pesaro and they tied him up. You know that he is the member of a very powerful family, so they dared not arrest him. But when the Doge heard, he ordered his imprisonment in the Lead Chambers. Now they're going to cut off his head. Did you ever meet him?"

"Never, thank God."

"I knew him quite well. He courted me at a ball, and I thought I'd never get rid of him; but luckily he drank so much that he fell asleep. Is the poultice all right? Have you got everything? Shall I stay with you?"

"No, thanks. I'd rather be left alone, if you don't mind."

"Of course, I don't mind. I'll come along tonight to give you a new poultice. But be on your guard against these Capras."

"All right, all right," he answered irritably. "But leave me now."

Marina brushed his forehead with her lips and was gone. Galileo stretched his clumsy right hand eagerly toward the book. He was soon buried in its pages. And, though still half conscious of the excruciating pain in his joints, he suddenly knew why Berni was his favorite poet. It was because he was a Florentine, and the music of Florence sang and clamored in his lines. He dropped the book and thought of Florence, the beloved.

"If only I were back there," he sighed, full of sweet longing for his home.

II

Vincenzio II, Prince Gonzaga, pomp-loving ruler of Mantua, received the mathematician whom he had summoned from Padua to his Court. Galileo had accepted the invitation, but he knew it would not lead to much. He had no desire to become Court mathematician at Mantua. Florence was the only city for which he was prepared to leave the Bo.

He had met the Prince before, having been presented to him in Padua. They had talked for a few minutes, but even these had been long enough for Galileo to discover in the Prince a capricious, rambling, crack-brained man.

Court etiquette was much stricter in Mantua than in Florence. Prince Vincenzio was celebrated all over Italy as a lover of every form of theatrical show. And he staged his own life with equally theatrical pomp. If he left the Appartamento Ducale to go to the Appartamento degli Arazzi, the simple move from one to another set of rooms became an elaborate cortège. Galileo was passed from group to group of stiffly moving courtiers like mutes on a gigantic stage, till at last he stood before the Prince. He bowed low:

"Permit me, Your Most Serene Highness, to prove my deep respect by presenting you with a humble invention of mine." And he produced a finely wrought copy of his measuring rod, made with especial care by the skilled Mazzoleni.

"What is it for?" asked the Prince.

"I call it a proportional compass. It can measure anything. If your Gracious Highness commands me, I shall be delighted to explain its use, especially in military matters."

"Military matters," the Prince repeated absent-mindedly. "Oh, yes, of course! Tell me, Messer Galilei, could you build a castle on the stage which would collapse at a given moment and burst into flames?"

"Why not? It is possible."

Prince Vincenzio became eager and animated.

"You could? Really? And listen, we want some angels to fly over the stage and scatter flowers on a martyr. But their wings must move. Could you solve it somehow?"

"Very easily. The angels ought to be towed on invisible wires, while they can move their own wings by cords."

"At last! At last! You're the very man! I have already written to you about it, but now we can discuss the matter personally. Would you care to take up a position at my Court?"

"It is a matter of finance, Your Highness, and a question of my time. I should have to know how much spare time you could give me for my own scientific work. And I have a large family to provide for."

"Yes. And could you construct an earthquake on the stage, with water and waves?"

"It could be done. Every technical problem can be solved."

"Marvelous. But the waves must have crests. You could do it. Wonderful! So you think you would like to come to Mantua?"

"I repeat, Your Highness, it is a question of salary and hours."

"Yes, yes. And could you arrange a naval battle here on the lake with lighted fire-ships?"

And so on, for the best part of an hour. It simply meant that the Prince needed a scientist to build stage machinery for his theater, to arrange parades, garden masques, and processions; but the money must be discussed with the fiscal authorities.

Finally Galileo was given a fine apartment and all the implements to draw up plans. Vincenzio was delighted with his results, but could not be pinned down to any serious commitment. Later Galileo tried to settle the matter with some Court officials, and finally learned that he could expect a salary of three hundred gold pieces a year, with full board for himself and his servant. Whereupon he left Mantua; and, though he gave little thought to the Mantua offer, he mentioned it to Fra Sarpi. He had been visiting the two *riformatori,* and he met the monk in Venice.

"Don't refuse it, my son, for heaven's sake. I can tell you beforehand: it will be very difficult to discuss the renewal of your contract, because all the authorities are so busy. It will be useful if you can frighten them with this Mantua business."

"I don't understand. Why are they so busy?"

"Do you mean to say you don't know? There are great things afoot. We are quarreling with the Pope."

"The Pope? But why?"

"Where have you been living, my son? Listen, I'll tell you once about it, so that you may know where you are. But I won't tell you again."

Galileo promised to listen carefully. Last year the Most Serene Republic had decreed that since the number of churches had increased out of all proportion, places of worship must in future be erected only with express permission from the government. This had enraged the Pope, and his anger was increased by the case of Sarraceno, Canon of Vicenza. This Sarraceno quarreled with the wife of a distinguished Venetian and insulted her in a most flagrant manner; whereupon he was arrested. The Pope angrily protested that Sarraceno must not be tried by a civil court. On the other hand, the Most Serene Republic, on the expert advice of Fra Sarpi, maintained that, if priests committed civil crimes, they must be dealt with by the civil authorities.

"So there are two parties now in Venice," Fra Paolo continued. "One led by the Papal Nuncio, Ofredi; the other by me. And now the whole machinery of state is whirring as if it had gone mad. There are twenty meetings of senators every day; couriers come in every hour from Rome with memoranda and counter-memoranda. But the main fight is still before us. The Senate has prepared a decree forbidding all gifts and bequests to churches and monasteries, which rob the state of large sums in taxes. There is going to be a struggle about that. Then there is trouble with the Abbot of Narvese, who is a common criminal. He is mentally diseased, and when he grows tired of his favorites, he hires assassins to kill them off. The Council of Ten is collecting evidence against him, and as soon as it is conclusive, he'll be arrested."

"Aren't you feeling nervous, Fra Paolo?"

"I am. I'd like to wear a coat of mail, but I can't. The Nuncio is having me watched. The other day he denounced me to the Vatican for not wearing sandals at home but slippers, although I am bound by the rules of my Order to go barefoot. The truth is that since my feet ache, I always wear slippers while I work. There must be a spy in my own house. So I have to look after myself without any coat of mail to protect me. I keep out of narrow streets, and never go out at night. But I warn you, my son, my friendship is becoming dangerous."

"I can well believe you," said Galileo. "But I'm afraid I can't do without it." And, in fact, he found it impossible to discuss his future with the authorities, although it was very important to clear up the question of his contract, which had one more year to run. Everyone to whom he broached the matter was on his way to a committee meeting or just back from one, so he took Fra Palo's advice and wrote to the two *riformatori* of his offer from the court of Mantua. He even visited Prince Vincenzio again, who rapturously praised his plans for theatrical designs and presented new problems to be solved. While Galileo talked of five hundred gold pieces a year and full board for three persons, the Prince discussed a volcano with real lava and ashes; the lava to be made of wine, the ashes of sugar. They could not reach an agreement, because the mathematician spoke only about his salary, while the Prince would only discuss volcanos.

He left it all unsettled and went back to Padua. But the Prince of Mantua turned out to be a most generous man: he sent Galileo a gold chain, a huge medal, and two silver dishes. All this was worth more than 2300 lire.

At the same time the two *riformatori* notified him that he would get a substantial increase in his new agreement, and that they would at once start paying this higher amount. The measuring rods were still selling fairly well, and his house was full of wealthy students. And now, after Marina had pestered him for years, he had consented to keep some sort of accounts. Yet his debts were still almost the same.

"They're robbing you right and left," she said. "But you don't notice it."

"Robbing me?" he sounded amazed.

"Of course. Did you think they'd be ashamed to do it?"

"But how can they rob me when I keep my iron chest always locked?"

"Oh, silly one! Your housekeeper charges you what she likes. The servants steal the wine. Mazzoleni cheats you as much as he pleases. It isn't my business, but after all they rob our children."

"Our children will always have whatever they need. You and the two girls come first. It's true, I'm careless about most other things."

Marina did not contradict. She knew her lover; nobody could change him; he would always star-gaze and stumble over pebbles.

Galileo had been twelve years in Padua. They were used to his hobbies and eccentricities; they did not mind his not having married Marina, nor did they reproach him for his indifference to public affairs, though at present he should really have shown some interest in them, since the tension between Venice and the Vatican found its echoes in Padua. Sarpi often visited the city; the professors all belonged to his followers, and excitement was rising day by day. But Galileo sat on among his students, and the greatest events of his life were letters from Michelagnolo and Kepler. His brother wrote complaining of his poverty, probably to escape having to pay any further instalment on the dowry; but otherwise the gay tone of his letters showed that he had fallen on his feet.

Kepler had more serious difficulties. He had inherited Tycho Brahe's position at the Court of Prague, but Brahe's son-in-law, Tengnagel, refused to give up the astronomer's instruments and manuscripts. Kepler could not work without these. It took him two years till Tengnagel could be forced to deliver Tycho Brahe's scientific treasure, and Kepler was commanded to write a book for the greater glory of Emperor Rudolph. He performed this task, but he wrote on optics, not on Copernicus, whose theory was slowly being forgotten. Even Galileo despaired of ever presenting it to the world.

His mother's visit brought some variety for him. He was ashamed to go to Florence because of Landucci, but he longed for his mother. Signora Giulia arrived one hot summer day, and to begin with they were all very happy. Then came a fierce quarrel, with both Marina and her son; and from then to the end of her visit Signora Giulia went back to her old ways, screaming and scolding, to the amazement and curiosity of the students. When she was gone, Galileo found it difficult to explain that his mother—suddenly an old woman—must not be judged by ordinary standards.

But then came something which revived the old fighting Galileo: the new star.

On a day in October when he had no lecture to deliver, but sat at home arranging his notes, one of his favorite pupils, the young Count Castelli, who was studying to become a priest, rushed into his study. Castelli was seventeen, destined, as a younger son, for a clerical career by his family. He had studied at a Benedictine monastery, and had chosen mathematics as his chief subject besides theology. Galileo liked him, not only for his quick wits and open mind, but also for his generous and excellent character.

The young Benedictine stopped in the doorway, completely out of breath and full of excitement.

"What's happened, Messer? Sit down and calm yourself."

"Your Excellency . . . Your Excellency . . . a new star. . . ."

"What? Sit down, my son, sit down, and get your wind. There. Now speak. You say a new star?"

"Young Capra and Mayr von Guntzenhausen have just discovered a new star."

Galileo laughed.

"A new star? Does that mean the end of the world?"

"Don't laugh, Your Excellency. His Excellency Giacomo Alvise Cornaro sent me to fetch you, as the chief member of the Ricovrati Academy, and as an astronomer. Monsignor Cornaro himself saw the star."

Galileo took his hat silently and set out. He felt a kind of malicious glee. Capra and Mayr, who were abusing him behind his back, had probably made fools of themselves this time, and would become ridiculous with Cornaro. Cornaro deserved it most because he was so self-important, so eager to play the part of a generous patron of sciences.

"Hurry! Hurry, *carissimo!* cried Cornaro. "Something incredible has happened. There's a new star in the sky. I saw it with my own eyes last night. I've sent word to our president, Count Querengo."

Galileo began to prick up his ears. There was something in Cornaro's voice which sounded convincing. "Sit down," Cornaro continued. "I'll tell you everything—just as the Capras told it to me. Six days ago, on October 10, 1604, young Baldassare Capra was looking with Simone Mayr at the fixed stars, as he does every night. As you know, Capra is studying astronomy, and has chosen Mayr for his master."

"I thought *I* was teaching him astronomy. He didn't say anything about Mayr, when he came to see me with his father, and . . ."

"Excuse me, that's another matter. Well, every night they scanned the fixed stars. On that day a friend of theirs from Calabria, a man called Camillo Sasso, was with them. Capra, as Mayr had taught him, fixed the quadrant in the astronomical latitude of Padua. They looked into its opening by turns. Suddenly Mayr called out that he could see a star in a place in the sky which used to be empty. Listen, I'll tell you where— just beyond the line connecting Mars and Jupiter. Sasso, who heard him calling, became curious and also looked. But, since he knew nothing of astronomy, he only asked: 'What do you call that star? I never saw it before!' Mayr didn't answer; he pulled Capra to the instrument. Only then did he say: 'There's a new star on the sky'—as he said it, his excitement made him grin. Capra was also amazed, because he had looked at the very spot eight nights running and seen no star there. They rubbed their eyes and looked at the new star again and again. After long hesitation they decided to keep the discovery quiet, because they were afraid of being laughed at. Next day they searched through all the available books, but could find no mention of a star in that particular place. They could hardly wait till it was night; but even then the sky was overcast, so they couldn't see anything. The cloudy weather lasted four days, and at last yesterday it cleared up. As soon as the stars came out, they looked for the new one. There it was—in just the same place! There could be no doubt about it! And at ten o'clock they sent for me. I've seen it with my own eyes! It's a star of the fourth magnitude, with a reddish aura. I watched it till an hour after midnight. On my way home I wanted to tell you, but the lights were all out in your house." Galileo remembered that at that time he had just left Marina's arms.

"It was my first duty to let you know. What do you say to this miracle?"

"I doubt it."

"But I tell you I saw it with my own eyes!"

"Our senses cannot always be trusted. I'll come tonight and see for myself. I can't say anything till I've convinced myself."

Cornaro was all impatience to have the endorsement of the official astronomer of the Bo. Galileo walked home, deep in thought. He looked up at the cloudless sky and tried to reckon out the spot in question: forty-nine minutes from Mars, in the line of the Mars-Jupiter axis. There was nothing to see there now. But Galileo's brooding mind pricked an invisible hole in that point of the mysterious dome of heaven.

He consulted his books, searched through them diligently, examining all the possibilities. There could be no star in that place. Cremonini came at noon asking his opinion, highly excited. Cornaro had spread the news through the university. At dinner the students were all speaking of the new star. In the afternoon came old Fabrizio and Alpino, the new botanist. Galileo had to lock himself in his study to escape all the inquiring guests. At dusk he went out into his vineyard and set up the quadrant.

He could not take observations from the window. There were too many trees hiding the sky. He took with him Castelli. The twinkling points of light grew gradually visible. Castelli shifted from foot to foot in his impatience, but Galileo motioned him to be quiet.

"We shall have to wait till we can see them quite clearly. Have patience. Don't stare at an empty sky." But he himself was becoming excited. In the course of his meditations that afternoon there had come to him a thought on which much depended. The sky shimmered with ever clearer diamonds. The young Benedictine could not stand still. At last Galileo drew a deep breath.

"Now." His eyes sought out the place in the sky. And a new star was really there. This marvelous newcomer hung in fullest splendor, a glittering secret. He might have looked up even earlier, and even without the quadrant found what he sought. Now he knew exactly where to look. Galileo shouted and threw his hat into the air; he flung his arms around Castelli.

"I've won!" he shouted. "I've won! I've won! Look, my son! There it is! The new star!"

The boy followed his pointing finger.

"I see it. But how has Your Excellency triumphed?"

"Don't you remember the first basic principle of Aristotle? 'The starry sky is eternal, final, and unchangeable.' Well, he was wrong! And now everything can be changed. Oh, how happy I am!"

Again he embraced the little count, standing there in his priest's gown. Anyone looking into the vineyard at this mad professor dancing round the quadrant, would have said that Galileo was crazy indeed.

III

It was November, the beginning of the new term. When the Head Proctor asked whether he would lecture on Euclid or the Almagest, Galileo answered:

"Neither. This year I intend to deliver a new series of lectures. I shall call it 'The Planets.' "

"Er . . . excuse me?"

"I spoke quite clearly. 'The Planets.' You can tell the students that after explaining the rudiments to beginners, I intend to deliver three lectures on the new star."

The Head Proctor shook his dignified head.

"Now, I really don't know what to do! The great hall of the law faculty will be too small. In the end Your Excellency will have to lecture in the open. There'll be thousands of them trying to get in, and they're certain to break down the doors."

Indeed, as soon as it was learned that Professor Galileo was to lecture on the new star, excitement took possession of all Padua. He got no rest from morning to night. His colleagues, partly from curiosity and partly because they wanted to learn his views on the new wonder, were continually knocking at his door. Cremonini, chief of the Peripatetics, who was a very good personal friend of Galileo's and had helped him once to get out of debt, had sneered sometimes at his enthusiasms for Copernicus and for the German astronomer's theories; yet this was only a sign of friendship and not of hostility. But this new star had changed the whole position. It alarmed the professors, who were afraid that Galileo might explain this wonderful apparition in some way to prove Copernicus, and that this might cause a terrible scandal, with Padua University as its center. Young Cornaro was equally excited. He wanted to exploit all this excitement to the advantage of his own Academy. And not only professors knocked at the door of the Galilei house; distinguished men arrived one after the other.

The situation was especially exciting in the first days. Even the town had changed its aspect. People no longer went to bed, but clustered in the street looking up at the sky. Rumors spread that the end of the world was approaching. Others felt sure there would soon be war.

The butcher who lived near Galileo's house, and who so far had only been renowned for his avarice, suddenly lost all control; every night he gave huge feasts in the neighboring tavern, spending like mad, in order to enjoy life quickly before the world came to an end.

Frightened people crowded round the confessionals to make sure at the last moment of getting to heaven. Several priests preached fiery sermons on the new star; it was a sign sent specially to Venice warning her not to defy the Church of God.

The world did not end; people got used to another star. Life returned to its normal course. But the learned were still very inquisitive, and Galileo was forced to shut himself up away from visitors from morning to night. He had mountains of correspondence to deal with, since now he was exchanging observations with other astronomers all over the world in preparation for his new lectures.

He could not find any peace at home, so he escaped. Most of his time he spent in the Benedictine monastery where Girolamo Spinelli, a monk, became his friend and assistant. This Spinelli was not an astrologer, only a very sensible, clear-headed man. Together with him and young Castelli, Galileo watched the mysterious point of light in the sky. The new star was losing a little of its radiance; it seemed to become smaller, although its position remained unchanged.

On the day before he delivered his first lecture on it, Cremonini sent an urgent request to see him. Although Galileo had scarcely a free moment, he could not refuse to see his friend and colleague. Cremonini arrived with a gloomy face, sat down, and came to the point almost at once.

"Galileo, I'm here to find out what you really think. For your sake, for the sake of Padua, and even for the reputation of science! You're apt to jump to fantastic conclusions. And I know that for some reason or other you've always mistrusted the tried and basic principles of learning."

"I don't. I only mistrust Aristotle. But I trust Plato and Pythagoras."

"Those are mere dwarfs compared with the giant. Aristotle is the beginning and end of science. What are your final conclusions about this alleged new star?"

"Alleged?"

"Well, in my opinion it isn't a star at all. It's a glimmering exhalation which has floated away from the earth and been lifted into the so-called elemental sphere. Just like a will-o'-the-wisp on a marsh which children may mistake for fire. Aristotle knew these phenomena; I can show you the passage . . ."

"Don't quote it, I know it by heart. Well, my friend, this is no will-o'-the-wisp. It's a star."

"Don't keep on saying it's a star when I know it can't possibly be a star."

"Of course it can be a star. Why shouldn't it?"

"You, a professor, ask me that? Because the stars are eternal, final, and immutable."

"Says Aristotle. But he made a mistake. It isn't his only mistake, by any means! The stars aren't immutable. That's what I'm going to explain. I've already proved that Aristotle made mistakes in mechanics. Now I'm going to prove by this new star that his system of the universe is untrustworthy."

"You really want to try and refute Aristotle?"

"By all means."

"But can't you feel how terrible that is? It is as though a priest should try to refute the Bible."

Galileo began to get annoyed.

"That isn't true! The Bible is a matter of faith, while this is a matter of knowledge. Haven't you spent your whole life in discriminating between exact science and theology? But now you refute yourself, Cremonini! Knowledge and belief are two distinct and separate things. Those are your very words!"

"Good. So you defy Aristotle, the eternal fountainhead of wisdom, the Supreme! Do you want to shake the whole foundations of our world?"

"I do. Because this foundation is the curse of the world. That's why we can make no progress. Everybody uses Aristotle's head to think with, instead of using his own. You can count on your fingers those who have dared to use their own minds in the last two thousand years. And what a hullabaloo it made when they tried it! Copernicus did; the new system of the universe was born. Giordano Bruno did; the new metaphysics were created. I did; the law of unhampered fall was defined; and the more I shake your idol, the more people will pluck up courage to think for themselves."

"Yes, till at last there will be chaos instead of the present wise and beautiful order. As many opinions as there are men! And no authority to bring order into the chaos. Galileo, I implore you, heed my words. Tell your pupils whatever you like, but don't tell them that this new phenomenon overthrows everything in which they believe. Look at the present world of the human spirit, how stable and happy it is in its twofold certainty: our faith the faith of Holy Church, its head the Pope; our knowledge that of the Peripateticum, its head Aristotle. This is an eternal and peaceful state. Why work against it?"

"Didn't you vote for Sarpi at the last meeting of experts?" Galileo retorted. "Thereby voting against the Pope? Weren't you forced to accept my refutation of Aristotle's theory of falling bodies? Is that your happy and stable state? It's really amazing how full of contradictions you Peripatetics are, closing your eyes, closing your ears! But now the human mind is in rebellion. There are secret leaders, clamoring martyrs of this revolt. Tartaglia, Leonardo, Moletti, Bruno, I myself, and Kepler. We won't give in till science is free to find out more and more. I know it isn't easy to fight the whole world, and I don't think I shall bring down the whole temple of Aristotle. I only mean to shake one of its pillars. The starry sky is not immutable; this is what I proclaim. Who can forbid me to say that? Do you remember the dinner at Pinelli's house when I met you for the first time? You praised the intellectual freedom of Padua! Have you begun to prevent it now?"

"I didn't come to forbid you anything, Galileo. I came to plead. Don't cause division among the scientists of the Bo. How can we teach two different things?"

"There is no need. Teach as I teach."

"Disown Aristotle? I'd rather die."

"And I insist that the starry heaven is not immutable."

Cremonini could only shrug his shoulders. He rose. He was very pale, and his hands were trembling.

"I see that our ways have parted. I am deeply sorry."

He turned and slowly went out of the room. Galileo stared at the closed door. He also was sorry to have hurt so honest and kind a friend; but he remembered he had no time to brood, and soon he was absorbed again in his work.

Next day it was almost impossible to get into the lecture hall. The Proctor and his assistants had hard work to clear a way for the professor. At last Galileo reached his desk, far away in the right corner, still not replaced by a proper rostrum. In the forefront of his crowded lecture room sat Capra, with a self-complacent face. Among his students were several colleagues, but the Peripatetics were ostentatiously missing. Cremonini himself had gone to Venice for the day.

Galileo decided to deliver a formal oration, not in his usual gay, witty, and personal tone, but in polished and elaborate Latin, so that the lecture could be printed.

"Testes vos estis, numerosa juventus, qui huc convolastis ..."

"You are my witnesses, young men who have come crowding hither to hear me speak of this new wonder. Some of you are shaken in spirit, a prey to vain superstitions. Some would fain hear tell of the evil omens which the incredible wonder represents, while others come in mere curiosity to find whether this is really a star."

He had planned to continue in the same strain, but soon he sensed with the sixth sense of a born speaker that he was disappointing his audience. They fidgeted and coughed. So he changed his tone and became less lofty. Now he was catching their full attention. First he explained that the miracle was not unique. Thirty-two years ago, in 1572, a new star had appeared in the sky and remained visible a long while. Then it had vanished. Astronomers tried never to mention it, because the subject was inconvenient. Had not Aristotle asserted that the heavens were unchangeably fixed for all time? His disciples had thought it best to deny its existence, and when it vanished had tried to forget the whole incident as soon as possible, and make others do the same. For some scientists have no use for obvious truth when that

truth contradicts their teachings; but try to distort reality to their
knowledge. If it did not suit them to admit one, they would teach
that there was no moon in the sky. It would be in vain for a simple
man to point to it; they would turn their backs stiffly and decree that
since the presence of the moon belied their principles, it did not exist,
even though everyone else could see it.

This brought the first applause. Galileo's courage increased. He told
of his observations regarding the new star and read letters received
from foreign astronomers. Everywhere, even in foreign countries, the
star had been seen at exactly the same point in the sky, and from
every country it was announced that, though this star had grown
imperceptibly smaller and paler, its place in the sky was still the same.
He ended his lecture with a summary of present results, and told his
audience that next time he would give details of all the explanations
which different people had given, and criticize each. Next time there
was an even bigger crowd. Collalto, a very rich student from Montepulciano, had asked his permission to bring his compatriot Lorenzini,
a dilettante astronomer, to the lecture. Capra and Simone Mayr, the
two proud discoverers, were also there.

Galileo raised the question whether the star was really a star. Many
people thought it was an exhalation of burning vapors from off the
earth. He traced from ancient times the history of this theory of burning exhalations and attacked it sharply. Probably it had happened in
every century that a new star had come into the sky and vanished
again. There was no real reason for supposing that this had happened
only twice in the course of the last five thousand years and once in
the last thirty-seven. Then he mentioned the hypothesis that the star
had been there all the time, but had been unnoticed before; thus the
sky had not changed, only human observation had improved. Galileo
laughed at this explanation. Was it possible that this wicked star had
avoided for two thousand years the sharp eyes of millions of observ-
ers? He mentioned a number of other stray theories, refuting them
all, and ended with the Jesuit explanation: God had created a new
star in that particular spot because, although the wise Aristotle had
declared that the heavens could never change by natural laws, God
was omnipotent. This gave Galileo his chance to praise the good sense

of Cremonini, who had said that God should be adored, but never involved in philology, geometry, or astronomy. When theologians look at the sky, let them seek for God beyond the stars, but leave the stars themselves in peace.

"In my third lecture I intend to give you my own opinion about the star and the conclusions I draw from it."

Loud applause welcomed this announcement. And the third lecture was attended by the Podestà himself, several distinguished gentlemen of Venice, and both deans. But while the first two lectures were easy to follow, laymen found very little to enjoy in the third. Galileo drew concentric circles on the blackboard, crossed them with mysterious diagonals, used the astronomical symbols of the planets: a small circle for Venus with a little cross underneath; another circle for Mars with an upward-pointing arrow; Jupiter was like the number four of the Arabs; Saturn like the letter *h,* crossed on top—even his pupils could not follow it all. They only understood the final conclusion: the star was really a star, up in the heavens, at a distance unimaginable for the human mind, its place being beyond the realm of the planets, in the farthest sphere. This mysterious star would vanish as mysteriously as it came. But the direction of its progress was identical with the axis of the earth. That was why we thought it was standing still, but at the same time we saw its size and radiance diminishing. One day it would vanish altogether, but the knowledge it left with mankind would transform the world.

"And now hear what I proclaim to you: I deny Aristotle's teaching. I deny that the heavens are unchangeable. Much in the firmament of stars is fixed and static, but much is changeable. The sun will probably never vanish, but there have always been wonders in the heavens, and there always will be. Aristotle has created his own system of the universe, which I teach you myself in the version of Ptolemy; but these are not dogmas, remember that! It is not certain that this system of the universe is the right one. Never forget, when in future I speak to you of astronomy, that all I say is mere hypothesis. And one day a new conception shall arise which will be truer, more natural, more correct; a conception which will have no reason to tremble because one single new light in the sky may suddenly overthrow our whole system. When I

teach you Euclid, that is different; you must simply accept that the sum of
the triangle's angles is one hundred and eighty degrees. But when I lecture
on the Almagest, you have to add to every sentence: 'Provided, and as
long as, there is no better system of the universe than Aristotle's.' And now
God bless you. I have done."

IV

Messer Antonio Lorenzini, the dilettante astronomer, stayed on in Padua. He proclaimed that he could explain the new star much better than Galileo. Apparently he had been working on his book for some time previously, because it appeared a fortnight later.

Galileo obtained a copy at once and read it. *The Treatise of His Excellency Antonio Lorenzini of Montepulciano in the Matter of the New Star* was written in the most classical jargon of the scholastics. It vehemently attacked all those who maintained that the new star was beyond the so-called elemental sphere. This was impossible, since in that case it could not have originated from the earth, but would have come out of nothing. And those who maintained that the star was vanishing were equally wrong, if it *were* a star. Had not Aristotle proclaimed that the sky was unchangeable? That a new star would cause the whole firmament to stand still?

There was a pencil in Galileo's hand while he read the book, and he scribbled caustic comments on the margins. It was a long time since he had come across such rubbish.

If someone maintains that the firmament originated in something else, he casts doubts on its perfection. To impair the perfection of the sky, earthly conditions are necessary. The sky, which is neither water, nor earth, nor air, nor fire, can only be designated the fifth element. But this fifth element contains in itself no taint of earth. Therefore it is by nature indestructible, since it has not the elements of destruction. I, therefore, ask the mathematicians—and let them answer if they can—how could the sky destroy the sky in such measure as to make it destructible?"

Galileo grinned and scribbled on the margin: "O indestructible fool!" Lorenzini maintained that the star was not a star but a comet, about as distant from the earth as the moon. It needed a long and involved explanation, which his reader could scarcely follow.

Next day he took it along to Spinelli and Castelli.

"Listen. I've never met such a perfect example of human stupidity.

213

My name does not figure in it, but it's obviously aimed at me."

He read out some passages with all the relish of a gourmet. There were pages which they could read three times, they found them so deliciously silly.

"What a luxury it would be to answer it!" Galileo said. "Every sentence is foolish enough to kiss! God bless the idiot Lorenzini!"

"Why don't you answer him, then?" asked Spinelli.

"I can't cheapen my name. I haven't published a book yet; my manuscripts are lying unprinted in my desk. I can't begin by refuting such a childish thing. And yet I've a splendid idea. The answer ought to be in the form of a dialogue between two shrewd peasants of Padua who have read the book and discuss it with their clear, human minds. And, of course, it ought to be written in peasant dialect, in that racy *pavano,* which I've learned, although I'm a Florentine. I like it better than anything else."

"Why don't you write it then, Your Excellency?" Castelli said.

"It would be a sin not to do it," cried Father Spinelli.

"But I tell you I can't use my name."

"That's easy," said the Benedictine monk. "Use mine. I'll help you, too, with the dialect, so at least I'll have some share in the book."

"Not a bad idea. Shall we do it?"

"Oh, let's!" young Castelli cried, delighted.

"All right," Galileo laughed. "We'll start tomorrow. It will be great fun."

Before they parted, Spinelli found a book in the monastery library. It had been written almost a hundred years before by a Paduan called Angelo Boelo. A popular collection of anecdotes, written in the *lingua pavana,* which they wanted to use for their humorous astronomical treatise. Galileo read it till late into the night, marking many words and expressions.

Next day they discussed the title. They even considered the question of not giving an author's name to the book; let the reader guess at the real name of this unknown astronomer, writing in the speech of the peasants. They chose the name of a village: Bruzene. Querengo, the president of the Ricovrati, to whom they wanted to dedicate the book, came from that village. Cecco dei Ronchitti da Bruzene should be the peasant author's full name. Two honest villagers, Matteo and Natale, were discussing the great drought of the year. Natale said that he had heard of a book, recently published, in which a learned doctor of Padua blamed the new star for the drought. Thereupon they began to discuss the book. Natale in racy peasant's speech recounted the learned doctor's arguments; Matteo answered with some of his own, as any sensible Italian peasant might do.

The book had three authors. Galileo contributed the scientific arguments, the free data of common sense; the Benedictine Father and young Castelli the expressions of peasant humor and village wit. They enjoyed the work so much that Galileo daringly denied the truth of the Almagest. He chose Matteo, the hard-headed simple Bruzene peasant, to voice the convictions of Copernicus for the first time in Italian speech.

"This here scientist," said Natale, "is always talking of someone called Aristotle. This what's-his-name says that if a new star should come on the sky, the whole thing would stop."

"That wouldn't matter so much," Matteo answered indifferently. "It may be that the sun is standing still and the earth is turning around it, only we see it t'other way round."

An asterisk pointed here to Copernicus. He was often mentioned further on.

"Won't you get into trouble over this?" young Castelli asked. Galileo only laughed.

"I don't think so! The worst that can happen is that the Peripatetics may get annoyed with Cecco dei Ronchitti. Perhaps they'll even hang him—if they can find him. But if they do, Cecco can always say that he isn't to be held responsible for the foolish talk of two peasants in the fields."

The printing press was already working on the book, when suddenly a new essay was published in Padua on the mysterious star, written by Baldassare Capra, the son of the fencing master turned astronomer. Galileo started to read the little book and soon came across his own name. Capra was apparently most polite, calling him "the eminent Galileo." But, after summing up Galileo's three lectures, he began to make some spiteful accusations. He reproached Galileo on three counts. For not having mentioned in his lecture that the star appeared on October roth; then, since he had not himself discovered it, for not having mentioned Cornaro's name. Thirdly: Why did he give only approximate information about the star's position? Why didn't he calculate in front of his hearers its exact scientific place?

Galileo threw the book aside. It annoyed him, but his anger did not last.

The Cecco dialogue interested him much more. He enjoyed the hubbub which followed its anonymous appearance. Everybody was intrigued by the mysterious Cecco dei Ronchitti da Bruzene. But the three authors kept the secret well. Padua laughed. Cornaro dropped strange hints that he knew a few things about Cecco, but could not speak. Everybody in town mocked Lorenzini. People who wanted to be funny would talk to him in peasant dialect.

But all this merriment was soon over. Galileo's rheumatism returned; both his knees swelled horribly, and his illness was costing him a lot of money. Every lecture he missed meant forfeiting a percentage of his pay; yet he needed money as never before. Both his brothers-in-law had lost their patience and were suing him.

In this plight he received the news that the Florentine Court wanted to ask him to undertake the mathematical education of the young Crown Prince. Prince Cosimo, the first-born son of the Florentine ruler, was fifteen; he had been carefully educated, but now his parents thought it necessary that he should be instructed in mathematics by the most famous mathematician in Italy, who was also a Florentine. Therefore they asked Galileo to spend his free summer months in Florence.

This request, which was also a great honor, touched Galileo deeply. Yet at the same time it only embittered him. If he went home now, he would be seized for debt and taken to the Bargello, and he was unable to pay. Galletti had sued him in Venice, Landucci in Florence. He would have to attend the court in Venice and, by trying to drag matters out, come to a compromise. At the same time he must urge the Venetian Government to increase his salary again, perhaps even give him some advance. But his illness kept him in bed. He could only curse the malicious fate which dropped the position of Ostilio Ricci into his lap at a time when he could not accept it.

As always when things were at their worst, he turned to Sagredo. And again the Venetian proved a helpful friend. He came over to

Padua and spent a whole day with Galileo, although he was very busy. His father had been made the governor of Candia, and all his family business was left to his son. Also, Pope Clement had just died, and every Venetian was deeply excited by the next stage in the war between Venice and the Holy See. Yet Sagredo willingly left all this and came to his friend. He loaned him money to settle the most urgent debts, never even mentioning former loans. He made Galileo draw up a power of attorney so that he could represent his case in Venice. He undertook to find a likely lawyer and to discuss the Florentine lawsuit with his jurist friends. He would also ask Fra Sarpi to visit the invalid.

Sarpi also came, although he was even busier than Sagredo. The quarrel between the Pope and Venice grew more embittered every day. The Senate, after lengthy discussions with Sarpi, had arrested the Abbot of Narvese on clearly demonstrable proof. The Abbot had even poisoned his own father. Now the question was who would be the next Pope. After Clement died the conclave elected Leo XI, but he soon fell ill and news came from Rome that he was dying. They furnished a special room in the Doge's Palace with pigeonholes, each hole representing a possible candidate. The Senators were *in camera* day and night, sending couriers and spies by the dozen to Rome. Sarpi had an important part in all this. Yet he gave up a day to come over to Padua with interesting news for Galileo. He had found a lawyer who knew all the loopholes of international jurisdiction. Galileo served the Venetian State; therefore he could claim the right to have his case tried in Florence by the court of aliens; he could raise the same objection in the Galletti lawsuit against the competency of the Venetian court.

When, after many weary weeks of torture, he rose from his sickbed, the new Pope had been elected. Old Leo XI had been Pope only twenty-six days, and could not do anything about or against Venice. His successor, in spite of all the intrigues of the Venetian Ambassador at Rome, was Camillo Borghese. He chose the name of Paul V, and his first action was to threaten Venice with the severest measures. This meant for Galileo that he could get no advance on his salary, since the officials were all too busy to be interviewed. He succeeded in dragging out his lawsuits, but this was only a temporary respite.

Sooner or later he would have to give something to his brothers-in-law. There was nothing to do but to turn to money lenders.

He incurred a terrible load of debt, but at least now he could leave for Florence without any qualms. He had received the formal invitation of the grand-ducal Court. Galileo took the letter to Venice and called on the Tuscan Ambassador, Messer Montauto. The Ambassador was very flattering:

"I've been informed of all this. Our Court is very proud to think that such a famous man as yourself should be a Florentine."

"I'm proudest of all to know myself one," Galileo answered. "It's good to hear the sound of Tuscan."

"You'll be hearing it all the time at home. My best congratulations on your appointment. But . . . there's something else I'd like to mention. I've been told that our Court is surprised that you don't belong to an academy."

"Oh, but I do. I'm one of the leading members of the Ricovrati at Padua."

"Yes, but not the Florentine Academy. And of course it would be only fitting that the Crown Prince should be instructed by an academician. Therefore the Court wishes that you should become a member of the Crusca. . . ."

"That doesn't depend on me."

"I know, but it isn't so very difficult. Do you know any influential person at home who would mention the matter at the Crusca? Because, you see, it would be a little awkward for the Court. . . ."

"Oh, yes, Your Excellency. The Prime Minister, Vinta, is an old patron of mine. . . ."

"Really? Well, it's no trouble for him at all. I'll write to him; it's more difficult for you. You know, to be a member of the Crusca is a great honor. These unimportant little academies hereabouts . . ." The Ambassador broke off and went to the open window. He looked out, to make sure that there was no one prying in the street. Galileo smiled to himself, but the Ambassador turned and noticed his smile.

"You probably think me a pompous fool, or at least you're surprised. But you don't know how careful I have to be here. Do you know the Venetian law about the dwellings of foreign ambassadors? If someone in my position rents a house here, the landlord must notify the authorities. If the houses on either side are not owned but rented, the occupants have to move out at once, and both houses are occupied by spies. Venice is a very strange state. It is like a merchant who keeps two sets of ledgers, one for himself and the other for his clients. It isn't governed by the public laws, but by the all-powerful and secret Executive Instructions. Shall I give you a few excerpts? 'If a subject of Venice addresses any petition to the Government, first of all it shall be ascertained whether his name does not figure on the list of political suspects which is kept by the agents of the Council. If a nobleman and a commoner go to law, the nobleman must always win the case, regardless of how the matter stands.' Tell me, Messer Galileo, do you care to serve such a state?"

"I have no greater desire than to return home. But truth is truth. I've always been treated very well here. I've never meddled in politics, but I've always tried to be useful to those who employed me."

"Perfectly right. But don't you think that you owe some of your fame to your own country?"

"Why must you torment me, Excellency? I long for Florence, but I'm a poor man. When I tried to serve Tuscany at the University of Pisa, both professors and students turned against me. And so I left. Padua welcomed me with kindness and treated me like her own child. If I leave here it would only be to go home. But how? I should starve in Florence."

"Yes, yes, I know it isn't easy. But we won't forget you. And, above all, when may His Highness expect to see you?"

"As soon as the term comes to an end, in the middle of August."

"Very good. Now let me make my notes. . . . The Crusca Academy . . . middle of August . . . permanent appointment."

He exchanged a few more polite words with his visitor before dismissing him. Galileo went away, pondering the incredible things which Montauto had said about the secret government of Venice. He felt like a man who has just heard evil stories about the past of a woman he loves. He visited the Palazzo Sagredo to broach the question, without mentioning where he had just been.

"Tell me, Messer, is it true that the Most Serene Republic is governed by Secret Executive Instructions?"

"Of course it is; everybody knows that. Why?"

"Because the republican government is so cherished here that it surprises me to hear the things which are done in its name."

"Don't let that worry you. It works well enough. After all, we're an independent state. Show me another state in Italy which dares to defy the Pope as we do!"

"That isn't my business. I've no quarrel with the priests."

"Well, with whom are you quarreling?"

Galileo was not quite sure himself. He changed the subject. But when he visited Sarpi, he put the same problem to him.

"Tell me, Fra Paolo, is there injustice even in a republic?"

"That depends, my son, on what you mean by injustice."

"If, for instance, a nobleman is involved in a lawsuit with a commoner—can he win his case even if he is in the wrong?"

"Of course he can. But that's no injustice from the point of view of the state. It is in the interest of the state that nobility shall be strong and powerful, to rule the masses. I have always opposed any death sentence imposed on noblemen, and especially public executions. If any member of the nobility deserves death, he ought to be secretly poisoned. Whatever is done for the good of the country is just."

"So the people can have no rights?"

"No. They're just cattle. Illiterate, uneducated, led by brute instincts."

"Couldn't we raise them from their ignorance?"

"Why? Do you think they'd be happier? They're much better off like this! Don't you believe that?"

"No. Because for me the most terrible thing is ignorance. And knowledge is the greatest joy. If I had the power I'd teach every peasant to read and to write, and explain to him the elements of Euclid."

"You're mad," Sarpi laughed. "I've always known it. Let's talk about something else. I hear you're going to Florence. I advise you to attend mass and confession most diligently there, because you may not have the chance to do so by the time you return. Things are going very badly with Pope Paul. He may excommunicate us. But we don't mind. Venice is free and independent, and we mean to keep her so. Don't be surprised if you hear that I've been stabbed."

All this bewildered Galileo. He had always thought that he knew Venice, yet slowly he now began to perceive that really he knew nothing at all of this city of secrets, where the greatest art and the foulest vices, bloody tyranny and the wildest love of liberty, went hand in hand. A new emotion served to intensify the homesickness which for years had been increasing. It was like the longing of a child lost in the woods, trying desperately to find its way back to home and safety.

In the middle of August he packed his things, said good-by to Marina and the children, and left for Florence. His first sight of the towers he had loved made him feel like a jubilant boy of ten. When his carriage came to the center of the town, he saw new houses in all the streets. One of his servants, Simone Gonelli, a Florentine boy, had accompanied him with delight. They called each other's attention to old buildings, former acquaintances. And at home, where brother-in-law Landucci received him with overwhelming joy as though they had never had any differences, they stayed up talking till the small hours. They told him everything that had happened since his mother's visit to Padua: the deaths and births, marriages and fires. Next day he left the house smiling like a man come back to his mistress. His first visit was to the Cathedral, which was adorned by a new dome and a cross. Then to the Medici crypt, which Prince Fernando was having built with fairy-tale pomp. The foreman, whom Galileo asked at the foot of the huge scaffolding, told him all about the wonderful details. The walls were to be covered with figures of lapis lazuli, mother of pearl, agate, chalcedony, and other precious materials. Later he had a look at the fortress of San Giorgio, which had changed both its appearance and name; now it was called the Belvedere. It was here they kept the treasures of the Medici: five million gold pieces, seven thousand Spanish ducats, and diamonds heaped up to a man's waist.

He caressed the marvelous wrought-iron figures on the gates of the Cathedral and Baptistery—gazed long at the soft-hued Campanile, walked across the Ponte Vecchio, stopping at the place where he had intended to kill himself, then remembered the time when he had heard the news of the death of Bianca Cappello and the Grand Duke. He turned into the Signoria and closed his eyes happily, to test his memory by naming the sights of the square: on the left the Loggia dei Lanzi, on the right the Palazzo Vecchio, beyond that the Nettuno fountain. Its chief figure had been wrought, as the family insisted with pride, by Bartolomeo Ammannati, his mother's kinsman. And beyond that the equestrian statue of Cosimo I, the Mercanzia with the soldiers waiting for their pay, and the Palazzo Uguccioni—he had only to open his eyes, and all these familiar things of which he had dreamed were his again, as though they belonged to him.

He spent the first day wandering about, and only began his business on the second. His first errand took him to Vinta, but the Prime Minister was away. The secretary guided him through the corridors of the Palazzo Pitti, haunted by Bianca's red-haired beauty. Marina's love, of which he had long been weary, crumbled away beside this phantom, rising from the very depths of his heart as an unattainable, mad, eternal dream.

The Court Marshal offered him a chair and strong but fine Spanish tobacco. Galileo was invited by the Grand Duchess to Pratolino, where the Court was spending the summer months. But he must stay a few days longer in Florence; the Crusca Academy would hold an election on the seventeenth, and then the learned Galileo would certainly be elected unanimously. After that he must proceed to Pratolino and report there to His Excellency Piccolomini, the Crown Prince's tutor.

He received the document in due course, but still he lingered.

Everybody wanted him to come home. This cheered him, but at the same time hurt him. How easy to tell him to give up his salary, his private lessons, his workshop, everything! And what should he do with Marina? He would have to marry her; but all Florence would gossip about their relationship. . . . It was a dream, this homecoming, nothing more. . . . Perhaps when he was older . . .

He had never been to Pratolino before. A beautiful avenue led through the carefully tended park which might have been a fairy-tale forest. Marble benches were set in the arbors, fountains among the rich flower beds. Above the treetops he saw the dim outlines of a gigantic statue of Appeninus, the work of Giovanni Bologna. When he reached it, he stopped the carriage. It was a giant's work; over sixty feet high, it showed the huge figure crouching. The ducal summer palace was just as imposing. He wondered nervously whether the princes would come to meet him. But he was only welcomed by servants who led him to a household clerk. The latter took him to his lodgings with a message that the Prime Minister awaited him. Belisario

Vinta, whom he had not seen for years, embraced and kissed him. He advised him how to behave at Court and whose favor to try to cultivate.

"Do your best to make them like you, my son; I may as well tell you that I plan to fetch you home."

"I want nothing better."

"Well, leave it to me. I ask only this: do nothing without me. Too many cooks would spoil the broth."

"I won't take a single step without Your Excellency."

"Good, I'll look after all the rest. You're to give your first lesson this afternoon to the Crown Prince. Be careful; never contradict the Grand Duchess; she likes to be always in the right."

The great moment came in the afternoon: Vinta himself led Galileo into the state apartment where the Grand Duchess Cristina, Crown Prince Cosimo, his tutor, Silvio Piccolomini, Sieur of Sticciano and Duke of Amalfi, awaited him.

The Grand Duchess had grown stout and matronly since their meeting in Pisa; she had just given birth to her eighth child. Piccolomini was an intelligent-looking man with an incisive voice and sharp clear eyes, a typical soldier. Duke Cosimo, the heir to the throne, was a tall thin lad of about fifteen, and not even his most abject flatterer could ever have pretended that he was handsome. His long sad countenance had the look of a face in a distorting mirror; on this long face a nose as shapeless as a gherkin and a mouth with broad thick lips. His voice was breaking; one moment it was treble, the next baritone.

But he seemed to be friendly and sympathetic, and Galileo liked him from the first. He graciously welcomed this learned man, who delivered a short address of homage and presented his gift, a beautifully chiseled copy of his measuring rod. Then he began to explain his invention to the Crown Prince, who listened with docile attention but looked very like a little boy who has just been presented with a plaything which his parents have forbidden him to use. Piccolomini praised the compass highly. He seemed to be interested in its military possibilities.

"What a pity it is," he said, "that scientists give up so much of their time to all kinds of abstract rubbish, instead of working to serve the state. Forgive me for talking frankly, but I'm a soldier. How much talk was wasted on this new star, while the most important problems are unsolved!"

"Perhaps Your Grace would mention such a problem?"

"Ten, if you like. Take, for instance, my guns. Bullets are projected from the barrel by the force of gunpowder. We know the force of gunpowder can be determined. We know the weight of the projectile. We know the angle of the cannon's bore and the horizontal line of the ground. Why can't science tell me where the cannon ball is going to fall? My best cannoneers have to go by instinct. Why can't science help? What is science for but to solve such a question?"

Piccolomini seemed obsessed with this thought.

Galileo glanced in surprise at the Duke: a sensible man. He bowed and answered:

"Thank you for the task you set me. I must think it over."

"What is the arch of the cannon ball?" the Grand Duchess interposed. "Any bullet travels in a straight line; that's natural."

Galileo would have explained impatiently, but Vinta restrained him in time. It was the Crown Prince who answered.

"Oh, no, Your Highness, it's different with a cannon. The barrel never points at the target. The cannon ball flies upward; then, its strength spent, begins to fall. If the aim was true, it drops on the target."

"But that's all wrong," the Grand Duchess exclaimed. "You ought to aim straight at the target and put more gunpowder in the cannon, so that it shall have more strength."

"The cannon would explode, Your Highness," Piccolomini remarked.

"Well then, make a stronger cannon—it's all very simple."

The courtiers eyed each other furtively. Vinta answered promptly:

"Of course! That will be another task for our scientist. And all the finer, because it was set by the consort of our reigning Prince."

"I am quite sure that our friend Galileo will set about it with enthusiasm. But there's one thing I don't understand. What use is this instrument of yours on the battlefield for measuring distances?"

Galileo nodded; he had begun to see how Court conversation should be conducted. He continued his explanation, using as many scientific terms as possible, to prevent any interruption from the Grand Duchess. She held her tongue with only an occasional gracious nod. They ar-

ranged the times for the lessons; Galileo was to teach the Crown Prince
geometry, astronomy, and the compass two hours daily. He would be
the guest of the Tuscan Court for six weeks at Pratolino.

Life was very formal in the summer palace. Galileo had his meals
with the lower-rank courtiers. He was never asked to the table of the
grand-ducal family. The Grand Duke he saw only once or twice on
horseback, as he rode out hunting or returning in a coach with his wife.
He had ample time to fish and swim, wander about in the lovely park,
and catch pretty maids in quiet passages for a quick kiss. It was not the
first time that he had deceived Marina; and, since she did not seem to
mind, he made no great secret of his fickleness.

One of his lessons was in the morning, the other in the afternoon.
Piccolomini attended the geometry and mathematical lessons; sometimes
he even brought his boy of six, Ottavio—the playmate of the younger
princes and a very intelligent child. But in the late afternoon the
Crown Prince was left alone with the scientist. They soon became
friends. Prince Cosimo was a kindly, dreamy, affectionate boy. The
difference in their ages vanished during their intimate talks.

"Do you see, Highness? That's the famous new star."

"It is very tiny. But I can see it."

"At first it was radiant and much larger. We shan't see it next year
at all. But I shall keep it as long as there's a breath in my body—as an
argument. If only I had time for my work! I've so many cares at
home. . . ."

"Cheer up, Messer Galileo, I'll do all I can. Tell me just how I can
help you."

"Dare I, Your Highness? Your Highness can do me a very great service."

"Of course, tell me. We're good friends, aren't we?"

"Your Highness is most gracious. The present *riformatori* of Padua . . .

He paused. One of them was a Cappello, Bianca's kinsman. So he
avoided her name and continued:

" . . . or one of them, Senator Leonardo Donato . . . he's the more
important. A very distinguished, wealthy gentleman, he may become a
doge at any time. If Your Highness would write to him in my favor
. . . that would mean a great deal. . . ."

"Is that all? Of course I'll have to ask my father's permission, but I don't think he'll refuse my request. I'll tell you what! You write the letter, and I'll sign it. But tell me: how are doges elected? Duke Piccolomini told me that it was the most complicated election in the world."

"I think I know all about it, Your Highness. First the Great Council, the Consiglio Maggiore, meets. They choose by ballot thirty senators. These thirty choose by ballot nine from their ranks."

"And one of the nine becomes the Doge?"

"Oh, no, that's a long way off. These nine meet again, and now they elect by open vote a council of forty. Listen carefully, Your Highness, because this is only the beginning. The council of forty chooses by lot a committee of twelve. These twelve elect a body of twenty-five. The twenty-five draw a lot for nine. These nine elect forty-five. Then there is a new ballot for eleven. These eleven elect forty-one. Here we are at the end. The doge is elected from these forty-one, but he must get at least twenty-five votes. Should he get only twenty-four, the whole thing starts all over again. All this serves to prevent any abuse."

"But tell me, Messer Galileo, does the doge's son become a doge?"

"Oh, no, Your Highness, he isn't anybody."

"What a strange country!" Prince Cosimo shook his head. "Well, it's time I went to bed."

The letter was duly sent to Leonardo Donato; the Crown Prince also wrote personally to Ambassador Montauto. Galileo showed his gratitude by inventing a little toy for the Crown Prince. It was a tank with glass walls with a red wooden ball inside it. Galileo had carved out the inside of the ball, put something into it, and closed the opening with wax. The amusing thing was that if someone pushed the red ball down it remained under water and did not bob up again to the surface. It floated on the level to which it was pushed and remained on the bottom of the tank if pushed there.

"How funny," the Crown Prince laughed. "What's this, Messer Galileo?"

"One of my arguments against Aristotle."

"What do you mean?"

"Aristotle had no idea of specific gravity. I put some iron grains into this ball which, being of wood, would float on the surface. Just enough for the specific gravity of the ball and the water to be equal. But what would happen, Your Highness, if we started to warm the bottom of the tank?"

Cosimo pondered the question. Then he said happily and eagerly: "The ball would sink."

"Excellent. Warm water is thinner; therefore its specific gravity is lower. The ball takes a longer time to get warm; therefore it would begin by sinking. . . ."

This tank with the red ball was inspected by the Grand Duke in person. Soon the whole Court had begun to play with it. Galileo became very popular. When the six weeks were up, he parted from the Crown Prince as an intimate friend. Vinta embraced him. Duke Piccolomini offered him his help wherever and whenever he needed it. His trunks were packed, and the coach with its team of horses was waiting—but still no official came to pay him his fee. He waited, still gossiping with courtiers, and at last got into the coach. Still nobody came. He looked at the coachman—perhaps he had the two thousand gold pieces stowed away? But the coachman said nothing. The coach set out.

The dynasty had simply commandeered the services of this Padua professor without payment. His lessons to the Prince had been given free! It was true, however, that he had formed invaluable connections during these six weeks. Perhaps that was almost as good as money! It was easy enough for these great lords. They could pay someone without having to spend a farthing.

"It's my fault," Galileo thought as they drove down the magnificent avenue. "Why was I born a Galileo? Why not a Medici?"

V

The Crown Prince of Tuscany had personally requested Venice to raise Galileo's salary; the Venetian Ambassador of Tuscany visited Leonardo Donato to inquire about the fate of Cosimo's letter. Donato sent for Galileo to inform him that he had called the attention of his successor to the matter. He himself was retiring from the office of the *riformatori*.

But even so the matter dragged, because the controversy with the Holy See had reached its pinnacle. At the same time Doge Grimani died. Galileo decided to wait till the new Doge had been elected and then call on Donato again. One morning Padua got news that Venice had a new Doge.

"Excellent," Galileo said. "Now I can go and see Donato. Who is the new Doge?"

"Donato. I doubt whether you'll manage to get near him."

It was Cremonini who brought him the news. When Galileo had rejected Aristotle's astronomy, Cremonini told him that their ways had parted. But this meant only that Cremonini eyed him pathetically, behaving with the conquettish sulkiness of a bride who has had a tiff with her groom. They were an odd pair, irreconcilable in matters of science but unable not to like each other personally.

"I won't hear a word against Cremonini," Galileo was always saying. "He's like a fine horse in blinkers. He could gallop anywhere if he liked, all over the fields of learning; but he sees only the beaten high-road in front of him. Yet I love him as though he were my brother. What a pity!"

"It's a pity about Galileo," Cremonini said. "He could do magnificent things if only he weren't so unrestrained. We haven't a single conviction in common, yet I'm very fond of him."

Now they were standing over the brazier where professors and students could warm their hands before entering the unheated lecture room. There was nobody around them, and Cremonini began a little diffidently:

"Galileo, I've read that Cecco book. It's an open secret that you wrote it."

"Well?"

"I think I ought to tell you as a friend. You remember Piccinardi? I've just heard all about his case."

"Well, what happened to him?"

"Piccinardi was a poor devil in Rome who wrote for his own amusement the biography of Pope Clement VIII. He seems to have said that Pope Clement's character was in some ways like that of the Emperor Tiberius. The Vatican officials somehow got hold of the manuscript and the new Pope read it. And what do you think has happened to Piccinardi?"

"Did they make things hot for him?"

"Yes, you could call it that," said Cremonini drily. "Pope Paul sentenced him to be beheaded on the bridge of the Castel Sant' Angelo for having slandered the Holy See. . . . I am only warning you, Galileo. I am fairly prudent; but even I got denounced at Rome by the Chief Inquisitor in Venice for saying that mathematics had nothing to do with theology."

"Many thanks for your warning, but you may not realize that Copernicus dedicated his book to the Pope of the time. The dedication was accepted. And isn't your warning a little ill-timed? Venice cares nothing for the Pope. You know yourself that Donato visits every night the house of Francesco Morosini, where the Sarpi party is meeting. The Inquisition is finished in Venice, *caro mio!* You're kind to warn me, but you can calm yourself. They're not likely to cut off my head."

"Please yourself," Cremonini said coolly. "The German Catholic Copernicus may have dedicated his book to the Pope; but now you're in the same boat with the German Protestant Kepler."

"Cesare," Galileo cried. "You say this? You who always kept religion and science strictly apart? You must know in the first place that Luther himself always called Copernicus a fool. And the Protestant Kepler has given his whole life to the cause of the Catholic Copernicus. And you must know that I have long disagreed with Kepler's theories."

"Disagreed?" Cremonini was surprised. "How?"

"In a hundred details. Kepler maintains that the planets have an elliptical orbit with the sun as their focal point. I say that they move along concentric circles with the sun as their center. And we have also completely different minds. I'm passionate, he's a dreaming man. My brain works like lightning or firecrackers. His is slow and strong, mulling things over for years. Do you know what he writes in the preface of his new book? When he read his work after he had finished it, he found it extremely difficult to follow the connection between text and diagrams, although he had constructed them himself. He is a thinker of the first water. But we have both found out from a hundred instances that we meet in our conclusions only once, if at all. Do you want to hear what he says about Lorenzini? Because he also has written a book about the new star. I'm just now reading it; here it is. Shall I read it out to you?"

"Don't," Cremonini protested. "I don't want to hear about it. The sky is unchangeable, I tell you. Good-by."

Galileo shook his head when his friend left. But he searched again for the place in Kepler's book and was filled with the same painful annoyance in reading it as the day before.

If our good Lorenzini had maintained that the calculation of the parallaxis is a difficult thing (and listen, you philologists, he even calls it a "parallapsis"), if he had said that astronomers are unable to decide a parallaxis with minute precision, I would have shared his view. But what does this wordmonger prattle? He doubts the capacity of astronomers to tell you whether a heavenly body is beyond or on this side of the moon's orbit. Therefore he doubts whether astronomers can measure an angle of fifty-two and a half degrees. What are you saying, Italian astronomers, Clavius, Ubaldi, Magini, Galileo, Ghetaldi, Rubeii, and you others? . . .

Galileo felt keen disappointment. "Clavius, Ubaldi, Magini, Galileo," so that was how Kepler valued him! He could understand that he put Clavius first; he was a German. Ubaldi was an old man, but . . . Magini, the ignoramus, the boneless sycophant . . . did *he* rank before the professor of Padua? This hurt him bitterly. At first he had fought against this emotion, but he could not overcome it. "Yes!" he admitted, "I care for fame. It hurts me to be ranked fourth by a man of such learning." His defiant pride did not permit him to renew his correspondence with Kepler.

But the stormy times soon made him forget his private vexation. The new Doge, who hated the Pope personally, as well as on political grounds, soon showed that he would stick at nothing; and one spring day messengers came galloping into all the towns of the Most Serene Republic. Pope Paul had excommunicated Venice, but the state considered the excommunication as unlawful and commanded all the priests living under her jurisdiction to say mass and administer the sacraments as if nothing had happened.

"Doesn't it interest you at all?" Cremonini remarked to Galileo, who was walking home past an excited group of professors.

"I have more important things to think about," he answered. "My brother has just come back from Poland."

Michelagnolo had appeared in Padua without any previous message. He looked well, he was decently dressed and, since he was now past thirty, had gained in dignity. Galileo could not express his happiness enough; he embraced him every five minutes, showed him over the house and workshop, introduced him to Marina, the little girls; he told his brother in a whisper that a third child was on its way. Michelagnolo kept nodding appreciatively, saying again and again how glad he was to see his brother so well and happy, but as usual he had come for money. Poland had been a disappointment, but now he had most promising connections at the royal court of Bavaria. If he had the money to go to Munich, he could get engaged in the court orchestra and even marry. He longed for a wife! Galileo was so delighted to see him that he carelessly promised to try and help. Michelagnolo took this for granted and considered the matter settled. But Galileo, that night in bed, unable to sleep, realized with a shock that he had promised more than he could perform—he would tell his brother that he was unable to carry every burden, and yet next morning Michelagnolo looked at him with such childlike faith and trust that he had not the heart to disappoint him. After a few days the young man said he would go back to Florence. He waived the matter of the journey-money to Munich—it was Galileo who asked his pardon for not being able to help just now. So Michelagnolo was graciously content with a small sum to tide him over during the days in Florence.

Galileo gave him the money, and when Michelagnolo had left, he hurried to Venice. He expected to have a long tussle with the authorities, but was surprised to find an entirely different atmosphere. Venice was triumphant and calm.

"Where's Fra Sarpi?" he asked at the bookshop.

"He'll be here soon."

While he was waiting, they told him the news. The Papal excommunication had eased the tension and brought complete success for the Serenissima, because her priests obeyed the state. The Priors of the monasteries followed one another to the Doge's Palace to take oaths of fealty. Many of them offered money because there were rumors of war: the Pope might attack Venice with his Spanish allies. The Bernardines gave a draft for a hundred and fifty thousand gold pieces. The only trouble was with the Jesuits, who were mostly foreigners and refused to say mass. The Council of Ten had sent them an ultimatum. Otherwise everything went its normal way: organs were pealing in all the churches, the bells of the Campanile echoing across the lagoons; there was again a queue at the confessionals because now people were curious to find out whether they could confess and take the sacrament. Venice had triumphed. Only from abroad did her ambassadors send news of minor incidents. In Cracow, for instance, two young men of the Venetian Embassy had been forbidden to hear mass; but the King of Poland had written the Doge a letter of explanation. In Vienna the Papal Nuncio refused to attend solemn high mass because he did not want to meet the Venetian Ambassador. But all in vain! Venice had triumphed.

Sarpi brought two strangers to the bookshop and said good-by to them in the door. His Secretary, a young Servite Brother, Micanzio, left with them.

"Who were your friends, Fra Paolo?"

"They are very good friends indeed. The English Envoy, Wotton, and his Anglican chaplain, Bedell. They're Protestants, but most honest and sensible men. And how is the world using you, my son?"

"I must find some money, but I'm afraid I won't succeed."

"Don't worry. Come along with me, we'll try one of the *riformatori*. We can talk on the way. I experimented with magnetism yesterday and made a number of small observations. You must take it up, my son. I've made some notes. You must see Sagredo; he has a magnet somewhere as big as my head. . . ."

"Thank you for the notes, but I'm more interested in your well-being, Fra Paolo. How are you?"

"Here . . . feel my habit. . . ."

Galileo obeyed. He felt a coat of mail.

"Yes, my son, anyone can denounce me now for not wearing the habit of our order. But I must be careful. Personally, I don't mind death, but my country needs me. The Pope has excellent jurists, and not everybody can meet them as an equal in our disputes. I call your attention to Cardinal Bellarmin, a very skillful politician and a dangerous man. Be careful if you should ever meet him. He is the Pope's expert in canon law, just as I am the Doge's. It's our duel, really. And it isn't easy to succeed against him. He had a good school: the Bo. He's one of the most talented Jesuits. One of his books has been put on the Index, although he is the Pope's intimate friend. He was the man who fixed the authentic text of the Bible, as head of the Vulgate committee. He took part in sentencing Giordano Bruno to the stake. The former Popes were mostly afraid of him, but couldn't do much, for he came of a very good family. His mother was the sister of Pope Marcello II. But the present Pope likes him very much. Now he's fighting against me. And he does it excellently."

"What are his arguments?"

"Mostly St. Thomas Aquinas. Quoting him at me. *Potestas secularis subditur spirituali, sicut corpus animae.* 'Even as the body is ruled by the soul, so is the civil arm ruled by the Church.' That is a very dangerous simile. Well, I'm not such a simpleton myself. . . . Now you'd better wait for me here."

They had reached the offices of the Doge's Palace. Galileo waited patiently while Fra Sarpi vanished behind a door. In a quarter of an hour the monk returned.

"It took me less time than I thought. Quirini can't see you now, but we settled the matter. You'll get an increase of two hundred gold pieces a year, and they'll make up the difference for the past year. I think that you'll be able to draw two hundred gold pieces in three or four weeks. Now you'll have a salary of five hundred and twenty gold pieces a year. Quirini told me that Moletti never had more than three hundred. Have I settled the matter quickly enough?"

Galileo could scarcely speak in his gratitude. He left Fra Sarpi and hurried back to Padua. The first thing he did was to visit Marinelli, the printer. He had for months carried in his mind a scheme which he could now realize. A message had come from the Tuscan Ambassador commanding him to be ready against next summer. Young Prince Cosimo had so enjoyed his lessons that Galileo was to be asked to Pratolino again next year. He wanted to present some worthy gift to the Crown Prince and decided to have one of his manuscripts printed and dedicate it to Cosimo. The best thing would be to enlarge and work out the explanation and instructions for the use of the compass. He soon agreed with the printer: he would pay about eighty Venetian lire for sixty copies. But Galileo made a strange stipulation.

"You must move your premises to my house, Messer Marinelli, and do the work there."

"It would mean much trouble, Your Excellency . . . and what use would it be?"

"Leave that to me. They can't steal the sheets from my house, but they can do it from here. There are many people who envy my invention. They would all like to manufacture compasses with the instructions enclosed."

After voluble protests the printer agreed. Galileo superintended the printing and read the proofs carefully. And when the first copy was ready, he stroked it as gently as his first-born.

A real child was born at about this time, though it came late. Marina had miscalculated the date of the event. It was August when Galileo was called out one early morning to Marina. He dressed hurriedly and ran out through the pouring rain. This time Marina bore a son, who was christened Vincenzo Andrea, after his two grandparents; then Galileo was able to leave for Florence.

On his way he already felt the chill which he had caught in that shower, and his joints began aching again. He spent a night at Florence and went on next day to Pratolino. He presented his book to the Crown Prince and was happy to see how much it pleased him. All the courtiers rejoiced, but Galileo's face was distorted with pain.

"What's the matter, Messer Galileo?" the Crown Prince asked.

"I beg your pardon, Highness, but I'm in terrible pain. My joints are torturing me. I'd like to ask humbly for permission to withdraw."

Grand Duchess Cristina raised her eyebrows and looked down her nose. This was an offense against Court etiquette. But Cosimo was already assisting the groaning, limping scientist from the room. Galileo went to bed at once and lay writhing; he bit his lips until they bled, so as not to cry out.

His fever began to make him delirious. He lay for ten days in the summer palace, suffering the tortures of the damned and only seeing the Crown Prince for five minutes every day. Then Vinta had him moved to Florence, where he was in bed for a week. When he got back after a terrible journey to Padua, he found there the gift of the ducal family. Grand Duchess Cristina sent him a thick velvet robe in return for the book dedicated to Cosimo. In Padua he was cured by Fabrizio.

It was late in November before he could at last get up and hobble round the room with the aid of a stick. Then he received the news that his former colleague, old Mercuriali, had died. He wrote off at once to the Grand Duchess to recommend Fabrizio for the best-paid professorship in Italy.

He spent his evenings at Marina's and was amused to see how the two little girls mothered six-months-old Vincenzo. One night he looked up curiously at the sky in search of the disputed star. But it had vanished. He recalled the arguments, the fun of the Cecco book. It was a long time since he had heard anything about Simone Mayr or the Capras.

But next day he heard a good deal. When he reached the university, the Chief Proctor handed him a book. He glanced at its title: *Usus et fabrica circini cuiusdam proportionis.* The use and manufacture of compasses for all proportions. And the author? Baldassare Capra! He began to read it. It was an exact description of his invention, the servile repetition of his instructions. And there was one paragraph which chilled his blood. Capra hinted unmistakably that there was a certain famous scientist in Padua who had stolen his, Capra's, invention, flaunted it in a shameless manner, and behaved like a common thief.

"Your Excellency. . . . In heaven's name!" the Chief Proctor came running up to him.

"It's nothing. I was feeling rather giddy. . . . May I borrow this book?"

"For as long as you like."

"Thank you. But stay with me, please, till I calm down—because now I feel like murdering someone."

VI

Sad news from Pesaro: Alessandro, one of Marchese del Monte's sons, wrote to him that his father was dead. He had died very peacefully. Galileo read the letter twice before he could realize its full meaning, and mourned deeply for the old gentleman. He had never been so fond of anyone and perhaps no one had loved him so much. Such great and pure spirits forsake the earth, while scum like Capra live and prosper.

In the Easter vacation he decided to take action against Capra's book. The court of Padua university was the chief authority in such matters. So his case would come before the *riformatori*. He went to Venice with the intention of getting satisfaction by any means.

Fra Paolo was the first man he visited. He found him in excellent spirits. And his young secretary, Micanzio, beamed at him.

"What do you say to my latest triumph?" asked the Servite monk. "Bellarmin has tried every trick; all the followers of the Vatican have intrigued; and yet I've won! The Pope has yielded. But you must have heard all about it in Padua!"

"Yes, I heard something about the approaching peace."

"It's already concluded. Venice is to judge her criminal priests in the civil court, and we've passed a law that nobody may leave his estate to the Church. Everything remains unchanged. It took a whole year to make His Holiness yield."

"And so the war is over and now you can rest, Father."

"Not a bit. I've just begun a vast new work: I'm going to write the history of the Council of Trent. It ought to clear up a good deal. And I'm still fighting. Rome won't forgive this victory so easily. I've heard that Pope Paul said: 'This Sarpi is more dangerous than the Calvinists. . . .' They'll get me yet. But I see that you're troubled about something. What is it?"

Galileo silently pointed to the passage in Capra's book, accusing him of plagiarism. Fra Paolo was amazed.

"This is really the height of impudence. How did it happen?"

237

"Now if I put two and two together, a number of small incidents become clear to me. These two Capras and the scoundrel Mayr were always spying around my house and trying to get a compass for copying. Now I've found out that Cornaro loaned them one. Capra was so incredibly shameless that he sent him a copy of the book. Cornaro read it and then came along to see me, quite distraught."

"Is he willing to be your witness?"

"Of course, he's ready to do anything."

"Well, then, I'm sure Capra will be heavily sentenced. We'll draw up the petition together. I'll be able to give you my whole day tomorrow. Then you can go to the *riformatori*."

They agreed to meet on the following day. At home Galileo carefully collected his proofs. He brought Capra's book, which had been printed on March 11th, and his own, dedicated to Prince Cosimo and already published on June 10th in the previous year. He produced letters received years previously, in which various people thanked him for having presented them with the measuring rod. He brought receipts from Messer Silvestro which plainly showed that for several years Galileo had been paying him a salary for copying out the directions for use. So it was easy enough to draw up the document. Fra Paolo was skilled in such formalities.

Next day the *riformatori* held a meeting. There were three of them this year: Francesco da Malin, Antonio Quirini, and Girolamo Cappello. Quirini was ailing, and Galileo addressed his words chiefly to Cappello. The distant relative of Bianca was a tall, fair, heavily built man, inclined to be stout. He had not the faintest resemblance to his lovely kinswoman.

He interrupted Galileo: "The situation is clear enough. We'll decide at once. Wait outside, if you can spare the time."

Galileo could certainly spare the time. He had to wait almost two hours till the two *riformatori* had finished consulting.

"We have sent orders," they informed him, "to both deans of the university, the Mayor and Police Prefect of Padua. The sales of the Capra book are to be suspended till further notice. We've also summoned Baldassare Capra ten days hence. We have fixed such a short time because we must give you the earliest opportunity to clear yourself of this grave accusation. It is our duty to see that no professor of Padua is suspected of plagiarism. We hope that this will satisfy Your Honor. Don't be afraid. You'll obtain justice."

Galileo bowed gratefully. He discussed further steps with Sarpi, then returned to Padua. As he passed Pietro Paolo Tozzi's bookshop, he quickened his steps, red with anger. From inside came the voices of Capra and Mayr, chattering gaily. They did not know that Capra was to be summoned to court. Galileo was beside himself with rage. He suspected everyone he talked to of having read the slanderous book. Perhaps every student he encountered was laughing at him behind his back. He could not bear to be in Padua and returned to Venice to await the trial there.

He had to wait twelve days, instead of ten, because the *riformatori* were so busy that they postponed the case. But now the court was sitting again—Galileo on one side, trying hard to control himself—on the other young Capra with his counselor and his evil genius, Simone Mayr, who must have incited him to the whole abominable business. The parties took no notice of each other. They were informed that the matter would be dealt with next morning, at nine. Galileo nodded, bowed, and departed.

On the following day they were not kept waiting. Malin and Cappello had taken their seats behind the long green-covered table, before them the documents of the case, the rival books, and the rest of the evidence. Mayr stayed in the anteroom; only the two litigants were allowed into court.

"We ask Your Honor," Malin began, "to present your case."

Galileo tried to speak impersonally. But the longer he talked the angrier he became; his wrong stung him into fury, till at last he roared like a lion.

"I protest most indignantly against the allegation that I have stolen my invention or even its smallest detail from anyone. And if this scoundrel will not give me full satisfaction, I'll . . . I'll . . ."

"Quite so," Malin said. "Remember this is a court of law. What is your answer, Messer Capra?"

Young Capra did his best to look innocent.

"Really, I don't know why I am standing here. I had no idea I had offended Messer Galilei. I only invented an instrument and wrote a book on it. I have no idea why His Excellency should accuse me of doing that . . ."

Malin interrupted impatiently.

"Listen, young man, we aren't here to waste time. Your book mentions a certain scientist, whom without naming him you accuse of having stolen the same invention."

"I wasn't alluding to His Excellency! What made him suppose I was?"

The *riformatore's* fist crashed down on the table.

"There is only one scientist who claims such a compass as his own, selling and explaining it. You can't shuffle out of it like this, young man. You state in your book that Galileo has stolen your invention. Well, give us your proofs!"

"It isn't exactly my invention. Or rather I should say, it's mine, but I borrowed its basic idea. From the same man as Messer Galilei."

"This sounds more credible. Well, from whom did you borrow it?"

"From . . . what's his name . . ."

"Well? Can't you even think of his name?"

"Tycho Brahe," Capra blustered. "It was he who really invented it. Everyone was saying in Padua that Messer Galileo had made the measuring rod on the basis of a foreign book, published in Germany. I haven't got the book, but I'm prepared to send for it and produce it. . . ."

"Oh, no!" roared Galileo. "I object to that! Must I wait for months till that alleged book arrives from Germany . . . and all the time be branded as a plagiarist? Your Excellencies, this fellow wants to drag out the case, but let me once get him by that throat. . . ."

"Quiet! Quiet, Messer Galileo. You'll be given your rights, but don't be so hasty!"

Galileo did his best to control himself. Capra resumed:

"I question the authority of this court. This is a matter for the learned. Messer Galileo has the right to answer my book with another one. And if he feels that his honor has been impaired, we can fight like gentlemen."

That was too much. Galileo sprang at the young man; the ushers had great difficulty in restraining him.

"So you want a duel, you little cur? You've become a fencing master again? First you steal my book and now you want to kill me like a gentleman?"

Words of abuse came foaming out of him. At that moment there was no difference at all between him and his mother, when rage possessed her. The two *riformatori* had the greatest difficulty in restoring order.

"Listen to me," Malin said. "The question has nothing to do with learning. You must prove, Messer Capra, that His Excellency Galilei has stolen your work. As we see, you're unable to prove it. You refer to some German book, but that doesn't concern us. You don't mention Tycho Brahe or any German studies in your work. But His Excellency Galilei maintains that your book is merely the Latin translation of his."

"That I deny!" Capra said.

"We'll ask an expert to decide that. Fra Sarpi is to give an official opinion. We fix five days for this procedure. . . . The next hearing will be on the twenty-fourth in the courtroom of the Criminal Council of Forty. This hearing shall be public. Now you can go."

Galileo hurried off to Fra Sarpi. The monk laughed.

"I knew it before you did, my son. I'll read the two books today and prepare the report tomorrow."

"And what will you say in it?"

"The exact truth, my son. Even if it isn't to your advantage."

The courtroom of the Council of Forty was packed. Simone Mayr was sitting on a back bench; his face betrayed clearly that this was his case really, not Capra's. All three *riformatori* were present; even Quirini had left his sick-bed to watch these proceedings.

Cappello read the report of Fra Paolo.

"There can be no doubt that in Capra's book, published at a later date, one can find every chapter of Galileo's Tuscan work in Latin translation. I found three sentences in Capra's book which seemed at first glance to be original, but after careful consideration I discovered that these thoughts were also present in Galilei's book. This expert opinion proves that the Capra book is a plagiarism. I request Messer Capra to answer the charge."

Capra rose. Mayr tried to prompt him, but in vain.

"I'm no thief," Capra faltered. "Whatever I wrote, I discovered myself."

"Your Excellencies," Galileo interrupted, "let me put a few questions to this man about his own book."

Malin, Cappello, and Quirini exchanged a few whispered words. Then they nodded.

"Tell me," Galileo turned to Capra, "how you calculate the double-edged acute angle within two planes and with the help of the semicircle divided into ninety grades."

"The double-edged acute angle . . ." Capra stammered, "you . . . I mean . . ."

He stopped. Mayr tried to prompt him again, but Cappello noticed it.

"What's that? I'll have you ejected if you disturb the hearing."

"I don't remember it now," faltered Capra. "I'm too nervous. But it's in my book."

"He hasn't got the slightest idea," Galilei countered. "Just a stupid thief."

He sat down. Capra shook himself and shrugged his shoulders.

"I'm willing to apologize publicly. If His Excellency Galilei wishes it, I'll have this formal apology printed."

The three *riformatori* looked questioningly at Galileo, who stared suspiciously at Capra.

"Wait a moment," he said. "And what about your book?"

"If I give you a printed apology," answered Capra, "that will completely take the edge off my book. What better proof could I ever offer of my good will and willingness to make amends? If Messer Galilei doesn't accept this, I don't know what more I can say."

And now the three *riformatori* seemed to be on Capra's side. Galileo felt that there was something wrong. The young man sensed that he had swayed the mood of the judges and the audience; he stared almost defiantly at his opponent.

"I'd like to ask something of Messer Capra. Does he intend to sell this book which he stole from me, yet accuses me of having stolen?"

"Excuse me," Capra answered, "but I still don't admit that I ever plagiarized. My book is my own work. I feel I have a right to sell it, even if someone raises objections. And if I publish my formal apology, I think I shall have given full satisfaction. I'll include it in every future copy sold."

"And what about those already sold? It was officially ascertained that you've ordered 483 copies. How many are left?"

"I don't know," Capra said, shrugging his shoulders. "I've still got those which haven't been bought or presented to my friends and acquaintances."

"I beg your pardon?" Galilei's voice rose. "Did you present copies to anyone? To whom? Friends or perhaps even foreigners?"

Capra evaded the question, but he got more and more muddled. Soon it became evident what he had done. He had sent copies of his book to all the famous mathematicians in Europe. Now they were reading at Louvain, Prague, Rome, or Göttingen that Galileo had plagiarized an invention.

"Are you willing to send your printed apology to those who have received your book?" asked Malin.

"I'm sorry, but I don't remember to whom I've sent them. If I had a list, it was lost."

"That will suffice," Malin said. "The offer of Messer Capra to apologize publicly was not made in good faith, and we cannot ask Messer Galilei to accept it. We shall formulate our sentence accordingly. The hearing is herewith closed."

The three *riformatori* rose and departed. Galileo was still blind with rage. He glared like a mad bull at Capra, but Fra Sarpi got hold of his arm at the moment when he wanted to rush at his enemy.

Capra only stood there, blinking, with a sallow face. Galileo still gasped with rage. Four people had to hold him and lead him from the room.

The judgment was proclaimed in Padua. It was also sent to the authorities, to the bookseller, and read out to his opponent. It forbade the sale of Capra's book and clearly described him as a slanderer.

The sentence was proclaimed at the university with all traditional formalities. At midday one of the janitors walked up to the corridor of the first floor. He sounded a bugle thrice. The courtyard and the corridors were full of students back from the Easter vacation. The Head Proctor read out the sentence. Galileo was loudly cheered. A young man shouted:

"Let's find Capra and thrash him for this!"

But the Proctor forbade such violence. The Police Prefect visited the Tozzi bookshop in person. Two officers collected and counted the books. They found 441 copies. Then they went to search Capra's lodgings, where they seized thirteen books. Thirty were missing. Several must be in Padua; the Head Proctor and Cornaro had each received one. Capra and Mayr had sent the rest to all the universities of Europe.

Galileo was desperate.

"What shall I do?" he raged when he visited Fra Paolo and Sagredo. "I can't write to every European mathematician!"

"Why not?" Sagredo answered. "You can write an answer, have it printed and distributed. It's only a question of money."

"Of course. I never thought of that. I'll get the money, even if I've to rob someone. I must defend myself at all costs against this."

But that was rather a rash assertion. When he tried to find out how he stood financially, he was appalled. He was in debt—up to his ears. He had Marina to keep, and his three children; he kept his mother; his brothers-in-law were always pestering him; what little he could manage to send them scarcely covered the interest on his debt. The main trouble was caused by Michelagnolo, for whose journey to Munich he had paid; but still his brother postponed his departure and finally he confessed in a letter that he had fallen in love. He wanted to get married first, and take his wife to Bavaria. But the girl, Annachiara Bandinelli, had no money at all. So now there would be the wedding to pay for and his journey as well. There was always new interest falling due.

Yet somehow he managed to raise enough money to print his answer to Capra's book. He would have been ill had he not rid himself of his spleen.

He wrote it with savage enjoyment. His quill almost flew across the paper: angry abuse splashed over the pages. And he himself noticed that this fury was something he had inherited from his mother. Yet the urge had to be appeased. He would not have a single moment's peace till he had freed his mind of this burden of hate.

It was finished, and soon it was printed. In August the *Difesa,* his defense, as he called it, was published. When he read it in print he found it exaggerated the case. But now it was too late to modify it. He drew up a list of fifty names, more than those two scoundrels could have used, and scattered his furious invective broadcast all over Europe.

Now at last he was calm again. He had a new interest: he had begun to experiment with magnets, in the company of Fra Paolo and Sagredo. It was half play and half scientific interest. They met in Venice and experimented. Sagredo had spent a large sum in constructing a very big magnet, weighing over five pounds. They investigated all its properties; putting it into water, heating it, cooling it, covering it in insulating materials. The two others were amused; Galileo was thinking. He was highly excited by the fact that one end of the magnetic needle always turned north, the other south. A miniature replica of the earth's axis, he thought. He tried patiently to fit this phenomenon into the Copernican system and use this strange machine as a basis for argument, rather than a pleasant toy. Since the new star had helped him to refute the most notable dogma of Aristotle, hope had risen in him again that soon he would be able to present his conviction as a proved hypothesis to the world.

One day in October he came to Venice. He hurried straight to Fra Paolo's lodgings. Micanzio met him with tears in his eyes and motioned him to be silent.

"What is it?" whispered Galileo.

"Fra Paolo was stabbed down last night."

"Stabbed? Is he dead?" cried Galileo.

"No, but he's dying. Only a miracle can save him."

"For God's sake, tell me, how did it happen?"

"We were at the Doge's Palace. He was consulting Fra Paolo on some legality. I waited in another room. At ten o'clock Fra Paolo told me to go home and copy out an urgently needed document. I hesitated. I didn't think it wise to let him walk alone in the streets so late at night. I begged him to allow me to wait, but he would only repeat his order. So I went home. At eleven he was attacked by two masked men on the corner of the Merceria. They must have known he was wearing a coat of mail, for they stabbed in the neck. He got twenty-three wounds. One of the stabs cut the main artery. They ran away and left him lying there in a large pool of blood. A few minutes later someone passed along and stumbled over his body. He raised the alarm. They carried him home. We couldn't find a doctor at once. So we fetched a barber, who sewed up the wounds. Fra Paolo didn't move all night. We sent word to the Doge; he came here at once. But this morning Fra Paolo recovered a little and told us what I've just told you. The doctor says he hasn't a chance. Forgive me, Messer Galileo, but I can't let anybody in."

The young monk was weeping again. He leaned against the wall and wiped his eyes. Galileo turned and hurried to the Rialto. He wanted to see Sagredo; they met in the street.

"Have you heard?" asked Sagredo.

"Yes. It's terrible. Have those scoundrels got away?"

"I've just heard a few more details. The Doge sent out his best *shirri* last night. They reported some interesting things. Several people saw two masked men boarding the ship which weighed anchor at midnight. Do you know whose ship it was? The Papal Ambassador's."

VII

The miracle happened. Fra Paolo did not die. He was bedridden for a long time, but recovered. Nobody ever found out who his attackers were. The monk himself did not press the investigation.

"You're my witness, my dear son," he told Galileo, "that I was prepared for such a possibility. I was fighting a war, just like any other soldier. In every war there's always the risk of wounds. Since this war is still being waged, I'm still in danger."

"How do you mean? The Holy See has made peace with Venice."

"Yes, but the Pope has not made peace with me. He doesn't see me as a monk, but as the incarnation of Venetian patriotism. His Holiness hates to think I'm alive."

"But you ought to be more careful at least, Father."

Fra Paolo smiled.

"The Doge said the same thing, but less gently. He scolded me so harshly that I was ashamed. The Senate has decreed that the excellent Fra Micanzio shall never in future leave my side. After this I shan't be able to send him on errands; he would cite the decree. And I ought to be the first to respect the decrees of Venice. But never mind all that. How are you? Do you need money?"

"Yes. I'm ashamed to trouble you with such a request again, Father, but perhaps you could ask the *riformatori* to give me a year's salary in advance."

"I can always ask, but I must tell you that it's against the law. Padua only gives advances when a professor marries off his daughter."

"I know, Father. When my sister married, I got some advance; only we put the word 'daughter' instead of 'sister' in the documents. Perhaps such a way could be found now."

Fra Paolo promised to do his best. In a short time he wrote to Galileo that he could draw the money but must find a guarantor among his colleagues. This was a new obstacle. It was hard to trouble another professor. They were all married and all poor men. None of them could easily guarantee a sum of five hundred gold pieces.

Next day Cremonini stopped Galileo in the corridor.

"I hear you're in trouble."

"Yes," Galileo replied, "things aren't any too easy."

Cremonini blushed.

"I only mentioned it because, though we may not think alike, if you feel I can help you . . . I'll be glad to . . ."

He stammered and was extremely confused.

"Cesare," Galileo said, deeply moved, "I don't know any better man than you are."

"I don't need your praises!" snapped his colleague. "I've always thought you a little mad. But if you like you can tell them that I'll be your guarantor, though I may as well say I consider your Kepler and Copernicus only fit for the madhouse." He passed on, muttering to himself.

Galileo smiled as he watched him go. In a few days the money was guaranteed. Most of it went to his two brothers-in-law. He kept only a small part to buy new clothes. The Tuscan Court had summoned him again, but this time to Artimino. He arrived to hear that Prince Cosimo was about to marry and Pratolino was being prepared for the future Crown Princess. Cosimo was just nineteen. The secret and involved intrigues of his father and Vinta, the Prime Minister, had been crowned by success: Cosimo had won the hand of the Austrian Archduchess Maria Magdalena, the daughter of Archduke Charles. This was an outstanding achievement of Tuscan diplomacy. The sister of the bride, Archduchess Margaret, was the wife of Philip III of Spain, while her brother, Ferdinand, would succeed to the Austrian throne.

This time the learned guest saw little of Cosimo, who from morning to night was choosing patterns for rich attire and examining plans for festal buildings. The whole Court was in a fever, and Galileo found himself neglected. But he managed to have a few words with Vinta.

"Do you still want to come home?"

"More than anything else."

"Well, try to keep the favor of the Crown Prince, who likes you very much. By all human reckoning Cosimo will be our ruler before long."

"Even that hope fills me with gratitude. But why not at once? Is His Highness Fernando angry with me?"

"Oh, no, my son. Not angry! He simply doesn't know you exist. I mentioned once that we ought to have a Court mathematician in Florence. His Highness only said: 'What for?' and that settled the matter. He's thick-headed and always suspicious of being swindled. You must wait for Cosimo."

When Galileo saw Cosimo, the Crown Prince raised the question himself.

"Messer Galileo, if I become the ruler of my country, I shall hope to talk with you about science. I must have you at my Court, Messer Galileo."

"It would make me unbelievably happy, Your Highness."

This conversation was interrupted by news that the fleet of Leghorn, which Fernando had sent to subdue the Turkish pirates, had won a great victory.

The wedding took place in Florence. Galileo, being no longer a guest of the Court, had to jostle in the crowd to watch the glittering cavalcade with its pomp of Austrian, Hungarian, Bohemian, and German nobles who had accompanied the bride. Feasts followed each other, and rich and poor rejoiced for weeks. Galileo returned to Padua.

Since the birth of his son, he had ceased to be Marina's lover. He talked to her as to an old acquaintance to whom he had nothing much to say except when they discussed the children. Their past love had vanished, leaving no trace. From time to time Galileo had superficial affairs with a seamstress or a pretty widow. Marina knew all about these, but she never deigned to mention his infidelity. Months passed without their exchanging a single confidence. Neither of them wanted to alter this; Galileo because he was ashamed, Marina because she was indifferent. And now, even if they had wanted to, they could not have found the way back to affection.

But when Galileo returned to Padua, Marina received him with the surprising declaration that she wanted to talk to him. They sat down in the courtyard so that the children should not disturb them.

"I want to tell you," Marina said, "that I have a suitor."

"*What?*"

"A man has proposed to me. It isn't very polite to look so surprised."

"Who is the man?"

"You don't know him. His name is Giovanni Bartoluzzi, a clerk at the Dolfin merchant house in Venice. I met him there when I was a young girl. We ran into each other by accident here . . ."

"While I was in Florence?"

"Oh, no. More than a year ago. He always visits me when he comes to Padua."

"Without my knowing it?"

"Don't try to be angry when you aren't," Marina smiled gently. "You're completely indifferent about it, aren't you?"

Galileo took some time to answer, but when he spoke it was the truth:

"Yes, I am."

"Well, Bartoluzzi tells me that he wants to marry me. I replied that I should have to speak to you first, because you kept me, and it wouldn't be fair to settle such an important question without you. And there are the children. . . . Bartoluzzi is a little afraid of taking the responsibility for them. . . ."

"And you? Do you love him?"

"As much as I *can* love. I wouldn't die for him. But he is a kind, honest man. I could live at his side peacefully."

"And you could leave your children?"

"I could," Marina answered calmly. "Though it's a little early yet to leave Vincenzo. He's still so tiny. He ought to stay with me a few years longer. The girls could do very well without me; they are going to a convent anyhow."

Galileo stared at her aghast. The longer he knew Marina the more mysterious she seemed. He could not deny that she had been an admirable mother. When Virginia had a dangerous colic, she had not gone to bed for four days. And now without the smallest sign of emotion this mother could relinquish her three children to marry someone whom she herself admitted she did not love. . . .

"This is all very important, Marina, especially since it's an easy way out of our relationship. You see, I want to go home to Florence. This is a secret now, and I expect you not to tell it to anyone."

"Surely you know me well enough for that. I won't tell."

"And if I go home, probably to take up a post at Court, it mayn't be so easy to have you with me. On the other hand, there's no sense in your staying at Padua with the children when I'm in Florence."

"Certainly not."

"So this marriage would be the solution to everything."

"Yes. But we can't get married at once. I only told you about it because it was too important to hide. You see, there's always money to be considered; and, as I know your financial position . . ."

"What do you mean?"

"Bartoluzzi has no money of his own, and he isn't paid enough by the Dolfin to keep me comfortably. Therefore he would like to keep his work, but at the same time start some small, independent enterprise. For that he needs capital. Not much, but . . . Why are you smiling so queerly?"

"I was just adding up how many people I was keeping. The Landucci's, with four children and a servant, that's seven. The Gallettis, with two children and a maid, five. My children and you, four. The Mazzolenis, five. I have four servants. I keep my mother. That's twenty-two altogether. Bartoluzzi would be the twenty-third. I don't complain, it tickles my vanity. Oh, yes, my mother's maid and yours. And myself, twenty-six. . . . And how much would this Bartoluzzi need?"

"He didn't mention any amount. I didn't like to discuss it with him. You two ought to meet and talk it over. Would you like to?"

"Of course I should. We're sure to come to some agreement. I'll take the two girls home and put them in a convent. Vincenzo must stay with you for the time being. We shall have to decide how long. Thank God that everything can be discussed so simply and smoothly with you. I wish everybody was like you. And you know all about my troubles. But never mind . . ."

"I often feel very sorry for you. And I've noticed for a long time now how much you have wanted to get away from here. And how are your chances in Florence?"

"I don't know. It may happen tomorrow . . . or not for years. God and His Saints ought to help me."

Marina was silent.

"Why don't you go to the Saint?" she asked.

"What do you mean? Which saint?"

"People are coming here to Padua from every country to touch the Saint's grave and ask him a favor. I always ask him for things. When Virginia had pneumonia, I promised him a gold piece, and Virginia got well. When I lost my pearl earrings, I made another vow. And as soon as I came home from church, I found them."

"Oh, nonsense! I should be laughed at by the whole university."

"Just as you like. But you can always promise him something and give it to the poor, if the Saint gets you this post in Florence. There's nothing in that. Everyone asks him for things."

"That's just idle talk."

They changed the subject, but it stuck in Galileo's mind. He often found himself hesitating on the brink of going across to St. Anthony's church, but could not manage to conquer his vanity. He, the cleverest man in Europe, to behave like an old woman going on a pilgrimage! Yet, on the other hand, he had always been devout and felt some reverence for the Saint. At last he turned to Fra Paolo again. But he heard such exciting news from the monk that he did not mention his own problem till the end of his visit.

Fra Paolo did not care in the least what the Nuncio said of him to the Pope. He liked to talk to sensible men. The English Ambassador and his Anglican chaplain were among his closest friends. He corresponded with Du Plessis-Mornay, whom they called the Huguenot Pope. Diodati, the Calvinist translator of the Bible, came to Venice especially to visit him. And now there arrived an even more interesting foreigner: Christian, Prince of Anhalt-Bemburg, the leader of the German Protestants, sent Christopher Dohna, an important member of his Court, to discuss with Sarpi the question whether Venice could not bring herself to break with the Pope and establish Protestantism. Fra Paolo was famous everywhere as an opponent of the temporal power of the Vatican. Dohna was almost certain of his success.

"And what did you answer him, Father?" Galileo asked curiously.

"I answered as a faithful Catholic. I sent a message to the Prince of Anhalt that I respected his convictions and held him in high esteem, but would not permit a single step against my Church. Not for the sake of the Pope, but of the Church. But such a step would never be successful. We Italians could never stomach Protestantism. We could never give up our church ornaments and pictures, our processions, our relics, our legends of miracles. So Dohna and I parted like two good friends. But that was all."

Then at last the shamefaced Galileo began to ask advice about St. Anthony.

"Father, do you believe in miracles?"

"Since I believe the Bible, I believe in miracles. All the doctors say it's a miracle I'm still alive. Why do you ask?"

"Because someone advised me to ask St. Anthony for a favor. What do you think?"

"It's quite simple, my son. If you really believe that the Saint can intercede for you with God, then go and ask him. If not, you'd only be behaving like a man who wanted to buy something at a grocer's. That would be beneath the dignity of a Christian. Listen, my son—because this applies to the whole of life. Be ambitious in matters of knowledge, feel yourself a much bigger man than Aristotle, and use your sharp brains to conquer him. But in matters of faith, be humbler than the humblest, as humble as any old woman who goes on a pilgrimage. Then God will be pleased with you."

"Excuse me, Father—but am I allowed to think of the temporal power of the Vatican? Because old women on pilgrimages never do that!"

"That's a matter of science—theology and canon law. I'm not talking of that. Be humble before God Himself and His Saints! The Pope doesn't concern you."

"Fra Paolo, I've a queer suspicion. I suspect you of being a Protestant at heart."

This both annoyed and amused the priest.

"And I suspect you of being a fool at heart. You say that to me—at a moment when I've just kept Protestantism out of Venice and all Italy! But to go back to St. Anthony—let me give you a piece of advice. Just ask your servant whether he ever prays to St. Anthony, and what he prays for; then go and do likewise."

"I understand. What kind of a saint was St. Anthony, father?"

"You're a funny man, living for sixteen years in Padua and asking me, the Venetian, about St. Anthony. But I can understand! I don't know a single foreigner visiting Venice and not climbing the Campanile, but there is scarcely a Venetian who ever has. The saint was a Portuguese, born at Lisbon. I think his family was related to the Bouillons, who gave a leader to the Crusades. His father was an officer. Anthony himself first became an Augustinian monk, but once he was present when the relics of five martyred missionaries were brought home from Morocco. This inspired him so much that he joined the Franciscan Order, which had just been founded by St. Francis. He went as a missionary to Africa but became so ill that he had to return. His ship was driven to Sicily by a storm. He visited Francis at Assisi, and they became fast friends. Francis ordained him as a bishop and sent him out into the world, to preach and to teach theology. So he wandered preaching from town to town. The Pope of that time, Gregory IX, heard him and called him 'the ship of Holy Writ.' He died in the Arcella convent, near Padua, at the age of thirty-six. People loved him. When he died, they called to each other sobbing in the streets: 'The Saint is dead!" He was canonized a year after his death."

"He was a Portuguese? How strange, I didn't know! And what miracles did he perform?"

"Very marvelous ones. My favorite is the one where a mother was accused of some crime and only her little son could have saved her, but the child was dumb. Anthony put his hand on the boy's head, and he began to talk. The mother escaped the unjust sentence of death. But he performed innumerable miracles. Once he preached to the fishes, as Francis did to the birds. I'd advise you to buy his prayer book. The prayers in it are very beautiful.

Galileo was too lazy to search for it. But when he went home to Padua he called one of his servants, old, sickly Alessandro, to his study.

"Tell me, do you ever ask the Saint for things?"

"Of course, sir. And he always helps me."

"And how do you do it?"

"You have to know the right words, sir."

"What right words?"

"The prayer to St. Anthony. You must go to the church, to the altar where he is buried. Then you have to walk round the altar and put one hand on the lid of his tomb. And then you have to say the prayer, thirteen times. At least we in the Abruzzi believe that. Because thirteen is a saint's number. Every saint is allowed to grant thirteen wishes to everybody. At home we always bake thirteen loaves from the new corn for the Saint's poor. But you must ask only one thing at a time."

"All right, but what are the proper words?"

"A rhymed prayer, sir."

"Could you write it down for me? Here's some paper."

Alessandro Piersanto scribbled with his heavy, uncouth letters the holy poem, in the dialect of his own country:

> *Sand Andonie de Paduve*
> *Che dde Paduve avaniste*
> *Tridece grazij a Ddio cerchiste*
> *Tutta tridece l'aviste*
> *Facete ne grazij a mme*
> *Pe le cinghe piaghe de Ggesu Criste.*[1]

Galileo read it. He shook his head.

"That isn't right. This prayer ought to be said in some other town. 'Who *came* from Padua?'"

"But it *is* right so, sir," Alessandro said. "It helped me, too."

"Very well, you can go. Wait a moment. When are you supposed to give the money?"

"Not until after your wish has been fulfilled, sir. One has to be so careful with money nowadays. You see, you might always get it wrong. For instance, you might say it fourteen times instead of thirteen. Then the whole thing would be spoiled and you'd lose your money."

Galileo kept looking at the slip of paper with the little prayer which his servant had given him. He began to be fond of it. He read it over and over again till he found he knew it by heart. Then he slipped on his winter coat and walked through the rain to the Church of St. Anthony. He was still rather hesitant and ashamed as he went through the dark church to the altar. There were only a few people there, scarcely breathing in the deep twilight.

He stood at the Saint's tomb in silence. He had always admired the candlesticks. Then he remembered that he ought to formulate his wish. He would like to get home to Florence. He would like to have his

---

[1] St. Anthony of Padua
Who came from Padua
And prayed God for thirteen favors
And got them all
Grant my request
By the five wounds of Christ.

financial burdens eased a little. He must ask for health for his children, a long old age for his mother. Suddenly he felt as uneasy as the
ragged beggar in a fairy tale to whom the beautiful fairy grants his
wish. What ought he really to ask? He gazed at the stone lid of the
tomb. Under it lay the mighty St. Anthony. What a great thing to
have been a saint, to have renounced with incredible strength the sweetness of life, not to have tasted the intoxication of wine and women, to
shine high above the sins of every day. Galileo bowed his head.

"I'm longing for purity," he told himself; "therefore my real home *is*
purity. Fra Paolo is a wise man. It was worth while to come here."

But still he did not go behind the altar; he kept putting it off. His
attention wandered to its architectural construction; his eye traced the
distribution of stresses in this marble frame. But at last he went round.
He decided first to say his thirteen prayers and then tell the Saint what
it was he wanted. He went to the back of the stone grave, through the
almost impenetrable dark. He set his palm on the cool stone and began
like an obedient child his prayer in the Abruzzi dialect: *"Sand Andonie
de Paduve . . ."*

He said it over thirteen times, playing all the time with the thoughts
of Florence, his mother, his children, his money cares.

And then he whispered: "I beg you, St. Anthony, to plead with Jesus
Christ for me that he should enlighten my mind and let me invent
something very great to further human knowledge."

He took his hand off the stone and stared amazed into the darkness.
So this was what he was really longing for in his deepest heart! How
deep and secret are human beings, since no man really knows what
dwells in him. He saw suddenly that it was easier to know the universe than oneself.

"Five gold pieces," he added.

He remembered that he had not yet fixed the amount of his vow.
And man is weak and fickle. If he gets what he asks for, he easily for-
gets his humbleness in asking. He repeated his vow, then turned beside
the equestrian statue of Erasmo da Narni, whom the people had called
Gattamelata, tiger cat.

At home foreign letters were awaiting him. He recognized the handwriting of his former pupil, the French Badouère. The Frenchman

informed him that according to rumors in France a citizen of the Netherlands had discovered a strange optic phenomenon: he had constructed an instrument which by adjusting different lenses showed everything several sizes larger. Galileo smiled at such foolish gossip.

The other letter came from Florence. The chamberlain of the Grand Duchess Cristina wrote to say that the Grand Duke was ailing, his wife very anxious, and asking Galileo to draw up Fernando's horoscope at once.

He did not start it that day, and he was disturbed the next. He kept putting it off. He did not like this kind of work and had lost many chances of earning money by this dislike. He did not believe in horoscopes, just as he did not believe in Ptolemy. And then came another letter from Florence: the Grand Duke was dead. His nineteen-year-old son, Cosimo II, would succeed him.

Galileo wrote at once to the new ruler, his former pupil, to send his cordial homage. Then he hurried to Marina, told her the great news, and explained that now he would probably go to Florence.

"It was you who advised me to pray to St. Anthony. He's granted my wish in a strange way. I asked him for something quite different, but that doesn't matter. Anyway, it's time I met your Bartoluzzi to talk things over."

"It's a pity you didn't tell me yesterday, when he was here in Padua. But I'll write to him now."

A week later a sturdy, red-faced young man, bursting with health, knocked at the door of Galileo's study. He introduced himself as Bartoluzzi. He was obviously much younger than Marina.

They talked easily. Bartoluzzi showed not the least embarrassment. He wanted to marry Marina—but how could he do it without a dowry? So he needed three thousand gold pieces and a monthly allowance for at least as long as Marina kept the boy with her.

Galileo tried to bargain, but bargaining had never been his strong point; and Bartoluzzi stuck stubbornly to his guns. Finally they agreed that Marina should get two thousand four hundred gold pieces as a dowry, one thousand at once and the rest during three years.

"Now, I have only to wish you luck. When do you mean to have the wedding?"

"A fortnight after I get my thousand gold pieces."

"All right," Galileo nodded. "I hope it won't be too long an engagement."

Bartoluzzi went off to tell Marina.

Galileo snapped his fingers angrily. Why had he not asked St. Anthony to let him simply marry Marina or something like that! If the whole of Italy thronged to Padua to take private lessons and buy his measuring rod, he would still be overburdened with debt. But in the end he shrugged his shoulders, as he always did when things looked blackest. It would all settle itself somehow.

There was something else which interested him much more. The letter of Badouère set him thinking, although he smiled at it. He sat down and read what science was saying about refraction. Then he asked Sagredo to take him to Murano, to the glass factory, of which his friend was a director. He explained to the foreman what sort of lenses he wanted: all possible combinations of the convex and concave in different sizes. At home he called on his old printer and told him to make strong tubes of thick paper. Some of them must be of equal diameter, the others narrowing to a point.

It was difficult to wait till they arrived. Whenever he could escape from Padua he hurried to Venice to spend his time with Sagredo. His friend had got tired of idling and decided to try work for a change. He wanted to be a diplomat; he had a real gift for diplomacy and an inclination to see the world. His father was overjoyed and had his son appointed as Venetian consul at Aleppo. So Sagredo was preparing for his journey and saying good-by to all his friends. He allowed himself to play a last practical joke on Galileo. He did not tell him the date of his departure, but one day he took him out in a gondola. They were rowed to the Malamocco, and there Sagredo said indifferently:

"God speed you, my friend. The gondola will take you back to Venice; I'm going to Asia. If we shouldn't meet again, think of me kindly."

And he hurried away without waiting for an answer. Galileo saw Sagredo's father waiting in the midst of a crowd of guests, all assembled to bid farewell to the young man. He understood: Sagredo hated sentimentality and long leave-taking. The gondola turned back to Venice; and, though Galileo did not look back, he felt as though he had lost his right hand.

At home he buried himself in his new experiments with the lenses, surrounding himself with scribbled sheets of calculations. He changed his lenses again and again, setting them at different distances. He spoiled one tube after the other, spending a considerable sum on new lenses and new paper funnels. He tried a hundred variants of them; but, when he looked into them, he saw only the dimness of his surroundings.

One day in July he had finished another such cardboard funnel. This was of equal diameter everywhere; one end bore a plano-convex, the other a plano-concave lens. He stood up from his chair to take a last look into it and then go out, having done enough that day. His window was open, the chatter of birds came from the treetops in the garden. He was just about to put down his paper tube, when something made him want to take it up again. One of the domes of St. Anthony's church towered above the trees. He directed his tube upon it and took a glance. What was this huge protuberance?

And now he stiffened. What was this? He saw part of the dome, but it seemed much bigger. He put down the tube and glanced at it. Then with the tube again: it seemed five times as big. He could clearly see the smallest dents and fissures, although they were not visible to the naked eye. Now he turned his instrument on the foliage. He saw the leaves in sharp relief; he could have counted them, although as a rule he saw no more than a green mass. He was so excited that he had to put down the tube and rest. He pressed his hand over his heart as though he were afraid of some shock.

Then he began again. He went to the window and spied out the different objects in the courtyard. As if they were moved by some devilish power, they sprang into nearness as soon as he spied at them through the tube. He could distinguish the single straws on the roof. He saw clearly the rusty nails on the garden gate. And suddenly he began to shout:

"Who's at home? Count Schultz! Salvati! Count Montalbano! Hurry!"

His servant Alessandro was the first to arrive.

"Do you see that pigeon on the opposite roof?"

"I do, sir."

"Take this tube and look through it carefully. But if you drop it, I'll kill you."

Alessandro obeyed. Suddenly he screamed in terror and pushed the tube back into his master's hand.

"What's this, sir? A devil's contraption!"

He crossed himself and shook with fear, edging away from the magic tube. The students came in, and Galileo shouted like one possessed:

"I've got it! I've got it! Send everyone here! Let the whole world come in and look!"

VIII

There was a huge crowd in the house. All the neighbors came thronging; even complete strangers crowded in at the news of this miracle. It was night before they consented to go away. Galileo stared for a long time at his candle. He went into the courtyard and watched it through the window with his tube. He could not have enough of the wonder he had discovered.

Next day he took it to the university. He put the tube into the hands of the first student he met. This was a Florentine called Marcimedici, scion of a distinguished family, a rather narrow-minded theologian. He glanced into the tube, and his mouth remained open. He stared at Galileo as if he had been Satan himself. Soon a crowd collected. Old Fabrizio, who was already pensioned, happened to be in the building and was one of the first to glance into the magic tube. He was horrified; he mumbled and shook his head.

"That I should ever live to see such a thing!"

Then came Cremonini.

"Cesare, hurry up, see what a miracle I've invented. Your Aristotle never knew anything about this!"

Cremonini glanced into the tube and was dumfounded.

"Incredible. But why attack Aristotle again? I'm sure this is somewhere in his books. There's everything in them."

"I'd like to see it," Galileo said indignantly. "I'll bet you a soldo you won't be able to find the place."

Other professors came. The whole morning schedule was upset. Everybody talked of the wonderful tube. At home he had to lock the house doors, since the curious infested even the dining room. After dinner Cornaro arrived and wanted to examine the invention in the name of the Ricovrati Academy. He asked Galileo to arrange a special demonstration at his palace. And Cremonini came too, highly excited.

"I've found it. I told you I should find it."

He had brought with him two volumes of Aristotle, *De Generatione Animalium*. He searched for a passage.

"Here you are! 'Whoever looks into a tube, sees further.' But here is
the other. Read it yourself. 'Therefore it can be alleged that from the
bottom of a very deep well we could see the stars even by daylight.'
What is a deep well if not such a tube? Your invention is splendid, but
you see Aristotle anticipated it."

"You're so stubborn, Cesare, that you don't mind how much nonsense you talk. It's just as though you'd taken me to Carrara to the
marble quarry, and said to me: 'No past or future sculptor counts for
anything, because every statue is already hidden in this mountainside.'
Aristotle had not the faintest inkling of my invention. That's the great
beauty of this new tube; it will show you people a few new things! I
say to you for the hundredth time: Aristotle stays in the same place,
while the whole world moves on. I won't die till I have conquered
you Peripatetics and broken the fetters you've put on human thought.
You can think with Aristotle's mind; I think with my own."

Cremonini sadly shook his head.

"I'm deeply sorry for you, because I like you and can see how mistaken you are."

He departed gloomily. But ten others came in his stead. Acquaintances, inquisitive women, priests, artisans, people of all sorts. The servants had no time to explain that His Excellency the professor was busy.
There were some who simply pushed through the gates. The house was
like a besieged fortress.

With his remaining lenses, Galileo made three other tubes. He was
deeply excited when he looked into the second, because he was afraid
that the invention, or rather the first copy, had some hidden, unknown,
accidental element which he had not included in the second. But, having looked, he danced for joy: he had placed in the second a plano-
convex and a plano-concave lens, and it brought the object just as near
as the first.

The uproar of the first days died down. He decided to present his
invention in fitting form to the head of the state. He wrote a careful
letter to Doge Donato.

He reported his discovery and expressed his delight that he could offer
Venice, in whose service he hoped to spend his whole life, some return
for her signal favors, something which would make her glory shine
even more brightly.

Marina read the letter. She looked up surprised at the end.

"You want to serve Venice for the rest of your life? I thought you wanted to go back to your own country?"

Galileo shrugged with a shy smile.

"I'm afraid I've caused a little confusion. I followed your advice and went to St. Anthony to ask him to send me back home as soon as possible. But at the last moment I changed my mind and asked that I should create something great in my field. And St. Anthony has answered my prayer. Now I've become superstitious: my other wish can never be fulfilled. But don't let that worry you; you'll be able to marry your Bartoluzzi."

He himself took the letter to Venice to present it to the Doge's secretary. But he also brought one of the tubes and showed it there to all his friends. That was enough to spread its fame. The small inn near Santa Lucia where he lodged became a veritable shrine for pilgrimages. The whole city was full with the rumor of this miracle. Commanders of high rank, most of them strangers, sailors of repute visited him. Senators wrote him letters and invited him to their houses. The Doge would have heard about his invention even if he had never received his letter.

Soon he was ordered to report at the Doge's Palace and discuss the best means of demonstrating his invention. Galileo proposed to choose some point of vantage from which distances could be seen through the tube. They agreed on the Campanile, but had first to ask the aged senators whom the Doge wanted to invite if they would be willing to climb so many stairs. The miracle had aroused such curiosity that even the oldest senator was prepared to stir his joints. Thus the morning of August 21st was the date fixed for the event.

The company met at the foot of the Campanile. It was a distinguished party, composed of the most powerful senators, whom the Doge had honored by inviting them to be present at this rare experience. They gathered under the tower, already enraptured by the invention. They snatched the tube from each other's hands to examine the frieze on the palace walls, the pigeons on the roof of San Marco, the horses over the entrance to the church. They were all full of admiration and praise. At a quarter past eight, the Doge emerged from his palace. He approached and graciously received the greetings of his bareheaded senators.

"Well, let us see this miracle of yours, Messer Galileo."

Priuli ventured to suggest that the Doge would enjoy it more if he waited till they had climbed the tower. Up there the view would be still more curious. Donato smiled and acquiesced. They began their climb with the sober dignity appropriate to such elderly gentlemen. They had often to stop to get their breath and mop their faces; the higher they climbed the more often it happened. But at last they arrived. They leaned panting against the dusty stands of the huge bells. Galileo was the last. This experiment promised new experiences even for him. It was a brilliant sunny day without a cloud. An azure sky hung over Venice. He stepped to the parapet and directed his instrument on Murano. His delight forced him to cry out. The tube showed him the steps of the San Giacomo church, and he could clearly see people going into it. He moved his instrument a little and saw the column on the corner of the Rio dei Vetrieri, the Glass-blowers' Row, with its moored gondolas.

"Hey, Messer Galileo." Someone touched his shoulder. "The Doge is waiting."

He was horrified at his own thoughtless rapture, and hastened to offer the tube to the Doge. Donato looked into it and exclaimed:

"Incredible! Why, I can see the *traghetto* clearly! Contarini, Contarini! I can see the dog in your park; come and have a look! This is wonderful! The dog looks like a small black dot. . . ."

Contarini stared at his dog. Then others took the tube, but soon the Doge demanded it again. The magic city of the lagoons spread out below them, the Grand Canal, green among the mass of red-shingled roofs and yellow-gray walls. . . . Everybody searched for his own house. Soranzo cried angrily:

"They'll drop that brat out of the window. . . . I'm always telling them to be more careful!"

They all laughed at this. Then they began to look farther. Chioggia, Treviso, the Lido, the Conegliano Harbor were all clear through the magic tube. And they were almost taken aback to find the mainland, the "terra firma," clearly outlined, the bell tower of the Santa Giustina rising out of the sea of houses: Padua. At last they looked out to sea, and found that where the naked eye could not even distinguish a tiny point, this wonderful tube gave them a clear sight of fishing boats with their gold-brown sails.

"What is the ratio of the magnifying?" asked the Doge, to show how much he knew.

"Ninefold, Your Highness."

"And how did you invent such a thing, you wizard?"

"I had heard, Your Highness, about a Dutchman who invented a magnifying tube. I thought I could do as well as he did. I tried different combinations till I found out the right one. And I am happy to have won the approval of the Republic."

The Doge put a hand on his shoulder.

"And you may rest assured that Venice can reward such genius. How much is your salary, Messer Galileo?"

"Five hundred and twenty gold pieces a year, Your Highness. My agreement has one more year to run."

The Doge glanced at Priuli.

"When is the next Pregada meeting, Messer Riformatore?"

"On the twenty-fifth."

"That's four days hence. Very well. We shall summon Messer Galileo to appear at the meeting. There we shall inform him how we plan his future affairs. But let me look once more into this magic tube. It's so difficult to stop looking. . . ."

When Galileo got back to Padua, he sent immediately for one of his workmen.

"I want a new tube," he said, "of exactly the same size, and as soon as possible. It must be a very fine copy, richly gilded and sheathed in a fine case. When can I have it?"

"When do you need it, Messer?"

"It's already too late!"

"I understand. You shall have it the day after tomorrow."

And Galileo took it—his new gold telescope—to the Pregada meeting presided over by the Doge himself. He was summoned into the room and asked leave to speak. The Doge nodded.

"I should be very happy if Your Highness would accept this instrument as the humble gift of your poor subject."

The Doge was delighted.

"What? What? You want to *give* it to me?"

"It would be a great honor if Your Highness would deign to accept it."

"Thank you," said Donato eagerly. "I thank you heartily. And we have decided that this invention of yours will be of the greatest use to the State, in many ways. We think that its importance is incalculable. Therefore we order twelve copies of this, er—what's-its-name. . . . Have you named it already?"

"I thought of calling it 'tubespectacles.' *Cannocchiale*."

"Splendid. Hereupon we order twelve copies of it. As for your future employment at the university, you shall receive our resolution in writing. God bless you, Messer Galileo."

Galileo bowed gratefully and turned to go. But he waited outside, since Priuli, the *riformatore,* had signed him that he had something to say. And not five minutes later Priuli appeared.

"Messer Galileo, I have great news for you. The Doge was so touched by your gift that he has fixed the terms of your new contract personally. Do you know how much you're going to get a year? A thousand gold pieces. No professor at Padua has ever been paid at such a rate. And for how long? For the rest of your life. I hope you're satisfied. . . . Of course, the Senate has to discuss it, but you can rest assured, it will be only a formality. I congratulate you, Messer Galileo."

He embraced him and hurried back to the meeting. Galileo came down the steps, lost in his thoughts. It was really incredible good fortune: his salary doubled, his position made safe for the rest of his life, and he could be sure that his invention would have an immense effect in the world of science. And this meant the end of money difficulties. He could live peacefully at home, cultivate his little vineyards, slowly pay off his brothers-in-law, get Marina married, and even gradually pay his remaining debts. He could work in peace, devote himself without interruption to the long-neglected Copernicus. Everything was hopeful, triumphant, and happy for him, and yet he felt sad—saddened by the expression, "for the rest of your life." Fiorenza! Fiorenza! he cried. But his patrons at home had long been silent; the Prime Minister did not write; the new Prince, his former pupil, seemed to have forgotten him.

He spent the summer vacation in Florence, but found nobody. The Court was away for the summer, and had not invited him. The town had started a new life under the new ruler. Cosimo II began his reign by closing down the Medici bank, from which his family took its origins and derived its power; the bank which had created a dynasty, in whose veins flowed the blood of the Kings of France. But the Austrian Grand Duchess did not want to be a banker's wife. Cosimo also decided not to live in town. He planned to enlarge the Pitti, but at the same time he was building a new palace for his bride in the hills near Arcetri. It was to be called the Poggio Imperiale.

Galileo went to inspect the Pitti. He was amazed to see the grand scale of the plans. The whole front had been enlarged; it had thirteen windows instead of seven. Two large wings were added, with a huge courtyard and a wide terrace at the height of the first floor. He felt like a disinherited son.

He had brought a copy of his invention to Florence, and the Landucci house was besieged by the curious. Landucci hinted several times that he would like to have a copy, but Galileo seemed not to understand him. Finally the invention led to a violent quarrel. Signora Landucci began to squabble with her mother. Signora Giulia made a scene. She ran out into the street and swore that Virginia had ceased to be a daughter of hers. She never wanted to see her again. Thank God she had still another child! In future she would live with Livia; but, till her quarters had been prepared there, she would spend a few weeks in Padua with her dear Galileo. She packed her scanty belongings and set off for Padua with her son.

Landucci tried to stop her, but it was no use. And Galileo knew why his brother-in-law had been so anxious to placate her. He had been drawing the money for her maintenance and did not lose on it.

After a few quiet days in Padua, the old lady was angry again. When they told her that Marina was going to marry, she railed at her day and night. She found a thousand faults with the upbringing, clothing, diet of the three children, and urged her son not to leave them for a moment with their mother. She tried to incite the little ones against Marina. And when Marina took all this with complete indifference, Signora Giulia became still more furious. Galileo and Marina met in the botanical garden to discuss matters in peace. Galileo wondered timidly whether they could not let his mother have one of the girls; perhaps she would be pacified then.

"She can have one," Marina answered, shrugging her shoulders. "Whichever she likes."

Galileo was amazed. How could any mother let her children go without more ado? But he said nothing. He was glad that he could restore peace, and decided to send Virginia away with her grandmother. The girl was nine years old, not a pretty child, but an enchanting one, gentle and docile. With her mother she was good and obedient. She adored her father. When they told her that she would go with her grandmother to Florence, she only asked whether her father would stay in Padua.

"Yes, my sweet, for some time; but I'll often come to see you and write many letters."

"Yes," answered the little girl, but her voice shook and there were tears in her eyes.

Signora Giulia finished off her visit obstreperously: she quarreled with her other daughter, Signora Galletti, who had come to fetch her. Now she wanted to go back to Virginia. She walked up and down in the courtyard, screaming and shouting. Little Virginia followed her everywhere obediently.

"Look here, mother," Galileo burst out in a fit of irritation, "it's all the same to me which daughter of yours you choose; but go, for God's sake. I can't work like this; you upset the whole house."

Thereupon her whole fury was turned on him. Everybody was relieved when at last she got into the coach, after deciding that she would go back to Landucci. She carried off Virginia, like a hostage.

Galileo returned to his work. He was busy in town, and it was nightfall by the time he got home. But then he was full of curiosity. He took up his telescope and began to examine the sky. This was the first time he had done so.

He was astonished. The tube reduced the stars instead of magnifying them. But where the naked eye had seen a radiant, glimmering uncertain source of light, the tube showed a precise circle. Galileo took a glance at all his old friends—Sirius, all the stars of the Bear, the single members of the Pleiades. He pointed his instrument at the spot where the "new star" had been but did not see anything. Just then the moon appeared from behind the clouds. He was feverishly excited to discover a whole maze of patterns on her surface. She seemed to have the form of a ball, and the upper half of her surface showed chains of what seemed to be mountains throwing extremely strong shadows and gigantic craters. Galileo watched with all his might. It was as though the full force of supreme joy had broken over him, almost brutally. At last he had set his feet on the right path. The old starry sky belonged to Aristotle; but he, on this autumn evening of 1609, saw a new sky, never seen before by human eyes. That night he stayed awake till dawn, as long as he could see a single glimmer of starlight. When he went to bed, no sleep would come to him. Why had this tube so enlarged the moon and at the same time diminished the stars? For the moment he could not solve the mystery, but even so he was supremely happy. He again watched the stars come out on the following evening. He again saw the huge craters on the surface of the moon, the mountain chains throwing those strong, ghostly shadows. He looked at the Milky Way and saw that it was no veil of mist as people had said for two thousand years, composed of some mysterious substance, but the conglomeration of thousands—hundreds of thousands—of tiny stars. He again stayed up the whole night; it was morning when he fell asleep.

His lectures started again at the university, and his private lessons increased. He gave up every social activity. He did not visit Marina, but asked her to send the two children twice a week at dinner time to his house. At supper he was rigidly abstemious and drank little wine; up to now he had enjoyed good cheer and gay company and gone to bed every night, if not drunk, at least a little dizzy. But now he bent all his faculties on discovering the amazing new country. When he heard from Florence that little Virginia was not happy with her grandmother, who spoiled her one day and whipped her the next, he sent word that she must be taken to the Nunziatina Convent at once. He wrote so harshly that they did not dare to defy his command—the angry father might stop his payments. And now he could give his whole mind to the sky.

He had a new tube made with much bigger lenses: a twenty-fold enlargement. He furnished a fair-sized astronomical observatory in the attic, where he had a table with reference books, writing utensils, and an oil lamp. If the weather was clear, he had his food brought up to him and spent only a few minutes over it. He ate at the common table only if the sky was overcast. Every night he sat there jotting down reckonings and observations. His real life began at night in this cosmic solitude. By day he was silent and absent-minded, not saying a word of what he had seen. His notes increased. He knew that the unchangeable sky of Aristotle with its one thousand and twenty-seven stars was a childish dream: he himself could have counted twice as many, even apart from the Milky Way. He had sketched a map of the moon with its mysterious abysses, crags, and shadowy craters. He had found out why his tube diminished the stars: because the severe impartiality of lenses robbed them of the mist which the naked eye imagined around them. He perceived that their real kernel, their real form, was much smaller than the human eye had seen, and his tube showed this tiny kernel twenty times magnified.

He made many notes, feeling his way toward some unity.

It was one o'clock in the morning of January 7th when he examined Jupiter. Standing in his frosty solitude, shifting from foot to foot to keep himself warm, he called out suddenly. He saw three very small but sharply glittering stars in the vicinity of the planet. Nobody had ever known of these stars. They could not even exist, according to Aristotle.

And yet they did. They shone like diamond pinheads along the straight line running parallel with the ecliptic. Galileo left his instrument and stared amazed into the darkness. He took another look. The three diamond points were still there. No, it was impossible. There must be some fault in the lenses. He stared at them for more than an hour and noted down their exact place.

Next day he could scarcely await the sunset. Again he saw the three points; but, when he checked them by his previous night's drawing, their position was different. Or perhaps Jupiter had moved. He rubbed his forehead. It might still be a flaw in the lenses. Next day there was a heavy mist over Padua, so he had to break off his observations. But the following night he looked again and thumped on the table. What devilish joke was this? Now he saw only two of the three stars, but in different places. But he saw clearly that this change was not due to the planet. The tiny stars had moved. On the following night there were two again, but a very important thing had happened: last time they had seemed to be completely equal in size, but now one of them was much larger.

He sprang to his feet. Yes, here was the solution. Here were three orbits around Jupiter, just as Venus and Mercury circled round the sun. One of them was now behind Jupiter, therefore invisible. The second had come forward on his orbit and therefore looked larger. So therefore Jupiter had its moons! It was a planet like the earth! If Jupiter was a planet, so could the earth be! The earth was not the center of the universe. Copernicus had seen the truth.

He waited for the third star to come out again. On the next night it emerged at about three o'clock in the morning. And another surprise awaited him on the night of January 14th: the fourth star! Three stars were clearly visible west of Jupiter and one to the east. Next night all four were on the west side. No doubts now: Jupiter had four moons, four stars of which astronomy had known nothing! This meant the end of the Peripatetics. On their "unchangeable" sky, Galileo had discovered four new stars!

He worked on feverishly at his notes to publish this earth-shattering discovery. His quill raced across the paper. In his introduction he described the invention of the new instrument, and then he built up his observations into a solid system. He left the moons of Jupiter till the end. He scarcely slept four hours a day. He strayed about, dazed as an autumn fly; but, when he was back again at his desk, after the effort of the first few sentences, his mind became suddenly clear and eager. Then, while he slept, his manuscript was copied by three clerks.

By January 29th he had finished. His book was called *Sidereus Nuncius*. The *Herald of Stars*. It proclaimed wonders which all, especially philosophers and astronomers, would have to take into account. And these wonders were proclaimed by *"the Florentine nobleman, Galileo Galilei, mathematician of Padua University—amazing discoveries, made with the help of a telescope recently invented by him, concerning the appearance of the moon, the innumerable fixed stars, the Milky Way, the Nebulae; but especially four planets which flew round Jupiter in different periods of time and with amazing velocity."*

Then he asked Vinta to present the enclosed manuscript to Grand Duke Cosimo. If necessary he would send an excellent copy of a "telescope," as he called it now, so that His Highness might follow with his own eyes what the book described. And the next courier brought his answer:

I have found your letter so remarkable that I read it instantly to His Highness. This last proof of what we may well describe as your superhuman talent has so impressed him that he would desire nothing better than to follow your discoveries with the telescope.

So a telescope was sent to Florence. The university authorities allowed him at once to print the manuscript. Baglioni's printers worked night and day. Galileo called several times daily to read the proofs, snatching an hour's sleep whenever he could. He was still watching the Jupiter moons to add still further observations to the last pages, if he should find something important. He hurried to Padua, lectured, and came back to Venice. He wrote to Vinta again, proposing that he should name the four "moons" Cosmicus, after Cosimo, honoring his former pupil in the finest way he could.

Vinta answered at once. He disapproved of the name "Cosmicus" because everybody would confuse it with the Greek word "cosmic." When the letter arrived, the book was already printed. The presses were stopped, the word "Cosmicus" covered over in the finished copies, and the title pages completely reprinted. The author added to the long title:

and which stars, discovered by the author, shall be called by him "the Medici stars," everybody being requested to call them by this name. Venice. Printed by Tommaso Baglioni, MDCX. With the permission and favor of the proper authorities.

When he held the first copy damp from the printer in his hand, he thought that if now he did not get home to Florence, he never would. He had really deserved to be recalled. He had really done what others only promised allegorically: he had fetched the stars from heaven for the Grand Duke Cosimo.

IX

One night he was hurrying back from the university when he met Cremonini. Though Cremonini opposed him even more fervently in science, he still remained a faithful friend.

"Have you read my book, Cesare?"

"I have."

"And you've nothing to say?"

"We'd better not argue about it. You'll never make me change my mind or betray the faith in which I grew up, the faith in which I hope to die."

"So you believe in the one thousand and twenty-seven stars? In the immutable sky? You believe in the perfect number of heavenly bodies and that the moon is a flat disk?"

"Yes, I do. αὐτὸς ἔφη."

"Cesare, come home with me! Look into my telescope. You'll see that Jupiter has four moons of which the Peripatetics know nothing. And besides Aristotle's thousand and twenty-seven stars, you can count several thousand more, if you have the patience. And you can look at the surface of the moon, which is full of blemishes. Come along, man!"

Cremonini thought for an instant, then shook his head.

"No. There's no object in my coming. All this cannot be. Aristotle never said it was so. There can't be any stars around Jupiter. I'm not coming."

"But, Cesare, do you think I am mad?"

"No, Galileo. Only wrong-headed. Those stars can't be there."

"I'd like to drag you home and force my telescope to your eye; then you'd have to see. Come along."

"No, let me go. It can't be as you say. Good night."

He freed himself and hurried away like a man chased by thieves. Galileo went homeward. He resolved that sooner or later he would break Cremonini's stubborn will. He had sent his book to every notable mathematician of Europe. Now he waited for their answers.

It would be some time before they replied. These European cities were all far apart. Only Grand Duke Cosimo wrote to summon him to Pisa for the Easter vacation. He would send a litter to meet his former tutor at Bologna. Galileo was very much excited. He knew that this invitation would settle his fate.

He did the journey by afternoon stages. Wherever he stopped for the night, he watched the stars, taking notes till dawn, then sleeping till noon. In Bologna he planned to visit Magini. He did not want to remain his enemy, and was curious to hear his opinion of the telescope and the miracles of the *Sidereus Nuncius*. A former pupil of his, Roffeni, lived in Bologna; he called at his house, and they went to see Magini.

His old rival, who had triumphed over him in Bologna but failed at Padua, received him with excessive amiability, with honeyed words through which his envy was still perceptible. He would not dream of letting Galileo spend the night in any other house. He presented a sharp-eyed young man with an ascetic face and harsh manner, who spoke Latin with a strange, Slavic accent.

"This is Messer Horky, a Bohemian mathematician, and my pupil. Kepler sent him to me."

"Oh, Kepler, my comrade in arms! Did he really send you here?"

"Yes," the young Bohemian answered. "He thought I could learn the most from Messer Magini."

That surprised Galileo, who pretended not to notice the insinuation. He asked after Kepler. Horky had come from Prague and seen him recently, and had many things to relate. Kepler had three children now; his daughter was married to a Bavarian physician called Ehm. On the whole he did not like his position. There was much strife in Prague. A strong party worked underground against the Emperor Rudolph to set Archduke Matthew on the throne; there was continual fighting in the streets. Kepler could not work in peace. He had visited Prince John Frederick at Stuttgart, trying to get a post at his Court, but had not succeeded. Now he was back in Prague. His wife loved fine dresses and display, and Kepler was forced to draw up horoscopes.

"But he's a kindhearted man," the Bohemian said. "He got me the money to come to Bologna."

"We also have Bohemians at Padua, and some of them are my best pupils. They enjoy looking through my telescope to spy out the wonders of the firmament. Will our kind host give me permission to use it now? I never miss one evening. If you are interested, Messer Magini, I shall be delighted to show you the sky."

"Thank you," said the honeyed Magini, "but I, too, have my work. I'm preparing a big new map of Italy. . . ."

"Perhaps Messer Horky . . ."

"Thank you"—the young Bohemian's voice was cold—"I have no time either."

But Roffeni, Galileo's former pupil, was full of eagerness.

"May I stay here and watch, Maestro?"

They gave Galileo a room from which he had a good view of the sky. He explained the details of the *Sidereus Nuncius*.

"Beware of these men, Your Excellency," Roffeni suddenly interrupted him. "Behind your back they are always abusing you. It turned my stomach to hear them praising you to your face. . . ."

"The Bohemian doesn't even do that," Galileo laughed. "It's odd, because he comes from Kepler. Well, never mind."

They worked till dawn. Galileo rose late. Magini bade him profuse farewells with assurances of respect and admiration. Horky had vanished. Galileo lay proudly in his litter. With the same pride he arrived in Florence, and halted before the Landucci house. Let them see how far Galileo had got in the world! Then he went to the convent where little Virginia was at school. She trembled with joy to see her father.

Next evening he would observe the stars from Firenzuola, the following evening from San Romano. And on the fourth day he faced the Prince in the very same room where, long, long ago, he had criticized the dredger of Giovanni de' Medici. Cosimo welcomed him with delight. They discussed the book, the wonderful telescope, and the significance of the four new stars. The Prince kept saying how grateful he felt.

"And what news of Venice, Messer Galileo? How goes the quarrel with the Pope?"

"I know little about it, Your Highness, only that Fra Paolo Sarpi has again been attacked by masked men who wanted to kill him. But he escaped. Later he denounced the Venetian Nuncio, Cardinal Borghese, and the Pope, for hiring the assassins. It's a very difficult case; the court does not know what attitude to take."

"What a violent and disorderly country. . . . How much better things are in our lovely Tuscany!"

"Oh, if only I could come home!" Galileo exclaimed, so fervently that his own eagerness scared him a little.

"You shall!" Cosimo nodded. "It is our wish that you should, and has been so for a long time. Now we shall realize it. We herewith invite you to return, and we shall summon you officially to our Court. The rest you can discuss with Belisario Vinta. Now we dismiss you, Messer Galileo; but we desire to see you again this afternoon."

Galileo could have shouted for joy as he left the audience chamber. But he had to control himself. Halberdiers were posted all down the long corridor, lined with Gobelins. He tried to find Vinta, but the Prime Minister was away. So he went to visit Castelli, his former pupil. He had pupils now in every city. They went out together in search of the house where he had lived as a young professor, and then to find his old student's quarters. They visited the Cathedral, in which he had watched the swaying lamp, then the Baptistery and Leaning Tower.

"Don't you want to go to the university?" Castelli asked.

"No, I never want to see it again."

This Easter vaction was very pleasant. He was often received by the Duke and the Duchess, Cosimo's mother and his family. Only Vinta was difficult to interview. The Prime Minister was busy from morning till night. But they arranged that he should find some post for Galileo of rank fitting to his celebrity. The details would be settled by letter. The Prince took very gracious leave, assuring him that he would soon be given a post. But Galileo still could not believe in such good fortune.

Many letters awaited him in Padua, but Kepler's interested him most. The German scientist sent his latest work, the *Astronomia Nova*. His letter told him that Kepler had tested every line of the *Sidereus Nuncius* and confirmed it, that he would tell all his friends of this wonderful book, and that a new edition was already being prepared in Prague, to which he himself would write a preface. Altobelli wrote from Ancona:

"Your *Sidereus Nuncius* has amazed me so that it shook me out of the lethargy of the past five years. . . . Hipparchus, Ptolemy, Tycho, Copernicus, the Egyptians, and Chaldeans would all be astounded that they did not know the half of what they believed they knew. Your glory has put them in the shade."

Even Munich was interested. Hermann, the Court physician of Maximilian, Prince of Bavaria, inquired—mentioning his good friend Michelagnolo, who was employed in the ducal orchestra—whether he could get such a tube to see the miracles himself. The French Embassy in Venice submitted the request of the French Court that if the excellent astronomer would discover a new star he might name it, after His Majesty Henry IV, "Henry" or at least "the Star of the Bourbons." Whereupon Galileo replied politely that he did not expect this opportunity to arise, for he had diligently searched the heavens, and would probably find no new star.

And Vinta also wrote regularly. The Florence appointment was being arranged through the usual official channels. The financial conditions were agreed, and the matter of Galileo's rank. He was to be offered the post of mathematics professor at Pisa, but without a chair, delegated for Court service, and would be paid a thousand Florentine gold pieces a year, which was considerably more than the Venetian currency; he would also be officially appointed Court mathematician to the Tuscan Court.

Galileo took the letter straight to Marina. He gave it her without a word. She read it calmly.

"When do you leave?" she asked.

"As soon as possible. I need a few weeks to settle my affairs. I must get my document of repatriation at Venice, give up the lease, sell the wine and all the furniture I don't need . . . I think I can move by the end of August."

"I see. Well, I wish you luck and happiness."

"Thank you. I'll take Livia, as we agreed. But the boy can stay with you for a while."

"Yes."

"As for Bartoluzzi, I'll try and get the money as soon as possible. I liked that young man."

"Yes," Marina smothered a yawn, "a very good man."

Galileo felt that he must say something.

"So we're parting now, Marina."

"There's plenty of time for saying good-by," Marina answered absentmindedly. "The end of August is weeks off. Do you mind if I send you away now? I've told them to prepare a bath."

Galileo left her, dejectedly. This was not how he had pictured the leave-taking. His vanity felt a little hurt. Marina, who had borne him three children, accepted the fact of their separation as though it were the most trivial event. He felt vaguely sorry to lose this beautiful woman whom even now people turned to look at in the street. He would have liked to possess her once again. Ashamed, he put away the thought, said good-by in his soul to his love, already dead, and went about his business.

When he announced at Venice that he wished to leave his post and take up the position of Court mathematician at Florence, it was some time before Contarini, the *riformatore,* could say a word. At last he answered very politely:

"The Most Serene Republic wishes nobody to be detained against his will. We have always done our best to meet your demands, and wish you all good fortune for your new post. At the same time we are very sorry that we could not satisfy you here. But at least we have done as much for you as we could. God be with you."

Galileo would have liked to answer, but found he could not. Contarini rose from his desk, the astronomer bowed and took his leave. So ended his connection with Padua. He went for the last time to the university to collect his belongings. He did not say a word to anyone. It was still some time before his departure. But, when he passed under the archway and glanced back at the winged lion, his heart was heavy.

Now he was busy all day settling his affairs and correspondence, while at night he still scanned the heavens. His daily work was less agreeable. By now he was receiving the first news of those mathematicians and astronomers who had not written to acknowledge the *Sidereus Nuncius* because they disagreed with its conclusions. The more moderate among them called it an illusion, an error. Even Clavius, the Jesuit in Rome, declared that it was impossible to believe what Galileo said he had seen. And stubborn followers of Aristotle plainly described it as idle prattle.

At last a book arrived, written by Horky, the Bohemian, Magini's pupil.

"Sally against the Herald of Stars," said the title. The contents were pure abuse, a furious and violent pamphlet. It did not try to refute anything; it simply stated that Horky had looked with the telescope at

the spots in the sky which Galileo mentioned, but had not seen what the Padua mathematician claimed to see. The whole pamphlet betrayed hypocrisy. Galileo could only wonder why all this had been written by Kepler's pupil. He wrote to Kepler, directing his attention to such strange behavior.

Meanwhile Alessandro, his old servant, was dying. This old man had been a dear friend; Galileo visited him several times a day and stayed with him as long as he could manage. Nobody quite knew what the matter was. The doctor said he was dying of old age. He seemed terribly afraid to die, groaning and weeping, praying incessantly to St. Anthony. But not even St. Anthony could help him. One night he died quietly. Galileo gave him a costly funeral, and himself collected his poor belongings to send them to Alessandro's family.

While looking through the dead servant's chest, he was surprised to recognize his mother's handwriting on some letters under tattered sheets. He read one of them:—

Above all don't forget to tell me in detail about the joy which my departure has caused; for I know you could never tell me enough. You can write whatever you like; all the letters will come safely into my hands. Only take care that Signora Marina reads none of mine. I want to know everything they say about me! I know that you were the only one who grieved to see me go; all the others were glad. . . . And now, my dear Alessandro, get me secretly one or two lenses for the tube-spectacles from your master. I want them for my son-in-law Landucci. Galileo has plenty of them; it ought not to be hard to take two or three. Put them in the bottom of a box and fill the box with the aloe pills ordered by Professor Fabrizio. I beg you to do me this favor. Galileo is very ungrateful to his brother-in-law, who has never shown him anything but kindness.

There were a number of similar letters: full of more than servant's gossip and the theft of lenses. Galileo read them with dismay. His mother showed herself as she was. Till now he had always excused, loved, and defended her in his heart. Her wild rages seemed to him only part of her nature. But these letters were inexcusable! So his own mother had even intrigued with his servant against him! There were few men living with so strong a sense of kinship as he, but now he felt that he had lost his mother forever. And suddenly he recoiled from the thought of living at home with her again.

He put the letters carefully away and did not mention them to anyone. But this was the deepest wound he had ever received. And he realized with a painful shock that his second daughter Livia took after her grandmother. While Virginia was sweet and kind, her young sister showed already all her grandmother's traits of greediness, selfishness, and violent rage. Galileo had to work early and late, burdened with a thousand cares, with an emptiness in his heart that nothing could assuage.

Only when the stars came out, did he find solace.

On July 25th he was about to finish his night's labor when he noticed that Saturn's shape was strangely changed. The longer he watched it the more convinced he grew. There could be no doubt: Saturn was no regular sphere. It looked like a sphere surrounded by a well-defined ring, and this ring was emphasized on two sides. But, since it did not seem to be possible that God should have set a ring round the planet, he at once rejected the supposition and tried to decide the real nature of the phenomenon. At last he came to the conclusion that this double emphasis must be caused by two separate stars dependent on the central mother star. Saturn was therefore a triple star.

He was alone in the night with the secret of the new miracle. He kept returning to his telescope, thrusting aside the Regiomontanus tablets. He buried his bearded face in his hands, and thought. Another wonder which his eyes were the first to behold. And what a strange, monstrous miracle—a triple star! What was the source of this relationship? How did these three stars keep on their course?

He told nobody what he had seen. He watched Saturn for five more nights, then wrote to Vinta that henceforth he belonged body and soul to the Medicis.

My eyes have seen another world, and I desire that Their Highnesses and Your Excellency should have knowledge of it. But I beg that it may be kept a secret until I have published my new book. But I longed to report my discovery to Their Highnesses. Thus it is I have seen that Saturn is no solitary star, but a group of three stars. These three are apparently welded, their positions never change, but remain on a parallel axis with the longitude of the Zodiac. The central star is about three times as large as the two others, as I intend to demonstrate in the autumn, when Their Highnesses will be better able to observe the motion of the planets above the horizon.

But the thought that someone else might notice the peculiarity of Saturn gave him no rest. Anyone could prepare a telescope now. All over Europe they were being turned upon the sky. There was an actual danger that someone would publish a sensational book about Saturn. How should he secure for himself the priority of this discovery without having to publish in a hurry? Finally he thought of a way. He set down the fact of his discovery in four Latin words, the letters of which he jumbled together. It resulted in the following cryptogram:

SMAISMRMILMEPOETALEVMIPVEMVGTTAVIRAS

This he sent to all whom he had chosen as witnesses in case he needed to prove his right—to Castelli, to a painter named Cigoli, to Clavius and another German priest in Rome, called Grienberger, with whom he had corresponded on astronomical problems, and in the first place to Giuliano de' Medici. Giuliano, who held a post at the Prague Court, at once passed on the riddle to Kepler.

It caused great excitement. All the recipients tried to solve the strange jumble of letters which Galileo told them contained the secret of his new discovery. Kepler was the only man who made any sense of them. He suspected that Galileo had discovered something about Mars, and took this as the basis of his solution, although one letter he could not place:

Salve umbistineum geminatum Martia proles.

But even this had very little sense, as Kepler himself admitted. He wrote to Galileo, imploring him to solve the riddle. But Kepler also had by now observed the moons of Jupiter. Up to now he had merely believed the *Sidereus Nuncius,* for he only had a faulty telescope, and could not clearly distinguish them. At last he had obtained a better one. Galileo was told that when Kepler saw the four Medici stars, he had cried like Julian the Apostate: "Vicisti, Galilei!"

But the victor did not tell him the new secret. This new discovery was his. Let whoever would, observe Saturn; it would be easy to prove his priority by the correct arrangement of the thirty-seven letters. He continued his work. In August he went to Venice and visited his old friends Fra Paolo, Magagnati, Zorzi, Boccalini, to say good-by. Then he returned to Padua. He had to make a number of formal visits. Fortunately most of the notables had left town. But he found Cremonini.

"I wish you all good fortune, Galileo. You know I have always been your friend."

"And I yours, Cesare. I know. But now for the last time I beg you to let yourself be convinced. Come to my house, let me show you everything. You'll see that till now you've been mistaken, and that the gates of a new astronomy have been flung open to mankind. You're a gifted man, and know so much! You too can enter by these gates and be useful to learning!"

"No! No! I'm not coming with you. You're only confusing me. I've just begun to write a book against you. Of course, not against you personally, but against your teachings. I mean to write a book on the moon, in defense of the classic teaching of Aristotle, the only true one."

"Write whatever you like; only come with me and use your eyes."

"No; I won't look into that tube. It can't be as you say."

They had a long argument, till finally Cremonini burst out:

"Listen, Galileo! The science of the world was built on the pillars of Aristotelian wisdom. For two thousand years men have lived and died in the belief that the earth is the center of the universe and man the lord of it. So that we, whom God has formed in His own image, are only lower than Him. After Aristotle, Our Lord Jesus Christ descended upon earth and saved us, giving us His wonderful gift, Christianity. This Christianity has perfected Aristotle, spiritualized him, made his teachings Christian knowledge. All that we know today, from logic to medicine, from botany to astronomy, is Christian and Aristotelian. A glorious structure of the human mind, every stone of which fits perfectly into the others. The greatest minds for two thousand years have worked on it, till they have made it a perfect and splendid whole. My life has been spent in the service and admiration of this structure. Learning and teaching have both brought me peace and happiness. Now I'm an old man with little time left. Tell me, why are you so cruel as to want to shake my belief in all that I love? Why do you want to poison my few last years with doubt and conflict? Don't hurt me! Leave me my peace of mind! I refuse to look into that tube!"

"But the truth, Cesare! The truth! Doesn't that mean anything?"

The trembling, fearful Cremonini still kept him off.

"No, I need my peace and happiness!"

"I understand. How strange! To me peace and happiness have always meant one thing: to seek truth and admit what I found. I suppose that really the whole world consists of us two, Cesare. Of Cremoninis and

Galileis. You keep the world back, we urge it onward. You're afraid to look at the sky because you may see there something which disproves the teaching of your whole life. I understand. Our task is heavy. And unfortunately there are many like you. But it's only we who can triumph."

"And if you do? Even if you manage to prove that our earth is really only a miserable little star like thousands of others? And that mankind is only a multitude of chance creatures on one of these stars? Do you really want to do that? Do you want to abase man, made in God's image? To degrade victorious man, the lord of earth, to a wretched worm? Is that what you and Copernicus and Kepler want? Is that the true purpose of astronomy?"

A long silence.

"I never thought of that," Galileo answered. "I seek for truth only because I'm a mathematician, and I believe that whoever admits truth is nearer to God than those who build up their human dignity on senseless errors. And I shall go on. I must continue my path. God bless you, Cesare."

"God keep you. And I stay where I am."

Those two who saw the world so differently, stood hesitant, unable to take leave; they faced each other, and suddenly embraced.

Next day, Galileo departed. He climbed into the coach with Livia, and was suddenly loath to leave Marina. He sat in such a way that he still could see her to the very last, standing there in the porch waving good-by to him. But it happened otherwise. The coach had not even started when Marina called her last greeting and turned back into the house with little Vincenzo. She did not even look over her shoulder, although she must have known that she would probably never see her daughter again.

X

Livia lodged with the Landuccis, while Galileo accepted the hospitality of Filippo Salviati, a former pupil. Salviati owned a pleasant villa set in a garden on the slopes of Monte Oliveto. It was called the Villa della Salve, and, early on September mornings while the astronomer was noting his observations on Saturn and the moon, the wakening birds chirruped outside as they had in the trees of the garden in Padua. But here even the song of the birds was different.

For the time being the "Court astronomer" had little to do at Court. He had to put in a formal attendance at audiences, which gave him no chance of saying anything. Cosimo informed him graciously that until he had settled into a house, he would not have any Court duties. Nor would his duties in general be very exacting; there was someone else to draw up horoscopes, and he need not trouble himself to attend Pisa University, of which he was an honorary professor. It would be his task to amuse the Court from time to time by his scientific explanations and conversation; he would be asked to give an expert opinion if a scientific problem should arise; but his main duty would be to pursue his investigations and make famous discoveries worthy of Florence and the Medicis.

That was what he himself desired with every fiber of his being. It surprised him to think how much free time he had. There was no need to deliver lectures, teach young noblemen the science of fortification and the use of his compass. At dawn he could sleep as long as he chose. Salviati, the perfect host, never disturbed him. He could have his meals according to his wishes. He took long walks, mostly into the hills, where he could look down over the valley of the Arno and over Florence. He loved the city as though she were a bride with whom he was on honeymoon.

For he was a Florentine—as Fra Paolo was a Venetian! He felt as tender to Florence as to his wife.

He stared at the multitude of domes and wooden roofs as if he would take stock of his own property. These towers and spindle-shaped cypresses were engraved on his heart. He saw them still, even if he closed his eyes. If he selected a point in the maze of the city, he knew all its past. There at the Palazzo Strozzi, a brother of Michelangelo had worked as a clerk. Over those stones, the great genius walked, with the thought of the Pietà in his head and the accursed love of handsome Tommaso Cavalieri in his heart. . . . The dreamy gaze of the astronomer slid over to the Signoria. The feet of Dante and Beatrice had touched the same flags where later the Dominican Savonarola, the fiery preacher, had been burned between his two companions. There beyond was the Santa Maria Meda Hospital, built by Beatrice's father. Here San Lorenzo, where Donatello worked for the great Cosimo; Donatello, who was always untidy and disheveled, who was always being presented with splendid new clothes by his Prince and next day walked about in rags. . . . His glance returned to the Strozzi, built by Benedetto da Maiano, who was not an architect at all, but a wood carver. And Botticelli, the painter of dancing, singing spring; and Leonardo da Vinci; and Arcagno, the grim giant; and all the others who had painted, carved, built, dreamed, and sung this jewel, Florence—served by the gold which streamed here, in exchange for wool and silk from Constantinople and Gallipoli and the Island of Rhodes; gold handled by the powerful bank of the Medici. Gold and genius were welded to create this Florence, and the welding was done by the Medici family.

Every Florentine, thought the astronomer on the hill, is devoted to the Medici from birth. It's like a kind of second religion. It would never be extinguished in him, although by nature he loved freedom. Yet in Venice, in the free republic, he had always somehow felt ill at ease; while here, where people bowed to the glittering Court, he felt safe and happy. But why was this? He knew no answer.

His heart was full of love for young Duke Cosimo. He was full of joy to think that he could serve and extend his fame; this fame should gather like a wave, its waters should break over the world.

The Emperor Rudolph complained bitterly that he could not use the Galileo telescope often enough, because Cardinal Borghese was always snatching it away. The Dowager Queen of France, Maria de' Medici, whose husband had been murdered last spring, had lain down in her widow's weeds on the floor to get a better sight of the moon. News came from all over Europe of the interest aroused by this invention, and of the stir caused in the world of science by his incredible *Sidereus Nuncius*.

Galileo considered it below his dignity to notice Horky's wretched screed, and allowed two of his pupils to answer it.

But there was someone else nearer home who could not be so easily settled: a Florentine nobleman called Francesco Sizzi. He had written a book attacking the *Sidereus Nuncius*. The dedication showed what had inspired it; the author had set Giovanni de' Medici's name on the title page. The same Giovanni de' Medici whose dredger had failed so ignominiously at Leghorn. He was seldom to be seen at Court, and Galileo had never met him since. Now he returned from the past with his old hatred, and used this Sizzi, a mere political adventurer, to take his revenge on Galileo. And it was quite an adroit attack, because even if the arguments were childish, the conclusions to which they led were dangerous.

The pamphlet mentioned seven different reasons why the four moons of Jupiter could not exist. First: astronomers had always maintained that there are seven planets and no more. Second: seven is a perfect number because the week, *set by God,* has seven days. Third: objects have four physical qualities: cold, originating in Saturn, dryness in Mars, heat in Jupiter, and humidity in Venus; while the other three planets regulate these qualities according to the horoscopes—which shows that more than seven planets are unnecessary. Fourth: the possibility of new planets is contrary to the astrological principle of the Spheres of Planets. Fifth: there are seven metals corresponding to the seven planets; there cannot be more. Sixth: the sages of the Old Testament knew of seven planets; this is shown by the seven forks of the Jewish candlesticks. And seventh: Giovanni Pico della Mirandola has proved in his work *Heptapolo* that Holy Writ knows only seven planets; therefore Galilei's alleged four new planets are contrary to the Scripture itself.

Galileo did not think that this book—which bore the title *Dianoia*—was of any importance; he only noted that he must beware of Giovanni de' Medici, the Prince's kinsman, whose hate was still alive. And at present something else engaged his attention. In his latest book Kepler had declared he had solved his cryptogram. Galileo decided to publish the right answer. He sent it to all those to whom he had submitted the jumble of letters:

Altissimum Planetam tergeminum observavi.

"I observed that the highest planet was a triplet." Kepler wrote to him at once. He himself had been observing Saturn after he had got Galileo's solution of the riddle, and he accepted Galileo's theory in everything. He only contended that the axis of Saturn was parallel with the axis of the equinox and not with the Zodiac's longitude. The others also answered, all of them amazed at the miracle. Father Clavius offered himself as a witness.

Galileo worked on, proud and happy, and found a new wonder; but this time something which meant the fulfillment of his dreams—he found proof.

It was given by Venus, the evening star. One night he noticed that the edge of the circular orbit of Venus began to darken. Next day this darkness increased. In a few days Venus had dimmed to a sickle shape which could be seen on the moon by the naked eye. And one night Galileo sprang to his feet with a great shout of joy. He took his candle and roused Salviati.

"Are there thieves in the house?" asked Salviati anxiously, rubbing his sleepy eyes.

"No thieves, Filippo, but a great joy. I've just made an amazing discovery. But first you'd better wake up." It was a freezing December night. The cold soon roused Salviati, who sat up in bed. Galileo sat on the bed beside him, and began talking about astronomy. "If I see a sickle-shaped shadow on a sphere, what body can throw it there? Only a sphere." There were fine winter apples on the table near Salviati's bed. Galileo took two of them and showed him on the coverlet how one sphere would cast its shadow on the other when it was moving. He talked of the difference between the inborn light of heavenly bodies and the light they receive from the sun. He had observed that Venus drew her light from the sun, while the planets had their own source of light. It was apparent that Venus moved around the sun, not around the earth. So Venus was one of the sun's moons! And so was the earth! Anyone who couldn't see that was either a fool or refused to see! Here was proof of the whole Copernican hypothesis. Copernicus had become reality!

The new world was born in Florence in a room in the Villa della Salve, early on a cold December morning.

"Yes," mumbled Salviati, who by this time was sleepy again.

Next day Galileo wrote a long letter to Clavius, to the headquarters of the Jesuits at Rome. He had been invited to dine at Court, and decided to announce his discovery.

"Your Excellency can voyage over the heavens," the Dowager Duchess Cristina observed, "like a new Columbus."

"And I have just as much trouble with skeptics as ever Columbus had, Your Highness. He decided that, since the earth was spherical, which nobody believed at that time, he would start for the Indies by sailing west, instead of east. He found a high protector for the plan in the person of Isabella, Queen of Spain. . . ."

"Take care," Cosimo gaily interrupted. "Columbus was sent by my wife's great-great-grandfather on his expedition."

"I too am sent by a great prince to explore the moon and Saturn. But, to continue, the plan of Columbus was examined by experts. They demanded proof that the earth was spherical and accused him of heresy. But later he managed to set out. *I* am in the same position. I have discovered the Medici stars, and this Sizzi accuses me of contradicting Holy Writ."

"His book is quite ridiculous," old Vinta remarked. "But a reference to the Bible is always effective. You must know that Archbishop Marcimedici is abusing you everywhere."

Galilei knew the Archbishop and disliked him heartily. Marcimedici had been his pupil at Padua and was a stupid and pompous man. But after dinner the Prince took Galileo aside.

"Listen, Messer Galileo," he said seriously. "It is a bad thing to antagonize priests. Now, you're the official Court mathematician. The Court is more or less responsible for anything you may say in your books, and it won't be pleasant if they assert that you are contradicting Holy Writ. I advise you to do something about it. The Archbishop is already your enemy."

"Your Highness, the Archbishop is everyone's enemy."

"I dislike him also. But he *is* the Archbishop. I won't fight the clergy. I don't imitate Venice. I'm on excellent diplomatic footing with the Holy See—for a hundred reasons."

"I'm at your command, Your Highness. What shall I do?"

"Do you know any powerful priests in Rome?"

"Of course, Your Highness. Cardinal Del Monte would do anything for me, if for no other reason than out of the reverence he feels for the late

Marchese. But I also have a very good Jesuit friend, the renowned Clavius."

"Excellent. I advise you to go to Rome and clear up the matter there. There are some very sensible men in the Vatican. If you can explain the *Sidereus Nuncius* to them, the priests here can talk till they're blue in the face. But if the Vatican dislikes it, you'd better stop the whole thing, before the Inquisition takes up the matter. Go to Rome. I'll supply you with a litter and servants. You can stay at the Legation in Rome. But you must settle this! You know, those stars are Medici stars. It would be most unpleasant for me, personally, if the Church were to put them on the Index or do something equally serious."

"Your Highness is so wise that I must bow to your judgment. When shall I go?"

"There's no hurry. The Court is moving to Pisa for Easter; that would be the best time. And I hope you return successfully."

Galileo felt an overwhelming happiness. He thought that this ugly, pleasant young man with the big nose had exceptional brains. In Florence they said that all the Medicis were near-sighted, gouty, and clever.

He began to prepare his trip. He collected some letters of introduction, among them one from Michelangelo Buonarroti, nephew of his great namesake whom he had known since his childhood, and who had important friends in Rome. He also announced his arrival to Clavius, mentioning the German priest Grienberger, who had recently become famous, and who lived in Rome as Clavius' pupil.

During his preparations he received a letter from Sagredo. His friend had returned from Asia to Venice and had found out that Galileo had left Padua for good. He wrote a long and rather reproachful letter.

Galileo began to read it with all the love of an old friend, but soon he threw it angrily aside.

"I know that he loves me," he told himself, "but why spoil my joy?"

And that whole day he was in a very bad temper.

XI

He would have started for Rome in January, since the Court spent the second half of the winter at Pisa. But his old ailment returned and kept him indoors. He had his bed drawn up to the window and spent the painful hours of the night with the telescope in his sound hand, watching the sky. He could not see through the leaded panes, so he had to keep the windows open. But he could not brave the cold for long, and must needs keep closing them again. As soon as he felt a little warmer, the lattice was again thrust open, and so it went the whole night through.

By day he tried to watch the sun. He had noticed for a long time in Padua that even the sun disobeyed Aristotle. If the sky was a little clouded so that his eye could stand the blinding rays for a short time, it seemed to him as if there were spots on the dazzling surface. After many efforts, he discovered that these dim, irregular spots were slowly moving. Therefore some mysterious things must swim on the surface of the sun, or they were stationary and the sun turned round its own axis, like a spun top.

He spent more than two months in great pain, writing letters with his good hand, but mostly thinking. He saw the blue universe in his mind, with the sun in its center and the spheres around him, the planets rushing in their circular orbits, preordained since the days of Creation; some of them surrounded by their own brood; the planes of the individual orbits intersecting at slanting angles, throwing shadows on each other in their alternative passing; while the fixed stars watch like a playgoing audience this hornets' swarming with a mysterious aim; and the millions of stars of the Milky Way stream across the picture in a white flowing veil. In this world there was no up nor down, no day nor night, since the sun shone perpetually, and nothing upheld the stars in the void. What was all this? And what was beyond the farthest stars where purblind Peripatetics wanted to set the limits of eternity?

"How much I have to do! How much!" he sighed, and did his best to think of himself clearly as a tiny being on one of the stars of the Copernican system, on one of its continents, in a certain room of a certain city's certain villa, while the whole universe was buzzing, circling and flying in the microcosm of his brain.

He recovered by March, so that he could set out on his journey. He packed his scientific arsenal: the best of his telescopes and his diary about the planets. He continued his observations on the way; not a single day was lost. He noted down every night the exact position of the Jupiter moons, except when the sky was overcast. By day he recalled the memories of his youthful trip when he had walked on this same highroad, sometimes begging for a lift. Now a ducal litter bore him to Rome.

He arrived on a beautiful spring day at the legation. Niccolini, the Tuscan Ambassador to the Holy See, had been notified of his impending arrival; he took from Galileo the Prince's personal letter. Then he conducted him to his suite with elaborate, rather frigid, courtesy. He lived in the city in order to be near the Papal residence, although the beautiful Medici villa, which the dynasty had bought a few years previously, stood uninhabited on the Pincio. Galileo had secretly hoped that he could stay there, but the Ambassador was so formal and stiff that he did not dare to ask him this favor.

He hastened to unpack. Then, carrying a telescope, he set out for the Jesuit College. He had some difficulty in finding it; almost twenty-five years had passed since he had last walked the streets of Rome. Instead of the virile, sturdy monk, he met now a toothless, bent, fragile old man whom he scarcely recognized. They embraced warmly, then Father Clavius presented the young Jesuit who was in his room.

"This is Father Grienberger, whom you know by letters. I hope you'll be good friends."

They spoke Latin, because Father Grienberger knew no Italian. He was a red-haired, gaunt Jesuit, a German from the Tyrol with a kind and good-humored face. In a few minutes they had started their work. The Jesuit College had an excellently equipped observatory with specially built windows, textbooks, and all the instruments known to astronomers. But Galileo had brought his telescope! For hours they watched all that had been described in his *Sidereus Nuncius,* and he himself added a wealth of details.

"Now tell me, my son, what has really brought you to Rome?"

"I have two reasons for my visit. The first is to find somebody of clerical authority who will examine my *Sidereus Nuncius,* endorse its statements, and verify the Medici stars. But I have another, more distant, aim. First I must tell you that an excellent pupil of mine, Castelli, has just been appointed to the chair of astronomy at Pisa. Castelli, of course, being my pupil, believes in Copernicus. Now, at Pisa everything is settled by the Chief Curator, Count d'Elzi. He is a stubborn Peripatetic. Before Castelli could get the appointment he had to promise to teach astronomy by the Almagest, and never according to Copernicus. Poor boy, he could only accept. And I myself would like to proclaim my faith in the Copernican system publicly. But this is a dangerous and decisive step. I must be careful. A man called Sizzi already accuses me of contradicting Holy Writ."

Clavius nodded. Then he said:

"Your plan is excellent. Sizzi is an ass; we have laughed at his ridiculous arguments. But I don't believe your Copernicus, my son."

"I'm always willing to argue, Father," Galileo smiled. "But first I must declare my convictions. For the present then, let us keep to the *Sidereus Nuncius*. Do you think such a clerical committee of investigation could be organized?"

"Of course, if you have the necessary influence. Have you?"

"As much as I need. With the Pope himself."

"Excellent." The old Jesuit rose. "The Pope is all-powerful, even in science. . . . But I'd advise you not to mention Fra Paolo Sarpi. I hear you were his close friend in Venice. And don't speak of your domestic affairs to His Holiness. . . . Come back and see me tomorrow morning; I'll introduce you to several mathematicians of our Order. Good night."

Old Clavius had lost his former zest—this was Galileo's first thought. He reflected on the Jesuit's attitude, and saw why he disliked Fra Sarpi. Fra Paolo had persuaded Venice still to keep the Jesuits out of the Most Serene Republic.

Next day he began his rounds. His first visit was to Cardinal Del Monte. This delicate-looking old man bore a striking resemblance to the unforgettable Marchese Guidubaldo, and was delighted to see Galileo. He said at once: "You must go to Bellarmin. He is the only one to do it. And he's a Jesuit." He smiled and added, "Haven't you brought a letter of recommendation from Fra Sarpi? There! There! You mustn't take me seriously. Let's hope that Bellarmin won't turn against you because you were friends with that wicked monk."

"Excuse me," Galileo asked, "but am I famous here in Rome as a dangerous enemy of the Church?"

"Well, Sarpi's friendship isn't precisely a recommendation. And everyone knows everything here in Rome."

"Even about me? In Rome? Am I such an important man?"

"Of course you are. You probably don't know how famous you are. For days I have heard nothing but 'Galileo is coming'. . . . If you need me, I'll take you to Bellarmin myself."

On this they parted. Galileo continued his visits in his litter. He had letters of introduction to other priests and had to visit the Jesuits again. One acquaintance brought him several others. He was surprised how well they knew him everywhere. Some people received him with enthusiasm, others with unfeigned dislike; but none were indifferent. He saw the Jesuits practically every day, got acquainted with the whole college, spending many hours among them, arguing and explaining, during their walks in the garden. And then the day came when he was received by Cardinal Bellarmin, the man whom Sarpi had described as a great intellect and a serious opponent. He was prepared to hear the famous Cardinal mention Fra Paolo at once. He had his answer ready; he had already told everyone how saintly Fra Paolo was and what a great Venetian patriot; let his actions be judged by these two qualities.

But Cardinal Bellarmin did not mention Fra Paolo at all. He was a dignified man of seventy, with a strong nose and a long mustache merging into his beard; the strange thing in his face were his eyebrows, which showed a downward slant from the bridge of the nose. He extended his hand graciously to be kissed, asked Galileo to be seated, and came instantly to the point. Galileo stated his request for an ecclesiastical commission appointed to examine the statements of his *Sidereus Nuncius*. It would be his greatest happiness if the Cardinal consented to be its president.

"I cannot undertake it in such a form," Bellarmin answered in a strong, incisive voice. "But we'll find someone else for it. I have read your work, and it moved me greatly. It would be desirable to see with my own eyes what this book supposes."

Galileo offered at once to demonstrate his invention any night. But the Cardinal was suspicious, and wanted to conduct his investigations alone. It would be best if he could use the telescope in the Jesuit College. Then he would send word to Messer Galileo about his decision.

"One of my *cannocchiali*, Monsignor, is always there at your disposal. I have brought several with me. Please use it whenever you so desire."

"Good. You must believe that I wish you well."

And again Galileo kissed this hand which had probably counted out the money for the hire of those Venetian assassins. His litter took him next to a great lord, the Duke Cesi. Cesi was young and very rich, deeply interested in science and poetry. A few years ago he had founded an academy in Rome which bore the name of "Lincei." The "Lynxes" had come together to discover new truth with their lynx-eyes, and fight against the torpidness of science. The Duke sent word that he wanted to visit Galileo, but the mathematician hastened to anticipate him. The young Duke, well-mannered and splendidly dressed, begged him at once to join the academy. Galileo could scarcely believe his ears.

"I see that you're surprised," said Cesi. "You must know that your name would be an asset to any academy in the world."

"Your Grace does me excessive honor. May I ask if you have read my book?"

"The *Sidereus Nuncius?* Naturally! And how I have fought on its behalf! It's amazing how stubbornly blind people are to the truth. But that's why we Lynxes are here. And so you accept my invitation? Thank you. But now let me show you my poor villa. I've a few interesting pictures, statues, and books. And my wife will be delighted to see you."

Galileo was soon sated with pictures, statues, and books. Cardinals and high Church dignitaries all insisted on showing him their collections. At first he rejoiced in so much beauty, but soon its prodigality wearied him. He had many engagements; Duke Cesi held a banquet in his honor at which he met so many people that he could not even keep track of their names.

But his business progressed. The Jesuits told him that Cardinal Bellarmin had visited them, had examined the heavens for a long time through the telescope, and so expressed his complete approval of what he had seen. To fulfill Galileo's request he had written to the Jesuit College asking them to submit an expert opinion on the five different statements of the *Nuncius*. A committee of four was to be appointed. It would be composed of the Germans, Clavius and Grienberger; the Belgian, Maelcot; and the Italian, Lembo. The Reverend Fathers fixed April 24th for their meeting. Galileo decided to take a rest. But almost immediately he was notified that the Holy Father would receive him.

He hardly expected it any longer, when suddenly a Swiss halberdier appeared at his lodging with a document which called him that same morning to the Vatican. He dressed very carefully, donning his doublet of black velvet, a snow-white cambric collar, and plumed hat. He kept tidying and brushing himself even in the litter. He arrived half an hour before his appointment. A young chamberlain received him and explained how he would have to behave: he must kneel and kiss the Pope's holy slipper, then await his questions kneeling till he was bidden to rise.

"Who is with His Holiness now?" he asked.

"His nephew, Scipione Caffarelli, the Secretary of State."

In the meantime a young man had come swaggering into the anteroom in magnificent clothes. He crossed the room with tripping steps, scarcely even nodding to the chamberlain, and went straight into the Pope's audience chamber.

"Who was that young gentleman?"

"His Excellence Borghese, General of the Papal Army. Another nephew of His Holiness."

"I see. And how old is the general?"

"Nineteen."

Galileo said nothing. After a long wait, well past the appointed hour, the two nephews returned, and he was told to enter. He hurried over to the figure in the middle of the room, knelt before it, and touched with his lips the white slipper encrusted with diamonds. He straightened his body; the Pope motioned him to his feet.

"I am glad to meet the renowned Galileo."

Galileo faced the Vicar of Christ. A portly man of sixty-odd, strong and majestic-looking. He wore a clipped square beard and a sparse mustache on his broad, round face. A very straight nose, a sweetish, almost sycophantic, smile. But his red, thick lips, which he kept on wetting with his tongue, were his most characteristic features. This was the man who had had an innocent dilettante writer beheaded for comparing a Pope to a Roman Emperor.

"My humblest thanks to Your Holiness for the signal favor of this audience."

"And how are your affairs in Rome progressing? Cardinal Bellarmin has told Us about it."

"The Commission meets the day after tomorrow, Your Holiness. I sincerely hope that the Fathers will support my views."

"Bellarmin says that your statements seem to be true. It is very commendable in you to try to obey the authority of the Church. So long as you remain Our faithful son you can always expect Our personal support in your researches."

Galileo bowed gratefully.

"Have you any favor to ask, Messer Galilei?"

"I would like to carry the blessing of Your Holiness to my master, Cosimo II."

"We gladly bless him, Our specially favored son. And we bless you, too."

Galileo hastily knelt again. Pope Paul made the sign of the cross over his head, and once again he kissed the glittering slipper. That finished the audience.

He was overjoyed. Now the world could say whatever it liked about the *Sidereus Nuncius* and the Medici stars.

The Commission's opinion was also favorable, apart from one minor objection. Galileo received a copy of the document addressed to Cardinal Bellarmin. These priests had found everything in the sky exactly as the Florentine scientist maintained. Only the moon caused some difference of opinion. "The great unevenness of the moon's surface cannot be denied; but Father Clavius thinks that it is not because the surface is uneven, but because the substance of the moon is not of equal thickness everywhere; this is the cause of the shadow we have already mentioned. Others consider the surface as uneven, but we have no certainty in this matter."

So Father Clavius still clung to Aristotle, who asserted that each star was a perfect sphere. Galileo, when he thanked them for their endorsement, approached this question.

"Father, I speak to a mathematician. Why do you confuse mathematics with metaphysics?"

"How do you mean?"

"There are no 'perfect' and 'imperfect' shapes. Shapes have no hierarchy. The most irregular piece of rock is a geometrical formation just like a sphere."

"Yes, yes, but what does that go to prove?"

"That the secret and beauty of creation is not to be looked for in its symmetry. Even if the moon's surface is rugged, God's marvelous universe will not be less wonderful. On the contrary."

"Why on the contrary?"

"Because, if this mystical game with spheres and horoscopes fails, I can replace it with a finer system. God's universe, as Copernicus sees it, is much clearer, finer, and more unified than Aristotle's. Only truth can be beautiful. Further, if you start to explain a phenomenon you can set about it in two ways. Either you begin with a preconception and twist and turn the connection of phenomena till you can force it into some Aristotelian role. Do I see the moon's surface as rugged? Impossible! Aristotle has told me that it is smooth. How, therefore, can I find some method by which Aristotle can still be right and yet I am still permitted to use my eyes? Let us say then that this smooth sphere is of equal thickness. That is one way. But there is another: to forget all one has learned and taught, and accept only the teaching of one's own eyes. Let them explain! If the sensible and natural explanation ends by overthrowing Aristotle, let him look to himself!"

The old Jesuit listened very carefully. He shook his head.

"I must think that over."

"Think, Father!" said Galileo warmly. "And please don't forget one thing. All matter strives to become spherical—naturally, since every community strives to group itself around the same center. But there is no perfect sphere, since a thousand components are always impeding the perfect grouping of the units. Aristotle's cosmical sphere is unreal and untrue. The world I mean to proclaim is life and reality."

Clavius frowned and remained silent. He did not seem to like what he had heard.

When Galileo returned to Florence, he entered like a triumphant soldier. He brought his prince the Papal blessing, and could show him a document which justified the Medici stars and his other discoveries. He also gave Cosimo a letter written by Cardinal Del Monte. Cosimo read it and gave it back with a smile. The kind Cardinal could find no words to praise the Court astronomer's Roman success.

"Were we living in ancient Rome," he wrote, "Galileo would have been certain of a statue in his honor on the Capitol."

Galileo went to visit his daughters. When he reached the Landucci house his mother was in the midst of one of her bad spells. She was screaming and slamming the doors again. The neighbors gathered to watch the sport. Galileo stopped and turned away. But at the convent, he heard quite different sounds. Someone inside was playing an aria from Monteverdi's new opera, and playing it excellently. He stood listening by the open window, enjoying the music. Who could it be?

He did not know that the nuns had such a skillful lute player. When she had finished, he entered the nunnery. He asked the sister at the gate:

"Which of your nuns plays the lute so wonderfully?"

"She isn't a nun. It's your own Virginia! I can't tell you how much she delights us all. She teaches all the others music."

Galileo hastened to the parlor to await Virginia. He embraced his daughter with delight.

"When did you learn to play the lute so well?"

"I practiced hard while you were in Rome."

"But really you have an unusual gift."

He turned her sweet, ugly little face toward him and looked into her eyes. There was gentle light in them.

"Can you give me any news of your mother?"

"No, sir. She never writes."

XII

Cosimo had interesting guests in September: two Cardinals passed through Florence and stayed with him for a considerable time at the new Palazzo Imperiale. One of them was Cardinal Gonzaga, a member of the Lombard ducal family; the other Maffeo Barberini, son of the rich Florentine merchant. Cosimo warned Galileo to prepare himself carefully for these dignitaries. Cardinal Gonzaga was a great patron of the sciences. Barberini was the author of classical poems.

Cardinal Gonzaga was an insignificant-looking man, while the other Cardinal was a tall, strong man with a queer thin voice. Barberini began by saying that they knew each other already.

"Where have we met, Monsignor?" Galileo asked, surprised.

"Why, here, in Florence. Aren't you the son of Galilei, the draper who plays the lute?"

"He played it once, Monsignor. He's been dead a long time. Yes, I'm his son."

"I'd have known you anywhere. I knew you as a little boy when you'd just come home from Vallombrosa. I was two years younger, and rather envied you because the other boys told me that you were the strongest. You once gave my brother Carlo a terrible hiding."

"Yes, I'm beginning to remember."

"You see, Messer Galileo, we did get acquainted. But now we won't fight. Or only with spiritual weapons."

"I hear that you've been in Rome and were much acclaimed," interposed Gonzaga.

"Monsignor, such things are mere vanity. My favorite poet, Berni, says . . ."

"You like Berni?" Barberini interrupted eagerly. "And know him? I'm glad. A very amusing poet. And a daring one."

The Cardinal glanced around with a mischievous smile. The Grand Duke was talking to Vinta, his wife to the Dowager Duchess.

"I hope His Highness won't hear it. Do you remember the poem, Messer, which he wrote against Pope Clement?"

"Oh, yes, I know it by heart.

> *And what did God do, Clement, making thee*
> *His purblind regent of the Holy See?*
> *Poor silly man, whose wits are all astray,*
> *Whose short-lived reason could not reign one day."*

"I find that a little too strong," Gonzaga said in a disapproving tone.

"I crave your pardon, Monsignor," Galileo replied at once. "I withdraw the quotation."

But Barberini was still laughing.

Now the lackeys opened the doors; the Master of Ceremonies led them into the dining hall. As soon as they were seated, the Prince turned to his mathematician:

"Well, let us hear. Tell us all about Rome."

Galileo nodded. He was used to sitting hungry at Court feasts, because he was always expected to talk. He was invited to amuse the great, and was paid for that. He spoke vividly and amusingly about Rome, taking good care to hurt nobody's feelings.

"Tell me," Barberini cut short one of his sentences, "did you find the Roman clergy intelligent?"

"Very intelligent, Monsignor. There are many learned mathematicians."

"Do you mean to tell me that all the priests at Rome have brains?"

"Oh, no, but the average is very high. I only met one stupid priest, a Dutch Jesuit, to whom I talked about ice. Well, he almost made me lose my temper—a very obstinate Peripatetic."

"This is interesting," Gonzaga said, "because I myself believe in Aristotle. And what had you to say about ice?"

"We talked about the fact that cold contracts bodies while heat expands them. I said that water was an exception to this rule, because when it freezes it expands. Ice floats on the surface. Therefore rivers begin to freeze on their surfaces and not in their depths. . . ."

"Forgive me," Gonzaga said; "ice floats on the water because it is broad, not because it is lighter. Aristotle explained that objects swimming in water remain on the surface according to their size and not their weight. A broad iron kettle doesn't sink, although it's heavier than water."

"They don't sink according to their weight, Monsignor, but according to their specific gravity."

"Specific gravity? Every species has some gravity. The bigger object is heavier, the smaller lighter."

"I don't call that specific gravity, Monsignor. But the weight which a cubic inch of the object represents."

"Well, and does a cubic inch of an iron kettle weigh less?"

"Yes, if it floats on the water. I'll explain why. If I add to the iron kettle the air, the vacuum which is in it, then, not the iron material but the kettle, has a smaller specific gravity than water. Therefore it doesn't sink."

"I am saying the same thing," said Gonzaga loftily. "This business of specific gravity, or whatever it is, originates in the shape of the kettle. Therefore Aristotle is right."

"But he isn't, Monsignor, because if I fill the iron kettle with water, it sinks. And yet its shape is unchanged; therefore, according to the Peripatetics, it ought to float. But, according to my physics, its specific gravity has changed: it has become more than the specific gravity of water; therefore it must sink."

This led him into a long dispute.

Galileo said something to the effect that in calculating the weight of an empty iron kettle, the air which is in it has to be taken into consideration.

"What?" Cardinal Gonzaga was startled. "Has air any weight? I've never read about it."

"Nor have I, Monsignor, but I found it out by my brains and proclaim it. Air has a weight. So small that we cannot measure it, but it has. Why does smoke go upward? Probably for the same reason as the bubbles of air do in water. It's lighter than air. The specific gravity of air is smaller than that of water, but the specific gravity of smoke is smaller than that of air. Yes, Monsignor, air has some weight."

Cardinal Gonzaga smiled politely.

"I think we can close this extremely enjoyable and instructive discussion before we begin to enter the country of fantasy. It's absurd to say that air, which is nothing, can weigh anything. Anyhow, we owe great gratitude to His Highness for giving us such an interesting evening."

"I am delighted," answered the Grand Duke, "that my guests were amused. But what Messer Galileo told us of the specific gravity of ice, I too find completely new and fascinating. We want you, Messer Galileo, to write a book about all you have explained here. We expect your report on that and express our due respect for your intellect."

The meal came to an end, and they went into another room where Cardinal Barberini sat down at Galileo's side. It was plain how much he liked this mathematician. He asked about his other work, whereupon Galileo produced a telescope. They went out into the *loggia* and looked at the sky—in the first place at the Medici stars. The Prince proudly informed the Cardinal that a Church council had endorsed them, because Messer Galileo had demanded the consent and approval of the Church in support of his marvelous new theories. Cardinal Barberini patted Galileo's shoulder.

"*Macte, puer,* as they say in Latin. Go on. You can always be sure of my support."

When they parted, he again stressed his good will.

Galileo went home with the feeling that he had won a most important protector in the Cardinal. He decided to visit him again, but illness prevented him. His joints began to ache. The doctor could do nothing to ease his suffering, and the sick man glared at him with angry scorn. His dislike of medicine, conceived during his years at Pisa, was still alive. He despised doctors, who knew no more than any herb-gathering village wife; at the best they were only skilled leeches. He thought of his father and wished that he were still alive to see how wrong he had been in wanting to make him one.

On his sick-bed, he began to discover that all this glory had its drawbacks. If he had believed that he had warded off every attack by winning the approval of the Church, he was finding now that the calm after Sizzi's book was only temporary. New attacks followed each other.

The first warning came from Cigoli, his friend in Rome. And strangely enough Cigoli told him about events which were happening a few yards from his lodgings in Florence, at the palace of Archbishop Marcimedici. The Archbishop had probably brought from Padua a strong dislike of Galileo and was working against him. He seized on a rather spiteful sentence in Sizzi's half-forgotten book which stated that Galileo's teachings were in contradiction to Holy Writ, quoting it again and again among his priests, advising them that someone should preach against Galileo, even

—as Cigoli discovered in Rome—commanding one of them to do so. But they would not accept the task. Even so, sooner or later a sermon was imminent.

Then new troubles came. When at last he recovered, he hastened to write the book suggested by Cosimo. As soon as he had finished it, he took it to the printers and hurried with the first copy to the palace. But now the Grand Duke had fallen ill. And his illness was a rather serious one, of which the doctors could make nothing. He lay in high fever, complained of nausea and headaches, though his "leech" could find no organic trouble. His lungs, heart, liver, and kidneys were all sound, yet he got no better, and always had a relapse after periods of comparative well-being.

Galileo began to feel very anxious. He remembered Sagredo and all that he had written about Court life. Now that the Prince had fallen ill, he suddenly began to feel afraid that his future work might not be appreciated. He valued praise above all else, although he denied this to himself. It was base vanity, no doubt—but he could not change himself.

He was very much pleased with this new book. He knew that it was completely original. He cleverly connected his subject with his own physical idea, *momentum*. His statements were clear, simple, and convincing; he simplified the problem of objects immersed in water and identified it with the problem of heat. He formulated the question of balance and explained that the object immersed in water and the supplanted water were related, exactly like the two pans of a balance. It rejoiced him to think how Cosimo would relish this observation, especially when he realized its importance to the whole future of mechanics. But instead of the ducal praise came a new sharp attack. An anonymous author. *Views of an Unknown Academician*—such was the title of the book which was dedicated to the Grand Duchess Maria Magdalena.

Next day he knew who had written it: Count D'Elzi, Governor of Pisa University, a rigid academic mind. This man, his personal enemy, could not forget that someone over whom he had no jurisdiction had entered the scientific life of Tuscany. Galileo read the book. A foolish pamphlet, full of contradictions and obscurities. He decided not to answer, but he asked the Grand Duchess for an audience. He had long to wait, for she spent her days at her husband's bedside. At last she received him, and he at once began to explain the errors of this anonymous opponent. She interrupted him almost immediately in words which showed that she could not understand him in the least—neither his book, the attack dedicated to her, nor his explanations. She assured Galileo of her favor and so dismissed him.

There was no remedy. But now came another attack.

A man called Nozzolini addressed a memorial to the Archbishop, expounding the innumerable errors of Galileo Galilei, Court mathematician, in his attempts to disprove the divine and immortal Aristotle. After him Ludovico della Colombo and Vincenzo di Grazie entered the fray to contest his book on objects floating in water. Galileo lost his patience. He wrote a fulminating answer, published as the work of Castelli—professor at Pisa.

He spent many weeks over it. At first he planned it as a short polemic essay, but he warmed to his subject and enlarged it. Castelli spent most of his free time with his master, and between them they composed the book. But it was Galileo who found all the decisive arguments and annihilated his detractors in crushing sentences. His restless quill could never stop.

Finally it became a treatise of deep thoughts, containing his experiences of life, his opinions on the phenomena of the world.

It is well if Princes can have scientists of different opinions and convictions at their Courts, because thus truth can more easily be found. It is the same when their ministers of state disagree and their subjects are divided by strife and party politics: this makes their property, life, and the commonwealth safe.

Be grateful to the man who relieves you of errors, and do not resent it as if you were roused from an agreeable dream.

It is a waste of time to refute an ignorant man, because you would need thick tomes to point out all his stupidities, and these tomes would be useless to the scientist and only a weariness to the many.

My opponents like to cling to theories of ancient times because they wish their ignorance to be common to all men, just as at the time of a pestilence death is less bitter than it seems in a world of healthy men.

Arguments are only useful if they touch doubtful matters and are based on these matters themselves, but not on the comparison and hair-splitting explanation of texts.

Silence can be the fruit of despair or conviction.

I value more the discovery of a simple truth than a lengthy pondering of the loftiest questions without any concrete result.

All this he needed as consolation. He had rid himself of his warring emotions since his troubles continually increased. Now followed the worst attack of all. Among those with whom he corresponded, he had a special friend and follower, the Mayor of Augsburg. Mark Welser was a highly educated and very courageous man. Their correspondence had lasted a long time, and Welser had always agreed with his discoveries. But now he wrote that someone else claimed to have discovered spots on the sun. He wanted to know Galileo's opinion.

Galileo sprang out of his armchair as if he had been stung by a snake. He had already forgotten something very important: he ought to have fixed his discovery and observation of the sunspots. There was no need to publish it prematurely; a jumble of letters containing the observation would have sufficed as in the case of Saturn.

Now someone had robbed him of the glory. This thought enraged him. Welser had enclosed three of the letters he had received from Galileo's rival. The mysterious astronomer signed them with the pseudonym Apelles. The letters gave a precise account of the discovery of the sunspots. They betrayed a highly trained astronomer, although he was a Peripatetic and had an Aristotelian explanation. There was nothing from which a deduction of his person or domicile could have been formed. This increased Galileo's fury since he had to fight an unknown enemy.

He left the letter of the Augsburg Mayor unanswered for a long time. At last he made up his mind. He wrote a long and detailed letter to Welser, telling him that he had seen the spots on the sun, eighteen months ago, and had pointed them out last summer to various priests and laymen in Rome. Then he dealt with the scientific part of the question. He explained that Apelles, who thought the spots due to the planets crossing the sun's orbit, could not be right. He shared the common fault of the Peripatetics: to search for possible and impossible arguments to prove the eternity of the sky, the fixed perfection of the stars. No, not even the sun is perfect. The spots are *on* it, just as the mountains are on the moon. Close observation of the moving spots revealed the miraculous fact that the sun turns around its own axis. This axis is vertical compared to the planes of the ecliptic, and faces always the same point of the universe. It takes the sun about one month to turn round its axis. A day lasts a month on the sun.

Galileo did not know that Welser would hide the light of this long letter, which was a whole astronomical essay, under any bushel. And this letter was an open avowal of Copernicus. He had crossed the Rubicon. Much sooner than he intended, but he had crossed it. His enemies were increasing day by day; one by one the Aristotelians were attacking him. Cosimo was still a sick man on the day when in the Archbishop's palace a whole committee gathered to discuss his affairs. Galileo had only one resource: to ensure swiftly the preliminary approval of the Church or at least find some important ecclesiastic who could be his stay in case of trouble. He tried to find out who was the highest authority on the Bible among the prelates in Rome. Most people said it was Cardinal Conti. He was glad of that because in Rome he had met him often and talked at some length. He wrote a letter to the Cardinal asking him to give his opinion as to whether the teachings of Copernicus were contrary to Holy Writ.

The answer arrived quickly; almost too quickly to be exhaustive and substantial. The Cardinal answered amiably, but too briefly. He explained that the Bible did not favor the theory of the immutable sky; rather it opposed such a conviction; therefore Holy Writ was not Peripatetic. The Fathers of the Church had always considered the heavens as more or less changeable; most of them had deemed it possible that men would discover new stars. In this respect the starting point of Copernicus did not clash with the principles of the Church. As for the movement of the earth, there are two kinds of movement: according to Copernicus the earth turned in the first place around her axis. This did not contradict the Bible. But the theory that the earth moves on a certain orbit around the sun was less feasible. It could be said that God had inspired the Bible for the use of the multitude; therefore He had written it in their language, and certain passages had to be interpreted accordingly. But this was a dangerous argument and only to be used as a last resort. On the other hand, there were doubtless theologians who defended Pythagoras, not Aristotle, and believed that the earth moved round the sun, not vice versa. The Spanish priest, Diego Zuñiga, had written an essay about that part of the Book of Job in which Joshua bade the sun stand still, and this Zuñiga had explained in a way which seemed to favor Copernicus.

It was difficult to draw exact conclusions from this letter. The wily Cardinal said neither yes nor no to the essential question. "Less feasible," he said. "On the other hand," he wrote. Galileo was in exactly the same position as before receiving the Conti letter. One of his attackers had hoped to turn Cardinal Bellarmin against him. They had sent arguments against the Court mathematician. Gallanzoni, the Cardinal's secretary, wrote to Florence asking Galileo to reply. Galileo lost his temper and in his answer called Colombo "a paragon of stupidity."

He felt like a wild boar surrounded by yapping dogs. There were too many of them, and he was alone. The Grand Duke was still an invalid; he could hardly see him. Vinta, his chief patron, was now so old that every complaint only made him nervous. Galileo had no one to whom he could turn. Virginia, whose angelic sweetness dispelled all his cares, he could see only seldom and for a short time. He did not like to visit the Landuccis because there was always a family quarrel there. Then the sad news came that Clavius, the kindhearted German Jesuit who had always been his affectionate friend, had quietly died.

His loneliness made him nervous, defiant. He decided to proclaim his belief in Copernicus whatever the consequences might be. In any case he must claim priority in the discovery of sunspots. He sat down, wrote all he had to say, and settled with Duke Cesi that his book should be published by the Lynxes in Rome. This book was very finely printed by the Academy, and contained his portrait.

When he received it from Rome he could scarcely restrain his joy. He read the well-known lines a hundred times and glanced at his picture again and again. He was very much pleased with his own test. There was no trace of the tone which he had used against Colombo and his other attackers. This unknown Apelles was a superior mind and a trained astronomer, so a different answer was due him. Galileo treated him with marked respect, even apologizing for differing with him. But he stanchly upheld the Copernican theory. Yes, the sun stood in the center, with his radiant body spinning on its own axis; and the planets moved around him like courtiers, among them the insignificant earth.

He felt deep relief. At last he had said all that had been on his mind these past twenty years. He considered the proof which the telescope had given, the newly discovered miracles of Jupiter, the Moon, Venus, Saturn, the Milky Way, and the Sun, decisive enough. They fitted wonderfully into the new system of the universe. It all depended now what the Church would say about his standpoint. He drew up a careful list of those to whom he would send the book. He did not forget a single important ecclesiastic who had shown him any good will while he was in Rome. And he sent the book to Cardinal Barberini.

He kept one copy always with him. When he met an acquaintance, he hastened to display his book and waited with childish joy till they had discovered his portrait. And the person to whom he bragged most about his new work could not even understand it—his son. Vincenzo was now six, and a good friend had brought him to Florence. Marina did not raise any objections. She had sent all the little boy's things to show that there was nothing amiss in her motherly care. But she sent no letter, not even a message. This hurt Galileo. Yet he soon forgot about it. The little boy was put to live at the Landuccis, where his grandmother welcomed him as a new object for her fickle love. A week later she abused him roundly for some mischief, and whipped him so hard that all the neighbors gathered in the street.

Whenever he had a little time, Galileo took his son for a walk. They wandered along the Arno and chattered together. Vincenzo asked so many questions that he couldn't even wait for an answer before putting the next. Galileo happily answered them all. He saw himself again in the child, searching in these wide-awake eyes for his own childhood. But he did not find much of his real self; Vincenzo was like any other intelligent boy of six.

Sometimes his father longed for him to grow up: he would appreciate all his triumphs. The book on the sunspots roused splendid echoes. Aguccia, an important member of the Pope's household, wrote a letter full of the highest praise. Duke Cesi had given him the book. Aguccia said that, though it contained surprising things and was bound to encounter much hostility, sooner or later the whole world would be forced to agree. But Cardinal Maffeo Barberini wrote in an even more flattering strain. He had written an ode to the great scientist:

> *Not all that shines has a shining heart,*
> *Even the sun has his blemishes*
> *Which you alone, O Galileo,*
> *See, with your art.*

Galileo went at once to the ducal palace. He wanted to pour out his happiness to his Prince. But Cosimo was not to be seen. The chamberlain told him:

"His Highness is deeply shaken by this sad news. He can see nobody. He has just returned from the sick-bed."

"But who is sick?"

"You hadn't heard? Vinta, the Prime Minister, is dying."

Galileo hurried away to the Palazzo Vinta, where everybody was walking on tiptoes; but he could not get in. A man to whom he talked in the doorway told him that Vinta's condition was very serious.

"What are the doctors saying? What's his disease?

"They only know that something is the matter with his intestines."

The old Prime Minister had a long fight with death. He was still busy on his deathbed, but Galileo never saw him again. One autumn morning he was informed that Vinta had died during the night.

Cosimo commanded the splendid funeral due the most eminent sons of Tuscany. Vinta was buried in Santa Croce. Two weeks later a requiem was held, celebrated by Archbishop Marcimedici. Galileo, who was present, was deeply shaken to see his Prince the shadow of his former energetic self. Constant low fever had weakened him terribly and set black rings under his eyes. By human reckonings he would not be likely to reign much longer. And what would then become of his mathematician? The Crown Prince, little Fernando, was only three.

After mass, the Archbishop blessed the Prince. As he did so, his eyes met Galileo's. A glint of stubborn hate was in those eyes, a gloomy hate which could not rest for a single second.

XIII

The identity of the mysterious Apelles could not remain a secret for long. Galileo found out that the observer of the sunspots was the German Father Scheiner, professor of astronomy at the university of Ingolstadt, a most worthy scientist. This explained his pseudonym. As a Jesuit he could not publish his book openly, only by permission of his superiors. To get it would have taken him some time, so he had chosen to write to Welser anonymously. According to news from Rome, Galileo learned that Father Scheiner did not truly mind being contradicted. He was a decent man, a serious scientist, who saw the whole thing as a matter of science, which did not exclude his personal esteem for an adversary.

But this was something which only the two opponents knew. Through mysterious channels of international communication within the Church, the identity of Apelles was made known to the Florentine priests. A Jesuit now assailed the Court mathematician whom Sizzi had already accused of contradicting Holy Writ. Galileo felt that the poison was seeping from the Archbishop's court to the minor clergy. Florentine priests who had seemed his friends became cold and formal. This hurt him deeply, since he longed to be friends with other men. But he could not stop every priest in the street and explain that he had no personal quarrel with Scheiner, nor that they kept exchanging the friendliest messages through the Augsburg Mayor. A priest called Lorini preached against the new system and warned his flock against believing in the teachings of "this Ipernicus." The main thing Galileo thought was that the higher authorities would support him. Let simple priests behave as they liked. Cardinal Barberini had written an ode to him; Cardinal Bellarmin had given him a document proclaiming the rightness of his discoveries; the Papal Secretary was one of his warmest supporters; even Pope Paul had assured him of his protection. He decided that after he had proclaimed his faith in Copernicus he would continue to collect his observations, try to find new and fuller arguments, and if he was ready with the material would write a large and detailed work setting forth his own cosmology, which was beyond Copernicus and Kepler, a new Almagest of Florence. It might take two years, it might take twelve. And while he worked at this great book he could always finish the smaller work which in the last years he had neglected.

But his thoughts were on a new track, suggested by a letter from Sagredo, whose sharp and skeptical mind raised an amusing question in connection with the fashion of horoscopes. Some Eastern potentate had ordered a poverty-stricken astronomer in Aleppo to prepare the horoscope of the Grand Mogul Akabar and had given the dates of his birth, but only incompletely. He knew the exact time: a quarter past six in the evening of July 13, 1551, but not the place. The Grand Mogul was born either in Malacca or on the island of Borneo. Sagredo was pondering on the fact that when it was a quarter past six in Malacca, it was a quarter past seven on Borneo. He raised a complicated question about the meridian, and Galileo was glad to play with these fascinating and intricate problems. This led him on to the latitudes and longitudes of the earth. And suddenly an idea sprang into his mind which gave even him a shock of surprise.

"I can give any country I like the mastery of the world," he thought, trembling at the implications of his discovery.

He had been considering the fact that ever since men had sailed the seas, the greatest sailors had been hard put to find their bearings. Ships sailing the open sea out of sight of land, with only the starry sky above, had to trust to luck in determining their exact position. To find latitudes had been easy even for the ancients, but longitude was a different matter. The best they could do was to use the eclipses of the moon in a rough calculation, though even that was not always possible. Now it had occurred to Galileo that the moons of Jupiter could be used. He sat down at once to calculate, and got results which seemed to be right. By such an invention he could give immense power to any nation with a strong navy. In war it meant an invincible advantage; in commercial shipping it meant great wealth.

He stared at his figures and suddenly thought: What would happen now if I had not left Padua? He could have gone to Venice, been received by Antonio Memme, the new Doge; he could probably have named his own price for the discovery. Venice would have made him a leading citizen. But he shook his head, remembering Florence. The thought of Florence warmed his heart. He had never really desired wealth. At last he had managed to pay off his brother-in-law; had sent his money to Bartoluzzi —Marina was probably married by now; he could keep his children and his mother. He had everything for his needs—why struggle for wealth? The most he could do with it would be to leave it to his son and give his daughters a decent dowry—provided they did not become nuns.

Next day he reported at Court, informing the chamberlain that he had extremely important news for the Prince. Cosimo received him the same afternoon.

"I am sorry, Messer Galileo, to welcome you so seldom, but you must know how glad I am to see you."

"That heartens me to continue my work, Your Highness."

"I do hope your work is progressing. Nobody is fit to tie your shoe-strings among those at Pisa. I know them, and they all weary me. Father Boscaglia, professor of physics, favorite of Count d'Elzi, was here last week, and I could hardly listen to him. If I think of the scientific standard of the country, you are the one by whom I judge it."

Galileo gratefully kissed his Prince's hand.

"Well, let's hear your news."

Galileo explained his new discovery; the Grand Duke listened intently and nodded. He seemed to grasp its world-wide importance. Galileo added:

"Of course, I offer this to Florence."

"We shall both profit by it," said Cosimo eagerly. "Both you and I. Tuscany has no navy worth speaking of. We cannot monopolize your invention for the sake of Leghorn. But we'll sell it. That will be my part. It will greatly assist my foreign policy. The state with which I share this knowledge ought to be extremely obliged to me."

"Were you thinking of Venice?" asked Galileo.

"Oh, no, my friend. It's against my interest to serve the Serenissima's navy. We'll offer it to Spain."

This surprised Galileo. Vinta had allied Florence with France instead of Spain. Was the pendulum swinging back again, now the old Prime Minister was dead? Perhaps it was really the Grand Duchess and the Spanish influence of the Hapsburgs.

"Leave the whole thing to me," said the Grand Duke. "Put everything on paper and let me have it. I'll settle it all in the diplomatic way. Let me bargain for you. You'll get the money. I only want the political credit. You mustn't say a word about it—not to anybody. . . . I hope you are well, by the way."

"I can't complain, Your Highness."

"I can well imagine it, especially as there are always complaints against you. I see no sense in telling you about the denunciations. My mother also gets quite a number. They are all alike: abusing you as an enemy of science and religion. Thank God, there are many people who envy you. You needn't trouble about them."

Galileo went home and at once wrote down his theory, by which any ship on the open seas could determine its position by the moons of Jupiter. He put it into a sealed envelope and delivered it to the ducal Court. In a few weeks he was again received by Cosimo, who told him that by a strange coincidence some French scientist had also offered a method of orientation to the Spanish Government, and now they were consulting experts.

After this he got no news for a long time. The Court moved to Pisa but did not invite him, and he fell ill again. His daughters gave him much to do. Cardinal Del Monte could not obtain for him the permission to keep Livia at the same convent with Virginia, so he turned to Cardinal Bandini, who seemed to have a greater influence and took more trouble. After that the permission was soon granted. Virginia had decided to be a nun, and now Livia insisted on following her elder sister's example. They both entered a convent of Poor Clares, where the Abbess happened to be a sister of the late Vinta. This convent was a long way off at the end of the lane of Giullari, which led along broken-down garden walls and through bare vineyards. Galileo took his two daughters in a cart, which kept sticking in the muddy road.

"When shall we be consecrated?" asked Livia.

"I don't know, my child; Suor Ludovica Vinta, the Mother Superior, will tell you that."

"But when Virginia takes the veil I can take it too, can't I?"

"I don't know, Livia. Virginia is thirteen; you're only twelve. But I'll ask the Abbess to let you both take the veil together."

They reached the convent and rang the bell. Galileo had to stay in the parlor. Soon the Mother Superior came, taking stock of the children's clothes, discussing the money which Galileo would have to pay. They would both become nuns at the age of sixteen. Livia began to cry because this meant that Virginia would be a nun a year earlier than she.

"Envy is not becoming in a bride of Christ," her father told her.

"Leave her to us," said Suor Ludovica. "She'll be washed clean of all her sins here. Say good-by to your father, children."

Livia kissed Galileo's hand. She curtsied once, and then seemed to forget all about him. But Virginia clung to him with desperate sobs. She did not cry out, but the tears were streaming down her face. And Galileo suddenly knew that there were also tears in his own eyes. When the children vanished behind the door, he asked to be shown into the church. He took his leave of the Abbess and went in to pray.

"God," his prayer was confused, his heart was full, "I am a sinner, a weak and useless man. I know well that I am also vain, ambitious, too self-assured; I cannot control my nature, eager for the lusts of the flesh. Often I drink more than I ought, and am not ashamed to hunt unworthy amours. But Thou knowest that my soul isn't deeply sinful. I am a child in that half of my heart which I have kept clean, as much as these children whom I have given to Thee. Let them find peace in Thee, even if they are just as useless as I am, because beyond all my faults I humbly believe in Thy Being, believe in Thee through that wonderful world which Thou has created me to explore and discover. Thou seest my heart, God, and knowest how faithfully and fervently I love Thee."

He looked around the tiny church. He was a little calmed. He wiped his eyes and went out to the waiting cart. He glanced back from the slope of the Giullari at the lonely building on the hill and pictured his two daughters arranging their clothes in the cupboard of a bare cell.

Down in the city he went on with his work-a-day life. He had many letters and spent every night watching the sky. He had to find new lodgings, for Salviati was going to Spain. The Prince gave him some temporary quarters in one of the Medici villas fringing the left bank of the Arno. One December day Castelli wrote him an interesting letter which caused him deep thought.

The Court, still at Pisa, had invited one or two scientists of the university to dinner, among them Castelli, the astronomer, and Boscaglia, the physicist. Their talk was of the Medici stars. The Grand Duchess Cristina turned to Boscaglia to ask him, as a confirmed Peripatetic, whether the followers of Aristotle admitted the existence of the new stars. Boscaglia was forced to answer that the Medici stars were really present around Jupiter. Castelli seized the opportunity to explain the immense importance of this discovery. As he talked he saw that Boscaglia was whispering to the Grand Duchess. After dinner Castelli had taken leave, but he was scarcely past the palace gates when a lackey came running to call him back. They led him to the apartment of the Grand Duchess, where he was surprised to see the whole company; and now he found out what Boscaglia had whispered to the Sovereign: he had said that Galileo's convictions were against the Scriptures. The Dowager Duchess requested Castelli to answer this charge.

"Forgive me, Your Highness," Castelli said. "I am a priest and I don't like to involve Holy Writ in any dispute."

"Boscaglia is also a priest," Cristina said. "It doesn't matter. This question has so often been raised that I'd like to find out at last whether our Court mathematician works against God."

Castelli obeyed and began to discuss the problem from the theological standpoint. He mentioned all the passages of the Bible referring to it, and tried to prove that there was nothing contrary to Copernicus in them. Cristina brought up one counter-argument after the other. It was evident that she wanted to clear up everything in front of Boscaglia. Boscaglia himself said not a word, and seemed ill at ease, since the Prince and his wife seemed to approve of Castelli's explanation.

Castelli wrote at once and in detail to Galileo, who pondered the matter for a long time. After all, Castelli had done everything he could have done himself. And the Medici dynasty was behind him. Yet this letter gave him the impulse to tackle the most burning question of his age: the relationship of faith to knowledge. He could not stop now that he had broached the subject. He spent whole days in trying to discover a form, and finally decided to have his say in a letter written to Castelli; his former pupil could show it to whomever he pleased. He weighed every sentence before writing it and tried to be concise and exact. After a short preamble he continued:

> The communication of Your Reverence has given me the opportunity to ponder the question whether Holy Writ can be involved in arguments on natural science and to consider the passage on Joshua which Their Highnesses mentioned, as a counter-argument against the movement of the earth and the immobility of the sun.

As for the remark of the Dowager Duchess, I found it very wise indeed. Your Reverence was right to answer that the Holy Bible could not lie or be wrong.

Every sentence in Scripture is a perfect and eternal truth. But I would have added that even if Holy Writ was always right, its commentators are sometimes wrong in various ways; the most frequent and most important of which is the clinging to the letter of certain passages. Such literal interpretations gave birth not only to contradictions but to heresies and to blasphemy. If we stick to every word we must equip God with hands and feet and ears, not to mention such human and physical passions as anger, hate, revenge, forgetfulness of the past, and ignorance of future things. There are many sentences in the Bible which, interpreted literally, differ from truth; but these have been clothed in words which the masses can understand. Therefore it is necessary that wise men should explain the real, inner meaning of such passages to the few who are entitled to think for themselves. And since it is not only possible, but necessary, to interpret different passages in a sense contrary to the surface meanings of the words, I believe that Holy Writ should be used as an argument in natural science only as a last resort. The Bible and Nature are both born of the Divine Word. Holy Writ is inspired by the Holy Ghost, but Nature is the executor of God's laws.

To confirm all this, let us take that passage concerning Joshua, of which Your Reverence had advanced three different explanations to Their Highnesses, among them my own. But now I would like to follow it up by some observations which I think I have not mentioned before. Our opponents say that Holy Writ has to be interpreted literally; for instance, that God stopped the sun at Joshua's prayer, postponing sunset and thereby giving victory to Israel. I still reserve my standpoint that my opponent is free to interpret the words of the text not literally: but at the same time, I maintain that this passage of the Bible proves that the world system of Aristotle and Ptolemy is wrong, while it fits in excellently with that of Copernicus.

1. I ask my opponent how many kinds of movement the sun has, according to our knowledge. He will answer, two. Every year it moves from west to east and every day from east to west.

2. I ask whether these two different and contrary movements belong to the sun itself? He will answer that, according to Ptolemy, only the yearly movement is a real, detailed, and peculiar one; while the other, lasting twenty-four hours, being the "primum mobile," is contrary to the movement of those planets which the sun is carrying along.

3. Finally I ask which movement causes day and night? He will answer: the primum mobile. The sun's own movement causes the seasons.

But if, according to Ptolemy, night and day are not caused by the sun, but the primum mobile, everybody must accept the fact that to prolong the day, not the sun but the primum mobile had to be checked. And whoever has learned the rudiments of astronomy must concede that if God stopped the sun, He did not then prolong the day, but on the contrary He shortened it.

For, according to the principles of Aristotle and Ptolemy, it would be quite impossible to stop the sun and lengthen the day. Now, according to Holy Writ, this happened. Therefore either Ptolemy's system is wrong, or we must differ from the literal interpretation of Holy Writ, saying that God did not stop the sun but the primum mobile. Only the Holy Bible has to conform to those intellects which would find it hard to understand sunrise and sunset scientifically. The Divine Purpose used words just the opposite of those which it might have used in addressing educated minds.

I must add this: It is scarcely feasible that God bade only the sun to stand still and left the other planets moving, since thereby He would have confused without reason their relations to distances from the sun and brought chaos into the whole order of Nature. It is feasible, however, to suppose that He bade the whole universe stand still and set it working again without confusion, without any change once the pause was ended.

And as we have agreed that we cannot interpret the words of Holy Writ according to their literal meaning, we must have a new system of the universe following closely the exact interpretation of words.

This has been done. I have discovered and proved that the sphere of the sun turns on its own axis, taking about a month for this gyration, just as the other heavenly bodies do. We can presume that the sun, the most gigantic creation of Nature, is the heart of the universe, and gives both light and impulse of movement to the stars and planets circling around it. If we follow Copernicus in the supposition that a twenty-four hours' movement is made by the earth, everybody must see that to prolong the day it suffices to stop the sun and thereby bid the whole universe stand still. This is what Holy Writ says in truth.

Thus we can prove without creating disorder in the universe and changing the words of the Holy Bible that by stopping the sun God lengthened the day.

It was late in the evening when he finished the letter. He read it over and found it good. He noted the positions of the stars in his diary and went to bed. Next day he woke with the memory of a dream about Cremonini. He tried to think why he had dreamed of his Peripatetic friend. And then he remembered that Cremonini, the most stubborn follower of Aristotle, had always clung to the rigid principle by which natural science must be kept strictly apart from theology. Galileo had always respected Cremonini for this wisdom. But now in the second half of his letter he had done the very thing he began by condemning. He had left his own ground and invaded the enemy's. Was that right? Was it wise? He thought it over, then shrugged his shoulders. He felt strong enough to vanquish anyone in argument. He trusted his brain and felt he was right. Holy Writ must justify him. If necessary he would convince the wisest Prince of the Church.

He sent the letter to Castelli and went back to bed. His joints had begun to ache again.

XIV

He had to spend many weary months in bed in inhuman pain. Moaning and groaning, he remembered that he was fifty years old. Nowadays he often thought of death. Not of his own free will, since he hated the thought. But the idea of passing into oblivion dogged him like an evil dream. Sometimes at night, when his thoughts were working without restraint, feverishly, he screamed in his dark solitude: No! no! Let me live—at any price. A long time. Forever! That was absurd, but life was miraculously beautiful and kind, even for the tortured invalid, since he could still relish food and drink, and it was still sweet to look out of the window at the towers of his adored Florence. He often remembered Fra Paolo's remark: "No one who loves life as much as you do, is born for martyrdom."

"I don't want to be a martyr," he cried to himself. "I want to live for my work, triumph with my great thought, and enjoy!"

While he struggled in his prison of pillows, an extraordinary man came out to him from a real prison. This was Campanella, a Dominican monk who had been tried four times by the Church for his restless and rebellious spirit. He had lain in prison with Giordano Bruno and had only just avoided the stake. He could not keep quiet and had tried to found a new state in his native Calabrian village, the tiny Stilo. He organized a conspiracy but was betrayed. His followers were beheaded, but he escaped punishment by feigning madness. The Spanish government of Naples did not know what to do with him, so he was sentenced to imprisonment for life. This "madman" wrote one metaphysical and political book after the other, and bombarded the Pope and the Italian princes with his world-shattering schemes. Even now he wanted to create the "City of the Sun," a strange, communistic, antidemocratic state, which would be under the unselfish government of exceptional minds. Many of his adroit philosophic phrases were used in scientific argument: *To know is to be. Three things are certain in this world:*

319

our own being, our own consciousness, and our own will—were some specimens of his brilliant, mad creations.

Now he wrote to Galileo to say that he was at work on a vast tome. He was trying to prove that both the Old and the New Testament supported Copernicus, or rather Domenico Maria Novara, late astronomer to the city of Bologna, who had been the great Copernicus' teacher. Because, Campanella wrote, the new order of the universe could not have been formulated by a German—only by an Italian. Copernicus must have stolen it from Novara.

Galileo was amused at this strange Dominican who had lived without cares and in excellent health for the last sixteen years in his prison; yet his praise flattered him, though he smiled at the patriotic fervor which wanted to claim the priority of Copernicus' discovery for Italy.

And there was another voice reaching him: Mayr. Simone Mayr von Guntzenhausen reminded the astronomer, now lying on his sick-bed, of the Jupiter planets. After the Capra scandal, both Capra and Mayr had vanished from Padua. Now he reappeared as Court astronomer of the Count of Brandenburg-Ansbach and had written a book called *Mundos Jovialis* about *his* discovery of these.

Galileo could scarcely believe his eyes when he read the book. Mayr's insolence was almost awe-inspiring. The treatise professed to be based on exact data and tried to tell the story of the discovery in a sensational way. Galileo shook his head, amazed. He was tired and ill. He flung the book aside and marveled. He postponed the answer until he was well again. His pain had never been so stubborn. And the time had come when his two daughters were to be professed; he wanted to be present at the ceremony. Virginia was often ill; she had much trouble with her teeth. Galileo sent his own doctor to the convent. Finally the two girls took the veil without their father or any of the family being present. They kept it a secret from their grandmother, because they were afraid that she might make a scene even in the holy precincts.

It was late summer before he could get up at last. He had to learn to walk again. His son, who visited him regularly, helped him down into the garden. He could go no farther. It took him a long time before he could get out into the street. His acquaintances scarcely recognized the thin, emaciated man. Since he could not walk the distance to the Arcetri convent, the Court provided him with a litter to visit his daughters.

He took young Vincenzo, and by special leave of the Mother Superior they spent the whole afternoon together. Vincenzo chased the chickens, broke a window, ruined the finest branch of a young fruit tree; but, although his father slapped him soundly for every misdeed, he was soon happy again. Livia was silent and sullen, sitting beside her father, playing with the folds of her habit and never smiling. "She's always like that," the sisters said. But Virginia was charming and eager. She had many little tales to tell, with a witty point to every story; she radiated superhuman kindness.

"I couldn't imagine the convent without Virginia," the Abbess had said. "I'd feel lost if she weren't here."

"A sweet child," Galileo nodded proudly.

"She is more than that. She's a little saint. There is such deep piety in her as I have never seen among the grown-up sisters. I don't know where she can possibly get it from. Forgive me, I didn't mean to hurt your feelings. . . ."

"You didn't, Suor Ludovica, but why don't you consider me pious?"

"Forgive me, but there's so much talk . . . of course, I don't pay any heed to it. They say you're denying Holy Writ. That you don't really believe in God. Forgive me, I know this is just wild talk, but I may as well tell you. . . ."

Galileo laughed and assured the Reverend Mother that he believed in the same God as she did. But when he returned with his son in the litter, he began to think. What could he do to end these rumors? If it were possible, he would gladly stand in the middle of the Piazza del Duomo and talk about it to the people. He felt as though seaweed were entangling his feet; invisible, dirty strands which, the more he kicked them, the stronger they twined around his limbs. Whenever he saw a priest in the street he got the unpleasant feeling that the man hated him. He ought to accost him and explain to him how wrong he was. But they passed each other in icy silence.

One Sunday morning his brother-in-law, Landucci, visited him. He was a rare guest, and Galileo seldom went to the Landucci house. It must be something very important which brought him here.

"Galileo, a most unpleasant thing has happened. The whole city is talking about you. And I can't deny that it's extremely painful for us too. My father was Ambassador to Rome; I owe it to his memory to take care of our name. My wife is weeping with shame; she wanted me not to come here at all."

"Why? What's happened?"

"They have preached against you in Santa Maria Novella. Caccini, the Dominican. The whole congregation stared at us. I simply didn't know where to look."

"What did he say? Did he mention my name?"

"Of course he did. I can't deny that he talked very skillfully. He chose two texts, one from the book of Joshua, the other from the Acts. The second was: "Why are you standing here, Galileans, looking at the sky?""

"Quite a skillful approach. At the sky. And my name. Very good. What did he say after that?"

"He abused you. For half an hour. That you contradict the Holy Bible with your doctrine about the movement of the earth. Your theories are against the Scriptures. You are spreading the poison of blasphemy in Florence, and are close to heresy. He shouted that nobody was allowed to interpret the Bible differently from the Church Fathers. Finally he began a tirade against mathematicians. He said mathematics were all invented by the devil and mathematicians ought to be driven out from every country, as the cause of all heresy. Well, Galileo, this isn't a laughing matter. I've never interfered with your affairs before, but now . . ."

Galileo raised his hand. He was just about to tell his brother to go, but before he could do that, a Court official came into the room.

"Her Highness, the Dowager Duchess, requests Messer Galileo to appear instantly at Court."

Galileo did not say good-by to Landucci, but hurried away to the Poggio Imperiale. He was announced at once. The Grand Duchess Cristina did not even wait for him to bow.

"Messer Galilei," her voice was sharp and frigid, "you've probably heard of the sermon which was preached this forenoon. A fine thing for our Court mathematician to be publicly accused of heresy! I haven't spoken to my son yet, since he is ailing; but he'll certainly be deeply grieved. I neither accuse you nor reproach you, but you ought to do something about it."

"Your Highness, I . . . I can't do anything, except be a faithful son of the Church, respect the Holy Bible, and do my scientific work. I should be deeply grateful if Your Highness would suggest to me what to do."

"That's just the difficulty. How should I know how to advise you? I only know that this business of Joshua and the Bible, these denunciations and what not, are making me nervous—just as they do the Prince. Don't look so miserable, we aren't angry with you. But it would be better if something could be settled. That was all I wanted to say."

Galileo hurriedly kissed her hand, bowed deeply, and backed out of the room. He went to see Picchena, Vinta's successor, who received him at once. He too had heard of the sermon.

"What shall I do? Shall I kill that priest? I don't even know him!"

"I do. He was transferred from Bologna, where he caused some scandal by a sermon. Later he had to apologize. He was transferred to the San Marco monastery."

"The San Marco?" Galileo ground his teeth. "Where Fra Angelico painted his frescoes? How can they allow such a scoundrel to walk those cloisters? What shall I do? How can I get satisfaction? The affair has become serious. The Dowager Duchess has warned me already. One day the Prince will get tired of all this, and then I can go and look for another post."

"Don't be afraid of that. His Highness likes you too much; he will never forsake you. But the Church is troublesome. Didn't you ever think that you might be denounced by the Inquisition?"

Galileo was startled.

"I?"

"Of course. I'm surprised that it hasn't happened before. I advise you to leave the sun and the earth alone for a while. Try to spend your time with something else. Later, if things quiet down, you can return to it. And be careful with priests. You have no idea what power the Holy Office wields. You can always count on me, needless to say."

The blood sang in his ears as he left the Prime Minister. He went home, locked his door, and began to think. Impossible to give it up. If they noticed that he had withdrawn, they would attack him all the more savagely. He walked up and down in his room, smoking pipe after pipe, sending out for strong wine.

When he felt calmer, he decided to address a detailed memorial to the Dowager Duchess, aimed at the experts. He would explain at some length that really he was faithful to Holy Writ, while his opponents contradicted it. Then he would write to his Roman patrons and to one of the distinguished Dominicans; perhaps they could muzzle Caccini.

He started the memorial and wrote letters from morning till night. A few days later came a letter from Father Maraffi, one of the most important Dominicans, and yet a Copernican. He abused Caccini, but could promise no satisfaction or redress. Other letters came, all friendly and consoling. But a little later, the Grand Duke himself warned him that things had gone wrong behind the scenes.

"I want to tell you something extremely secret. A member of the Church, whose name doesn't matter, asked my mother's confessor whether you haven't sent her the same letter which you sent to Castelli."

"No, I only sent it to him."

"I know. I wanted to tell you my suspicion that something is brewing around that letter. Where is the original?"

"Castelli has it."

"Ask him to send it back. And never mention this talk to anybody. Although I am much younger than you, I'm a Medici, and let me tell you that letters of that kind can freely circulate in the world as copies, because they *are* copies, and copies are no use as evidence. But the original should be at home, carefully locked away."

Galileo did not understand all this. He could safely say all he had said in that letter in front of the Pope. But a dim instinct told him also that something was preparing against him. Castelli sent the letter back at once, and a few days later had an interesting story to tell.

Bonciani, Archbishop of Pisa, had sent for him. He began by reproaching him for following Copernicus. He advised him firmly that as a priest of the Holy Church, destined for a distinguished career, he ought to give up this foolish theory, which was also blasphemous. Castelli maintained humbly but obstinately that Copernicus did not contradict the Bible. The Archbishop mentioned Galileo and added that he too would do well to give up this absurd delusion. He, the Archbishop, could disprove and convince Galileo, if only he would hear his arguments.

"He wrote some letter to you," said the Archbishop, "in which he enumerated these arguments."

"Yes, Your Lordship, I have a copy which I can show."

"No, no! copies are often faulty. I want you to show me the original."

On this they parted. Castelli asked his master to send back again the original letter. Galileo was scared. Castelli was an excellent mathematician, but a gullible and artless man. The ruse by which the Archbishop of Pisa wanted to get hold of the original was only too transparent. The Grand Duke's warning was based on exact information: for some reason there were people who wanted to get the letter.

He waited a long time, then sent a copy in his own hand, but did not sign it. He worked on the memorial and deluged his Roman friends with letters.

But bad news came from Rome. Duke Cesi wrote that Cardinal Bellarmin, who had been so kind in verifying the observations of the *Sidereus Nuncius,* had suddenly become cold and unfriendly; he said that, in his opinion, this Joshua problem was most delicate, that he considered Copernicus as flatly contradictory to the Bible. There were distinguished princes of the Church who had been full of kindness to Galileo, hailing him as a great scientist; now they became reserved and distant. Some did not even answer his letters.

At the same time, a priest called Foscarini, one of his most enthusiastic followers, published a book in Rome upholding the Copernican system. This made the whole theological question even more exciting. Rumor said that Foscarini would get into trouble. It was even whispered that the Inquisition would investigate Copernicus' work and probably put it on the Index.

Galileo walked the streets of Florence like a man frightened of ghosts, and appeared only in open daylight. Important people suddenly shunned him as if he had shown symptoms of the plague. The symptoms were like concentric circles, but their common center could not be found. Galileo's uncertain and hesitant fingers felt that something formidable and dangerous was sliding past his reach in the darkness; but, try as he would, he could not catch it.

He was losing sleep, was often roused by a nightmare. And when he had finished his memorial, he stared at it blankly. He could not give it to the hidden mysterious forces at work against him.

Now he was completely bewildered. Every moment threatened a blow, but he could not tell who would deliver it. And one night a young nobleman called Attavante slipped into his room; he had met him once or twice at Court. He stole in, glancing nervously over his shoulder like a thief.

"There's nobody here; you can talk safely."

"Your Excellency, I have been questioned on your account. I had a long struggle with myself whether I should come, but decided to risk it."

"Tell me all about it."

"Well, it was like this. . . . Last spring I was walking with Father Ximenes, the Dominican, in the garden of Santa Maria Novella. You know Father Ximenes? That Spaniard. . . ."

"I don't know him."

"It doesn't matter. Well, we talked about theological problems, mostly about the existence of God. I used several atheist arguments, to learn their rebuttal from Father Ximenes. When I took my leave, I noticed that something was rustling behind me. I just managed to see Father Caccini slipping away. I knew at once that he had listened to our whole talk. But I didn't think it important, and then I forgot all about it. The day before yesterday, I received the summons to appear in a certain place."

"Where?"

"Don't ask me, Your Excellency. I took a solemn oath not to tell anybody. I have perjured myself as it is. So, please, don't ask me."

"All right. Go on."

"I obeyed the summons and was questioned. To my great surprise they wanted to find out whether these arguments against God, which I had used to Father Ximenes, had been learned from you."

"From me?"

"Yes, from you. I told him that I have never spoken to you about God, that I had only had one or two opportunities ever to enjoy your conversation. When I talked with Father Ximenes, we didn't mention you at all. And that was all. Believe me, Your Excellency, I feel deeply disturbed because I think that there's something brewing against you. And now I must go. But you must swear that you won't betray me to anyone."

Galileo hesitated: "I'd like to tell this to the Grand Duke; but, of course, without mentioning your name or Ximenes'. Do you mind that?"

"No, not if you *must*."

"I must. For my own sake. And thank you very much for coming."

Attavante slipped out into the night. Galileo scarcely slept. Next morning he hurried to the Palace. He told the Prince every detail of the mysterious visit, except the names. Cosimo listened to him attentively.

"This is very simple. You've been denounced to the Inquisition. The hearing of the witnesses has already begun. That young man who visited you had been summoned to one of the inquisitors. Of course, they made him swear to keep silent."

"But why did they denounce *me*, Your Highness? What have I done?"

"It must be the same story: that you contradict the Holy Scripture. They've a masterly organization, a terrible power. Be on your guard."

"What am I to do, Your Highness?"

"Go to Rome at once. My ambassador, Guicciardini, has great influence. I'll give you letters of recommendation, money, a litter, a train of servants. Discuss all the details with Picchena. Don't look so troubled; nothing can happen to you. If necessary, I'll write to the Pope myself."

"I can't go at once, Your Highness. I had a very important idea recently, and now I'm trying to work it out. I've a new theory about the cause of the tides, of ebb and flood."

"That's interesting. Can you sum it up?"

"Very easily, Your Highness. Imagine that I am pushing a vessel filled with water in a certain direction. What will happen with the surface of water in the vessel? This is a proof that the earth moves. I want to take it to Rome completely finished."

"It sounds convincing enough. Well, hurry up with it. You may meet my brother, Prince Carlo, at Rome; he has recently been made a Cardinal. Perhaps he could help you too."

Galileo hastened to put his theory of tides on paper. One November morning he set out for Rome in pouring rain.

The new Tuscan Ambassador, Guicciardini, lived in the Medici villa above the Trinità Church. When Galileo told him that he wanted to parry a blow of the Inquisition, Guicciardini froze at once. But the personal letter of the Grand Duke, commanding quarters, servants, and a scribe for the scientist, was on his table. So he frowned and shook his head. But as soon as Galileo had unpacked he came along to his apartment, to discuss the *modus procedendi*.

"Did you receive any warning or summons from the Holy Office?"

"Nothing. My last official contact with the Church was the formation of a committee of four which examined my astronomical observations and verified them. This was ordered by Cardinal Bellarmin."

"Then you mustn't seem to know anything about the Inquisition. Keep this advice of mine well in your mind, wherever you go."

"What shall I do then?"

"Make contacts."

"What do you mean?"

"Be friendly with everyone. Look innocent, go visiting, talk, get connections. And try to turn the conversation to those matters which have been raised. Keep saying how good a Catholic you are, how much you respect the dogmas, and that you have never spoken to an enemy of the Pope."

"Well, that's rather difficult, you know. Fra Paolo Sarpi is a good friend of mine, and I correspond with the Mayor of Augsburg and Kepler, although they are Protestants."

"All right, all right," the Ambassador snarled, "but why say that to all and sundry? And above all, don't get involved in any theological argument."

"Excuse me, but we came to Rome to prove that my theories do not contradict Holy Writ."

"Leave your theories alone for the present. Show yourself a good and faithful Catholic. Should the Inquisition demand a declaration, you can call all the Cardinals to whom you have spoken as witnesses. Though really I can't understand why you want to meddle in questions which are always troublesome. Why don't you invent war machines or a new method of cartography?"

"What?" Galileo cried. "Am I to give up my cosmology which I have thought out for the benefit of mankind?"

The Ambassador rose and bowed sardonically.

"I think the stars would still come out tonight even if you neglected them for a while. I give you my advice and warn you again . . . what's the matter with your left hand?"

"An inflammation of the joints. It's chronic, but this is a slight attack."

"And you've come to Rome . . . in November? You couldn't have chosen a worse climate in all Italy! On the whole I think this trip to Rome . . . but never mind! If you need something call the *maggiordomo*. I'll see you later."

Galileo stared resentfully at his back. What would Euclid have said had he been advised not to write his geometry? Laymen ought to be kept away from the exact sciences. This reminded him that he had written on theology, although he was doubtless a layman there. He grew still more angry, cuffing his servant and tipping him in the next moment.

His first call was on Duke Cesi, whom he found in deep mourning: his wife, Artemisia Colonna, had died. But the mourning was only outward show. The Duke told him that he would soon remarry. Then he came to the point.

"I want to beg you, and all my Lynxes agree with me in this, not to enter upon any theological argument. We must be careful of our Academy. It's rumored that we deny the truth of Aristotle, as some of us do, while the Church is on the whole Aristotelian. Also, I have the impression, which may be groundless, that against you . . . that you . . . I mean, you ought to be on your guard against the Inquisition."

"I think the same. On what does Your Grace base your impression?"

"Whenever a Cardinal hears your name he becomes reserved. And this is a rather bad sign. Of course, they never say anything openly."

"What shall I do?"

"Renew all our connections, show them what a good Catholic you are."

Duke Cesi repeated Guicciardini's advice—almost word for word! He added that the Holy Office must never be mentioned.

"But can't you tell me who the leaders of the Inquisition are?"

"I only know that the French Cardinal Saint-Cecil is the president of the Index Committee. And Cardinal Bellarmin is a member. There are the Qualificators, who are experts on the theological side, but not judges, like Cardinal Setani. But, please, leave that question alone."

He went on to the Jesuit College to see Grienberger. Since Clavius had died, his place had been filled by the ever-smiling red-haired Tyrolese. Galileo avoided the Inquisition and Joshua; he only mentioned his theory of the tides. They spoke of Scheiner and the sunspots. Galileo hinted that he was considered as an enemy of the Jesuits, although there was no foundation for this rumor. They parted apparently as good friends.

He stopped his litter in the street. He did not know what to do or where to go.

At home he prepared a list of people to visit. His wallet was full of the Grand Duke's letters. He had a long list ready: from Count Querango, whom he had known at Padua, to Cardinal Del Monte, the Dominican Maraffi, and Cardinal Orsini. He noted every word of his hosts, every shade of the manner in which they received him. He could not mention the Inquisition or the Bible, so he said that his scientific theories had brought him many foolish enemies, on whose account he had gone to Rome to proclaim his faith in the Catholic Church and demonstrate alike to laymen and experts that his theories were clear, correct, and reasonable.

Some nodded, and did not understand a word. Others liked the strangeness and novelty of the Copernican system. Some attacked it violently. But all this referred to Copernicus and not to the person of Galileo. And this was really the only thing which interested him: he wanted to know what was going on around him invisibly. Sometimes he convinced himself that everything was idle fantasy. The official Church had nothing against him. The Castelli letter did not mean anything, nor did the Archbishop of Pisa. Attavante's dramatic visit was of no importance. There was really no need to have come to Rome at all. But, since he was here, he would do a little sightseeing, take a trip to Naples, which he had wanted to see for a long time. And he would visit Loreto, the famous shrine. Virginia had asked him to do that.

But, though he felt reassured, he was still thoughtful. What if the Inquisition had secretly instituted proceedings against him? For then everything would fit in. The Archbishop of Pisa might have received orders to get hold of the original letter as decisive proof. Witnesses would be summoned, perhaps ten or twenty; but he was certain only of one. Were they collecting data against him? Those who could have told said nothing, yet withdrew from him as if he were a leper. And while he was trying to puzzle it out, they were discussing him in some mysterious room of some palace or monastery, and might at that moment be deciding that the time was ripe. Even Galileo Galilei could vanish into the Castel Sant' Angelo.

In a strange frame of mind, he continued his visits; a hunted man, himself pursuing invisible phantoms. He had no greater wish than the certainty that really there was something afoot. Was there really anything? Even to know the worst would bring him peace.

At last he attained an inkling of this knowledge from Cardinal Bellarmin. It needed three visits for him to be received by that mighty prelate. Galileo at once led the talk to Copernicus. The Cardinal took up his challenge.

"Keep away from all that, Messer Galilei." His voice was cold. "This theory contradicts the Church."

"Monsignor, I'm convinced of the truth of this cosmology, and I know that it comes much nearer the spirit of the Church than Aristotle. Unluckily I've schooled myself never to discuss theology, or I could show Your Excellency that Copernicus and the Holy Bible say the same."

"It would be useless to advance such a theory—which concerns theology. Leave it to the theologians. They will deal with it on two counts. First, as concerns Foscarini's book, or rather his open letter. Secondly with regard to complaints from Florence."

"From Florence, Monsignor? What complaints?"

"Certain persons there are deeply concerned with the interests of our holy religion and have complained that your followers there are harming the Faith. This matter will have to be examined."

"Forgive me, but may I ask some questions?"

"That depends on the kind of questions you ask."

"Were these complaints against me personally? And to what authority were they addressed?"

The Cardinal ignored the second query, but answered the first:

"I repeat that the complaints were against your followers or, if you like it better that way, against the followers of Copernicus; there was no question of your person. But I warn you to give up this theory. This is my best advice. What you do in the matter is your affair. And now I must leave you. I have been summoned by the Holy Father."

Galileo bowed deeply and withdrew. Now he knew a little more. Someone in Florence had been complaining against his followers, openly, in a way which could reach Bellarmin. Probably a direct attack by the Inquisition.

Maraffi, the Dominican, told him more. Caccini, who had preached against him, was in Rome. The other monks at San Marco only knew that he had been summoned by a higher authority. Another link in his chain of conjecture. But soon came the decisive news, that Father Lorini, the Florentine priest, who had called Copernicus "Ipernicus," was now in Rome. What was he doing here? Slowly, very slowly and dimly, Galileo began to see the outlines of the case against him.

But he was happy to realize how useful his visit was. Several prelates, who at first had only consented to receive him after many postponements and then only at the urgent request of a friend, had shown themselves stiff and inclined to be hostile. But when Galileo stressed his deep religious feeling and mentioned his two daughters in the convent, their icy stiffness melted away.

This encouraged him. He visited the important people again and complained of the slanderers working against him. And now he was pleased to see the effect of his early visits. They all consoled and reassured him. Five Cardinals told him on the same day that he had nothing to fear, the Princes of the Church had long been assured that the rumors of his atheism were merely the kind of libelous inventions which often go with bitter sanctimonious hate. What he heard seemed to point to the conclusion that a secret investigation had acquitted him as a Catholic. Slowly he began to breathe more freely and grew accustomed to the thought that, though he might never learn what had taken place behind closed doors, his integrity as a Catholic had not been impaired by the secret investigation.

This whetted his appetite for arguments. His increasingly numerous acquaintances began inviting him to dinner, just as they had on the occasion of his last triumphant visit to Rome. And at these gatherings he deliberately began to plead for Copernicus. There were always one or two people who sponsored his views and ten who stubbornly contested them. He was in his element now. But he had to learn again and again what he had never learned during the scientific discussions of thirty years: very few of his opponents would give in, even under the pressure of irrefutable proofs. But he never tired. His sharp wits were always radiant, his gay irony was alive. Every argument started by ten people talking at the same time, but finished with Galileo speaking alone. There was something of the born actor in his fine voice and lively gestures. And very often the table applauded him as though he really were an actor.

While he worked on stubbornly and tirelessly to re-establish his good name, he received the last and certain satisfaction: Caccini visited him at the Villa Medici. Galileo was frankly amazed when the servant announced him one afternoon, immediately after dinner.

A smooth, courteous monk came into the room. Galileo realized now that he had seen him often at Florence, but had not known that he was Caccini. He judged him to be a dishonest man—at first sight. And now, as they sat there face to face and the priest kept bowing, rubbing his hands and shifting his glance again and again, Galileo took a violent dislike to him. He remembered those kind and blessed priests whom he had loved so much during his life, and compared them to this softly reptilian man. He would have liked to catch him up by the scruff of the neck and shake him well—but this thought was foolish.

"I am here," said the monk, in an unctuous voice, never meeting Galileo's eyes, "to ask your pardon."

"I thank you, and accept your apology."

"Since I preached my sermon, which was inspired by my fervent love of the faith, I have convinced myself that Your Honor is a diligent and loyal son of the Church. Several prelates here in Rome have told me this. I come to offer you any satisfaction you may require."

Galileo eyed him closely. Even in this self-abasement, there was some repulsive self-righteous vanity. He was just as much an actor as Galileo —or, indeed, as all Italians are. But this was a bad actor. His apology had a false ring. Yet why had he come?

"Thank you again, but I can get no satisfaction from Your Reverence in the field of learning. As for the Church, my affairs are in order."

"I wasn't thinking about learning. In this respect I follow Cardinal Bellarmin, who considers these teachings mistaken. I was thinking of human reparation. But believe me, Your Excellency, it would be unjust to let me bear the whole brunt of your anger. There are cases when we have to be silent, though we suffer for the sins of others."

"What are you hinting at, Father Caccini? You should speak frankly or not at all."

"Quite right, Your Excellency. But I had no wish to hint at anything. Let this whole sorry business be buried forever. Yet my fault is smaller than, for example, Lorini's. I only warned my flock in Florence to be on their guard against erroneous theories; whereas he denounced these theories in Rome, and so might have done you serious harm."

Galileo sprang to his feet.

"You say that Lorini denounced me? While you were preaching against me, he denounced me at the same time? That was well thought out! But why, why? When did I ever offend either of you?"

"We did it to defend our faith. We took our oath as priests to defend it."

"Well! Well! That may be as you say. And where did this Lorini denounce me? At the Inquisition? Please tell me that! You refuse? I see. It would have pleased you both to see me burned alive."

"But I haven't admitted denouncing you to the Inquisition."

Galileo eyed him in silence and drew a deep breath. He could see the whole thing more or less as it was; terrifying shadows were put to flight. These men had denounced him at the instance of his former pupil, the Archbishop of Florence. Caccini had preached against him, Lorini—the "Ipernicus" Lorini—had denounced him—of course at the Inquisition—accusing him of heresy and atheism. The Holy Office had started proceedings; had demanded evidence. The Archbishop of Pisa had done his best to get hold of the original of his letter. Witnesses had been summoned and heard—Ximenes, his brother monks, and Atta-vante. But this investigation had brought no proofs. He had come to Rome and made an excellent personal impression. The matter was fin-ished. And now one of his slanderers sat before him.

"Very well, I won't press you, Father Caccini. Only, tell me quite frankly, what is it you want?"

But now their talk was interrupted. Duke Cesi arrived bringing with him two Lynxes. Galileo presented them to Caccini and sent for wine. Soon they began a lively argument in which, to Galilei's astonishment, Caccini joined with a sharp attack on Copernicus. But he used all the stalest arguments, which even Duke Cesi could easily refute. Galileo kept his eyes fixed on this priest with his narrow skull, his smooth, feminine hands, and listened carefully to his voice. This was a small and malicious mind, an evil spirit. Such men as he, in certain circum-stances, might bring the greatest genius to ruin, men of whose teachings they knew almost nothing. And why? To get promotion in the Church, even perhaps to die a bishop! A horrible thought!

Duke Cesi took leave. But Caccini still insisted on staying. He began again in a sing-song, unctuous voice:

"Now that there's no anger between us, let me turn to you as your spiritual father, as a priest of your faith. Give up all thoughts of this new cosmology."

"What the devil!" Galileo laughed with annoyance. "Do you think I'm mad?"

"Listen, Your Excellency. The Church will never endorse this theory. And, after all, your salvation should mean a hundred times more to you than any number of learned axioms. Remember! the Church can save you from hell. Bethink yourself, for the sake of Christ's seven wounds . . ."

"Thank you for your ghostly counsel, but I've thought it over for twenty-five years. This thing which I hope to proclaim to the world will only serve the Church's glory."

"This devilish Protestant invention?"

"Why Protestant? Surely Pythagoras was no Protestant. And Copernicus was a canon of Thorn and dedicated his work to Pope Paul III. Leave all this, Your Reverence? It would be easier for you to persuade me to join the castrated singers of the Sistine Chapel."

But still Caccini would not go. He sat gabbling on like a missionary among the aborigines. When at last he took leave, Galileo hurried to see the Ambassador. He informed Guicciardini that nothing further kept him in Rome, that he had even received the unlooked-for satisfaction of a direct apology from Caccini.

"He arrived at two and left at six, God bless him! You see, Your Excellency, you were wrong. It was a wise move for me to come to Rome. My hand is no worse, my legs aren't aching very much, I don't even limp very badly—and I've managed to settle with all my detractors. Did you ever watch a great stone being lifted from its place among the ruins? The swarms of parasites and worms living under its protection go wriggling off—the sun is too strong for them."

Guicciardini seemed to be really glad: "And when will Your Honor return to Florence?"

"Return to Florence? Not yet, believe me! No. I mean to stay here for a while. There's something more important to defend than my own skin: the cause of Copernicus. You must know, Excellency, that this rascal Lorini was very astute: he did not denounce me personally, but the 'Galileists.' His immediate aim was to get the Church to condemn my system. And after that he could easily dispose of *me*. But it won't be as easy as all that. Tomorrow I'll start again on my visits."

The Ambassador's face plainly showed his impatience.

"You really are a difficult man! It will do you no good to be so persistent. But I can't interfere. It is the Duke's will which decides how long you can be a guest in this house, which isn't mine."

"Am I not welcome then?"

"Your company is always delightful. But it riles me to see you so unrestrained. Why trouble the world with this new cosmology? What's the good of it all? You're scarcely clear of one set of difficulties when you start another. And all for what? But do as you please. It's not for me to advise you!"

The Ambassador turned back to his papers, to show that he wanted to be alone. Galileo shrugged his shoulders and returned to his rooms to dictate letters to his scribe.

Next day he started off on his round of visits: first and foremost to Cardinal Gaetani, whom he knew to be one of the Qualificators of the Holy Office. Up to now Gaetani had always found some excuse for avoiding him. This time he received him at once.

It was the first time Galileo had been inside the Holy Office. It was housed in a monastery of Dominicans, next door to the Church of Santa Maria Sopra Minerva, beyond the Via Lata, which was always thronged with motley crowds. This monastery had the look of a rocky island rising out of a sea of smaller buildings; only the towering dome of the Pantheon could equal it in bleak severity. An irregular, rambling colossus of brick and mortar, like a harsh challenge to the world. It was as though all the Dominicans of Christendom had built themselves a separate metropolis in the midst of Rome, the Christian capital. Yet this immense building inspired respect rather than terror. Its fine church was warm and really devout-looking. In one of the tiny chapels St. Catherine of Siena rested in her glass coffin; her relics, splendidly enshrined, seemed to give forth a mysterious influence, which made the whispering visitors to her shrine speak in even lower voices. The sexton shuffled across the floor on sandaled feet, extinguishing candles on the high altar with his long-stemmed snuffer, kneeling and making the sign of the cross for the fiftieth time as he passed the tabernacle. Not fear, but a kind of exaltation hovered about this Church of the Inquisition. And on the floors of the farther wing, where the rooms of the Holy Office were situated, the early spring sunshine poured gaily through the large windows, lay brothers came and went with bundles of documents or stacks of faggots for the fires. The whole place was more like an Archbishop's palace or some other distinguished ecclesiastical place than any hair-raising tribunal for judging sinners, whom it tortured and sent screaming to the stake.

Cardinal Gaetani received his visitor kindly. He congratulated him on the manner in which he had cleared himself of these accusations and poisonous slanders. What could he do for the learned man?

"I have to see you, Monsignor, on behalf of a German canon long since dead. I wish to be informed whether the Holy Office is investigating the teachings of Copernicus and his followers?"

"I am forbidden to give you information about the business of the Holy Office. But this Copernican question interests me. I have read all

I could get about this matter. At the moment the whole question still puzzles me, but I rather incline to the old, well-established teachings. Yet, since you've come to me about this, tell me the name of an impartial and authoritative expert."

Galileo did not hesitate: "Campanella."

"H'm . . . Campanella . . . in prison at Naples. It might not be such a bad idea, if I consult him privately. In any case, thank you for the suggestion. And how is your health nowadays? Would you care to smoke a pipe?"

There followed a long and pleasant talk on indifferent subjects. Yet Galileo still kept mentioning Copernicus. He referred to Foscarini's case; but the Cardinal smoothly avoided important issues and inquired about Florentine wines. Galileo could not even get him to say when and where a commission could meet to deal with the fundamental issue, or who would be likely to compose it. So he went on to see Cardinal Orsini, whom he had left as his last resort. Orsini was under an obligation to the Florentine Court and a special favorite of Pope Paul. Galileo brought a warm letter of recommendation from Duke Cosimo.

"Monsignor," he told the lively, gay, and wise little old man, "I come to beg for your support. And on a rather important issue."

"Go on, my friend, go on."

"I won't weary you with preliminaries. The main thing is that a basic question of astronomy is going to be decided by the Church; only I don't know which high ecclesiastical authorities are likely to be appointed to deal with it. But in any case it's His Holiness who will speak the decisive word. . . ."

"One moment, *caro*. What is this astronomical problem?"

"Whether the sun circles around the earth or the earth around the sun."

Cardinal Orsini laughed.

"Does it matter so much? Look out of the window and see how beautiful the spring is, with those trees in bloom. Heavens above, what useless things men plague their minds with, instead of being grateful to Our Lord for this glorious world! Well?"

"I maintain that the earth moves round the sun. His Holiness probably cares very little which moves round which. I want to ask you most humbly to put in a word with His Holiness and beg him to say that I am right, and not my adversaries."

"Is that all? I shall be delighted. Tomorrow there happens to be a Cardinals' meeting. I'll speak to His Holiness. Come back here tomorrow afternoon, and I'll tell you what I've managed to get out of him."

Again, as they were taking leave, the little white-haired Cardinal shook his head with a lenient smile. To think that grown-up men should plague their minds with such childish questions!

When Guicciardini heard that Galileo had asked Orsini to influence the Pope, he did not attempt to disguise his annoyance. He thumped the table in his excitement.

"Messer Galilei, you really do the stupidest things! Why, this fixed idea that you, single-handed, can triumph over the stubbornness of the priests in this city makes my hair stand on end! Why can't you leave this matter alone? Why not go back to Florence and wait there for the Church to decide! The priests may let it drop, and you'll hear no more of it. Then you can continue your scientific arguments in peace. But, no, you wouldn't listen to reason! And now you've made another gross mistake."

"I can't see that."

"Had you troubled to ask me, I could have told you that Pope Paul knows nothing at all about natural science. All these questions only irritate and annoy him. It is usual at the Papal Court for prelates to brag of their ignorance in these matters in front of the Pope, because he is always glad to hear it. Yet now you send this old Orsini to pester him with a problem of astronomy! I simply don't know what to say. Tell me, what makes you defy fate, again and again?"

"There's no question of defying fate. Nothing can happen to me. But I fight because I want to win."

"Win? Alone? Against the whole of Rome?"

"I am not alone. The truth is with me. And truth can defeat the whole of Rome."

Guicciardini angrily shook his head. He invoked the heavens.

"God Almighty—listen to this man! I only wonder the roof doesn't fall about our ears when a grown-up man starts talking like that. Messer

Galilei, I myself don't know why I'm always arguing with you. In the
end you always make me so angry that I tell you to do whatever you
please. And I say it again. I wash my hands of you. But there's one
thing you'd better hear. The *maggiordomo* reports that last night you
returned home more or less intoxicated in the company of your scribe,
Messer Annibale, and two rather gay and noisy ladies."

Galileo could not answer this charge. He hung his head like a little
boy caught red-handed in an orchard.

"And, since I am responsible to His Highness for the reputation of his
Embassy, I must really beg you never to repeat such conduct. I won't
even mention the daily sums you spend on wine, although the bills are
paid by my chancery. That concerns His Highness—it's *his* money. But
I have the right to protest against such nocturnal episodes. So please
remember what I say."

"I'm very sorry indeed, Your Excellency. I'll be more careful in future."

"Careful about what? The house or your own business? But I won't
go into all that again. And to choose of all men Orsini, for such an
errand! You'll see tomorrow how right I am. Now go, and try to drink
less tonight."

Cardinal Orsini kept his promise. He asked the Pope next day to
decide the astronomical question in Galileo's favor. The Pope frowned
and answered that Orsini would do better to persuade Galileo to rid his
mind of all this rubbish. But the old gentleman stood his ground, maintaining that after all it wasn't important which star moved and which
stood still. The Pope cut him short with the sudden warning that this
matter was in the hands of the Inquisition.

"But I oughtn't to have told you that, my friend; it slipped out before
I remembered I'd promised. Well! Well! Now there's nothing for it!
I'm glad that I was able to bring you the good news."

"Good news?"

"Of course. You have acquitted yourself splendidly in the eyes of the
Holy Office in your own business—and now you'll see, it will be the
same. By every sign, they like you there very much. I may as well tell
you that His Holiness at once took Cardinal Bellarmin aside, to discuss
it privately."

"But this isn't good news, Monsignor. Bellarmin disapproves this
theory."

"Does he? Well, well. . . . Isn't it all the same to him? Men make such trouble for themselves!"

Galileo went straight to Cardinal Bellarmin, who began by saying that he could not spare him more than two minutes. He refused all further information and expressed his regret that Orsini should have been so indiscreet as to babble about the affairs of the Holy Office. Such indiscretion carried the severest penalties. He allowed Galileo to kiss his hand, but then at the last minute changed his mind, and asked him to wait a little longer.

"Sit down, Messer Galilei. I want to talk to you plainly as a friend. Listen to me. The Holy Office cannot possibly countenance this doctrine."

"Why not, Monsignor?"

"I'll tell you why. But remember, I count on your sense of honor not to repeat my words to anyone. Even if you did, I should have to deny them, and I don't imagine that your word would be taken against mine. Well then, has it ever occurred to you what a wonderful organization our Church is? With what splendid skill she has managed to make use of everything which can bind and uplift the human soul? Think of our churches and their splendor, the very sight of which comforts the poor, since we make them feel that the shimmering gold of holy vestments, the pomp of the processions, is really theirs. Think of the works of art which the greatest genius of centuries has created in paintings and statues for the Church. Think of the deep and soothing beauty of our music, the lulling harmony of our plain chant—of the fumes of incense which chain the believer even through his senses to his religion. Think of the sacraments which sustain human beings from birth to maturity and still assist them until they die in the arms of the Church. Think of the confessional, that wise and glorious institution which has given millions of human beings peace of mind and the courage to go on living, and quiet sleep. No movement of the human soul can escape the loving vigilance of the Church in her battle with the weakness of sinful men. And yet the whole miraculous institution, whose wisdom cannot be praised enough, is grounded on the truth of Holy Writ. Every rite, every word of the Mass, has its origin there. Our Church, as it stands today, springs direct from God. Her holy orders, her governing bodies, her world-wide authority, are divine. Whoever doubts this is a heretic."

"God forbid that I should ever doubt it, Monsignor."

"Well, listen. We priests who by God's mercy have been raised to posts of command and authority have the sacred duty of defending and strengthening this wonderful institution. We must wisely adapt its government to any problems that arise. Long before the triumph of Christianity, Aristotle and later Ptolemy created their pictures of the universe. Christianity has endorsed their view, because it seemed to agree with its holy aims. God created Adam and Eve, and through them mankind; He redeemed us by His Only Begotten Son. The whole cosmos relates to humanity—to man's struggle to save his soul. Nothing can be of more significance than the salvation of a single individual, of the poorest beggarly human being. Not even the sun means so much to the Church, our Mother, because the sun, the moon, the stars are only parts of this human universe in which was played the terrible tragedy of redemption. The soul of any beggar out of the multitude who has lived and grown in the hands of God's Church, knowing that nothing else is essential to him save his personal relation to the sacrifice of the Body and Blood of Christ, is worth more to me than all your learning. This beggar trusts the God who came to earth and was nailed to the Cross. Can I permit the thought to enter his mind that the earth is only a tiny satellite and the sun the real center of the cosmos? Can I let humanity form this terrible thought that the earth, with its men seeking salvation, is not the heart of all created life? Can I allow doubt to invade their minds? This would be a greater blow than the Reformation and all other heresies. It would be enough to undermine the civil authority of the Papacy, and hence the wise and merciful power of the Church. This first doubt would be followed by a hundred others. The whole structure would crumble. Instead of faith, capricious disputation would be supreme; men would lose even their earthly happiness. No, Galileo Galilei; as long as I remain here in authority, I will never permit you to do this thing."

"Monsignor, may I ask one question?"

"Ask what you please."

"Is it inconceivable that these teachings can be true?"

"I don't know. They are alien to all my conceptions: my mind is lost in them. But they may be true for all that. I am not interested, however, in their truth. I am only concerned with teachings. What can I allow people to believe in the interests of the Church and their own salvation? Is truth in science so important? It may be so, for the scientist, to enable him to dispute. For me the faith of millions of poor people is far more essential. But I'll go further. Even if your teachings were proved true, my faith could withstand them. It is strong enough. I can imagine the holy mystery of salvation even on an earth which moves round the sun. But I cannot measure the faith of those millions of small, undeveloped souls by my own."

"This was the point I wanted to reach, Monsignor. It's the same with me. I believe that mine is the true cosmology, yet I remain a faithful son of the Church. And I don't expect any chance member of the multitude to believe the opposite of what he sees. Why should he suppose as I do that it isn't the sun which really rises at daybreak? I ask that only of learned men whose faith is strong to withstand this trial. Human beings learn very slowly; they advance and develop by slow degrees. According to the Holy Bible: Be perfect as your Heavenly Father is perfect. The time will come when the faith of hundreds of thousands is strong enough to bear the truth of Copernicus so that in the end even the multitude will accept him, and still believe. Why am I forbidden to reveal this truth to learned men?"

"Because there are many priests among them. And a priest mustn't think with his own mind, but with the Pope's. No priest can ever persuade his hearers with a sermon in which he doesn't believe."

"And the learned laity?"

"How can you separate the two categories? I can't ask the Inquisition to prepare two different Indexes. You must resign yourself to the fact that I can never permit this system to be expounded as a truth. Listen. We like you here very much. I have no hesitation in letting you know it. We esteem your scientific work, and His Holiness, who has no time for science, respects in you the courtier of a prince who has done great service in furthering the foreign policy of the Church. We treat you with the utmost consideration. For instance, we haven't raised any objection to your book which describes the spots on the sun, although it's in the spirit of Copernicus. Nor have we the least objection to any proof that the sun is imperfect. In other words, we treat you with much more respect than we should, for instance, Foscarini. We might even consent to close our eyes, if you will promise to treat your system as a strange and curious *hypothesis,* without any possible bearing on reality. But I won't let you proclaim and defend it, because I'm a good priest, a good

Catholic, and want to see all God's children happy. I leave it to your conscience as a Catholic to do whatever you think fit. For myself I have already decided. And I may as well tell you that His Holiness has also settled this question in his mind. His paternal heart is in full agreement with what I feel. In due course you will hear what we have decreed."

And Galileo was soon notified that the Qualificators of the Holy Office had met by order of the Pope to pass a theological judgment on two questions: First, whether the sun could really be considered as the true center of the universe and its movement in the heavens as only apparent. Second, whether it could be proved that the earth was really a mere planet which only spun daily on its own axis.

The Qualificators met on February 23rd in the Palazzo Sopra Minerva, and proclaimed that the first thesis was erroneous, in flat contradiction to all philosophy; that it contradicted the text of Scripture in many passages, as well as the interpretation of the Fathers and learned theologians. That in essence the second thesis was open to the same objections and was, at least in theology, fallacious.

Such was their considered judgment, although from his prison in Naples, Campanella had written a dissertation proving that Galileo was right. This learned screed did not influence the decision.

Galileo awaited news in the Villa Medici. At last it came. Bellarmin summoned him immediately. He hastened to obey the summons. When he came into the Cardinal's presence, he found him with several unknown Dominicans. These monks offered to withdraw, but the Cardinal ordered them to remain.

"The question is decided, Messer. It is the sun which moves round the earth."

"I've heard the decision, Monsignor. But, forgive me, that doesn't settle the matter. We only know that this is the view of the Inquisition. The earth can still move round the sun."

"Perhaps. But, in what I say to you now, I must remind you of a recent conversation. In this question truth is not essential. What matters is the welfare of Catholic humanity. In my opinion, the civil authority of the Papacy might be wrecked on the teachings of Copernicus. I have to inform you that the Index Committee of the Holy Office bases its judgment on this decree. I have summoned you here to draw your attention to the bidding of our Holy Father that from now on you are to cease your arguments and assertions, even among your private friends. The Church has spoken."

"I understand, Monsignor, and I obey. But I can't deny that I'm still firmly convinced of my own truth."

"No doubt. It was scarcely to be expected that the findings of the Qualificators would instantly cause you to change your mind. But I repeat most solemnly that henceforth *this theory must only be treated as a hypothesis*. Even Copernicus treats it thus; therefore we do not forbid his book. We only mark it, *donec corrigeretur*."

Galileo knew what this technical expression meant. The *donec corrigeretur* books were given over to some Church expert. Until certain words or passages had been changed, the book was "suspended." After such corrections it could be read again. His heart beat furiously.

"And may I ask what changes they will make in Copernicus?"

"You may ask, of course. Indeed, it is essential that you should know. We intend to omit those lines in his dedication to Pope Paul III in which Copernicus affirms that his theory does not contradict the Scriptures. In one or two instances, we shall probably alter the word "star" wherever he calls the earth by that name. Otherwise everything is to stand. But again I insist that we spare Copernicus only because he treated his whole theory as mere hypothesis. I insist on this, in order to let you see my friendship. Study the corrected Copernicus and let yourself be guided by that."

Galileo looked straight at the Cardinal; then he said:

"Such limitations will make my work exceedingly difficult. But may I say that I feel the deepest respect for your wisdom and the strength of your faith, Monsignor."

"Such a compliment from so learned a man! Of course, it pleases me. And in return I have good news for you. His Holiness intends to receive you, and offer you his fatherly consolation for any harm which our decision may have done to your position as a scientist."

The visit ended with Galileo's humble thanks and cordial leave-taking. At home, having considered these events, he did not feel the position as very serious. Really, it might have been much worse. When he came to Rome first, it would not have surprised him very much to find himself suddenly in prison. Now he experienced only courtesy at everyone's hands. It was rather a pity that the Church should so strongly object to the theory of Copernicus. But if he could still treat it as a hypothesis, it meant only a formal limitation. It was half a success and half a failure. That nauseating Caccini had triumphed, inasmuch as the Church had denounced the new theory as in contradiction to Holy Writ. On the other hand, he, Galileo, had not been defeated, since he was still permitted to continue the greatest work of his life, though in a more complicated form and hindered by the necessity of carefully choosing his expressions.

On March 5th the Holy See published the decree of the Congregation.

Inasmuch as the Congregation had been notified that a certain false teaching of Pythagoras, in flat contradiction to Holy Scripture, concerning the so-called motion of the earth and immobility of the Sun, as further was maintained by Copernicus in his book entitled: *Von den Bewegungen der Himmelskörper,* on the Book of Job, was spreading and finding credit with many; furthermore as this was proved by the work of the Carmelite friar, Foscarini, in which the above-named Father tried to prove that the thesis of the Sun being the center of the universe, was true, and not contradictory to the Holy Bible: therefore to prevent such opinions spreading further, to the damage of the Holy Catholic Faith, the Congregation resolves that the works of Copernicus and Zuñiga shall be suspended till they have been corrected, while the book of the Carmelite Father Foscarini shall be prohibited and banned, together with all such works as teach the same theories.

The Papal audience was arranged for March 11th. Pope Paul V received the scientist very kindly, with marked favor. When Galileo had kissed the glittering slipper, His Holiness commanded him to rise, and addressed him almost consolingly:

"My dear son, We very much regret that you have encountered difficulties in your science. But We know that you are a pious Catholic and We also learn that Cardinal Bellarmin has explained to you Our Holy standpoint."

"Yes, Holy Father."

"Well, you must manage to do your best. We have no fear for your personal safety—you have sharp wits. But enough of this. What is the news in Florence?"

They talked for almost an hour. Not another word was said of Copernicus, astronomy, or the movement of the planets. They talked of the

Medici family; of the visit of young Carlo, the Prince Cardinal; of Tuscan folklore and Florentine life. But at last Galileo felt that something
more must be said of his own business.

"Life would be beautiful, Holy Father, if I had not so many slanderers
and enemies. I can't describe what distress I've suffered. I shouldn't sur-
vive it a second time."

"You need fear nothing more. We are fully satisfied of your innocence, as well as your diligent faith and honest thinking. The whole
Inquisition knows you as an excellent and upright man, and We ourselves esteem you as such. Every famous man has had his slanderers.
But while We live, you have nothing to fear. Whenever you need Our
paternal power or good will, as long as you remain a faithful Catholic,
you can always turn to Us for protection."

He kissed the Pope's hand and again his slipper, and went proudly
home. Few people could boast of the fact that Pope Paul V had expressed to them his regret at having to take a decision. He hastened to
describe his audience, proudly and in detail, to the Ambassador. Guicciardini nodded and said indifferently:

"I'm really glad to think that the whole matter is settled. As long as
Your Honor remains in Rome, I must keep my ears pricked like a grey-
hound for fear lest you blunder irreparably—in the name of truth."

"But, Excellency, I shan't be leaving you yet. I settled it with His
Excellency Picchena that I'm to wait here for the arrival of our Prince
Cardinal Carlo."

Guicciardini sighed. This unruly, argumentative, violent, and extremely
unpleasant man, who was also a strong drinker, had been quartered on
him for four months. Now he had hoped to be rid of him at last. But
no . . . the weight of anxiety was off his mind, and Galileo wanted to
enjoy himself. It was seldom that he felt completely well. The arrival
of the young Medici Cardinal did not interest him very much, but there
were so many amusing and clever people among the Lynxes; there was
such good wine in the inns of the Trastevere; the cocksure Duke Cesi,
now out of mourning, knew such a bevy of pretty and not overvirtuous
young girls, that he always found some new distractions. . . .

And soon he found new cause for staying. The prophecy of the Pope
that he would always have slanderers, was proved true with unexpected
swiftness. The rumor had spread through Rome that he had had a

great quarrel with the Inquisition and had been forced to deny all his teachings under oath, in front of Cardinal Bellarmin. His peregrination started all over again. He wanted to get to the root of this ugly gossip. It was almost a police investigation, following a twisting trail. But, as usually happens in such cases, the original scandal-monger could not be found. All whom he asked where they had picked up the ridiculous rumor answered with a sly, innocent smirk: "Everyone says so."

There was nothing for it but to get another audience with Bellarmin and complain to him of this new calumny. The Cardinal listened without the slightest sign of impatience.

"I've heard the same rumor. It's really vile. Don't you even suspect somebody?"

"Everybody and nobody, Monsignor. I'm helpless."

"But I may be less so. Tell me what you think I can do."

"Dare I ask you to give me a written denial?"

"Gladly. The truth is always the truth."

And at once he wrote out the following document:

We, Cardinal Roberto Bellarmin, having been apprised of certain slanders against Messer Galileo Galilei, to the effect that he has been forced under oath to deny his teachings in our presence and do penance for them, herewith declare at his request and in the interest of truth, that the aforesaid Messer Galilei was never constrained to deny any teachings under an oath, neither in our presence nor in that of any priest in Rome—nor, according to our knowledge, in any other place—and that he was never commanded to do penance. He was simply notified of the prohibition of Our Holy Father the Pope, published by the Index Congregation in reference to the Copernican system. This decree forbids, as contrary to Holy Writ, any defense or maintenance of the teaching that the Sun stands at the center of the universe, not moving daily from east to west and that the earth revolves around the Sun. The above which is written by me personally I attest as true on this the 26th day of May in the year of Our Lord 1616. Roberto Card. Bellarmin.

This calmed him a little. He waited for the arrival of Prince Cardinal Carlo, who entered Rome in great magnificence, through dense crowds. It was a great procession of horses, pikemen, and halberdiers, a dazzling display of Medici wealth. In the Villa Medici they presented him to this brother of the Grand Duke. Carlo received him very graciously and permitted him to kiss the hem of his cloak, though this was an honor usually reserved for members of the dynasty. Then, on his last day in Rome, he went back to Santa Maria Sopra Minerva, the Church of the Inquisition. He knelt and prayed before the high altar. "I'm still alive," he muttered gratefully. "They haven't burned me. . . ."

He came out of the church, stopped in the small square, and looked back at the huge block of buildings. He glanced up at the windows on the left, where the Inquisitors usually held their meetings, where they passed their judgments and spoke their sentence. The sun shone clear in the radiant sky—the gigantic sun around which, at this moment, spun the earth, as it had through ageless æons of time, a tiny ball of stone and clay.

A few human beings, the millionth parts of a speck of dust, had come together on a tiny point of this little ball, hurtling through space, invisible to the naked eye, to proclaim that the ball itself did not move. Yet still the ball spun onward through immeasurable space, and they along with it. Galileo looked up at the windows, and shouted with the gay impudence of a street urchin: *"E pur si muove!"*

XVI

The ailing Grand Duke, whose constant fever no doctor could alleviate, was not able to receive his Court mathematician. Galileo reported to Picchena, the Prime Minister. He delivered the Papal blessing for his Sovereign, and all his other news. He had, for instance, spoken to the Spanish Ambassador on the subject of his navigating invention. By now it had collected dust for nearly four years in the Spanish archives. But at last the Ambassador, who had just been recalled to Spain, had promised to rouse the officials. Galileo also delivered a confidential request from Duke Cesi, who had chosen a rich and pretty Countess, a Salviati, for his second wife. The Countess was related to the Medici, and the Duke wanted Cosimo's support with the rest of the family.

"And what about your new cosmology?" Picchena asked.

"I'm forced to keep quiet for a while. It isn't easy though, especially now. A very sharp-witted Ravenna man called Ingoli has just sent me an open letter in which he enumerates all the arguments against Copernicus. My fingers simply itch to answer him, but this isn't the time. Why, just as I was leaving Rome they arrested the bookseller in Naples who had printed Foscarini's book! Foscarini himself died of the shock. So for the present I can only work on in secret, but I'll come into the open again one day. I shall write some work which treats the whole subject as a hypothesis. Just as Copernicus did. . . . But now I must move into my new house."

"Where do you intend to live?"

"On the south side, on the road to Monte Oliveto."

"A charming neighborhood. Have you taken the Villa Segni, by any chance? If so, we shall be neighbors."

"Yes, the Villa Segni! It makes me so happy to think of living there! At last I'll have plenty of room. There's a big garden, the view is magnificent, and there's a splendid room for my observatory. It will be a sheer delight to live there. I shall give my enemies all kinds of material to use against me."

"That reminds me of some interesting news which I'd forgotten to tell you. Do you remember Sizzi?"

"Of course I do. It was he started the ball rolling, instigated by Messer Giovanni de' Medici."

"That's right. Well, you've nothing more to fear from Messer Giovanni. He has taken service with the Venetians. We found him rather a nuisance here at home. But let me tell you about Sizzi. He went to Paris and got involved in some French conspiracy—and we've just heard that he has been broken on the wheel. An ugly end."

"He deserved it," Galileo roared—but he calmed down at once. "Although it was a terrible punishment. It must be too horrible to be tortured . . . the wheel. . . . A whipping would have sufficed. Poor man. I pity him already. Is His Highness better?"

"Sometimes he is better and sometimes worse. He's a shadow of his former self. Pray for him, Messer Galileo! Your prayer will be more efficacious, now that you have been blessed by the Pope."

The new villa in Bellosguardo was quite different from his former Florentine homes. It was almost a palace; even its entrance showed that a distinguished master had been living in it. Beyond the gate was a gardener's lodge. The villa itself was hidden farther in the park, as if it had been built in a forest. Galileo looked about for a likely housekeeper. Many came to apply for the post. He chose the woman who asked the highest wage and looked the prettiest. As they bargained he gazed at her with such fervor that this virtuous widow lowered her eyes with understanding modesty.

Life went on in its usual course. Every night he watched the stars, prepared his notes, and rose late next morning. He was seen at Court, talking with any friends he happened to find, sometimes with Picchena himself. Now and then he was received by the Prince or the Dowager Duchess. He had many letters to answer from all parts of Europe, from famous and unknown men alike. He still wrote to his old friends. He always knew something about Sarpi, Sagredo, Cesi, and of Bartoluzzi, who, according to visitors to Padua, was living happily with Marina. He knew what Kepler was doing. The German astronomer had moved to Linz and had there taken a second wife to give his small children a mother. After the ambition and luxury of his Barbara, he seemed to long for simple domesticity, since he had taken to wife a serving-wench of Baron Stahremberg. Two children were born of this second marriage, and the children of a good-for-nothing brother also lived in his house. Then the post brought news of other acquaintances. Old Fabrizio, the Padua professor of medicine, had died during the windy spring. Magini, his rival at Bologna, who had been intriguing against him these thirteen years, passed away suddenly. He had no time to finish his work on the exact orbit of the Medici stars in which he wanted to question the fame of their discoverer. But the letters of his innumerable pupils in Portugal, England, and Poland contained news about unknown people. An Englishman, for instance, wrote that one of the notables of his country, a well-known player and writer of plays, had just died at Stratford-on-Avon. Galileo, however, could not make out his name; he had never heard of him.

Every day after dinner his son visited him. He himself taught Vincenzo the rudiments. Though the boy was not exactly stupid at ten, he already betrayed the fact that he was never likely to be a genius. He hated his lessons, no subject especially interested him, while as for his character it surprised his father more and more to see how he took after Michelagnolo—the same shiftless reliance on other people. The same eye to the main chance.

Michelagnolo seldom wrote from Munich. He also had two children of his own.

When the boy left, Galileo took his hat and walked down into Florence. It was a long walk from Bellosguardo, but his nature needed constant exercise and the sight of other human beings. If there was no one to visit, he dropped in at the Grazzini pharmacy on the corner of the Piazza del Duomo, the ancient meeting place of distinguished Florentines, where in times long past Machiavelli had stood disputing with his friends under the shelves and flasks, or he went to some meeting of the Crusca Academy, where one could always hear interesting news. The great Italian dictionary had been published and had brought the Crusca such renown that other nations were following its example. The Germans had founded a similar patriotic academy to compile a dictionary at Weimar, calling it *Fruchtbringende Gesellschaft*.

But his happiest day was Sunday, the time for a visit to the convent. Vincenzo did not come for lessons, and directly after dinner his father set out on his long walk. It led him down to the river bank, then into the beautiful alley of the Poggio Imperiale, and so on to the footpaths which led to Arcetri. If the weather was fine, he did not mind climbing the narrow mountain tracks behind the city. His daughters were always waiting for him at the usual place, in an empty outhouse of the convent yard. There was a bench here on which the two nuns were sitting sedately. They had ceased to be Virginia and Livia. When they had turned sixteen and were both professed, they had each taken a solemn oath in the presence of Coadjutor Pandolfini, Governor of Convents, to live by the triple rule of Poverty, Chastity, and Obedience. And so, to symbolize their rebirth, they had taken new names. Virginia became Suor Maria Celeste—Sister Heavenly Mary; and Livia, Suor Arcangela—Sister Archangel. But these solemn names soon became pet names for Galileo. His elder girl became "Celeste," the younger "Angela."

The two nuns kept their childhood characteristics even as grown-ups —indeed, they were even more pronounced. Celeste was spiritual and elfin, celestially gay, as though she had stepped down into the world from one of Fra Angelico's frescoes. Angela was suspicious and moody, sullenly nursing every grievance. Celeste was celestial life itself; Angela was earthly. Their father tried to love them equally, but in his heart he felt a much greater affection for Celeste. Angela's voice and bearing were icy and distant as a stranger's. Celeste adored, but Angela didn't even like him. All her love was given to herself. Every time her capricious temper vented itself in high-pitched words, Galileo sadly recognized and remembered his mother's voice. He tried to put this thought out of his mind; filial respect was still deeply ingrained in him, and he hated to think of the old woman's faults, though even in her old age her foolish temper was just as violent. But her son scarcely suffered from it now, since he seldom visited the Landuccis. He had never mentioned the letters of the dead servant, but he still kept them locked in a drawer. Whenever he was saddened by the sight of his mother's vixenish temper in Angela, he found ample consolation in Celeste. Celeste was kind, patient, long-suffering. She could understand and forgive all things. She was full of love. Galileo was happy when she scolded him for his slovenly clothes, and resigned himself to taking all the physic which she kept prescribing for him.

Not that her physic did him much good. Inflammation of the joints started again, with increasing severity. A stabbing pain shot through his kidneys. The doctor nodded. It would be a miracle, he said, if his kidneys did not suffer from so much wine. But, like all doctors, he could only explain the pain without alleviating it. The sick man did not care if a crowd collected outside his room to listen to his screams of agony. He could not read; his crippled hand could not hold the telescope. The brother of the Grand Duchess, the Austrian Archduke Leopold, visiting Florence, had come to see this famous man. Galileo needed all his strength not to cry out in the Archduke's presence, forcing himself with a monstrous effort to talk to him with fitting ceremony; he asked Leopold's permission to dedicate his work on the tides to him. But when at last the royal guest took his departure, Galileo found that his lips were bleeding, and the nails of his sound hand had left deep marks on the palm.

He had to stay in bed for long months, without comfort save for Celeste's letters. She often wrote to her sick father, entertaining him with the small stories of the convent, and putting into every word her warm affection. She implored him to go on a pilgrimage to Loreto and the Holy Virgin; then he would certainly recover. He promised, to please her. But even this pious vow was slow in vanquishing his illness. After six months he was able to get up at last. And as soon as he recovered part of his strength he really went on a pilgrimage to Loreto.

The Dowager Duchess, who usually was not inclined to be generous, gave him a litter chair. She was more a pious Catholic than her son, and encouraged this learned man to go on pilgrimage, especially as he was meddling with dangerous teachings. It was June, and an oppressive heat spread over the world. The sick man sat panting and sweating in the jolting litter, his temples throbbing. It was a long way to the Ancona seashore, but at last he arrived. The lovely little shrine enraptured him and filled his heart with gratitude to Celeste. His nerves, made more susceptible during his long illness, were sensitive to every impression. His servants carried him to the hill where the shrine stood. Among a host of pilgrims he listened to the sermons of the priests. The house at Nazareth in which the Archangel Gabriel had greeted the Virgin had been lifted by angels on the night of May 9, 1291, carried across the Heavens and put down near Tersatto. There it had stayed for four and a half years. On December 10, 1294, they moved it again to the neighborhood of Recanati; then in a few months a third time, depositing it finally here, on the hill of Loreto. The small Santa Casa was surrounded now by a cathedral. Galileo knelt with the other pilgrims from all over the world, in front of the two steps of the altar. Then, with great difficulty, he managed to climb the Campanile, because Celeste had told him to do it. But when he rested and began to talk to people he found that war was their only topic. In the countries beyond the Alps a great religious war had broken out, and the superstitious Italians could talk of nothing but signs and wonders. Many affirmed they had seen the statue of the Virgin on the altar of the Santa Casa with tears in its eyes. Others had been in places where blood had fallen instead of rain. The cows had monster calves in many villages. Not one heavenly sign was missing.

When Galileo returned, exhausted, to Florence, his first visit was to the convent. And here, too, signs had been seen in the heavens on an August day of the year 1618, when the great war started. The pilgrim had paid no heed to former miracles nor did the war especially interest him. But the new signs excited him unspeakably. For three comets appeared in the sky. Two were small and scarcely noticeable; but the third, appearing at the center of the Scorpion constellation, shone with a clear and almost formidable radiance. Florence was half crazy with excitement. "An Evil Omen." People did not sleep for days; they stood in clusters in the streets staring up at the menacing sky. Panic went shuddering through the crowd.

For the man who had most interest in these stars, they were really ominous. His pilgrimage had done no good. He had to take to his bed again. His pain was less racking than it had been in the first half of the year, but it kept him from working. He could not watch the comets, having neither the strength nor the nervous energy for such work. He had a friend, a former pupil of his, Mario Guiducci, who visited him every day and described what he had seen the night before. But the sick man listened indifferently and did not answer. Once more he was laid up for months. And when he rose again after enduring pain, exasperating boredom, and impatience, the comets had begun to fade. In January they vanished completely, so that the most famous astronomer in the world was unable to observe these stars which might have an immeasurable importance. And now when he could work, they faded away.

Someone else went with them. A broken-hearted letter came from Padua. Bartoluzzi wrote that Marina had died of some inner malady, after a short illness. The doctors could not give it a name.

The first person whom Galileo told was his son. Vincenzo burst into tears when he knew that he was a motherless little boy; but, when he thought he had done his duty, he asked for money to buy some Murano marbles. Galileo gave him the money and suddenly remembered Murano, the heavy scent of Sagredo's enchanted garden, the gondola waiting at the bridge.

Then he went up to the convent and told the nuns that their mother was dead. Angela did not seem much disturbed.

"I scarcely knew her; she never cared for me. But I'll pray for her soul. Only it will have to be tomorrow; I've too many prayers today, as it is."

Celeste said nothing for a long while. Then she said:

"I'm terribly sorry for her, because she started her life at such disadvantage, and she couldn't love. No one could have a worse fate than that. It's as though she hadn't lived at all. But because she was kind she's now in Heaven with the angels. And she's full of love. Do you see, father, how merciful God can be?"

Galileo stroked his daughter's hand silently. Then he said good-by to them both. He had some important business to see to in Florence. He went home and called on his neighbor, the Prime Minister.

"Your Excellency sent for me."

"Yes. I was sorry to trouble you, but I thought it would be easier for you to drop in here than to see me at my office. I wanted to ask you something. Caterina, my daughter, has fallen ill. That means plenty of trouble for a widower like me. But I must go with the Court to Pisa, for a long stay. Would you mind looking in on my daughter every day while I am away?"

"It will be a great honor for me. My sister, Signora Landucci, who is a kind woman, can move into my house for that time. She can spend the whole day with your daughter if necessary."

"I knew you'd help me. But how can I repay your kindness?"

"Let me take you at your word, Your Excellency. I have three illegitimate children. The two girls are nuns; it doesn't matter about them. But it is more important for my son. I've wanted to legitimize

him for a long time, but couldn't because by the time I got the idea
his mother married someone else. But now she is dead. I wanted to ask
you to submit my request to the Prince. It's only a formality."

"That's all right. I'll settle it for you."

Galileo stood up to take his leave. But his attention was caught suddenly by some pictures which were standing against the wall.

"What paintings are these, Your Excellency?"

"Court pictures from the collection of Grand Duke Francesco. But
Fernando banned them from the Palace. I had them brought down
from the attic. Time enough has passed; they can be hung again. That
one at the end is a portrait of Bianca Cappello."

Galileo ceased to hear his voice; he stood there lost in contemplation
of the face that once had wakened his soul. His young heart beat again
like a fluttering mysterious bird. He looked again at this face to which
he had prayed, and was staggered to see that Marina had really never
resembled it at all. And yet the mere fancy of this resemblance had
made him fall in love with Marina. It was not Marina he had loved,
but the Bianca in her. Yet why? Why did he think that there was such a
close affinity between the two?

He stared amazed at the portrait which showed a face utterly different from hers. His memory showed him the perfect image of a com-
pellingly lovely, red-haired woman. How could he ever have made
such a mistake! And he thought that the secret of human beings is
even more wonderful and mysterious than that of the stars.

XVII

Even after Marina's death Bartoluzzi kept writing to Galileo. His love for his wife lived on in their friendship. And now he questioned the great astronomer about these mysterious new comets which still excited the whole world. He was not the only one. Even during his illness Galileo received hundreds of inquiries from all over the world. He was the safest man to ask. But he did not answer. He could not tell them honestly, because he did not know what these three new stars were. He discussed them often with Guiducci, but at best he could only form uncertain theories, which he himself considered as provisional. Therefore he did not answer the many questions.

But finally he received inquiries from two places where an answer was imperative.

One was put by the Court. The Dowager Duchess sent for Galileo, receiving him in the company of her daughter-in-law. The two ladies were more conscious than ever of their dignity. The Emperor Mathias had recently died; and his nephew, Crown Prince Ferdinand, a brother of Cosimo's wife, succeeded him. So the brother-in-law of the Tuscan Grand Duke had become the Emperor of the Holy Roman Empire, Lord of Germans, Bohemians, Croats, Moravians, and Hungarians; and Archduke Leopold, who had visited the sick Galileo in the Villa Segni, was now Crown Prince. The Florentine Court could talk of nothing but the Emperor. The Grand Duchess kept finding occasion to say: "His Imperial Majesty, my brother." Her children mentioned "Uncle Ferdinand, the Imperator," every hour. Even the sensible Grand Duke Cosimo liked to talk of "Our brother-in-law, the Emperor."

At present, however, His Imperial Majesty's position was not an easy one. The Bohemians would not acknowledge him as their ruler, and elected in his place Frederick V, the Elector of the Palatinate, head of the Protestant Union. Another Protestant prince, Gabriel Bathlen of Transylvania, was besieging Vienna. All this caused much anxious stir at the Florentine Court. Therefore they had sent for the Court astronomer.

"Tell us, Messer Galilei, but quite frankly, what the three comets mean. The holy crusade of His Majesty the Emperor to exterminate heresy causes us the deepest anxiety. And we hear so much about the secret importance of these stars that we felt we had to ask your advice."

"Your Highness," Galileo answered, "that is a metaphysical question. I don't deal in the secret meanings of the stars. I leave that to theologians and astrologers."

"I know that you have never drawn up horoscopes," the sister of Emperor Ferdinand said frigidly; "but we hoped that you would be prepared to talk, when it's an affair of His Majesty, my brother, and the Faith itself. Can you tell us nothing about these stars?"

"Nobody on earth can tell you anything definite, Your Highness. Science hasn't yet solved the mystery of these so-called comets or how they are formed. These radiant apparitions appear and vanish at irregular intervals. No system is able to account for them."

"Of course there's a system," snapped the Grand Duchess. "Even a child knows that they always appear before a war!"

"Naturally, Your Highness, since so far there has never been an age without a war somewhere or other on this earth. When the comet appears, it is always wartime. I have a theory which I have mentioned to His Highness, Archduke Leopold, but I won't vouch for it. These comets may not be stars at all, but burning agglomerations of gases freed from the atmosphere of the earth, which can travel extraordinary distances— as far as the moon. Their tails of flame can be explained more or less by optical laws and the imperfection of our sight. Then the gas flare burns out, and the comet vanishes. Once I taught exactly the opposite of this. But I have changed my opinion. I believe that a comet is no star, but a mass of vapor."

"Yes, but what does it *mean*," the Dowager Duchess insisted.

Galileo found a way of escape.

"Your Highness, His Holiness the Pope has forbidden me personally to deal with theological questions. But if Your Highness would petition the Holy See to have this changed . . ."

"No, no!" the Dowager Duchess interrupted him nervously. "If that is a command of His Holiness, we'd better leave it. There was nothing else we wanted to ask you."

After such audiences Galileo always called on Picchena to tell him every word of the conversation, and ask for advice and information as to how he stood in the favor of the reigning family. He did it now. Picchena frowned as he listened. Then he said:

"Do you know the Cavaliere Cioli?"

"Not very well. I feel that somehow he dislikes me."

"I advise you to gain his friendship as soon as possible. I have good reason to think that very difficult times are before us. I know you take no interest in politics, but your own eyes may have shown you the trend of events. This is the great day of reckoning. The Papacy is fighting its last battle with Protestantism. Europe's most powerful ruler, His Majesty the Emperor, is a fervent Catholic who brooks no contradiction. He longs to exterminate all heretics. As a good Catholic I must applaud him for this. But I dislike the civil authority of priests. And this fight means that the Jesuits are all-powerful everywhere. You must know that this whole battle against heresy, every detail and phase of this huge struggle, was inspired and organized by the Jesuits. The Emperor Ferdinand is their pupil. So is our Grand Duchess and the Dowager Duchess. But not His Highness Cosimo or myself. I can work excellently with our Prince. As long as he is still alive we'll always be good friends with the Holy See, yet remain independent. As long as he is still alive! But to my unspeakable grief we may have to reckon on losing him in the prime of his life. And, Galileo, my position will be bad indeed. They won't leave me a week in my post. The Jesuits will demand my head. The power will be in the hands of two women who have already chosen my successor: Cavaliere Cioli, a favorite of the Society of Jesus, one of the humblest slaves of Rome. The Jesuits will rule Florence. Messer Galileo, take my advice. For your own sake, try to gain Cioli's favor, and be on your guard."

"I've never had any trouble with the Jesuits. On the contrary. I've many friends among them. I never took part in the actions of Padua University against the Fathers. Father Clavius, the Roman professor, of blessed memory, was almost a father to me. Cardinal Bellarmin, the greatest Jesuit, has always shown me particular favor. Even Father Scheiner, the Jesuit astronomer of Ingolstadt, always treats me with great respect in controversy.

"These are individuals. But I think that the Jesuits as a whole mistrust you as a follower of Copernicus. Take my advice: be on your guard."

Galileo promised to remember. And now he was confronted by the second question about the comets which had to be answered. The Jesuit Father Grassi delivered a lecture in Rome, explaining at length that they were really stars. The lecture also dealt with the latest developments in astronomy, but did not mention Galileo's name. It was as though he had said in so many words that the man who had invented the telescope had done nothing; as though the moons of Jupiter did not exist; as though no one had ever heard of the amazing new attributes of Venus and Saturn. A copy of this lecture arrived in Florence. Guiducci brought it to his master, highly indignant.

"Messer Galileo, you must answer!"

"No, no," he protested. "I don't want to quarrel with any Jesuit."

"Very well, I'll answer it myself."

He was soon ready with his reply, and showed it to his master. Galileo hesitated; some dim instinct still warned him to drop the whole matter and ask Guiducci to keep quiet. But, when he read the essay, he could not control himself. He corrected the text, changing the order of the words and creating thereby a new clear meaning in a whole series of muddled thoughts. In the end he did not hinder Guiducci. Let him take the responsibility; he was independent enough! And so his answer was published by the Florentine Academy.

A few weeks later there came a reply to Guiducci's answer. *Astronomical and Philosophical Scales, on which Lotario Sarsi Sigensano measures the theories of Galileo Galilei expounded and recently published by Mario Guiducci at the Florentine Academy.* Lotario Sarsi Sigensano was only a pseudonym; the book was written by Father Grassi himself.

This was no scientific argument with Guiducci, but an open, violent personal attack against Galileo. He mentioned the comets only as a scarcely important issue. The whole essay dealt with Galileo's person. It started by belittling his scientific stature. It doubted whether Galileo Galilei had ever invented or discovered anything. All the successes he claimed were due to others. He had not really invented the telescope. His compass was created by Capra. The moons of Jupiter had really been observed by Mayr, the sunspots by Scheiner. Galileo was a garrulous thief of other people's achievements. And these insults were followed by a very skillfully laid trap: What of the Copernican system to which Guiducci had not referred, but in which Galilei believed so stubbornly? Did he uphold, or not, the accursed theory which "insults truth as much as the pious ears of the faithful, and which must be abhorred by all God-fearing men"?

Galileo could not sleep for weeks after this wild attack. He did not know how he could answer it. If he replied to the last question, he had either to renounce the main idea of his life or adhere to it—but then he could prepare himself for the Inquisition. While, if he kept quiet, he was shamefully admitting these charges, accepting these insults to his honor. Whatever he did, Picchena's words were coming true: he found himself fighting a Jesuit, behind whom the whole world power of the order threatened him.

No one could advise him usefully. Everyone had a different suggestion. One warned him not to reply a single word. The other tried to incite him to a violent counter-attack, while at the same time he must praise the whole Society of Jesus, never mentioning Copernicus at all. The third advised the usual form of a letter addressed to one of his friends. The fourth suggested that he should defend Copernicus as a hypothesis. All this bewildered him. He was so nervous that he could scarcely keep quiet. He felt he had lost his own sober judgment, and when his nerves seemed about to snap, one day his sister, Signora Landucci, came to his house, crying and sobbing. It took her a long time to compose herself:

"Oh! For God's sake, stop that noise! How can I help you unless you tell me what's the matter?"

"Benedetto . . . the scoundrel . . . after thirty years of married life. . . ."

"Well? What about him? Has he begun to beat you?"

"He's left me. He's gone off with his mistress. He left me with the four children and your Vincenzo and Mamma . . . and without a soldo in the house . . ."

"What! When did he go! How? I don't understand. . . ."

Virginia recovered a little and told him everything. Benedetto had had a mistress for months; he had picked up a girl from some poor family. Recently he had been behaving intolerably at home. Often he slept out. Husband and wife did not speak to each other; they communicated in writing. Now Benedetto had packed all his clothes, sent for a coach, and driven away. He had not even kissed his children. He had left a note on the table, saying that he could not stand this life, and was leaving Florence. Virginia began to cry again. Galileo now felt very sorry for her. She was forty-seven, fat, a middle-aged, prematurely gray-haired woman. Landucci, the model citizen, who was so self-righteous and greedy about the dowry, had left her. . . . Galileo sighed.

"Don't cry. You can move over here at once with Mother and the children. As long as I live you've nothing to fear."

Virginia embraced him, shedding copious tears. She abused her husband and babbled words of gratitude at the same time. They started to move in on the same day. One family scene followed another. When Galileo's mother arrived with Vincenzo, the whole Bellosguardo family gathered around the house. The old lady stopped the cart and, using it as an orator's stand, began to abuse the niggardly scoundrel whom she could never abide. Slowly a large crowd gathered. By the time Galileo arrived, the whole roadway was full. They had great trouble in persuading her to come into the house. Then the four Landucci children brought all their belongings; the eldest was almost a young man. Virginia, standing in the door, embraced every one of them and cried.

There was plenty of space in the roomy house, but the new arrivals were numerous. In the first days there was an almost unbearable racket of furniture being arranged; and, when at last they had settled down, his mother began to quarrel with his housekeeper. She hobbled out into the park screaming and cursing like a mad woman.

Galileo bore it for a month, but not longer. When he awoke one morning and felt the well-known pain again, he said nothing, but dragged himself into the town and wandered about till he found more modest quarters. They were near the Arno, on the steep slope of the Costa San Giorgio, in the direction of the Belvedere. He took a pleasant little house, with four windows to its one-storied front. It even had a little garden with a friendly green medlar tree. It was empty, and he did not bargain much. Next day he moved in with his housekeeper to be ill in peace. The pain assailed him. He moaned and screamed. Whenever it abated a little, he had to think how to answer the Jesuit. He was still undecided, but now at last he had found the best means to avoid the question about Copernicus. And after all, whatever happened, two great men had assured him of their protection as long as they were still alive: Pope Paul V and the Grand Duke Cosimo.

One February night all the bells of the city began to ring suddenly. Galileo sat up and tugged at his bell rope, until his housekeeper was aroused. He told her to go into the street; perhaps she could find some late passer-by who would tell the reason for all this clamor. Sullen and half asleep, she obeyed. There was much running about at this late hour. She was soon back, sobered by the shock.

"The Grand Duke is dead."

The sick man nodded and sent her back to bed. He wanted to be alone with his thoughts. He put out the light and began to weep softly in the darkness. He recalled the picture of the young Crown Prince listening with his kind, ugly face to the explanation of the compass, the joy of understanding in his eyes. Then he remembered an evening in the park of the ducal summer palace where he pointed out mysterious stars to him, and the boy was amazed and moved by the thought of infinity. He followed Cosimo through his whole short life, refreshing the memory of their conversations, and ached with the thought that a kind, good man was dead, who had loved him and whom he had loved as every Florentine loved the Medici.

They buried the thirty-year-old Grand Duke in the wonderful Medici crypt, a grim jewel case inlaid with precious stones. But his loyal Court mathematician could not even attend the funeral. He listened to the news of the outside world in an agony of physical pain. The ten-year-old Crown Prince succeeded his father, taking the name of Fernando II. Cosimo had given detailed instructions in his will, commanding that Fernando's mother and grandmother should act as regents, assisted by a council of four. But Picchena did not remain a member of this council for long. It all happened as he had foretold it: he was pensioned off, and Cavaliere Cioli took his place. The Jesuits were ruling Tuscany.

The sick man often remembered the Sagredo letter written soon after he left Padua. Every word of that letter was coming true. He tried to console himself by calling up the picture of the Venetian dandy, his small waxed mustache and forked beard, his cut velvet doublet, buckled shoes, and always ironic, skeptical, and teasing smile. He longed to see him again and talk to him. Sagredo had kept sending him invitations to his different estates, but he never went. Now he decided to go and see him as soon as he was well enough to move. This decision lightened his heart and made even his pain endurable for a day.

Suddenly there came the news that Gianfrancesco Sagredo was dead.

He had the old letters of his friend collected from among his papers. The dead voice could be heard in them all.

The other dead man sent a message. One forenoon a coach drew up in front of the house. His housekeeper came rushing into the room announcing the arrival of the Grand Duke. The little Prince followed her into the bedroom with his Jesuit tutor and Prince Enea Piccolomini. He was wearing a stiff black mourning dress with a white ruff and a richly chased gold rapier. He came to the sick-bed and allowed Galileo to kiss his hand, who had great difficulty in taking advantage of the honor.

"Our father of blessed memory," the child ruler repeated his lesson, "commended you to our special favor on his deathbed. In obedience to his command, but also to our own feelings, we come to wish you speedy recovery and so assure you of our good will."

"I thank you humbly, Your Highness."

That seemed to finish the conversation, but Prince Enea Piccolomini leaped into the breach. He brought greetings and best wishes from his brother, the tutor of the late Grand Duke.

"Do you remember young Ottavio? He was a tiny boy when he had the good fortune to listen to your lectures in Artimino. Now he's twenty and a soldier. He joined the army which Tuscany sends to assist His Imperial Majesty Ferdinand against the Bohemians."

The Jesuit, who had not spoken a single word, solemnly nodded. The Grand Duke again extended his hand to this famous man, inherited from his father. Galileo kissed it with the same difficulty.

"There will be a marble tablet on this house, Porzia," he said to the still-astonished housekeeper.

Then he returned to his grim thoughts. His mind was preoccupied with death; all day he felt it skulking around his bed. His dreams were nightmares; the fear of leaving the world appalled him. Every night he forced himself to sleep, in terror of the morning's news.

He had not long to wait. One morning Virginia came sobbing, with her the gently, indifferently crying "Nencio," as they called Vincenzo in the family.

"Galileo," she sobbed, "Mother is dead."

It was a hard shock. He could only long for her. All the shame, trouble, and scandal she had brought on him faded away, as if a garment had fallen from his naked soul which writhed, still clinging to its parent, according to the ancient bonds. He moaned and shuddered in his bereavement, as if he were not fifty-seven but a boy of five. "Mother! Mother! Mother!" he cried again and again, like a lost little boy, and clung with his sound hand to Virginia. It was only later that he could bear to listen. The old woman had been poorly for weeks, but they had not dared to trouble him in his illness. Her last days had been unconscious; she had died so gently, nobody even noticed her death. She was eighty-three. Her funeral was very lonely; Livia and her husband could not get to it in time from Venice. Lena and her family lived in a far-away village among the hills. Michelagnolo was in Munich, while the two granddaughters were cloistered nuns. There were three of them now, because one of the Landucci girls had joined the order as Suor Chiara. Galileo was ill. Virginia and her four children were the only ones present of the family.

Who had he left? On whom could he count? Who would help him when he could get up and work? Dimly he wondered how to answer the Jesuit. No violent pamphlet. No open letter. Something great and fine, a confession of his whole science, his whole thought. He would take time over it, work it out carefully. He would present it personally to Pope Paul and Cardinal Bellarmin, explaining to them what it was all about. A vast work in which even the Copernican system was only a detail.

He set to work slowly, sometimes with a yelp of pain when he moved carelessly. Every day his visitors brought him the exciting news of a world in arms. One November morning they came to tell of a great victory: the Catholic army had triumphed over the Protestants near a mountain called Weissberg. Young Piccolomini had commanded a regiment of cavalry and proved himself a gallant leader. The Court was jubilant; there were great festivities in Rome. Pope Paul had arranged a splendid procession of thanksgiving. But all the excitement proved too much for him. He died of a stroke.

Galileo was beginning to live in fear. All those of whom he thought with trust and affection were dying off, as though his thoughts had poisoned them. He became superstitious, murmuring village spells learned from his housekeeper. But they could not dispel his terror of death. In the last few months he had aged ten years. As he sat working at his table or resting in his armchair, there was always a look of strain and fear on his face.

The Cardinals chose a frail and ailing old man, Alessandro Lodovisi, to succeed him. He took the name of Gregory XV. He could not fill his office; his kinsman Ludovico Lodovisi governed in his place, skillfully gathering all the reins. Only a few old Cardinals, as, for instance, Bellarmin, still had some say.

Galileo's state of mind improved. He was working more easily. He was especially glad to have found a good title for his book. Grassi had called his attack *The Astronomical and Philosophical Scales*. Galileo would call his the *Saggiatore*—"The Gold Scales." A fine instrument of precision to show the exact difference between gold and glittering dross.

Summer arrived; the pain had gone out of his kidneys. His joints were almost supple again. The book was making excellent progress. He had already finished a number of chapters when one afternoon Guiducci visited him.

"Maestro, I've just had letters from Rome. Cardinal Bellarmin is dead."

The room was shrouded in gathering dusk. The objects around him lost their perspective. He swooned and slid down off his chair. His unconscious hand still clutched the quill. . . .

XVIII

Two and a half years had passed since the publication of Grassi's attack, and still the answer had not been heard. Grassi's adherents had more or less achieved their aim: their opponent had been put to silence, a silence which seemed shameful surrender. In Rome the Peripatetics rejoiced. Duke Cesi clamored for the manuscript of the *Saggiatore*. One of Galileo's former pupils, a priest, was also impatient to see it. This man had become very influential. He was Monsignor Ciampoli, one of the priests attached to the Vatican and chosen as his Breve Secretary by the new Pope, Gregory XV. Galileo became especially diligent now that the Pope's secretary hurried his work.

But he could not give up all his time to it. Either one or other of his daughters was often ill. Then he had to settle the business of the oldest Landucci boy, who had fallen in love with a strikingly beautiful young girl, Anna Diocianti. His father had strictly opposed this love, and now that he had deserted his family, the mother continued the same objections. There were so many well-to-do girls; let her Vincenzo marry one of them! But the boy refused to give up his choice. He sensed his only friend in his uncle, and brought along the girl to see him. She was really beautiful and very much in love with young Landucci. And Galileo took their part. They visited him almost every day to tell their plans and ask his help. Mostly it was a question of money. Neither of them had a soldo in the world. And even the girl's family were against it, since quite a number of rich cavaliers were prepared to marry the pretty child. But this love story reached its climax in a letter from an unknown place written by the fugitive father, again forbidding his son to marry this girl. This so enraged Galileo that in his first fury he offered to dower the girl and pay the expenses of the wedding. Now even Virginia, the austere mother, was silenced. She could raise no objections; Galileo was keeping the whole family; he had every right to decide in this matter. But his generosity only brought a crop of slanders. The beautiful girl was often seen going into the house at the Costa San Giorgio. Tongues were set wagging; the old rascal, they said, was not content with constantly changing his housekeepers, but he must needs hook to himself a virgin, and then, as soon as he was tired of her, force his nephew to give her an honest name. So Galileo sent Anna to a convent till the wedding, and gave the boy a written warranty for her dowry.

Another Landucci boy became a Benedictine novice. One of the girls was a nun in the same convent as Angela and Celeste. The second girl, who also feared the world, was placed in the San Giorgio convent. Virginia was left without any children.

Only Nencio, Galileo's son, stayed on with them. He was sixteen now, and attended the university. He seemed to possess no special talent. He was used to having everything his own way. He had begun to dress like a rich young noble; he wheedled small sums out of his father. When Galileo tried to discuss his future, he pulled a sour face. He was too lazy ever to want to work. It seemed to him the most natural thing in the world that his father should keep him.

"I don't understand you," raged Galileo. "Have you *no* ambition? Does nothing urge you to prove your mettle, show the world what you are?"

The boy looked sullen, and did not answer.

"At least look into yourself and, if you can't find any ambition, try to find some desire. How would you like to live as a grown-up man? How do you see yourself in the future?"

Nencio mumbled and said at last: "I seem to see myself as a diplomat or some kind of courtier."

"Well. That's something at least. I don't want to interfere with your leanings. You can become anything you like, only I wish you would do it with a good will. All right then, you'd better study law."

He had thought of sending the boy to Padua. But it was not so easy. As usual, he had taken on himself new burdens which were almost crushing him. It would cost too much to keep the boy at Padua in a state befitting his father's scientific rank. But perhaps he could get a Court stipend for him at Pisa. Also he felt some dim pang of conscience. He did not want to hear that people were saying that Galileo despised a Tuscan university for his own son. So one fine day he packed Nencio off to Pisa. He gave him some good advice at their parting, but his son's expression clearly showed that he was only listening out of duty, and could scarcely wait for the lecture to end.

The Villa Segni became empty again; only Virginia remained there. Galileo moved back, since he longed for the garden, but kept on the house in the Costa San Giorgio. It would be a refuge if anything happened again to fill the Bellosguardo villa.

In the midst of all these domestic troubles and problems he continued to work on at the *Saggiatore*. The manuscript grew thicker and thicker, and still he was nowhere near the end. He had so much to say. Whenever he put one thought to paper there were ten others clamoring to be expressed. His friends in Rome would wait no longer. They brought out an essay to stop the mouths of triumphant Peripatetics till the "Gold Scales" should be in print. This was written by one of the Lynxes, Stelluti. He defended Guiducci against Grassi, but did not mention Galileo for fear of anticipating the arguments of the *Saggiatore*. The Lynxes sent copies to Florence, but still kept clamoring for the manuscript.

At last it was finished, three years after the Jesuit attack. He read it through, enjoying it like another man's book. He had succeeded in realizing his plan. It defended his own science and its results, and disposed of Grassi's accusations.

Everything was contained in it. It showed clearly that he did not complain of the Church for the blow he had suffered at her hands by the banning of the Copernican system. But he explained that he had not given up the hope of working out a whole new cosmology. Every sensible man could read between the lines what his yielding to theology really meant; yet the Inquisition itself could not have objected to one sentence. Finally it showed Sarsi that his rascally intention had been seen through.

He sent the manuscript to the Lynxes at Rome. They received it with loud acclamations and submitted it in the greatest secrecy to the Papal censorship. Monsignor Cesarini himself wrote to Galileo that the Jesuits had somehow found out about the manuscript and had taken almost unbelievable trouble to get a sight of it. But it was safe in the desk of Monsignor Riccardi, examinator to the Dominicans, who was already reading it. Now everything depended on whether the Church would permit an attack on a Jesuit to be printed. This meant delay. Nobody knew how long it would take. Riccardi would hasten matters as much as possible.

So Galileo waited. This time of waiting was filled with sadness. Fra Paolo Sarpi died at Venice. In the long chain of deaths this shook him again, made him gloomy, and robbed his nights of sleep. Vincenzo was behaving very badly at Pisa; the faithful Castelli, who tried to watch over his master's son, was compelled to write that the boy was leading a dissolute life, fighting, drinking, bragging, always picking quarrels. If he continued like this he would certainly lose his scholarship. There was always trouble at the convent. Celeste suffered continually from toothache and, although she was only twenty-three, most of her teeth had to be pulled out. But she bore the pain with angelic patience. Not so Angela; she had contracted some mysterious ailment and a pain nobody could assuage. To make thinks worse, Virginia also was taken ill.

The censor took four months to reach a decision, but it was worth waiting for. His report was preceded by a private message to Galileo: He longed to make the personal acquaintance of the man who had written such a books as the *Saggiatore*. Duke Cesi urged Galileo in a joyful letter to come to Rome. He enclosed the official text of the examinator's report:

At the command of the Very Reverend Papal Chamberlain I have read the work entitled *Saggiatore*. I found in it nothing offensive to Christian morals, nor any matter contrary to the truth of our Holy Religion. But, above all, I found in it such beautiful disquisitions on the natural sciences that I fully believe that our century should take pride in such a man, who not only has inherited the knowledge of past scientists but has penetrated nature's manifold secrets. Things which remain hidden from former men of learning, this author's acute and lucid mind has revealed to all. I am happy to have been born in this age when the gold of truth is weighed on the finest of all scales. Fra Niccolò Riccardi.

After this there was little hope for the Jesuits' ever stopping publication. The Lynxes sent the book to the printers. And now everyone talked of the *Saggiatore,* even before its text became known. Wild rumors circulated. The Jesuits had stolen the manuscript. The Lynxes had been intimidated, and did not dare to publish the book. Galileo stayed with his ailing sister and daughters, and could not go to Rome. But these rumors scared him. Could they be true? He sent a messenger. The messenger returned from Rome with proofs of the two folios from Duke Cesi.

But the last death in a terrible series spoiled his good news. Virginia died. She had suffered terribly, probably with cancer; the doctors were unable to give it a name. Her husband had left her, her children were scattered. Only her brother had stayed at her side, himself ailing, his nerves on edge. When the poor woman gave up her soul, it was Galileo who closed her eyes, knelt down to pray, and think of his children, muttering in his tear-stricken grief:

"Enough, O Lord, enough now. . . ."

His sister was buried. Galileo lived alone in the Villa Segni and the Costa San Giorgio house. His shoulder was twisted, his limbs weakened, the old fire was dim in his eyes. He was almost sixty. Only his children remained. All his other friends had gone, and his life was empty. It was in vain he tried to disperse these shadows. Through the lonely dusk a long procession of ghosts moved across his eyes: his mother, his sister, Marina, Fra Paolo, Sagredo, the Grand Duke Cosimo, Pope Paul, Bellarmin, old Fabrizio, Father Clavius, watching him with horrible beckoning glances, stiff in the transparent pattern of their hovering faces. Sometimes he felt an unbearable fear of death. He cried out in the dark to hear his own voice, like a child lost in a huge forest. He lit his lamp and stared with trembling horror into the flame. He was old and tired, sick in mind and body. Yet he wanted to live, to live at any price! To live and see the *Saggiatore* in print, thumb its pages, enjoy it, go to Rome, enjoy success there, then come back home, to live on and never, never, never die. Even if alone, even if robbed of his beloved . . . to cling to life.

In these grim, anxious, brooding days, almost forsaking the wonderful joys of science, he heard some news which suddenly filled him with jubilation. He heard it at Court, where a courier from Rome had just arrived. He took a carriage and drove up to Arcetri to the convent. Angela was in bed, but Celeste came to him at once.

"Something's happened, father? Something bad?"

"No, no. I have great news. Important for the convent. Poor old Pope Gregory has died. There's a new Pope. Do you know who he is?"

"Well, who is he?"

"Maffeo Barberini, who loves me so much. Who wrote a poem to me.

Now everything will be different. Ask the Mother Superior whether she has any important request to make. I'll get it for her. I'll settle everything. As soon as I am strong enough to travel, I'm going to Rome. To see His Holiness—he'll embrace me! We'll joke and discuss old times together. We'll talk about my book. The Jesuits will have to be careful of me. Everything will be different. After so much pain and suffering, the good Lord has changed it all. . . ."

Celeste stroked her father's hand happily. His happiness shone on her thin face like the sun's radiance on the moon. Galileo shouted suddenly:

"And now I'll *make* them accept Copernicus! Everything will be altered now!"

He rose and stretched his arms. Suddenly he felt much better.

III

III

I

HE ALWAYS kept every letter, even if it seemed unimportant. He liked to rummage among old correspondence, read a few lines here and there and put the letters back in their orderly files. Now he got out the letters which the new Pope, Urban VIII, had written him as Cardinal Barberini. They were all full of expressions of the warmest praise. He found the one which the Cardinal had sent him, together with the ode:

> The enclosed lines express the deep esteem which I have always felt for your person and the services you have rendered. Though my verse is hardly worthy of your works, it can at least be counted as a token of my appreciation that I want your famous name to shed its luster on my humble poetry. Therefore I send you no lengthy apologies, but only beg you to accept this humble token of my great sympathy. With heartfelt greetings, wishing God's fullest blessing on you.

These lines still made him glow with satisfaction. Was there any other living scientist to whom the first ruler of the world would address such words? And in Florence everyone knew of the poem and letters. His status increased tenfold. Strangers bowed low to him. The Pope's friend! Priests who before had passed him with expressionless faces stopped now and asked affably how he did. The Court suddenly began to take him seriously again. Since Cioli had become Prime Minister, they had paid him very little attention. But now he was as welcome a person as he had been in the reign of the Grand Duke Cosimo. The two Grand Duchesses often invited him, and he had opportunities of speaking to Fernando II, the child prince. Their conversation nearly always led him to the new Pope, and Galileo never missed the chance of saying carelessly:

"Yes, it certainly is a great joy to me that such a good friend of mine has been raised to St. Peter's throne. I am impatient to visit him in Rome and have a long talk with His Holiness."

"The Embassy is always at your disposal," the Dowager Duchess hastened to answer. "The young Marchese, Francesco Niccolini, our present Ambassador, is an exceedingly nice man."

"And his wife is enchanting," Cioli added.

"When were you thinking of starting?" asked the Grand Duchess.

"Your Highness, I should like to start at once; but my health would never stand such a journey. I am afraid to go till I feel quite well again, and they tell me the roads are unsafe. I hear there are floods everywhere. . . ."

"Well, I hope you'll feel better. Before you go, we'll provide you with letters of recommendation."

He waited patiently, but this time his illness seemed to be chronic. Sometimes he felt almost well enough to go, when suddenly he would be forced back into bed. And one day fresh misfortune befell him. He was pruning his rose trees, and tried to roll away a boulder which hindered him. He put his shoulder against it and strained hard. Suddenly a wave of blood flooded his brain; he sank down in a faint. He soon recovered consciousness, but when he tried to get up he felt a burning, stabbing pain. His hand went instinctively to the place, and he was horrified by a strange experience: his fingers touched his body before they expected it. A great swelling jutted out of his stomach. He fingered himself in consternation, still lying on his back. Then he unbuttoned his clothes and examined himself. The wall of his stomach had a rupture.

Cautiously he tried to get up, pressing his palm against the swelling. First he managed to get to his knees, then to his feet with trembling wariness. He leaned on the rock which had beaten him. At last he stumbled to the house. He dared not even call his housekeeper, for fear of enlarging the rupture. He found her, and with a deathly pale face told her in a whisper to run for the doctor. While he waited, he prayed and stammered with fear. He could not gauge the extent of his danger, had no idea what was happening in his body. He was horrified to think that he might be dying. His eyes were full of tears, and he implored God with sobs to let him live.

At last the doctor came and examined him. It was an ordinary rupture, nothing more. He would have to bandage it up closely and keep his bed for a long time. And in future he must always wear a bandage. It was a painful and unpleasant illness—it could not be cured, but it was not especially dangerous; he might still live to be a hundred.

So now two illnesses kept him bedridden. But at least there was no danger that he would die. This gave him courage to suffer patiently.

Celeste consoled him with tender letters. But what helped him most was the thought of the Pope, which restored his strength, hope, and belief in life.

He had long been debating in his mind whether he ought not to send His Holiness a letter of congratulation on his election. But he decided that it would be assuming too much. God's immediate representative on earth stood far too high to correspond with him. Nor did he want to give the impression that he was taking advantage of their old friendship and hastily calling the Pope's attention to their former intimacy. So he contented himself with a letter to the Papal Court, which was answered immediately. Monsignor Ciampoli, the Breve Secretary, invited him cordially to Rome, assuring him that he could hope for the warmest reception.

Duke Cesi reported happily that they had almost finished the setting up of the *Saggiatore,* and it would greatly help in the success of the book if the author would come to Rome for its publication. Then the news followed that the book had been published at last and the first copy was in his hands. The sick man stroked its pages tenderly; whenever he read a passage, he was well satisfied. Then Monsignor Cesarini wrote him a jubilant letter. "Your work has already achieved such a high esteem that His Holiness is having it read to him during meals." What an honor! Galileo was deeply touched. Yes, and this was the real Pope! Even during meals he could still be interested in science. How wonderful to imagine Pope Urban dining in one of the beautiful rooms of the Vatican with his Court around him and to think that now everybody would hear how the Jesuit Grassi was slowly pulverized under the hammer blows of the Florentine scientist's arguments. Then came news of Grassi himself. Francesco Stelluti wrote a few days later:

I am sending Your Excellency sixty copies of your book. I must tell you that it has aroused great interest everywhere. The Chamberlain of the Vatican had a copy and gave it to the bookseller Sole. Grassi hurried along and asked for it. He began to read it at once there in the shop, and his face changed color. He remarked that you have delayed three years with your answer; but, even so, it might prove a rash and precipitate one. Then he put it into his pocket and left. I heard no more, except from a member of the Jesuit College, who tells me that he has read the whole work and found it excellent; Grassi would have a hard task to reply, he said. The Jesuit Fathers are all of opinion that the tone of the book is unimpeachable and that you speak with appreciation of the Jesuit Order.

But all this joy only healed his spirit, not his body. He suffered for months and could not even think of setting out. They were writing from Rome that the roads were impassable, the Tiber had risen again, and the Orso quarters were flooded as usual.

It took six long months before he could walk again. Weak, dizzy, stumbling, he set out. It would have been impossible to accomplish the whole journey without a rest, so he decided to visit Duke Cesi at Acquasparta. The Duke, who had succeeded in marrying the Countess Salviati, had retired with his young bride to his country estate, and spent little time in Rome. Galileo reached his house at Easter, and stayed on there for two whole weeks getting the strength to go on to Rome.

The idyllic quiet of the castle, the enchanting kindness of the Duke and Duchess, the fresh and lovely spring, were like balm. For two long weeks they discussed the prospects of the Lynxes. It was certainly extremely significant that the Pope was giving so much time to the *Saggiatore*. They already saw the Academy of Lynxes as the greatest and most decisive power in Europe's intellectual life. They saw Copernicus reconsidered. Even the Inquisition would change its stand under the rule of the all-powerful Pope. It was nearly daybreak, they told each other happily.

He was still at Acquasparta when the letter reached him assuring him that the Pope was overjoyed at his coming and would receive him at once. What should be the next step? To use the opportunity to the full and persuade Pope Urban to annul the decree of the Inquisition which proclaimed that the sun moved round the earth, and that any other teaching was forbidden.

After two weeks' rest he started for Rome with the certain conviction that he would succeed. The litter shook his aching bones, but his spirit seemed to soar out of his body.

Again he saw the lovely Medici villa on the Pincio. But some miracle had changed it completely. The last time it had been a cold official palace where even Grand Duke Cosimo's favorite was careful not to raise his voice, and behaved naturally only between the four walls of his room. Now it was no longer the frowning Guicciardini who gave the keynote to the house, but the Niccolinis, of whom he had heard so much, but whose personal acquaintance brought him even more in beauty and kindness.

Galileo decided on the first day that he had never before met such a likable pair. They treated him like intimate friends from the very first moment; their glances betrayed affection; they were untiring in their care and attention. Now he received quite a different suite, at the front of the palace, one reserved for notables. There were flowers in his rooms, a volume of Ariosto and one of Berni on the table by his bed. A large flask of his favorite Grignano wine on another table. What time and pains these wonderful hosts had wasted, to find out all his small preferences and habits! At their first supper his favorite Florentine dishes were served. The Ambassadress had dressed especially to please him and was lovely in the candlelight, like a dream. And they both were young, fond of fun, and gay. One witty remark followed the other; they were laughing all through dinner. Then they rose like people who had spent many years in close companionship.

"Let's go and look out over the city," said Signora Caterina. "I never miss it for a single night. We'll sit in the loggia. There's no finer view of Rome."

Galileo hesitated, suddenly remembering his health; it would be dangerous to sit out on the loggia, heated by wine, in the chill spring air, without a cloak. But already a gold-embroidered lackey was standing with a thick cloak at his elbow. These people could even read his thoughts. He smiled.

They went out on to the moonlit balcony. The miracle was repeated: he had never seen this city so beautiful as in the company of these two. The ancient center of the world, the eternal maze of stones, the Rome of Romulus and Numa Pompilius, Cicero, Horace, and Nero; of Peter the Apostle and the first Christians; then of the mystic age of Byzantium; and finally the Rome of the Popes, of the Borgias and now of Urban VIII, lay spread at their feet. Two thousand years of history hovered over this landscape, its darkness touched with blue and silver by the moon, which invested it with amazing beauty. The strong moonlight drew firm clear outlines. The tall oval of St. Peter's dome, the bronze angel on the Castel Sant' Angelo, here and there the deep black masses of umbrella pines, and the jutting shapes of glimmering, silvery, ornamented towers . . . and there, beyond all, on the ridge of Monte Mario, a line of cypresses tipped with silver. . . . Galileo drew a deep breath. He searched for old acquaintances in this silver drawing of geometrical lines. He picked out the dome of the Pantheon and tried to find the outlines of the Sopra Minerva Church, headquarters of the Inquisition.

"Perhaps the Pope is looking down over his city just as we are," he said slowly.

"I don't think so," said Niccolini. "He always goes to bed very early. But he rises at dawn. Every morning he goes riding. He is very fond of it, and is a very good horseman."

"It must be beautiful to ride in the morning, in the freshness of the dew, among singing birds. . . ."

Niccolini smiled: "It isn't quite like that! There are no singing birds in his garden. They disturbed His Holiness' sleep, and he gave orders to have them all exterminated. They've killed them in thousands. Now only a stray titmouse ever wanders there, to its own destruction. As soon as the palace guards hear a single twitter, they rush out to kill the bird."

"But how sweet they sound here on the Pincio!" said his wife. "Every morning I wake hearing them. I wouldn't give them up for anything!"

"This woman," the Ambassador laughed, "won't eat singing birds. She refuses to have them on our table. If ever I want to eat a nice ouzel, I have to go to an inn."

They all laughed. But Galileo laughed half-heartedly. This Pope who exterminated singing birds aroused a queer feeling in him. Strange that a man who wrote verses and wanted to be a poet, could not bear the sound of birds singing. But the next moment he was defending Urban VIII. He needed his rest; all the cares of Christendom were his; he answered for the whole world to God; it was his duty to wake with a clear head every morning.

For a little while longer they enjoyed the silvery vision of Rome, but soon they were shivering in the cool air. They said good night; Niccolini came to his guest's apartments to make sure he had everything for the night. Galileo stayed awake for a long time thinking of the Pope and listening to the birds. Their song woke him in the morning and brought the Pope again to his mind.

His first visit was to Cardinal Carlo de' Medici, whose splendid entry he had watched during his last visit. He presented to him the letter the

Grand Duchess Cristina had written personally and a copy of the *Saggiatore,* and answered his questions about Florence; then he kissed the hem of the young Cardinal's garment and went to call on Cardinal Hohenzollern, to whom he also brought a letter of recommendation.

"I've heard much about you in these last years," the German Cardinal said, "but even if I hadn't, His Holiness often mentions your name. And always affectionately."

"That is an old affection," he answered happily. "His Holiness even wrote a poem addressed to me."

"Oh, yes, we've heard about it often. You'll end by remaining here as a . . . as a Cardinal!"

"I'm too old for that. And yet, when I was a little boy, I wanted most of all to become a priest. Now I'm too old, although I might be certain of a career in the Church."

"Nonsense! You should join the Jesuits. They govern the world now. . . . Oh, but that reminds me! You aren't in very good odor with the Jesuits. Why are you so angry with each other?"

"The anger is certainly not on my side. Indeed, there are many Jesuits whom I like and deeply respect. They're angry with me. They honor my humble person by calling me the Antichrist, a danger to the Church's power on earth."

"A danger? How?"

"Because, Monsignor, I follow the teachings of a compatriot of yours, Copernicus, though I have changed them according to my own thoughts."

"Of course! Of course! Now at last I shall be able to learn the truth. They're talking such nonsense in Rome. Tell me in a few words what it's all about."

Galileo began happily, like a street vendor who has found a customer. Cardinal Hohenzollern listened attentively. They warmed to their subject and spent almost two hours over it.

"Frankly," the Cardinal said at last, "all this seems convincing. I'm going to think it over; and, if you can spare some more of your valuable time, I'm sure to have all kinds of questions for you."

"With the greatest pleasure. But I ought to warn you, Monsignor, we are now in the shadow of excommunication. Pope Paul issued a decree forbidding anyone to proclaim and teach this theory, as contrary to the

Bible. Even *I* put the whole thing to you as a hypothesis, for the time being, because I've a very great plan. I want to persuade His Holiness to revoke that decree. Will you help me, Monsignor, if I ask you?"

"First you'll have to convince me a little more. But, as I said, your explanation seems almost conclusive. Let me think it over, then I'll be able to tell you how I feel about it."

As soon as he had performed these two formal visits, Galileo hurried to the Lynxes with his glad news. This famous member of their Academy who had parried the Jesuit attack was received with a fittingly triumphant ovation. They all considered the *Saggiatore* their own personal triumph and now crowded jubilantly around the leader of their vanguard.

"I've just heard in a roundabout way," said one of them, "that Father Grassi has read the book and expressed his opinion of it."

"Well?"

"He seems to have said that, though it was a dangerously well-written and clever work, he was surprised at your reserved and moderate tone. He was prepared for the kind of abuse usual in learned disputation. Instead he found a reasoned argument. This impressed him so much that he wants to meet you. I think it would be useful. We could get farther in friendship with the Jesuits."

"Nonsense!" another Lynx cried violently. "It's just a trap; I know them. They pretend friendliness and stab you in the back. Let us continue the fight. Up to now we have nothing to complain of."

The third thought that they ought to spy out the land through some impartial acquaintance. They disputed confusedly. Galileo listened and pondered everything. Perhaps a world organization would help to have that decree withdrawn; it might succeed more easily. But then he remembered that there was no need to waste his time in barren, useless arguments when he could settle the whole thing personally.

"You gentlemen," he said at last, "are debating something which, after all, is a personal affair of mine. If Father Grassi wants to make friends, I don't mind. He can always find me. If his intention to make peace is really so strong, he'll discover ways and means to let me know officially. I am going on my prescribed way, and intend to speak to His Holiness."

They started to discuss the possibilities of the Papal audience. Galileo shrugged, smiling at their excitement.

"I'm not worrying about it. His Holiness has given me so many flattering proofs of his personal good will and even friendship, that I'm sure to attain all that is humanly possible—more than anyone else. I'm calling today on Monsignor Ciampoli, the Breve Secretary, who is a good friend of mine; and I'm going to ask for an audience. I'll visit Riccardi, who granted the permission of the censors. He's related to the Tuscan Ambassador, because the Ambassadress is a Riccardi girl. We don't need to angle for any introductions. Tell me, what is the standing of Ciampoli and Riccardi at the Papal Court?"

He was deluged with information. Some said that Cardinal Maurizio of Savoy was the best spokesman with the Pope, because he represented the French orientation. Cardinal Barberini became a Cardinal at the wish of the French Court, for during his ambassadorship in Paris he had joined the French clerical party against the Spanish. Others said that the Pope clung most to Cardinal Aldobrandini. Someone else contended that the road to the Pope's heart led through the arts. There was this young Neapolitan sculptor, Bernini, whom Cardinal Borghese had discovered. His Holiness covered him with favors.

Galileo felt a little pang of jealousy when they spoke of Bernini. For many months he had played with the splendid illusion that he was the Pope's favorite—he, the world-famous scientist whom the Pope had honored by an ode. But now it seemed he was only one of many. He only hoped that the Pope had written no poem addressed to Bernini.

"No," he said to the Lynxes, "I don't want to turn to anybody just now. I'll try to use only my own strength, then we shall see. I'm going to the Vatican now."

Monsignor Ciampoli, the young Breve Secretary and his former pupil at Padua, received him with sincere delight.

"How pleased His Holiness will be!"

Then, like a good Florentine, he demanded all the news from home. But at last they came to the main point.

"What is the standing of the Jesuits with His Holiness?" Galileo asked.

"That doesn't really matter." Ciampoli shrugged. "There's no other will here except his. He can't be influenced, he's suspicious and terribly strong-willed."

"But you enjoy his especial favor?"

"Thanks be to God, I can't complain! Whoever writes such poems as I do is sure of a favored place at Court. His Holiness rides out in his coach

every day with different members of his suite . . . but they must be
poets. Usually myself or Cesarini. . . ."

At that moment Cesarini entered. He was tired and complained of a
headache, as he always did; but he endeavored to show how pleased he
was to be able to welcome the famous visitor. He was a frail, soft-spoken
priest, the third son of Prince Giulio Cesarini, who had to take orders
and who carried all the burdens of overbred aristocracy on his frail shoulders.

Soon they were all three discussing the possibilities of Galileo's great
scheme. And both priests were of opinion that if Urban VIII could be
convinced of the truth of the new system all would be well. Whatever the
whole College of Cardinals, the far-flung Jesuit organization, all the
Peripatetic scholars of the world might say, the Pope could simply instruct
the Inquisition that from now on the earth must be considered as a moving
and gyrating heavenly body, instead of the sun. On the other hand, if he
did not accept Copernicus, there was no power on earth which could
move him.

"We'll see," Galileo said hopefully. "When may I expect the audience?"

"Most probably tomorrow. Be prepared. His Holiness would rather
postpone someone else's audience to receive you. I'll report to him as soon
as he returns. He has gone to Santa Maria delle Valle, the family chapel
of the Barberinis, which contains relics of St. Sebastian. His Holiness
likes to pray there. It may be that I shall send you word about the audience tonight."

And he kept his promise. Galileo was notified the same night that
His Holiness was looking forward to the visit of the great scientist. He
talked all the evening about the Pope with the Niccolinis.

"What sort of a man do you think he is?" Galileo asked.

"A born ruler, an extraordinary talent in politics, and a merciless tyrant. His life shows how a statesman can train himself. He has a very
hot temper, the blood easily rushes to his head, but he is calm just as
quickly again. He has accustomed himself never to decide anything while
he has a fit of temper. Although his moods change quickly, he is slow in
settling matters and doesn't take advice from anybody."

"Is he good-hearted?"

"No one can tell. If someone provokes his anger, he can be merciless.

Sometimes his sheer implacability makes me feel afraid. But there's also kindness in his nature . . . there must be. . . ."

"Of course, he is a poet," Signora Caterina interposed.

"That doesn't mean much, my sweet. Nero was also a poet. Poems express some of the feelings and tendencies of their author. But not all of them. I know that there's kindness in him, because his nearest subordinates adore him, love his good heart. That's why I say he's a born ruler. But if someone doesn't submit to him, he can be inexorable. He is only kind to those who acknowledge his rule."

"I admire his stupendous culture," Signora Caterina continued. "I've often talked with him at official receptions and also in private conversation. I was always amazed at his knowledge of classical literature. Wherever you start Virgil, Ovid, or Horace, he continues at once—to the very end. But he knows the minor poets equally well."

"He has another quality," Niccolini added, "and that's mistrust. My colleague Possevino, Ambassador of Mantua, tells me that there's no human being whose innermost characteristics Pope Urban will not find out at their first meeting. I don't doubt that he is a good judge of men. But not an objective one. He is so jealous of his power and authority that he probes into everyone for hidden lack of respect. Therefore it's very difficult to deal with him, because, though he expects the utmost reverence, he despises and persecutes flatterers. On the other hand, if someone stands up to him like a man, he sees in him an impudent rebel against Papal authority. So all I can really tell you is that His Holiness is a very difficult man. But why need I explain all this to you, who are one of his oldest acquaintances and favorites? . . ."

Galileo really had known Pope Urban long enough to feel entitled to be considered as his favorite. But now, when he prepared himself for the great meeting on which the whole new age of astronomy depended, he had to confess his failing: he was no judge of men. A single tiny star of the Milky Way interested him more than all the millions of his fellow mortals. The only people who could always count on his interest were his children and his nearest relatives; all other humans, although he admitted their existence, he divided into two distinct groups—those he liked and those he disliked. The only person whose qualities, instincts, talents he analyzed with the greatest attention was—Galileo Galilei. And in this respect he possessed the necessary courage and sincerity. He was never afraid to look into himself, because he was never afraid of seeing something unpleasant. "If that's how I am, I can't help it," he would tell himself secretly. He was too lazy to look for the faults of others, but he knew his own very well. He knew that he was too eager for fame, that he could not control his longing for pleasure. And he knew that in his strangely constructed mind there were two opposite qualities: a great and exceptional spirit soaring to the farthest heights, and mere human foolishness —almost the foolishness of a child. Though he could clearly define the errors of human thinking as it had existed for the last two thousand years, he was so gullible in everyday affairs that anyone could deceive him like a boy. Now, though he sat nodding indifferently at the Ambassador's remarks, he knew in his soul that really he had no clear idea of the being of the man whom he was approaching in such an important matter.

The great moment arrived. The huge doors opened and there in the middle of the study stood—Urban VIII, Christ's Vicar on earth, with his athlete's body, square-cut black beard, and alert, light blue eyes. Galileo approached him, knelt and kissed the white slipper. Then he felt the Pope raise him to his feet. Just as Pope Paul had done. The smiling face of Urban VIII radiated friendship and kindness without reserve.

"We were expecting you, Messer Galilei, with real joy."

But he was using the majestic plural. And not Galileo's Christian name.

"We hope that you have stood the tiresome journey well."

"I did, Holy Father, because of my gladness at the knowledge that in the end I could kneel at the feet of the World's Ruler as an old acquaintance—this gave me strength to bear it."

"Yes, We also rejoiced to have known you for a long time . . . but let us not stand here; we must talk more comfortably. It gives Us so much pleasure to see you that We won't let you out of Our sight very soon. . . ."

They sat down. The Pope's tone was friendly. He talked as he would to an old friend. Galileo tried to adapt himself to this tone, yet remain respectful.

"Your Holiness makes me happy to remember our evenings spent at Florence. Monsignor Gonzaga was less understanding then . . ."

The Pope laughed.

"Do you remember how angry he was because ice proved to be lighter than water?"

"Oh, yes, I remember," Galileo also laughed. "And does Your Holiness remember that we didn't dare to quote Berni's poem aloud because he had written a satire against Monsignor Gonzaga?"

In an instant the Pope's whole expression changed. His face became grim, his eyes hardened with anger.

"Never mention that Berni. A shameless, insolent knave. How dare anyone speak of a Pope as he does? To call Pope Clement a half-wit! If he were alive today I'd soon send him to the Inquisition!"

Galileo sat in panicked silence. The Pope's rather high-pitched voice rose almost to a screech of fury. He thumped the table.

"Such rabble are worse than Protestants. The only reason why I didn't have his book publicly burned was that I didn't want to call attention to it. Miserable scoundrel."

There was a deep silence. Galileo would have liked to sink through the earth. He saw at once that he had committed a terrible blunder. The Pope was panting in his fury; his chest heaved up and down like a smith's bellows. There was a piece of paper on his desk which he crumpled with a vicious strength as though it had in some way rebelled against Papal authority. But the fit of anger passed. He was smiling again.

"But We won't talk of things that make Us angry when We have you. Tell Us how your health, so precious for science, is behaving?"

He was kind and affectionate again. Galileo began to explain his ailments haltingly. The Pope's face was really gentle and full of sympathy.

"We are sorry to hear all that. How old are you?"

"Sixty, Your Holiness."

"That's no age. I'm sure you lead an unhealthy life—not enough exercise, no moderation. Look at Us, Messer Galileo. We are fifty-six and Our health is excellent. Though We can never thank God enough that it should be so. We live temperately. Do you speak French? No? We learned a French proverb when We were in Paris. 'Help yourself and God will help you.' A very wise saying. We mustn't wait idly on every mercy of God. We have to earn it diligently. We'll pray for your health to God. And the Lord shall certainly listen to Pope Urban, His servant. . . . But now, about those "Gold Scales." We had the book read to us. A very fine work, worthy of you. But what was the quarrel really about? What did this Grassi want of you?"

Galileo's heart missed a beat. Now at last he could mention his business. . . .

"The rage of the Peripatetic, Holy Father. Since my early youth I have been struggling to free science from the prison which Aristotle built. Of course, only the courageous, the independent thinkers are on my side. And they are few. The others anxiously guard their safe comfort at the trough of conventional sciences. I was the one who disturbed their whole world. They hate me and want to silence me. But they can't."

"Excellent. Admirable. You must fight them."

"If I know that the greatest King of the world is my protector, I shall continue my fight with added strength. Aristotle was a great thinker, but his errors must be corrected."

"What were his errors?"

Galileo's heart leaped for joy. He enumerated all he had proved against Aristotle; spoke of how he, Galileo, discovered the laws of unhampered fall; of his new theory of movement. He explained that the whole method of scientific research must be given up because it was bad; it must be replaced with his system, which had brought to light amazing new things, while the Peripatetics had seen nothing new in nature for two thousand years. The Pope interrupted again and again. Galileo tried hard not to be too technical, so that His Holiness might not lose the thread. He forgot time. He was just about to take up the theory of the tides, and so skillfully pass to the wonders of the sky and then to his great theme—Copernicus. But the Pope rose suddenly.

"We're more than sorry," he said, "to have to dismiss you. This talk has been so marvelously interesting that We should like to continue it till sundown. We have to let you go now, but We shall summon you again in a few days. Our best regards to Our dear son, Niccolini."

He put an arm round Galileo's shoulder and led him to the door. Outside Ciampoli received him amazed.

"An hour and three-quarters! All the kings of Europe would envy you for this! Well, quick, tell me what you've achieved!"

"Nothing," answered Galileo. "I haven't even begun. But His Holiness was unspeakably kind to me. I should dance in my joy if my legs could bear it."

He arranged with Ciampoli that he would always leave word at the Embassy where he was, in case another summons came from the Vatican.

He also paid his respects to Ginetti, the Papal *maggiordomo*. Then he hurried to the Academy of the Lynxes and gave them, with the airs of a conqueror, all the details of this wonderful audience. He repeated it at the Embassy. Next day he called on the new Cardinal Barberini. The first Cardinal Barberini had become Pope Urban VIII, and had conferred the Cardinal's hat on his nephew, the twenty-six-year-old Francesco Barberini. This young prelate felt that it would only be polite to be very friendly to such a favorite of his uncle. Galileo returned to Cardinal Hohenzollern for another discussion on the new cosmology.

He waited to be summoned again. A week later came the messenger. He hurried to the Vatican, but the audience lasted only a few minutes. While Galileo was in the Vatican, a courier came with urgent news. But Urban gave him a few friendly words, asking him how he spent his days and whether he needed anything, after which he patted his shoulder and assured him that when he came again orders should be given to close the doors so that nobody could disturb the audience.

So Galileo had still to wait. He spent his time in visiting, in discussions with the Lynxes, and in arguments with Cardinal Hohenzollern. Or rather, there was no need for arguments, since the Cardinal proclaimed himself convinced. He promised that if it should be necessary he would even sponsor Copernicus to the Pope.

"Your Eminence is full of kindness, and especially courageous to advocate truth."

"I think you have many other followers."

"Some I have. Most of them Lynxes. Cesarini, Ciampoli. Yes, there are some. But that doesn't mean much. There's still so much to teach, to explain. Does your Eminence, for instance, know that delightful Father Riccardi?"

"The Monster Priest? Of course I do. Everybody knows him in Rome."

"Why Monster Priest?"

"When he was in Madrid, the King of Spain gave him that nickname because of his incredible size. Or have you ever seen a fatter man?"

"No, never! Well, the Monster Priest was kind enough to grant me the Papal imprimatur for my *Saggiatore*. I was convinced that he would be an enthusiastic follower of the new system of cosmology, and if necessary help me with the Pope. Yesterday I went to see him. What do you think, Eminence, he said of systems of cosmology? That he didn't believe in any of them. In his opinion all the stars were moved at God's command by angels. Others could teach whatever they liked. He believed that, and it could never get him into trouble! I am thankful Your Eminence has not chosen such a comfortable standpoint. As soon as His Holiness has received me again, I'll report our talk."

Ten days later he was again summoned. The Pope kept his word: he gave orders to announce nobody while Galileo was with him. The latter would have liked to begin again where he had left off. But that was impossible. The Pope took some manuscripts from his desk—his own poems—and he began to read them, one after the other. They were undeniably fine poems, the classic meters impeccable, their language rich in the traditions of Horatian verse. But they had to discuss each poem separately, and some the Pope read a second time. This lasted almost an hour and a half. Then the head of the Church dismissed Galileo with great benevolence. He would see him again in a few days.

But he sent no word for the next two weeks. Galileo waited. Apart from anxiety for his great plan, he lived very pleasantly. He was invited to many distinguished houses; sometimes the Ambassador gave banquets with the famous scientist as chief guest; and he enjoyed his fame—told gay stories of Florence, or, if he found a good opponent, argued for hours on end. But he liked the evenings best when he was alone with the Niccolinis. Signora Caterina played the harp. Galileo always carried a lute in his luggage. He had played very little during the past years, because he could scarcely use his left hand. But now there was no pain to hinder him. Their music floated out from the loggia into the silence of the Eternal City, and it pleased them to sing old Florentine airs. *"O Rosa, mia gentile"* was the favorite song of the Ambassador, *"Leggiadra damigella"* of his wife. Harp and lute made delightful concord. Signora Caterina sang with gentle sweetness. Galileo watched her and listened in silence. Never in his life had he liked a woman so much.

"That was so beautiful, Signora, that I feel I must sing to show my gratitude."

He took his lute and stroked its strings, then he began in a resonant baritone:

> *"Vicin, vicin, vicin,*
> *Che vuoi spazzar camin. . ."*

The Niccolinis joined in at once. They sang gaily like three happy children out for a holiday. Then they looked down on sleeping Rome, and Galileo went to bed with the kindness of Signora Caterina in his heart.

Two weeks later he was called for a new audience, the fourth. Galileo asked for permission to continue the explanations which he could not finish at the first audience.

"We shall be very much interested and are already eager to listen."

Galileo began by saying that all Aristotle's other errors were as nothing beside his blunders in astronomy. As soon as he examined the sky through his telescope, by God's grace he was enabled to perceive things which no one had seen since the Creation. It had been clear to him that Aristotle's basic teaching must be incorrect: the sky was not unchangeable. It was always changing. Then those who believed the moon a perfect sphere were also wrong. And so were those who taught that the sun was without spots. The whole world system of Ptolemy built on Aristotle was untenable.

The Pope interrupted at once.

"The only thing you mustn't try to explain is Copernicus. We can't accept *him*."

"But that was just what I wanted to do, Holy Father."

"Listen to me. Seven years ago We were glad to help you out of your trouble. We have often talked about Our poor friend Bellarmin of blessed memory. He didn't take a definite stand in the matter. He told me that it was all the same to him what was moving and what wasn't. He was only interested in the . . . how did he phrase it? . . . in the integrity of the holy structure of the Church and the Faith. But *We* have a definite standpoint. We consider the thought of Copernicus an impossibility. We tried to help you as far as We could, but only for your person's sake. And We still think that the theory of that German is impossible."

"Forgive me, Your Holiness, may I ask something?"

"Of course, We'll gladly do anything for you."

"I only ask for patience and the chance to explain. I can prove that it isn't the sun circling the earth, but the earth moving around the sun. The tiny sphere around the huge one, as is natural."

"Sphere? Why sphere? It isn't certain at all that the earth is spherical."

"But Holy Father, Columbus . . ."

"Your Columbus started westward to arrive in the East. I know. He wanted to reach India that way. Did he? No. He reached a new continent, and not India. How do we know what is beyond that? And on the other side, beyond Japan? I've talked to missionaries who came from there. They don't know. Nobody knows anything for certain."

"I do, Holy Father, I do. I do know that the earth is spherical. Let me tell you why."

The Pope nodded. Galileo almost began to lecture. The Pope listened with great interest and fixed attention. One could see that his brain was hard at work.

"Marvelous," he said at last. "You're a wonderful man. We know now why We always esteemed you so highly. These are excellent arguments. We can find no objection. Or . . . why doesn't blood rush to our heads when we're on the lower side of the sphere?"

A new explanation followed. In the universe there were no "ups" and "downs." These concepts were relative. Man is never "upside down." His body is always in the same relation to the earth's radius, and, like every other body, strives by his weight toward the soil. But blood has also some weight. It cannot rush from human legs to heads, unless driven by the arteries.

"Bravo!" cried the Pope, and his sharp eyes sparkled. "Every time we speak together you manage to show us a new world. Continue."

Galileo went on a little haltingly. For the first time in his life he was feeling nervous. He knew that on his words the fate of science depended for the next twenty, perhaps the next hundred, years. He began carefully and lucidly explaining the Copernican system. The Pope listened for a while, then shook his head.

"No, no, that's impossible. So far We've been able to follow you, but We can't go on. Why, We only have to look at the sky to see with Our own eyes what is happening there."

"Did Your Holiness ever look into flowing water from a bridge?"

"Of course. Very often. In childhood, from the Ponte Vecchio into the Arno."

"And didn't it seem as though the bridge were rushing against the stream and the water standing still?"

"Naturally. But that was a delusion. When We looked at the banks, it vanished."

"Wouldn't it vanish in the sky if the sky had shores?"

The Pope pondered. But he rejected the idea.

"No," he cried, and shook his head. "It's impossible. And it goes against all common sense to substitute something complicated which I can't see, for the simple and obvious thing which I see every day."

"Must we accept a mirage for the reality, then, merely because it's so difficult to explain it optically?"

The Pope laughed.

"The Devil take you! You've an answer for everything! God gave you uncommonly sharp wits, but you won't convince Us so easily. But go on! Let's hear your other arguments."

Galileo continued. He was now warming to his task. He rose, went to the desk, used the inkstand for a symbol of the sun, the seal-press for the earth. And so he demonstrated the two different movements of the earth. But Pope Urban had always a counter-argument ready. Galileo had to acknowledge that the Pope had an exceptional mind. He was absolutely untrained in astronomy, yet he argued like a learned Peripatetic.

"No, no, We see now that you'll never convince Us. And it would be better if you employed your mind and time on worthier things than idle phantasies."

"Holy Father, I live and die with these phantasies. If I was unable to convince Your Holiness, I'm sorry. But I want to ask you to leave me my conviction."

Pope Urban smiled, shrugging his shoulders.

"We cannot interfere with anyone's belief. But we must warn you that seven years ago you received the answer of the Church in this matter. The Church did not ban this theory; and, since We see no special heresy in it, We won't ban it either. But We haven't forgotten that the College of Cardinals has declared it audacious."

Galileo's heart missed a beat. So the Pope did not remember the decree, or did not remember it correctly! In the official dictionary of terms used by the Inquisition, the word *temerarius* did not stand for anything serious.

"So I must consider this theory," he asked tensely, "audacious, although not heretical?"

"Yes. And I'm sure you'll find out soon by looking at the sky with your magic telescope that you are—mistaken. . . . Oh, by the by, I've something very interesting. Wait a moment. . . ."

He rang for the *maggiordomo*.

"Listen, Ginetti. Two years ago a German was here from Cologne. I

don't remember his name. He wanted to demonstrate some strange magnifying contraption to Pope Gregory, but the audience was always put
off and the man from Cologne died here, before he was received by the
Pope."

"I remember, Holy Father."

"But he left his instrument here. Nobody can put it together. Some
learned Fathers came from the Jesuit College and experimented with it,
but without any success. Go at once and find the documents and that
strange instrument. If there is anybody in the world who can put the
thing together, it's Messer Galileo."

Ginetti bowed deeply and left. The two returned again to Copernicus.
Galileo continued his arguments stubbornly. He explained his theory of
the tides. The masses of water on the surface of the earth which spins
like a ball—that is to say, the seas—keep shifting with this oscillation.
But the Pope did not accept it. They argued for a long time, till finally
the Holy Father used an unanswerable argument.

"Wasn't it, then, in God's power to create the ebb and flow? As He
did the earth? To doubt that would be to doubt the power of God."

Galileo sat dumfounded. He would never have looked for such an
argument from a reasoning man. But Pope Urban was not only intelligent, he was despotic; he had suddenly shown that he meant to be always
in the right and did not scruple as to his choice of weapons. No answer
was possible. The Pope looked through the window and sighed.

"Alas, we're sorry to interrupt such an interesting talk again. But We
have so much to do. War keeps Us busy. But it's worth the effort."

"Has Your Holiness received good news?"

"Excellent! The war has lasted since 1618—that is, for nearly six years
—and already God has permitted us to win back huge territories from the
heretics, and incorporate them with the lands of the True Faith. If God
grants us strength and health, we will carry the flag of God's Lamb everywhere! And follow the ecclesiastical invasion with civil conquest!"

"Your Holiness plans the enlargement of the Papal State?"

"What else? Is it not my duty? Did not Christ Himself lay the command on Us: 'There shall be one fold and one shepherd.' We bow ourselves before His will. We shall manufacture cannons, my friend, with
the brass of monuments if need be. We shall pull down the Castel Sant'
Angelo! Our army is being carefully organized. Believe me, the Pope

doesn't lie on roses! There are many cares, and few people of any use to us! When you get back to Florence you can hint that sometimes the Medici family saddens our paternal heart. Why, only yesterday I was saying to Cardinal Carlo de' Medici . . ."

"Holy Father, for heaven's sake! What have the Medicis been doing?"

"King Louis XIII is a Medici, and he allows this Richelieu—whom probably you only know of by hearsay, but I know him very well—to give him very bad advice."

Again a sudden fit of anger overwhelmed the Pope. Again he bellowed and thumped the table:

"But I'll show them! Huguenot rabble! And if they provoke us much longer, they'll live to see something they don't expect. We have our cannon." He puffed with rage.

But when Ginetti entered he received him with a pleasant smile.

"Thank you, Ginetti, I see that you know what order means! My congratulations to everyone in charge of the archives. Well, let's see what we've got here. Come on, Messer Galileo, stand at my side. Let's read these documents together."

From the documents it appeared that the whole package had been left by a German named Jacob Kepler, who had died at Rome without being able to show the Pope this discovery: the invention of his relative, a Dutchman named Drebbel. A further document stated that experts, summoned by the Pope, had been unable to put together the separate parts of this new machine.

They opened the wrapping and found a pile of brass objects and some thick lenses. Galileo sorted them out eagerly. He began to finger the separate parts, and at once his brain began to work on them. But no clear image came to him yet.

"Well, now, show Us what you can do and put it together! Let it be ready by the next audience. We know you can do it! And now may God's blessing be upon you."

Galileo had planned three important visits that day, but he decided at once to postpone them all. He hurried back to the Embassy and locked himself into his room with the invention. He enjoyed the task; it was half science and half game.

But it was not easy. He scarcely knew what he was expected to construct from these finely worked pieces of brass and lenses. He only knew that it ought to magnify. He started to experiment both in a theoretical and a practical way. That same night he was ready; he had finished the construction. It became a pretty little machine, and the object for magnifying had to be placed under a lens and looked at from above. But he could not use it in artificial light. He put a scrap of paper under the lens, and saw dimly some great pitted and fibrous blankness, but nothing else.

That night he had been asked to supper by Cardinal Santa Susanna. He found a great company. It was hard to say nothing about this new machine. But partly because he wanted to convince himself of its usefulness, partly because he thought it would be unseemly to spread the news of such an interesting sensation before the Pope himself had seen it, he held his peace.

Next morning he woke much earlier than usual. His strange excitement had not been sleeping and woke him now. He hurried in his nightshirt to experiment. He pushed the table to the window and put a bread crumb under the lens. He looked, and cried out. Instead of the crumb he saw a fair-sized rock with cavelike hollows. Dimly, yet he saw it. He judged it to be a hundredfold enlargement. And he felt a twinge of admiring envy of this Drebbel. After all, he, Galileo, could just as well have invented this instrument! Its fundamental principle was identical with that of his telescope.

He could hardly wait till the Ambassador and his wife were up. He took the machine to them, put it on the window sill, and placed a tiny grass seed under the lens with the point of his penknife. They all three looked at it. It showed a huge bean. Signora Caterina clapped her hands; the Ambassador shook his head.

"Your friends are always experiencing miracles."

They amused themselves for an hour by examining all sorts of small objects. Then Galileo wrote a letter to Ginetti asking him to inform His Holiness that he had succeeded in accomplishing his task and found the machine extremely interesting. He went back to his room to experiment further.

This machine was not perfect. The pictures it showed were dim. This contraption would have to be manufactured for individual use, just as they made different spectacles. The outlines of the object under the lens were surrounded by a mist of rainbow lines. It was also inconvenient to push the magnified object under the lens, because there was not enough space.

"I'll have work enough to last me a fortnight," he thought gaily, "till I fix all this."

He took it to pieces and put it together again. Kepler must have brought several copies, because there were unnecessary spare parts, and some seemed to have been made for a larger machine. He was working on paper now, drawing lenses, pencils of rays, refraction diagrams. This was the real construction of the invention: he set down its essence in precise scientific terms.

In two days the Pope summoned him to bring his invention. He placed a poppy seed under the lens.

"What does Your Holiness see?"

"A big black ball with multicolored edges. What is it?"

"A poppy seed, Holy Father. Those rainbow colors are added by the machine because it's still imperfect. But I'll fix it. Within a few weeks it will show everything clearly."

"Galileo, you're possessed by a devil! What else could we put under it?"

"Anything. The end of this thread from my cloak, for instance."

He pulled it out. They saw rough, irregularly twisted rope. The Pope cried out:

"And today's Saturday!"

"Why does that matter, Holy Father?"

"Every Saturday I go to confession at Santa Maria Maggiore and stay for vespers. . . . So I shall have to wait till tomorrow to examine this marvelous thing. Your learning amazes me. You can ask me any favor you like. I promise to grant it. Not even the best Jesuit scientists were able to put this thing together. . . ."

"Holy Father, I would have one request. For you it's only a stroke of the pen—for me it means the crown of my life."

"Well? Let's hear it. I remember now—you have a son. Does he need a stipend?"

"I should be deeply grateful for that, of course. But something else is in my mind. Holy Father, give the earth permission to turn round the sun."

The Pope did not hesitate for a second: "No. I won't do that! I've told you already that the Church has defined this theory as *temerarius*. That cannot be changed. Ask anything else."

"But Holy Father, let it be *temerarius*. Only let me be permitted to write about it. To prove and proclaim it."

"Wait a moment. What did you agree upon with Bellarmin?"

"He told me that I was forbidden to teach the theory as the full truth, but allowed to expound it as a hypothesis."

"Aren't you fibbing, Messer Galilei? Did Bellarmin really say this?"

"I'm willing to take an oath that he did."

"Well, what more do you want, then? Treat it as a hypothesis. Whatever the College of Cardinals has said, I have said."

"Holy Father, this is a terrible burden for science. It's unspeakably difficult to write like this. I have to ponder every sentence for hours to avoid making trouble. When I had to mention Copernicus in the *Saggiatore*, that one chapter took me ten times as long as any other."

"So you mentioned him in the *Saggiatore*? We hadn't noticed it. But there's no sense in wasting time over such an argument. *Quod dixi, dixi*. You must obey the commands of the Church."

Galileo could feel he was treading on very dangerous ground. The Pope had forgotten the decree issued eight years previously. He did not remember that the Inquisition had branded the new teaching as contrary to Holy Writ. And now he was keeping all this from His Holiness. Would it not be better to accept defeat and not bring up this decree? If ever it occurred to the Head of the Church to have this decree brought from the archives, he would see at once that Copernicus' teaching was no longer merely *temerarius*, but plainly heretical. He had kept the essential part of the decision from Urban VIII. Still, it would be fine to go on fighting—and perhaps win. . . . All this took a moment to cross his brain.

"Holy Father," he continued doggedly, "I obey. Nothing is more natural than that. But as Your Holiness mentioned Bellarmin, may I tell you something else? I have a document signed by the Cardinal of blessed memory, in which he states that no ecclesiastical authority can force me to deny this new theory."

His heart stood still again. Perhaps the Pope would want to see the document. It was certainly true that it had stated that he could not be forced to deny the theory. But Bellarmin had also included the warning that these theories must not be upheld or taught. There was no mention of any "hypothesis" in it; Bellarmin had merely added that by word of mouth. Now he was dead and could not bear witness. But the Pope made no further inquiries.

"Tell me," he changed the subject, "aren't you ashamed to follow the same teachings as the heretics? There's this Kepler, a Protestant! And I hear that many follow him among the Protestants. Do you like that sort of company? What kind of a man is this Kepler?"

"Your Holiness, the poor fellow has paid for his heresy with much grief and suffering. Not long ago his old mother was denounced as a witch. Luckily, he heard of it in time. If he hadn't arrived at the last moment to defend her, she would have been burned."

"I see. And what witchery did they accuse her of?"

"Nothing, Holy Father. They were just trying to force money out of her."

"Yes, yes, we know that sort of abomination. If the victim pays, the accusation is withdrawn. To our sincere regret we have heard many similar cases. The Holy Office is really a holy institution, but men are loose and will use even a pillar of the Church to further their wickedness. But why don't you answer our question? Don't you feel it unpleasant to be associated with Protestants?"

"Your Holiness, let me tell a story. At Padua I had a colleague, Cesare Cremonini, a man with a heart of gold, but a stubborn follower of Aristotle. He was so angry with me over Aristotle that—I found it out later—he sent one of his pupils to spy at my lectures, and in his next lesson he taught the opposite of everything I had said . . . out of revenge. I couldn't do a thing like that! If a heretic happened to publish the truth, I wouldn't like to say it was untruth, simply because he was a heretic."

"You've an answer for everything," the Pope laughed. "But so have We. The sun moves round the earth. That's Our last word! It's for you to find out how to deal with any other hypothesis. And now go in peace and think over what you would like to have for this machine."

The Holy Father again embraced Galileo. He even led him as far as the door. There was nothing else to do but to kneel and take leave. The door closed. Outside, Ciampoli was waiting eagerly. Galileo sadly shook his head.

Next day he gathered the Lynxes again. He gave them the details of all these audiences. Though they did not rejoice, they were not too downcast.

They debated the position and found it satisfactory. The possibility that in the future Galileo might write of this great thought—even if only as a hypothesis—still remained. It was a good sign that the Pope had not remembered the text of the decisive decree. . . . This showed that to him the whole problem was of minor importance. And finally, it was the greatest asset for progressive science that the Pope liked Galileo so much. This was known now in all Rome; even the most dogmatically Aristotelian Jesuits would think twice before attacking the Pope's favorite.

"And that reminds me," said Guiducci. "Not long ago Grassi sent me word that he would like to meet me and make friends."

"He meant with me," laughed Galileo. "I have no objection. Make friends with him first, then I'll join you. In the end we'll make him a follower of Copernicus."

"It's only fitting," Guiducci continued. "It was I who first had to quarrel with Grassi, so that you could write the *Saggiatore*, and now I'll make our peace between you. I think the Jesuits aren't really so black as they're usually painted."

"I'm sure they aren't," Galileo said. "And I begin to believe that Grassi's attack wasn't an organized action of the Order. It was an individual affair. Nowadays the Jesuits care nothing about Copernicus, only about the great war."

So they finished their discussion hopefully. Then Galileo proceeded to tell them of his wonderful new discovery. He asked the members of the Academy to get him a coppersmith at once and an optician who could work quickly, cheaply, and well. He also needed a skilled technical draughtsman. His announcement caused great excitement. He was besieged by a hundred questions. There were five different Lynxes who knew of artisans.

Next day he had a draughtsman, a coppersmith, an optician. And now he spent all his time over the invention. As a last hope he visited Cardinal Hohenzollern and asked him to plead with the Pope. The Cardinal promised to do his best, but they must wait till he could catch Urban VIII in a good mood. In a few days Galileo had made decisive improvements in the new machine; it could be adjusted to anybody's sight by increasing or decreasing the distance of the two lenses by means of screws. Soon he found the best distance for his own eyes, and was himself amazed by the wonderful sharpness of the picture when he put a strand of tobacco under the lens. He constructed a special little shelf for objects to be magnified. He had long discussions with the optician till they could eliminate the rainbow-colored outlines. When the first magnifying instrument, Drebbel's invention in Galileo's version, was shown to the Lynxes, they could find no praise worthy enough. He had no trouble about money; the Academy provided that. They ordered a number of copies of the marvelous instrument.

"Now, of course, you'll spend years in developing it," said Stelluti.

"Not at all. I shall play with it a little in Florence and then put it aside. I've other more important things to do."

"What are they?"

"I've to write my own cosmology. It won't be an easy task to write it as though I didn't believe in it. But somehow I must state my belief."

"I shouldn't have thought you'd find any difficulty in the writing."

"Really? Was the *Saggiatore* well written?" It always delighted Galileo to be told that he was a good writer, and soon he encountered further compliments. That night when he got back to the Embassy he was welcomed by Signora Caterina.

"I've wasted a whole afternoon," she said, "reading a badly written book. Now I must go back to the *Scales.*"

"Really? Did it please you so much? Is it well written?"

"Is that a serious question or are you mocking me?"

"You? How can you ask me that, Your Excellency! I'm really curious to know what you think of my style."

"I think it's perfect. I can't use any other word. You'll always be read as one of the greatest stylists in Italy . . . in hundreds of years. No one could be more Italian. It has a flavor like the best *tagliatello,* you know, well mixed with cheese. Thank heavens you didn't write it in Latin."

"And God's blessing on you, Excellenza, for such pleasant words to your parting guest."

"What? Are you going away?"

"Alas, I must! I've finished my business more or less, and I long for my daughters. And then my hand has begun to ache again. I'd prefer to stay in bed at home. . . . Surely you're not sad, Signora?"

"I'm silly." She smiled shamefacedly. "But I can't deny that you've made us like you very much. We've somehow been thinking you'd stay here forever. I must confess that I feel for you, as though you were . . ."

Galileo's throat ran suddenly dry, and his heart beat furiously. He stared at this charming woman, waiting breathlessly till she finished her sentence.

"Well—as though you were my father," she said.

He nodded, but his face fell. He kissed her hands with gentle reverence.

"Let me remember you then as my third daughter, for I have to leave you. I'll wait till I can take leave of His Holiness, and then go home to do some work."

The Ambassador himself informed the Pope that the scientist wanted to leave Rome. And Urban VIII at once found time for a farewell audience. Ciampoli was beside himself with amazement.

"Do you realize that no crowned head would have received this favor? Six such long audiences! The whole of Rome will be talking about it!"

The Pope did not even let him kneel. He embraced Galileo.

"So you are going away. . . . You don't know of what pleasures you are robbing Us. But, if go you must, We can't selfishly keep you here. As the token of Our gratitude for the unforgettably interesting hours spent together, We intend this picture for you. It was painted by Cigoli: the Holy Family. We have chosen it because We've heard that you were a good friend of this early deceased painter whom We also liked. But, stay a moment. Here are two memorial medals to commemorate your visit to Rome. The one is gold, the other silver; and here a package of sacred pictures, some depicting the Lamb of God and blessed by Us. Give them to whoever you like, to your children. We also intend to grant a stipend to your son. Tell Ciampoli to remind me if I should forget. And take this letter addressed to your Prince in your praise. And now take Our apostolic blessing together with Our deep affection."

Galileo knelt to receive the blessing. He stood up and thanked His Holiness for the gifts. Then he added, hesitating:

"Is there no way to grant my special request?"

"No, none! Hohenzollern tried to argue with me yesterday. We informed him also that this theory was *temerarius*. We wish you Godspeed and command you to take care of your valuable health."

Galileo knelt again to kiss the white slipper. Urban raised him in a last embrace. No mathematician had ever received such favors at the Papal Court, and a man who was Kepler's friend and Fra Paolo's!

He spent the last evening with the Ambassador and his wife. They went out for the last time to the loggia and looked down over the loveliness of Rome. Signora Caterina touched his arm. She suddenly said:

"Francesco. . . ."

"Yes, my dear."

"Would you mind if I kissed Messer Galileo?"

"Mind? I'd like to kiss him myself!"

And so they both kissed and embraced him. He responded warmly to the Ambassador's affection, but he turned only his cheek to Signora Caterina and tried hard to think no sensual thought.

Next morning he left Rome. He had two companions on his way: a bishop and Michelangelo Buonarotti. When they passed the Piazza di Spagna, Galileo gave a cry of surprise. He had noticed someone in the square.

"Who is it?" his fellow travelers asked.

"Someone I haven't seen since my early youth. Scipione Chiaromonti, a scientist, if you can call an ass a man of science. Many years ago I had such a violent quarrel with him at the house of the Marchese del Monte that we almost came to blows over Aristotle. Strange that he should still look just the same. I recognized him at once . . . how many years ago was that? Twenty-six at least. . . ."

II

Fernando II, the fourteen-year-old ruler, offered his hand to be kissed by the Court mathematician of sixty-one, and accepted the letter Pope Urban had written him. He himself broke the seal, as was his right. Then he passed it to his Jesuit tutor to be read aloud. His mother and grand-mother reverently made the sign of the cross. The Jesuit began reading the Latin letter:

Our greetings and Our apostolic blessing to Our beloved son, the worthy ruler of Tuscany. The whole of Italy esteems the Grand Duchy of Tuscany a mighty power both because of the rich yield of her taxes and strength of her armies, but even the most distant nations call Your Highness happy because of the glory of your subjects and the great talents of the Florentines. Since these embrace new worlds with their souls and discover the very secrets of the ocean, turning now even the fourth element of the universe into a monument to Your Highness' name. As long as the blissful star Jupiter shall shine in the heavens, so long shall Galilei's fame be borne onward, as its everlasting companion. For a long while we have followed the course of this great man, whose honor glows in the heaven and spreads its radiance over the world, with Our paternal affection. For in him we have seen not only a triumphant scientist, but a pious believer; we have found many qualities in him fully deserving our Papal good will. When his intention of congratulating Us brought him into the capital city of Our See, We embraced him with great affection and listened to him gladly while he increased the fame of Florentine eloquence with learned conversation. We cannot allow him to return to his country without the signs of Our love, now that he is recalled by the magnanimity of Your Highness. We know what rewards the great rulers have given him for his deserts and the amazing results of his genius which fixed the glory of the Medicis among the stars. Many say that they are not surprised at the bounty of great achievements in a State, the munificence of whose Princes feeds them with such plentiful rewards. And to show you how beloved this man is to Our Papal soul, We were pleased to issue this honorable testimony to his talents and religious diligence. And We add that We shall be glad to see all the bounties with which

Your Highness will honor him, not only imitating but surpassing Our paternal favor. Written in Rome under the sign of the Fisherman's Ring, on the 8th June, 1624, in the first year of Our reign.

The Jesuit kissed the letter, gave it back to the child ruler, and crossed himself. Fernando looked inquiringly at his mother and grandmother. Grand Duchess Cristina spoke in his place:

"The heart of His Highness, the Grand Duke, is filled with filial joy by the message of the Holy Father."

Then the two women looked at each other, a little uncomfortably, and it was the Dowager Duchess who spoke again:

"His Holiness speaks of certain rewards which he expects from His Highness for you. Perhaps you have some financial request to make? Because it would be better to address that to Messer Cioli. . . ."

"Thank you, Your Highness; but just now I have no such request. But I brought something as a token of my respect for His Highness. I am certain he will know how to reward my humble gift."

He beckoned to the lackey to whom he had given the magnifying machine. He began to explain it to the ducal family. They were all excited by the strangeness of this new invention. Galileo opened his handkerchief in which he had brought all sorts of small objects: wings of flies, grass blades, tiny pieces of crystal. Grandmother, mother, and grandchild were delighted with the interesting toy. The little Grand Duke pulled out a hair from his own grand-ducal head to look at it under the lens.

"Will you give us this instrument?" he asked anxiously.

"Of course, Your Highness, that's why I brought it. I'll make another copy for myself."

Grandmother and mother glanced at each other again. This time it was the mother who spoke:

"We wish to express our warmest gratitude. His Highness will provide the fitting reward."

Galileo bowed himself out of the room, after cordially greeting the Jesuit. He knew him well and was very friendly with him. It was the priest's doing, not his. When Urban had become Pope, the tutor had turned very friendly.

The audience had been smooth enough, yet he sighed as he left the palace. He remembered the time when Cosimo had become Grand Duke and Vinta was the Prime Minister. Then he had someone with whom he could discuss his more important problems at Court. The two Grand Duchesses had no mind for anything except pomp and dresses. *And* the Church. The proud ducal palace where Cosimo had started his reign with such hopeful strength and wisdom had become a resplendent monastery in which the subservient piety, the incense-laden unctuousness, oppressed all hearts: it was the opposite of the Arcetri convent where poor, simple nuns lived their gentle lives, but which the real presence of God filled with a gaiety which lifted all care from the souls of visitors.

Galileo spent some time over the magnifying machine, improving and enlarging it, finding a number of small alterations which all made it more efficient. He examined all kinds of possible and impossible objects, from parings of his nails to a raindrop. His mathematical mind turned farther and farther from a conception of the universe in which man was the center. Man seemed to be now an inconsequent speck of dust among the million wonders of nature, yet at the same time Godlike, because he possessed a mind, and the wings of this mind could take him from the infinite great to the infinite small.

He looked at everything he could find. He enjoyed the excitement of finding fleas formidable monsters under the lens: flies were nauseating and hideous with their multi-angled eyes; while mosquitoes were lovely in their finely constructed slimness, and moths amazingly beautiful.

Then he became bored with it all. Living creatures had never interested him very much. He loved life for itself and because it was his. He often wondered whether it was this strong instinct for life in him which had prevented him from wanting to study life, since such studies bring to our minds death and impermanence, things of which he dreaded the thought. On the other hand, everything inanimate interested him all the more, from the miraculous flaming sphere of the sun to the stone rolling down a steep slope. He longed to fathom the world which nature had created around man, to formulate it in an equation like a problem in algebra: he was pondering the ever half-perceived solution of this huge riddle even when he seemed to wander farthest afield.

The new conception of the universe which gradually had taken shape in his mind was so much finer, more logical, more harmonious than the old imperfection of the Almagest, that it revealed a thousand times more clearly the marvelous being of God. He found a formula for himself: The more one knows, the more wonderful the world seems, the greater the power, glory, and perfection of God. Religion could have no higher object. If the worst should happen, if Bellarmin's misgivings proved true, this new conception of the universe might shake the sixteen-hundred-year-old organization of the Church. It might so happen. But enlightened men would be the real believers, and the damaged organization would be replaced by something better and firmer. *Ad maiorem Dei gloriam.* His duty was clear—even as a young man he had never known so clearly that he must teach the world everything he discovered.

Every night he looked at the stars with his telescope, but often he put it down and stared at the sky with his naked eye, taking stock of the universe. He knew the sky as well as a geographer knows a map of the earth. He glanced with trained eye toward the seven stars of the Great Bear. He followed the prolongation of the line of stars and saw the shining Arcturus. Then, turning his head slowly to the right, he named to himself the Serpent, Hercules, Vega, the Swan, threw back his head to look at Ursa Minor, and in the midst of heaven, the Stella Polaris. Then he turned round and his eyes caught the radiance of Orion above the horizon. He searched for planets among the fixed stars; he knew where they were moving and wandering, just as a father knows the movements of his traveling children. Each of them represented a period of his life. Jupiter recalled the excitement of discovering the Medici stars; Saturn the riddle he had sent to Kepler; Venus the great sensation he experienced when he saw her sickle form. And, among the innumerable glimmering diamond points crossed like a fluttering silver veil by the Milky Way, he saw the moon, the melancholy wanderer of the sky, the eternal, circling serf of the earth which had moved since eternity on its orbit with the sharp-shadowed precipices of its lifeless mountains, and would move on in the same way to the end of all time. Then he closed his eyes and searched in his imagination for the sun. The face of the earth on which Florence lay had turned away from it. He set the center of fire down in front of himself as if now he were placing it in the universe, and began to turn the planets round. They all moved around the sphere of light at different distances, on differently sloping planes, with different velocity, some of them turning on their own axis and drawing one or a number of satellites after them. This disquieting, rushing, complicated wheeling in empty space with its majestic and mysterious silence, this glimmering, radiant play of light, enraptured his soul. He conceived an adoration for his science which he knew as the only perfect one, because he could not presume a grain of discord in the distribution and balance of the myriads of heavenly bodies with their immense weights and circumferences; not an inch of divergence in the millions of miles of their distances. His soul rose at such times beyond the Polar Star, and his torrent of feelings merged into dim, happy gratitude. In his youth he had never felt how important it was to proclaim all this to mankind.

The magnifying machine had served to rest his mind while he recovered from the strenuous trip to Rome. Now he began work. The only thing he did not know was where to start.

But, while he was putting his old papers in order, he found this starting point. He discovered the attack of Ingoli, the Ravenna lawyer who had tried to refute him and Copernicus eight years ago, at the time when the Inquisition had taken up the matter. He had not answered it, being glad that he could avoid trouble. He decided to reply now. He would try to keep within the limits set by Bellarmin. But he had no idea of sending the answer to Ingoli. He wanted to send it to the Lynxes at Rome; they should judge whether it was advisable to have it printed, whether he had succeeded in defending the theory of Copernicus in such a way that the Inquisition could not lay hands on him.

The weeks passed quickly, and he was completely immersed in his work. What had begun as a letter became a book. Ingoli's little pamphlet of a few pages was very crude and ignorant. A serious scientist could only smile at his arguments. But this work was a witty experiment—to refute Ingoli without drawing the final conclusions.

He enjoyed writing it very much. He simply lectured his opponent about parallaxis and zenith. He warned him that the discoveries of astronomy were based on eternal rules against which there was no appeal, and could not be settled by legal hair-splitting. He composed the whole thing lightly, in a language which all could understand; but he wove into this seemingly light tone the daring new theories.

He sent the manuscript to the Lynxes in Rome and waited for their opinion. They seemed to be reading it very slowly; it took them a long time to answer. And when it came their answer was hesitant and cautious. Guiducci wrote that somebody—nobody knew who—had denounced the *Saggiatore* to the Inquisition. The attention of the Holy Office was directed to the defense of Copernicus contained in this work. The denunciation had been made some time ago, but since the Inquisition treated every case with the greatest secrecy, the Lynxes had not heard of it until now. But now they knew the result. The Inquisition had sent the book to the Minorite Father Guevara, whose report had gone against the accuser. Guevara could find nothing in the *Saggiatore* which upheld Copernicus. He praised it as a work of science. The case had ended well for Galileo, but should serve as a warning to be very careful. The reply to Ingoli, Guiducci wrote, could not be printed for the time being—not even shown to Ingoli, because he would run at once to the Jesuits or the Inquisition. All the Lynxes were of opinion that this manuscript was an unmistakable testimony for Copernicus.

The letter depressed Galileo. So he had been denounced at the Inquisition. By whom?

Who was the mysterious denouncer, and why had he done it? Surely it was scarcely conceivable that the Jesuits, after Grassi's defeat, had ordered him to strike up a sly friendship with his opponents to make quite sure of him? This was no more than a supposition, but seemed so satanic and involved, so much in the style of hysterical pamphlets against the Jesuits, that Galileo refused to believe it. But the feeling of eight years ago was again surrounding him. He felt as if an invisible enemy were lurking in the dark. Even now when Pope Urban had praised him as a good Catholic to all the world.

He followed the advice of the Lynxes and did not urge the printing of his work. But he asked them to have it read by some reliable man. Perhaps the times would become easier and his book be treated as a not too apparent confession of the Copernican thesis. The Lynxes fulfilled his request. But they kept it from the knowledge of Ingoli, who had come back from Ravenna to Rome and was living close to the Lynxes' Academy. He had no idea that Galileo had thought his attack worth a reply. He himself had forgotten all about it.

So Galileo waited, still wondering who his denouncer could be. He investigated—but without success. Certain acts of the Inquisition were apparently guarded by seven seals, though a great many others seemed to leak out. The Inquisition had just dealt with the case of De Dominis, a monk who had led an adventurous life, a correspondent of Fra Sarpi, a man who had himself been a Jesuit and a bishop in Dalmatia. He had left the Order, gone abroad, turned Protestant, and begun to abuse the Pope from a safe distance. James, King of England, made him a Dean of Windsor. But in England, he found no peace and had gone to France, been reconverted to Catholicism, and done penance. The Pope had forgiven him. He had come back to Rome, and Pope Urban's predecessor had granted him a pension. He had begun to write books about science, asserting among other things that the rainbow did not really exist; it was an illusion of human sight based on refraction. One of the first acts of Pope Urban's reign had been to stop De Dominis' pension—not on account of the rainbow theory but because he did not forgive this rebel for his apostasy. De Dominis loudly demanded his money from the exchequer of the Vatican. Thereupon the Inquisition summoned him. He was probably asked whether the rainbow was God's creation, and if it was, how could one say that it did not exist? They imprisoned him in the Castel Sant' Angelo, where he died. But this did not content the Holy Office. He must publicly atone for his sins even after death. A procession carried his body, together with all his books, to the stake. Both books and corpse were publicly burned.

Galileo was horror-stricken to hear of all this; yet he could not keep silence. He wrote again and again to Duke Cesi, Guiducci, and the other Lynxes.

His pride in science helped to keep up his courage. The most famous mathematician of France, Gassendi, had sent a letter. Gassendi was a young man, born when Galileo was appointed to the chair at Padua. At thirty he had become a university professor at Aix, and was rumored to be one of the sharpest opponents of Aristotle. Galileo had heard this from several of his acquaintances who had traveled in France, and he was very much interested in this newcomer, whose development he had probably helped to influence. Now Gassendi wrote him a long letter. He openly subscribed to Copernicus' teachings. He offered in terms of the deepest respect to correspond with Galileo, and added interesting and original observations on sunspots. By the use of a simple camera obscura he had projected the picture of the sun onto a sheet of paper, and so could examine the spots at leisure without braving the fierce heat and radiance of the sun itself.

It filled the elder man with delight to find that his companions in science were ever increasing in number. Gassendi was no heretic; he was even a priest, having studied theology at Avignon. His letter gave a new impulse to Galileo. He sent a manuscript copy of his last work to Monsignor Ciampoli, begging him to present it to His Holiness and ask his opinion.

He had to wait a long time for the answer. This was not surprising. The Pope had far more pressing cares. The European war had now lasted for seven years; and, instead of ending, it spread over and enveloped wider and wider territories. Holland and Denmark had entered it, the whole of Europe was watching it—the theories of Copernicus were forgotten. And in all Europe the Pope had the most reason to be concerned with the struggle of the Church—and the least to trouble himself with astronomy.

But at last came an answer. It was a single sentence among other news, a letter from Monsignor Ciampoli. "I've been reading your reply to Ingoli, and related most of it to His Holiness, who was delighted with the example of the sieve, your details about the weight of bodies and movement, and the fascinating experiments which you instance."

That was all. The next sentence dealt with the stipend to Vincenzo. It had not been forgotten; but, on account of the holidays, the work of the Papal exchequer was in arrears. Galileo studied this one sentence minutely, trying to draw conclusions from every word. It was Ingoli who had first mentioned the sieve. He had argued in his attack that when a sieve was being used, the gravel always collected in the middle. Therefore if the earth moved round like a sieve, the heavy objects on its surface would all gather at its center. Galileo's manuscript easily disposed of this childish argument. And if Ciampoli had explained this part to the Pope, he would have had to tell him that it was the refutation of an argument *against* Copernicus. If he had explained "most of it" to the Pope, it was impossible not to betray that every sentence referred to the Copernican theory. And if the Pope sent him word that he was delighted, that seemed an unmistakable answer. He was ready to wink at his favorite's indirect assertion of Copernican truth.

He went to see his daughters. He said happily to Celeste:

"Our Pope is a wise man and very kind to me. Pray that he may live long to the blessing of science and mankind. And pray for me, because I have much to do before I die."

"What are you thinking of doing now, father?"

"I must write my book. The great book, the crown of my life. I must still think it over carefully, and its form will be also very difficult. It will take me years. And I'm ailing and getting older and older. . . ."

III

The Pope kept his word: he granted a yearly stipend of sixty gold pieces to young Vincenzo, till he had finished his studies. There were certain formalities attached to it. A Papal scholar must wear the cassock of a priest, he must have his hair cut in a tonsure, and every day say a certain number of prayers for His Holiness. Galileo was delighted. The sixty gold pieces were very useful, and it would do the boy no harm if his priest's gown kept him out of taverns and idle pranks. For Castelli, who was still at Pisa, had nothing good to report of Vincenzo. He often missed his lectures, bragged of his celebrated father, and was always talking of his distinguished connections at the Florentine and Roman Courts.

One day he appeared unexpectedly in Florence.

"What's the matter?" Galileo asked anxiously. "Do you need anything?"

"Oh, no, but I had to talk over this business of the stipend with you, father."

"There's nothing to talk about. You've only to have the top of your head shaved and buy a cassock. It would be also fitting to write and thank Monsignor Ciampoli."

"But I want to write to the Pope and beg him to let me off the conditions."

"Are you crazy? Write to the Pope? Do you think it possible to correspond directly with the Pope? I think you must have gone quite mad. His Holiness has showered his favors on me, but I should never dream of such effrontery. Who are you? Are you the Grand Duke of Florence? *He* can write to the Pope, perhaps—but not a law student of Pisa. And what have you against the conditions? You should be glad to study at the Pope's expense. Not many students can boast of such a thing in all Italy."

The young man answered with a sulky stare:

"But I don't *want* to shave my head."

415

And he smoothed his locks as though to protect them. His father flew into a rage.

"You ridiculous ape! Am I to pay sixty florins a year for your pomaded hair—five gold pieces a month to let you strut about like a cockerel? I work day and night to keep you. You've never known what it is to want, and all your gratitude is wenching, drinking, and idling about, instead of studying. And when you could do a little to ease my burden, you come and whine about your hair! It's a sorry thing for a man to see his son such a windbag, such a worthless, empty-headed fool as you!"

Silence followed. Vincenzo seemed to think his own appearance much more important than his father's views. He answered grimly:

"And I'm not going to wear a cassock. I'm not a priest, and I'll never make one."

"Nobody wants you to be a priest. But you seem to have no idea of anything. Why shouldn't you put on a cassock? There is no necessity for you to strut about all day in front of women with your plumed hat. You put on that habit! It's time you started work in earnest."

The boy broke out into vehement protests:

"I'd rather jump into the river. Why don't you write to that Ciampoli and tell him I can't fulfil these conditions? You could settle it with a single word."

"Young man, if you make me lose my temper, I'll box your ears. Am I to give orders to the Pope? And do you think that with this great war raging, Ciampoli has nothing better to do than to discuss your lovelocks with His Holiness? Go back to Pisa this instant!"

"Father, I'm young and I want to live. Am I to bury myself during my years as a student? Please don't spoil my life with this tonsure and cassock. Why are you angry because I enjoy myself in Pisa?"

"It isn't that which annoys me. It's that you don't care in the least about *my* interests. It seems quite natural to you that I should keep you in state. Your sister Celeste is very different. She always worries about my affairs, my health, everything. I might die like a pig in a ditch—and you'd be only anxious about the money spent on barbers. All right, all right, we needn't talk about it. You never caused me joy, only anxiety. And if you don't fulfill these terms, you won't get a soldo from me. You'd better try and earn your own living. Now go back to Pisa; you have no business here in Florence."

The boy shrugged sulkily and left. He knew the house well and discussed the day's dinner with the housekeeper. On the pretext that he could not get a coach to take him back, he stayed on three days. His father saw almost nothing of him. Vincenzo was out visiting all day at houses where there were girls to flirt with, while at night he roamed about with his friends. On the third day he mentioned the matter again. And when his father told him finally that what he asked was impossible, he began to cry like a little boy. Already he was growing a beard, a much thinner beard than his father's, and Galileo began to ask himself whether at the age of twenty he would have cried in the same circumstances. Nothing came of their argument. Vincenzo still rebelled with all his might against the tonsure and habit, while Galileo insisted with all his authority.

"I don't understand you, sir," the boy whined. "Don't you hate priests? Haven't they caused you trouble and worry enough?"

"Don't talk like a fool. I've also been attacked by laymen and befriended by priests. There's Castelli, a professor at Pisa and a priest. I have few better friends."

"Yes, but the Jesuits. People are always saying in Pisa that they mean to ruin you."

"I've had trouble with one or two Jesuits, that's true. But also with Dominicans and others. It's absurd to say the Jesuits want to ruin me. Gullible people will chatter about anything."

"You know best. But they say in Pisa that Grassi was appointed officially by the Order to crush you."

"Father Grassi," Galileo smiled, "is on the point of becoming a follower of Copernicus. He's almost running after us. Praising me everywhere. He's probably very sorry he attacked me. At heart he's a kind and well-intentioned man. You should never generalize about life. And now go and put on that cassock or never speak to me again. I don't want to discuss it any more. When do you start?"

"Tomorrow morning. I must go to supper with the Bocchineris tonight. And there are other things I have to see to."

"And when are you going to see your sisters?"

"I'm sorry, I shan't have time for that. Tell them, sir, that I send my love."

Galileo was beside himself with rage.

"Get out of here. I don't want to look at you. Anyone who behaves like this to his sisters is less than human. They're always talking of you. For weeks they wonder what gift to send you. And now you've been home for three days without even seeing them. Get out; I don't want to talk to you."

The young man shrugged defiantly and departed.

Next morning he was out of Florence before his father was awake. Galileo was deeply grieved about it all. For days he had nothing on his mind except his son and the stipend. And to top everything, Castelli wrote him from Pisa, deeply indignant: his boy was proclaiming everywhere that he would rather leave the Church than shave his head and take the habit. Galileo went to his daughters and complained bitterly of their brother. Angela listened indifferently, but Celeste defended him. She always defended everybody, never judged harshly, was never angry. She said that the tonsure was a holy seal and the habit a holy garment. Whoever felt that he could not wear them worthily showed a sense of honesty in refusing them.

After a few days, Galileo's fury was spent, and he himself was finding excuses. Children are not born to flatter their parents' vanity. The boy had grown up without a mother, and that was his father's fault. He tried to remain strict and unyielding but saw that he could not change his own nature, that his son's will would be stronger than his. When the first of the month came, he sent Vincenzo his allowance. He wrote a grateful letter to Rome and found some excuse for delay in taking up the stipend. He was even ready to renounce it, but felt ashamed when he thought of Ciampoli's reaction to such an odd and unprecedented step.

But fate provided the solution. A letter came from Michelagnolo in Munich. His brother seemed to be getting on well among the Bavarians and if he had any worries, it was on account of his large family. They were expecting their seventh child. Their eldest, who was called Vincenzo, just like Galileo's son, was close on eighteen. They intended him to be a musician, and only Italy could train him properly. So Michelagnolo had gone the round of the influential courtiers at Munich till he was granted a stipend for his son. Maximilian, Prince of Bavaria, had allowed two hundred and twenty gold florins a year for the training of this future Court musician. Quite a respectable sum, but Michelagnolo also needed money most urgently to spend on the other children. He could not give his son more than half the stipend when he started for Italy. And this was not very much. Michelagnolo also wrote that he was longing for a sight of his kinsmen; and next year, if God granted him health, he would come on a visit with his whole household. Galileo was rejoiced at this prospect of seeing his brother again. It was years since he had embraced Michelagnolo. And it struck him suddenly that he need not, after all, give up the stipend. These sixty gold pieces were granted already; why give them up, why not have them transferred with a little machination to another Vincenzo Galilei? For the Pope it was a sum of no importance; it would mean a great deal to Michelagnolo. So he wrote to Ciampoli, hinting at this solution very tactfully, and when he saw that it would not be difficult, he put the request frankly and soon received a notification that the stipend had been transferred to his nephew. So the money remained in the family, while Vincenzo would still be able to strut and display his perfumed locks before all the girls of Pisa.

This turn of events soothed him a little. It was pleasant to think that next year when Michelagnolo arrived, he would have such a fine gift to offer him. His financial position was quite satisfactory. He could live easily on his Court salary; his daughters did not need money; it was only his son whom he had to keep. And he often received substantial sums for a magnifying instrument or for other scientific odds and ends from the Court or other notables. He spent his time peacefully among his papers, calculations, and correspondence, pondering the outlines of the great book he wanted to write and sometimes smiling at his erstwhile fear of the Inquisition. If anyone had the right to be fearless, surely it was Galileo, the Pope's favorite!

About this time he received a new book, printed in Paris. He was surprised to see that Sarsi—or in reality Father Grassi—had attacked him again. *The Reckoning of the Scales and the Gold Scales,"* the long title began, *"in which Lotario Sarsi Sigensano offers to the judgment of scientists what to believe about comets according to the Astronomical Scales of Lotario Sarsi and the 'Gold Scales' of Galileo Galilei.* Excitedly he started to read it. Sarsi began by saying that someone had turned the tails of the comets into incendiary torches, setting everybody and everything on fire, the author included.

What shall I do? Burn and keep silent? Shall I not even stamp out the flames? Oh, no! I must be courageous and put them out everywhere and prevent this sin from remaining as a danger for coming centuries and spreading even farther afield. I will take away inflammable materials from the proximity of danger so that the greedy conflagration shall eat itself up, lacking fuel. And although the person who criticized my book, piece by piece, was not prepared to submit to any restraint in tone or arguments, threatening me at the very outset with the licentiousness of masked revelers, and later on fulfilling this threat, I will not follow his example. I, who have taught not only natural sciences, but ethics for many years at the Roman College, I shall take the path which shields me from insult, yet at the same time triumphantly refutes all.

Galileo was staggered. Here was an unmistakable hint. Copernican thought must be "stamped out." So Father Grassi had shown his real face. All the time he had been sending flattering messages and paying friendly visits—or so they had seemed—he had been working at this outrageous attack. What a devil, what an incredible monster of perfidy, hypocrisy, stubborn malice, and corrosive hate the man must be!

He read on. Soon he was hot with anger and shame. He had often gone out to feasts in Rome and drunk much wine. Sarsi made puns on the title *The Gold Scales,* the *Saggiatore,* which he called the *Assagiatore,* "the wine-taster."

> Thus we might call Galilei's work "Wine-taster," "Wine-sipper." Such names are appropriate, since the book was published during the vintage—the introduction confesses that this work left the printing press in October. But a scientist can hardly find such titles suitable. I should prefer more sober ones.

And so on through hundreds of pages of violent personal invective which in every line showed the writer's malignancy. He misquoted Galileo's text, then refuted the misquoted passage triumphantly. Wherever he found a printer's error in the *Saggiatore* he proclaimed it as the ignorance of the author, and mocked at it. He ignored the list of *corrigenda* at the end of the book. It was a violent and insulting attack. But also terribly dangerous in its effect.

Galileo was horrified. This sophist was trying to use the shades of a technical term in physics to prove that he was denying the miracle of the Holy Sacrament; therefore denying the most essential dogma of Catholicism. If this was not a denunciation to the Inquisition, then he was blind and deaf! And Grassi was denouncing others. Galileo found a passage in the book, cunning and tortuous, like Grassi's mind:

I know what you want, Galilei; to hear the cry of Julian the Apostate: Vicisti, Galileae! But you will never hear the words from me which the Monster uttered.

So he denounced the poor Monster, Father Riccardi, who had granted the Papal censor's imprimatur for the printing of the *Saggiatore*.

When Galileo looked up from these pages, he found himself sitting in the twilight. He had sat down to read the book as soon as he had finished dinner. This new attack had shaken him so that he had forgotten time. But he struck no light. He let the book drop onto his knees and began to think. He discovered that he was trembling with nerves; his breath came painfully and in jerks. Again the horrible feeling of being tracked down, the nightmare of an invisible pursuer, which had tortured him so horribly before.

He waited desperately for news of the reactions the book had caused in Rome—whether the Pope had read it, and especially what the Inquisition would do. Rumors slowly reached him. The book had not caused any sensation, had remained practically without effect. Everybody was weary of the pointless squabbles of this Jesuit, which more resembled a market brawl than a scientific dispute. He also heard that Grassi had not been able to find a publisher in Rome and so was forced to go to Paris, where he got some financial help also, since the Jesuit College was apparently unwilling to bear further costs. The Papal Court was keeping silent about the whole matter, nor did the Inquisition make any move. It was obviously most improbable that the Holy Father's Inquisition would start proceedings against its own censorship, which had commended the *Saggiatore* in such flattering terms.

There came another edition of Grassi's attack; he had managed to get a Naples firm to print it. This disturbed Galileo again. But the nightmare faded, because nobody cared in Rome about the book. Everybody was occupied with the news of the great war. Wallenstein, the newly discovered Imperial General, was leading the armies of the Catholic Princes from one triumph to the next. The defeat of the Protestants partly narrowed their territory, partly provoked the entrance of hitherto neutral states into the war. Any moment might bring news of world importance. Those who rose and went to bed every day with the events of history did not even open Father Grassi's priggish, classicist work.

Galileo became reassured again, but one consequence of the long distress remained. He had to acknowledge how little of a politician he was, though any man in public life ought to possess some political guile, even if he is a master of abstract sciences. It was once more proved to him how gullible he was and how poor a judge of men. He often talked about it to Celeste, whom he found as wise as an old sage. This twenty-seven-year-old nun drew a wisdom from her own deep, clear soul. It was staggering how she could have acquired so much experience of life within the walls of the convent, such clear-cut views and opinions. She's more grown-up than I am, her father of sixty-three thought, as he talked to her.

"There's nothing sadder," Galileo said, "than disillusionment. Not perhaps for others, but my soul is constructed in such a way as to cling to belief and trust."

"Such a soul pleases God," Suor Celeste nodded. "Faith is the foundation of our world."

"Then why must we be so often disillusioned?"

"To test our faith. We ought really to pity the person who disappointed us. He is the unhappy one, not we. He is wicked, and therefore can have no peace in his soul. But we are left the divine gift of faith."

"What if it slowly turns to dust? It's terrible to be alone."

"You can never be alone, father. God, whom you can trust, will be always with you. And you won't be disappointed in me, ever. Perhaps you will in everybody else and yet, I say, love men and trust them. Because, you see, to love is a much greater happiness than the pain of disappointment can ever be. Love can be perfect, but not disillusionment, because there's always consolation in God. Therefore the trusting man is right, because, if he subtracts the sorrow of disappointment from the happiness of trust, a larger sum is left."

Galileo kissed his daughter fondly.

"You *are* a mathematician's daughter," he said, laughing happily. "But I must go now, to prepare for Michelagnolo's arrival."

"When are they coming?"

"Some time during the next month. I'm sorry that not everything can be arranged as I planned. You know, Michelagnolo's wife has got a sister, Massimiliana. He told me that she was a very kind, nice, honest person, a spinster. She wanted to accompany them, and I thought I might keep her here. I'm often ill, and these paid housekeepers do not nurse me well enough. It's quite different if you have a relative in your house. But

Massimiliana doesn't want to leave Munich, and Michelagnolo seems not to care about the idea, I don't know why. His eldest girl isn't coming at all; she is staying with Massimiliana. I can well imagine how sad the poor girl is; she looked forward so much to meeting you. Where's Angela today?"

Celeste smiled gently, sadly.

"Angela is angry with me. And yet I asked her forgiveness."

"Why, what happened?"

Celeste hesitated and seemed loath to talk. Apparently she did not want to say anything to blame her sister. Galileo decided something serious must have happened, and went to the Mother Superior.

"Suor Virginia, what is the trouble with my daughters? I know half of it, but would like to know the whole."

"I want you to know. I was going to send you a letter. Suor Angela and Suor Celeste have parted company."

"I know. But why?"

"There is no living soul on earth who could live in the same cell with Suor Angela. Only this angel, this Suor Celeste of unending patience, could live with her. I'm sorry to say such things about your own daughter, but Suor Angela has a very difficult temper. She is always complaining and reserved; she has always some objection or fault to find; and sometimes she turns into a fury. She shouts in the passages till the whole convent is full of her voice. She even makes scenes in the courtyard. I have often to punish her, but I haven't told you because Suor Celeste asked me not to. But punishment is no use. Lately she's caused a scandal every day, and always about her sister. You see, nobody can quarrel with Celeste. At last Angela declared that she would not live in the same cell. For no reason. It really touched me to see what Celeste did. She, the innocent, asked this vixen to pardon her. She did a special penitence to ask God to give Angela more patience. She came twice to my study to take her part. I couldn't do anything but separate them—for the sake of our peace. I know that I was doing wrong, and I confess that I was a little selfish: I took Suor Celeste as my companion. Her company is blessing and peace itself. But tell me what to do with Suor Angela? How can I change her?"

"You never will," Galileo shook his head. "She has the same temper as my poor mother had, God rest her soul. I can only ask you to be patient with her."

"Oh, Suor Ludovica Vinta, my blessed predecessor, asked me the same thing . . . But you can't see Angela now for a time; she has to keep to her cell. Alas, that is more of a reward for her than punishment. She likes to be alone. Mine isn't an easy task, believe me, Messer Galileo."

Galileo thanked her for everything, expressed his regret about his unsociable daughter, then went back to say good-by to Celeste. They embraced like two people who need no words to see one another's souls, and belong to each other in eternity.

Soon Michelagnolo arrived from Munich with his family. The children were like a row of organ pipes. The oldest, Vincenzo, was a gawky boy of nineteen. Alberto was ten, then Cosimo, Michele, Elisabetta, Anna—down to the few-months-old baby, Fulvia. They were lively and noisy children, talking quick, nasal German among themselves. Even Michelagnolo had become quite German. Being past fifty, he had grown the huge paunch of a "family father," and after the first joy of welcome asked for beer. His wife, who had been slim and pretty Anna Chiara, had also grown fat and dragged her unwieldy body panting along streets and through the house. She talked German to her husband. They were nine in all, mother and father and seven children.

At the same time young Vincenzo came home for the holidays from Pisa. The Villa Segni, where Galileo had dwelt alone in bachelor peace, had now to lodge eleven. The deep silence which had only been disturbed by the song of birds was broken now by noisy comings and goings, shouting, crying, slamming of doors.

But Galileo did not mind. He was happy to be surrounded by his family. As both boys were called Vincenzo, they had to find some way of distinguishing them. Galileo's son remained "Nencio," the name they had called him by as a child, while the boy from Munich was called "Cencio." Nencio and Cencio got on very well together. They did not spend their time with the other children, but went out together every night. The small ones were put to bed by their mother; and the three of them, the two brothers and Michelagnolo's wife, sat down in the cool of the garden. Michelagnolo drank beer, while Anna Chiara sipped sweet lemonade. They talked for many hours, exchanging all the varied happenings of twenty years. Michelagnolo complained just as his brother did. He had his family and good health, but no peace of mind. He was afraid of the war. The Bavarian Prince took part in it on the Catholic side, being a good friend of Emperor Ferdinand, both of them having been educated by the Ingolstadt Jesuits. Thirty thousand Bavarian soldiers fought in the Imperial Army, and up to now had been victorious, so that Bavaria had escaped the terrors of war. But the fortune of arms was always changing, and Michelagnolo was anxious about what would happen to his family, should the Protestant soldiers capture Munich.

Galileo complained about his health. He told his brother how he was often lonely and racked with pain, exposed to the indifferent care of sleepy and inattentive housekeepers. His son was in Pisa, his two daughters in the convent, he had no one in the world. Sometimes he thought of making his peace with brother-in-law Landucci, who had come to Florence after the death of his wife. Landucci's son, the third Vincenzo, was married and a clerk; the girls were in a convent. He had no one in the world to care for, yet when he met Galileo in the street they did not greet each other.

"He was very cruel to poor Virginia, and yet I sometimes think of patching up our quarrel, I am so lonely. I can't tell you how happy I am that you were able to come. But I won't let you go so quickly now."

"We also are very happy here," said Michelagnolo. "I only wish the beer was better."

Galileo searched the whole town till he found beer which satisfied his brother. He tried to fulfil his every wish, playing with the children, flattering his sister-in-law. There was no talk of their going home. Michelagnolo declared that he was afraid to take his family back to Bavaria, Galileo complained about his loneliness—till their wishes met, and one day Michelagnolo himself brought up the idea.

"I can't bear to think that I shall return to Munich and you be left here without proper care. I'd be willing to leave my family here."

"Leave them, leave them!" Galileo was joyous about the offer. "You'd make me very happy."

"It won't be easy, but I'll try to set up house with my daughter and my sister-in-law."

He told his wife, who had no objection to offer. They were cramped with the children in their Munich house, while here they had so much room in the spacious villa and park. The children all shouted wildly in their joy when they were told that they would stay. Only their father would return to Munich—but for the time being even Michelagnolo did not leave. He felt himself in his element, proved himself very popular in company, began to go out a lot and invite guests without asking Galileo. There was plenty of cooking and baking in the villa, and a young valet had to be engaged besides the gardener and the butler. The household expenses began to swell alarmingly, but Galileo told himself that he must not grudge the money when he saw his own family once in twenty years.

The noisy and crowded life of his house became an everyday pattern. Galileo began to attend to his papers again. The news from Rome was all reassuring. The number of his followers there had increased: Castelli had been invited to the chair of mathematics at the University of Rome. The Lynxes worked for him with unchanging fervor, and his correspondence with the dignitaries of the Church was as friendly and affectionate as ever. The nightmares called up by Grassi's latest attack began to fade. He could even smile at them when he told the long story to his brother. He did not even take Grassi seriously now.

Others interested him much more. Kepler had published a new book at Prague entitled *Tabulae Rudolphinae,* containing his astronomical observations. Galileo read it as if it were the most exciting novel. He corresponded with the Frenchman, Gassendi, a great follower of new thought. And he gave much time to a young scientist who had lately appeared. This was a Jesuit, Bonaventura Cavalieri, almost a scientific grandson of Galileo's, for he had studied under Castelli. Cavalieri had visited him in Florence, asking his help in getting some professorship. This Jesuit was an ugly, malformed, strange man with a very long head, and a huge potato of a nose in the middle of a very high, narrow face. But he seemed to be an extremely charming, clever, and likable man. Galileo tried everything to get him a job. Magini's successor, Cataldi, had just died at Bologna. Galileo sent out scores of letters from Florence, and Castelli did the same from Rome. The matter was moving very slowly, but it seemed to be progressing.

"Why are you doing so much for this man?" his brother asked him. "Haven't the Jesuits hurt you often enough?"

"That is foolish talk, Michelagnolo. Shall I hate every fair man because a fair-haired man has once been cruel to me? The Jesuit Grassi is a scoundrel. The Jesuit Cavalieri has a heart of pure gold. *And* genius! Listen to this, how he builds up the whole world of geometry with a single thought: 'Every line is an indivisible infinite of points, every plane is an indivisible infinite of lines, space itself is an indivisible infinite of planes.' Isn't this wonderful?"

"Yes," said Michelagnolo, scarcely listening. "But still, he's a Jesuit. I see at Munich what they're capable of. One can't move at Court without them, although our Prince is a real ruler. What sort is yours?"

"I don't know. A reserved, frightened child; a puppet manipulated by his grandmother, mother, and the Court priests. Now he's gone away on a long journey all over Europe. He'll be eighteen next year and take over the government."

"I've heard about it. The priests will be even more powerful then."

"I don't mind; I've no trouble with the Church. And I don't think that priests are, generally speaking, bad fellows. It's the custom of young people to abuse them. Once I always recited the poems of Berni, mocking priests. But later you get wiser. A bad man is bad, even if he *is* a priest. A man can be good and still be a priest."

"And what about this war? The priests started that."

"Well—your son got the Pope's stipend."

The stipend had been transferred without any difficulty to Michela-gnolo's son; the Munich musician fell silent at this remark and laughed. He was the kind of man who considered every gift as his due. He had lived six months in the house of his brother, and now he was leaving his wife and seven children with Galileo. The latter hoped to the last mo-ment that his brother would offer him even a small sum toward his ex-penses. But Michelagnolo was careful never to mention money. He sent his son off to Rome and asked for a letter of recommendation for himself.

"To whom?"

"Anybody will do, in Venice. I'm going that way and want to stop there. I'd like to amuse myself a little. I need someone so as not to be quite alone in a strange city."

Galileo did not know to whom to write at first. But suddenly he re-membered Bartoluzzi, Marina's husband. Sometimes they still exchanged friendly letters. So he wrote to him now, asking him to take care of his brother. When Michelagnolo said good-by, Galileo's eyes filled with tears.

"I feel," he said, "as if I were seeing you for the last time in our lives."

"Don't be foolish; I'm coming to visit my family next year. And per-haps the war will be over by that time."

The day after Michelagnolo departed, Galileo was unable to get up.

Sickness overtook him suddenly. Now, as before, with slowly increasing pain, then unexpectedly, with raving force. He had never experienced such torture. He groaned for a time, grinding his teeth; but later lost control over himself and roared with pain. The whole household gathered in his room. The six children stared at their roaring uncle. Chiara fidgeted helplessly round the bed. It was soon evident that she was anything but a good nurse. She was even more frightened and excited than the sick man himself. And then she became absent-minded and clumsy. If she tried to nurse his suffering body, she was always sure to touch him in an especially tender spot. Yet she was full of good intentions. Every night she pulled up an armchair, heroically announcing that she would sit up with him. But she fell asleep almost at once. If Galileo wanted a little water he had to shout her awake. Thus the night went by. He suffered as he had never suffered before. He strained every muscle and nerve in his body, holding his breath to deaden the pain. In the morning, while he fingered himself gingerly with his good hand, he noticed aghast that his rupture had become enlarged. His entrails were swelling in a hump under his skin. He asked for a strong bandage; but, when Chiara saw this monstrous rupture, she screamed and fainted at the bedside. He shouted for help, but they only thought that he was crying in his pain, and knew that Signora Chiara was with him. At last Chiara regained consciousness unassisted, but her hands trembled so that the gardener had to bandage his master. This led to a quarrel. Chiara felt insulted and ran from the room. She sulked in her own part of the house.

Galileo sent for the younger serving man. Since both of them were called Giuseppe, this one's name had been shortened to Gepe. An alert and lively peasant boy, he was much more useful to the sick man than his sister-in-law. Gepe had to sit at the bedside and await the orders which his groaning master gave by nods and grimaces.

After dinner he asked Gepe for something, restraining his constant impulse to scream. But Gepe did not answer.

"Speak up!" he shouted at him. "Why don't you answer?"

Then he was horrified to see that, though the valet's lips were moving, he could not hear a word he said. He had gone deaf. Although he loathed doctors, now he sent for one. The physician examined him, found that every form of cure Galileo had used was correct, and prescribed herb tea and a warm bandage around his head. He went away with puckering eyebrows and a disapproving shake of his head.

The sick man knew that he had high fever. He fingered his rupture under the bandage; his left wrist and knee ached terribly. The inquisitive children often came into the room and annoyed him. And suddenly he grew terrified of death. He shouted to the servant to fetch his son. He felt death approaching. The man rushed out with a deathly pale face to do his bidding.

Nencio came to him three days later. Galileo spent these days half-conscious. He was still in horrible pain, but his head was clearer, although he could not hear everything.

"I'm going to die, Nencio," he said, weeping and feebly stretching out his hand weakly. "I feel death on me. Be with me, my son. I'm so alone. . . . Don't answer me, I can't hear you. If it's very important, write it down and hold the paper up to my eyes."

His son gently stroked his feverish face. Galileo stammered:

"Send for your uncle Benedetto, I want to make my peace with him."

He swooned again. He awoke to see Landucci at his bedside. He gave him his hand.

"Let's make it up, Benedetto, I feel my death. Let's forget everything. I don't want to face the judgment with anger in my heart."

Landucci nodded self-importantly, and held a slip to Galileo's eyes:

"*Do you want a priest?*"

"No, no!" he cried desperately. "If I take the Last Sacrament, it will all be over. Only at the very last minute. Don't send word to the girls, either. Now you can go, Benedetto. . . ."

Landucci took himself off, politely gloomy. Galileo felt faint, his strength ebbing. He swooned again and his last thought was: This is death.

But he did not die. When he woke, Nencio was sleeping in the armchair. But he was conscious only long enough to realize that he was alive. This happened again and again. Slowly he returned to life and was overjoyed to find that he could hear.

"Nencio . . . I don't want to stay here. . . ."

"What do you want, sir?"

"I want to be taken away. I'm beginning to hear those noisy brats again. There's no peace. . . ."

"Yes, father. Where shall we take you?"

"Barbara, my former housekeeper, lives now in the Costa San Giorgio, my old house. She was my best nurse. Take me there. But not now. I'd be ashamed to be carried like this along the streets in broad daylight. Find a stretcher by the time it gets dark, and send a message to Barbara. And tell Chiara, but be careful so that she won't take offense."

"I'll do everything, father."

Somehow he got through the long day. In the evening, Nencio and the two servants brought the stretcher. Chiara was deeply offended. They carried him through muddy darkness down the long road. By the time he woke up, Barbara was at his side.

He found peace and quiet here, and his old housekeeper knew his every glance or movement. Slowly he returned to life. They gave him Celeste's letters which had arrived from the convent during his days of unconsciousness. He read them and wept.

Nencio went back to Pisa, where he had important affairs to attend: he had finished his law studies and was waiting for his graduation. The sick father improved only slowly. His hearing was completely restored, but the pain in his joints did not lessen. Or, if they did, his nerves were so racked by the trials of his long illness that he felt even the smaller pain more keenly. Often he had a fit of weeping, which brought a little relief. Then again there was always something to excite him. He had much trouble with his nephew. He had sent him to Castelli, and the faithful friend was forced to report even worse things of the Roman Vincenzo than he had about the Vincenzo in Pisa. Cencio had brought shockingly bad manners from Munich. He swore great oaths to prove his manliness. He was lodging with a family called Crivelli, and the Crivelli ladies were always complaining of him. But this was nothing. He abused priests and mocked at the Church, although he wore a priest's frock. When Crivelli reproved him, he answered impudently: "I'm not a madman like you, to adore a painted wall." Crivelli was so enraged that he threatened him with the Inquisition. But first he talked to Castelli, who reported all this in a longer letter to his master, and asked him to call back the young man to Florence at once.

All this retarded his recovery. He was heartily ashamed that this young scoundrel, who was studying at Rome with the Pope's stipend, should behave like this. If any word of this scandal should reach the Vatican, he never could repair the damage. Now that he was able to write again, he sent his nephew a sharp letter ordering him to return at once, and told Chiara about it. She had calmed down now and came to see him regularly. She too complained that the boy had always been a boor, but said it was Michelagnolo's own fault for never having tried to keep him in order. He had even given him a bad example with his own godless behavior.

Galileo was recovering after the torture of six months. He had moved back to the Villa Segni, no longer finding the noisy children unbearable. He especially liked the second boy, little Alberto. He was a pretty child, polite and lively. Galileo did not have any difficulty in getting him a page's place at Court. When the boy donned his gorgeous page's dress for the first time, the whole family celebrated. On the same day Cencio arrived. He listened sulkily to a severe scolding of his uncle, but when he faced his mother, lost all restraint. He shouted at her as though she were a servant. Galileo was amazed. He dared not think what would have happened if he had spoken like this to his own mother.

A little later Michelagnolo returned. He began to discuss the situation in rather an insolent tone, reproached his brother for hurting Chiara's feelings, and violently defended his son. They could not avoid the question of money arising. Michelagnolo, whose family had lived for a year in his brother's house, saw an insult behind every word. At last they had an ugly quarrel. Michelagnolo gathered his wife and his children together, shouting that he would never cross the threshold of this house again. Galileo did his best to appease him, even to the extent of putting himself in the wrong; but his son interposed:

"Let be, father. Don't you see how things really are?"

"What do you mean?"

"Uncle Michelagnolo has found out that he couldn't let you keep such a large family for nothing. But he doesn't want to pay you a single soldo. That's why he has become so proud suddenly."

And so they made off. The little page cried bitterly because he had to leave his Court dress and ducal service. The young man with the stipend did not even trouble to say good-by. Nencio kept back Galileo, who wanted to rush after them at the last minute. He was sensible enough not to want to squander his patrimony on half a dozen cousins.

One hot summer afternoon, Galileo was resting in the park and making notes. He had begun to prepare his greatest work. His son sat down at his side.

"Do I disturb you, sir? I have something important to discuss."

"No, I don't mind talking; only don't ask for money because I haven't any. I've just received the bill from Pisa for your graduation fee. Two hundred and sixty-two lire! Well, at least you're a doctor now. So don't ask for money, son."

"Don't worry, I won't. I'd like to ask you to visit the Prime Minister. I had an audience with him today, and he's expecting you."

"Cioli? Why?"

"Because I've great plans, father. I want to marry and need your consent."

"Go on! Go on! You've made me inquisitive."

"I want to marry the Bocchineri girl, father. I've settled everything with her, and need only your consent. Also, her father insists that he should get a promise from the Prime Minister. That's why I ask you to see Cioli as soon as you can. He's willing to talk to her father, but wants to see you first."

"Wait a bit! Wait a bit. You mean Carlo Bocchineri of Prato? I know one of his sons well. He's the secretary of Cardinal Carlo de' Medici at Rome. Is it the same family?"

"Yes, father."

"It's a good family. . . . Wait a moment, I know the girl too. That pretty little dark-haired one who had supper with us when your uncle Michelagnolo invited some guests?"

"Yes. She's called Sestilia."

"A very nice girl too. I saw that she was in love with you, but didn't think it was so serious. And what about the money? What dowry is she getting?"

"I don't know the exact sum yet, but she'll get something. We thought that with your help we might buy a house. Perhaps that one on the Costa San Giorgio."

"Well, that isn't so easy, Nencio. But we've time to talk about it. You can stay with me for a while; there's plenty of room here. But the most important thing we haven't discussed yet. You spent seven years at the university, more than most. But now at last you have your degree. What are you going to do? How are you going to keep your family?"

"That's what you ought to discuss with Cioli, father. I hope they can give me a post at Court. I don't want to live on you forever, father. But I would like to ask you to help me in the first years if possible."

"All right, my son, you know I'll always do whatever I can. I'll go to Cioli as soon as I'm able to walk . . . when do you plan to have the wedding?"

"In January."

"Excellent. There's no sense in waiting. And remember, my first grandchild must be a boy!"

"I can't promise you a boy, sir," the young man said proudly. "But by next year I promise you shall have a grandchild."

"All right, son. Do your sisters know about it? You ought to tell them."

The boy grimaced.

"Arcetri is so far away, and I have so much to do now. Won't you write them, sir? I must leave you now."

He hurried away, and Galileo felt a little ache in his heart. But this was not the time to be angry. He got up and shouted for his servant. He dragged himself, leaning on his shoulder, to the villa, and sat down to write a letter.

"Great news, Gepe," he told the boy radiantly. "Your master is going to be a grandfather!"

The little serving boy gaped and grinned as though he had heard something rather indecent.

IV

There was no delay with the wedding: young Galilei married the Bocchineri girl at the end of January. The Prime Minister himself was present in church, and a great many notable persons accepted invitations for the wedding feast. Cioli proposed the first toast, exhorting the young people to live piously, in the fear of God; and he promised the young husband to find him a post at Court if he would be patient.

The bride and bridegroom stayed with Galileo. Nencio had nothing to do except to be happy. Yet he always complained of being so busy. He had a hundred things to see to and visits to pay. Galileo would have liked to use him as a secretary, but whenever he suggested this the young wife made a tearful face. So he left them to their love-making. He had become very fond of his daughter-in-law, who was a kind and gentle little soul, gay and modest, fitting in with Nencio's selfishly masterful nature. Celeste also liked her very much, and Galileo noticed indulgently that even so good a girl as his daughter could still be jealous. Though she praised Sestilia very warmly, she clung more to her father than ever before. He found it difficult to make the long journey into the mountains, and these letters were balm for his weary heart.

Galileo was the convent's watchmaker and general handyman. The nuns were very poor and could not afford to call in artisans if their clocks stopped or something went wrong with the chain of the holy lamp. There were always letters coming and going between Arcetri and Bellosguardo, especially in winter time, when Galileo was unable to get there over the bad road. It was tolerably good up to the Pozzo Imperiale, but the slope of the Giullari offered a hard task to man and beast alike. Gepe, the little serving boy, was the postman, carrying letters, cakes, books, messages.

In the meantime, the old man started to write again. Now he felt comparatively healthy, and the crowded days of his son's marriage were past. The moment had come for him to start the greatest work of his life. He had most of his material ready, but the main problem was not what to say—but how to say it. His task was to proclaim his faith in the stationary sun and moving earth in such a manner as to make it seem, not a positive statement, but always within the limits of hypothesis. He thought out many ways, but none of them pleased him.

One day, while he was browsing among old books, he came upon one by Erasmus of Rotterdam: *The Praise of Fools*. At first he fingered it absent-mindedly, then suddenly it began to interest him. Its skill amazed him, as he read. Erasmus made Stupidity voice everything he wanted to say about his age and the world. He expressed everything freely, but could not be caught. Had the Church called him to answer for any statement, he could calmly have said, "These are the sayings of fools, and therefore not to be taken seriously." It was an excellent form and, for a time, Galileo was tempted to use it. But he changed his mind. It might prove a double-edged weapon.

Yet he kept something of it. He decided to write the book in dialogue form. Two characters should discuss his deepest thoughts. He gave them real names. One he called Sagredo, the other Salviati. The first was his friend of Venice, who had died young; the other his Padua pupil and later his host in Florence. Both of them were long since dead, but while they had lived they had followed Copernicus. His book should be a monument to their kindness—it should free science from the shackles of the Peripatetics, in their names. And yet he felt it would be monotonous to have two people talk, both of whom represented the same views. He needed argument and discussion, refutations and contradictions. Someone had to represent the Peripatetics so that "Sagredo" and "Salviati" should have an opponent. He invented a symbolic figure, the stupid man. The narrow-minded, stubbornly lazy creature, slavishly keeping to the rut. He called him "Simplicio." This figure was the personification of the whole Peripatetic conservatism, of all he had fought and hated for the past forty years.

He made excellent progress. The three characters could hold a lively discussion. This dialogue made it easy to pierce the joints of the whole armory of creaking Aristotelian arguments. He could give free rein to his gift of words, could describe in subtlest detail the thinking processes of a stupid man. Nothing interested him more than the mental caliber of human beings. A clever man—even an opponent—always delighted and attracted him. A stupid man aroused his combative instinct as the scent of games provokes a hound. Now he had Stupidity in his hands, all the foolish enemies of his life as a concentrated extract in this Simplicio. He could revenge himself for all the suffering caused in forty years by silly opponents. He mocked them all with a savage lust, putting into Simplicio's mouth all the arguments which fools had ever managed to find against him. He jotted them down on separate slips of paper—and there were plenty of them—though he had for the most part forgotten who had used them during the long decades.

Dialogue on the Two Chief Systems of Cosmology, those of Ptolemy and of Copernicus, he called his book. He divided it into three long chapters. In the first he intended to enumerate the phenomena to be observed on earth according to the two conceptions. In the second he would examine the signs of the heavens; while the third would be an exposition of his scientific theories of ebb and flow of the tides. He considered this an even more important and decisive proof of Copernican truth than any other. Kepler was of a different opinion, thinking that ebb and flow were due to the effect of the moon, but Galileo upheld his own theory and destined it for the third part of his work. Thus he called the three chapters "three days." Sagredo, Salviati, and Simplicio met on three successive days to discuss their scientific problems. "First Day" was the first chapter, "Second Day" the middle, and "Third Day" the closing chapter.

He was progressing well with the First Day when spring came, and he could at last visit his daughters at Arcetri. But, instead of the quiet happy meeting for which he had hoped, he found the whole convent in confusion. The Mother Superior, who had taken Celeste for her cell mate, had tried to kill herself the night before. She had waited till Celeste fell asleep, then slipped into the corridor and stabbed herself several times. But some instinct had awakened Celeste. Perhaps she had felt that she was alone. She lit the lamp and saw that the Mother Superior's cot was empty. Suspecting something wrong, she hurried out into the corridor, where she found the old nun lying groaning in her own blood. She ran for help; the nuns woke and began to scream; some of them had fits of laughing hysteria, others fainted; the convent resembled a madhouse. The Mother Superior did not die; they managed to drag her back to life. But she had lost her will to live. She struggled and sobbed; three sisters had to hold her down to prevent her from jumping out of the window. Even on the following afternoon the whole convent was still hysterical.

Almost every nun trembled and cried. Only Celeste was unchanged. Her deep pity did not affect her faith, which sprang from the summits of all belief, was kin to the infinite. She spoke with deep understanding about the error of the poor old woman, saying again and again that God would forgive her because she could not have been sane. Galileo discovered only now that for long weary months Celeste had known that she was sharing her cell with a mad woman. But she had tried to calm, console, and hearten her, and had stayed at her side with unspeakable patience and courage.

"Why don't you tell Uncle Galileo," Suor Chiara, her cousin, said, "how she tried to stab you once?"

"That wasn't serious," Celeste answered, gently and yet very decisively. "And there was no sense in my telling father, because the thought that I was in danger would only have worried him."

"I hope you'll be the Mother Superior now," Galileo said. "Even though you aren't old enough."

Celeste shook her head.

"I'm much too young. But that doesn't matter. What matters is that He should never let me become an abbess. It would be terrible for me to have to command and punish others, and it makes me so happy to obey. Father, please do all you can to prevent their selecting me."

Galileo came back from the convent feeling very humble before Celeste. He saw her as something sublime and himself as unworthy of such a daughter. But at the same time he felt a happy pride that this saint should be his blood and body, a soul sprung from his. All that had become so divinely perfect in this angel, had its seeds in his own soul. Therefore he could consider himself as inclined to good—even in spite of his many faults. At home he spent a long time in prayer, a thing he very seldom did—only when his heart was so deeply moved that he had to pour out his sorrow or joy at the feet of God. Then he resumed his task of showing the miraculous world of God as even more wonderful than men realized, so that all could share these marvels with him.

Sestilia had been married four months when her husband, who was still idle, told his father that he could expect his grandchild in the month of December. He swaggered as much as though he had built a cathedral single-handed or triumphed alone over the whole Danish Army. But Galileo really did consider it an equal feat. He took Nencio stormily in his arms and hurried to find the young wife, fondling, embracing, kissing her with affectionate glee.

"Children, now we start an exciting race," he said exuberantly. "You expect the baby in December, and by that time I'd like to have finished my book. We'll see whose child is born first."

Sestilia blushed and stroked the gray head of her father-in-law. The future father strutted across the room, stopping suddenly in front of Galileo.

"Father, it's time we talked about that house."

"All right," said the sobered Galileo. "And we must do something about getting you some work, too."

"Oh, of course." Vincenzo sounded reproachful. "I'm ready to start whenever you like. It isn't pleasant to spend my time idling. But the first question is the house. I *must* give my family a home. You've shown, sir, very magnanimously how much you love Sestilia. Now you can prove it to your grandchild. We trust your fatherly heart."

"All right, I'll see what I can do. Tomorrow I'll visit Cioli and urge him to get you something to do."

Cioli did not need any urging. He kept his word. A few weeks later the Grand Duke appointed Doctor Vincenzo Galilei a junior clerk of the Chancery. His salary was very small, but it was money. And now his career depended on his own exertions. He might even become a Prime Minister. So Nencio started his work. The Grand Duke had received the new clerk, to whose father he sent his warmest regards, saying that the war raging through Europe unluckily took up so much of his time that he had to deny himself the pleasure of seeing the great scientist more often. Nencio gave the message to his father in a slightly patronizing way. After all, he was almost a member of the Government, which handled the fates of all Court employees. He took his work extremely seriously, never coming late to his office and always staying there after hours. He was twenty-three, but he had all the characteristics of old age: a little clerk who places his little life in a safe rut, and will never leave it til! the end.

Meanwhile the *Dialogue* was progressing; the manuscript grew thicker and thicker. He had become used to the careful tone in which he must write, to the treatment of his subjects as a hypothesis. And he attacked only the minor Peripatetics; Aristotle and Ptolemy he handled with much more consideration. He had given a well-defined character to all three figures: Salviati was the absolute follower of Copernicus; Sagredo the sensible, understanding, and open mind; while Simplicio remained the stubborn fool. The whole discussion took place in a rich Venetian palace; therefore its tone was suave and ceremonious. In this form he voiced the deepest thoughts of his whole life. He spoke not only of the two systems of the universe, but also about the greatest things which a scientist, searching the connections of God and men, could meet on his way. Whenever he found a chance of expressing some philosophical concept, he did not hesitate to digress from the main, astronomical theme. He maintained that science is the equal of theology—though he did not put it quite so bluntly. He also said that human thought can attain a knowledge of God, even through nature, since we can recognize the perfect truths of mathematics and geometry—perceiving in them the necessity of God. No higher degree of perception could exist. As he wrote this down, he became shocked at his own daring. For the first time in the history of Christianity someone dared to say: "A scientist can reach God just as well as a theologian." But he did not delete it.

In the next pages he fell back into his easy-flowing, anecdotal style, proving some truth contrary to Aristotle's principles in a way which even the simplest man—Simplicio himself—could understand. Simplicio, for instance, was unable to accept the statement that the moon, with her dark, scarred, and uneven surface, could reflect sunshine much more strongly than she would have done had her surface been completely smooth, as Aristotle had maintained.

"Would you mind," Salviati told him, "taking that mirror from the wall and bringing it into the courtyard? Come on, Signor Sagredo, fix it on the wall here, in the sun. Let us go back to the shade. Now you see the two surfaces on which sunlight is falling, the wall and the mirror. Tell me, Messer Simplicio, which of them is brighter? Well, why don't you answer?"

But Simplicio cannot answer, because the mirror—what a wonder!—is really darker than the wall. This is an experiment which any child can make. But it is also natural because the millions of small protuberances on the wall can reflect more rays than the mirror. Simplicio remains silent, and the three characters of Galileo start a serious discussion on philosophy. Thus he connected at random the great with the light, the holy with the

gay, just as he had learned it from his favorite poet and master in literature, Ariosto.

His achievements in physics were also dealt with. His figures detailed
the law of unhampered fall, which he had discovered and considered
of the greatest importance. He explained the ideal essence of weight.
This was the first time he hinted at the physical principle of "endurance,"
which nobody had followed before: a body in movement would keep on
moving infinitely if the resistance of the medium did not prevent it. That
was why the planets moved around the sun, because they had received
the impulse of their original movement from the sun, and no medium was
limiting them. Every theory and principle led to the statement that the
earth was moving. Only those whose imagination was limited were unable to accept this. He followed it up with a detailed explanation of ebb
and tide, so that he had to add a Fourth Day to the original three.

He was nearing the end of his task when frightening news came: the
plague had broken out in Milan. This was one of the scourges of war.
An Italian soldier who served with the Spaniards had brought it to Italy,
after passing through territory contaminated by German troops. He had
bought some clothes from the Germans, and these contained the germs
of the plague. The soldier died in hospital; soon his two nurses and the
monk who had given him the Last Sacrament were taken ill. A few days
later people were dying like flies. The frontiers of Tuscany were closed
on the Milan side, but there were still some old Florentines living who remembered that Italy had been visited fifty-three years ago by the plague,
and no frontiers could stop it.

The little family was terrified. They bought plenty of rosemary and
vinegar, hurrying with their purchases, as many others were doing the
same. There was no immediate danger though, and the first fright soon
passed. They were waiting for the baby, and Galileo continued his work.
He had found something exciting which made him indifferent to war
and plague. He had discovered that a horizontal and a vertical projectile
force appearing at the same time compromised into a parabola of movement. Or more simply: the cannon ball which leaves the cannon horizon-
tally but tends to a vertical line on account of its weight, follows the course
of a parabola. It was the answer to Prince Piccolomini's question, put so
many years ago. He hesitated whether he should include it in his *Dialogue*
but decided against it. He wanted to prove the thesis to himself by ex-

periments. He did not know how he could do it, as he had no cannon; but he left that to the future.

Sestilia won the race. On December 5th her boy was born. Cialibino was an ugly, red, long-headed baby, always squalling; but his grandfather thought him the loveliest baby in the world. He was so happy that he kissed his son, his daughter-in-law, his grandchild, the midwife, and even the bedroom door.

"We'll buy the house, son. You can start bargaining."

"I've finished it long ago," the proud young father answered at once. "The lease is ready, too; it only needs signing. And we've made a plan of the rooms. Sestilia's two brothers are going to live with us. I'll give you the lease, sir, so that you can read it."

"You discussed all this . . . without telling me a word about it?"

"I didn't want to disturb you, father."

Galileo felt furious—for a moment. But he would not spoil his happiness by a quarrel.

"I want to tell you something else, sir. About the name of Cialibino. I've agreed with my father-in-law that our first-born should be named after you—Galileo."

The grandfather smiled. He was quite won over.

"All right, let me have that lease."

On December 20th they had the great christening. The young mother was already about again, while the youngest Galileo Galilei screamed all day and night, except when he was feeding or asleep. His own sleep was all that mattered to him. On the twentieth his son came into his room.

"Could you come along today to the notary public, sir? Only if your work permits, of course."

"It does, my son. Half an hour ago I finished the *Dialogue*. And now I'm very sad."

"Why? Aren't you satisfied with it?"

"I am very well satisfied. It's a great work. But I'm sad because it is finished. It was such a great delight to write it. . . ."

V

Whatever he did, he never forgot to watch the sky. His instrument had now received an international name—one of the Lynxes, Demisiani, had christened it "telescope." "An instrument which looks afar." Just as the magnifying machine had been named by Faber, a German scientist living in Rome and a great Greek scholar, the "microscope."

The Florence telescope one night showed a marvelous thing to Galileo. The moon was not standing motionless in one place, but moving, sometimes to the left, at other times to the right. It was a tiny movement, but he noticed it. He discovered precipices on the edge of the moon which he had not seen before. He was surprised to find that mankind could see more of the moon than the actual side which she turned toward the earth. Yet, if she were motionless, only this exact half could be seen. Now he could draw a map of almost four-sevenths. Only the other three were invisible. The moon was swinging, like a pendulum which had not come to complete rest. The moon had received an impulse of movement from the earth, but by some mysterious process this impulse was slowly becoming spent, and was now nearing its end. However, this would take hundreds of thousands of years, a period which scarcely counted in the universe.

He tried to include this discovery in his great work, and found a place for it in the First Day.

When he sent his bulky manuscript, which came to about eight hundred printed pages, to Rome, the Lynxes welcomed it with delight. Duke Cesi wrote at once that they were willing to publish it. Castelli notified him that he had spoken with the fat Riccardi, who promised willingly to read it as soon as possible and not to raise any difficulties about the censorship. Ciampoli, the Pope's secretary, wrote to him in the old friendly tone. But most important was the news of some words spoken by His Holiness.

They had been spoken in connection with Campanella, the dream-weaving and adventurous priest who wanted to found states and reform the world. After twenty-seven years, the Spaniards had let him out of prison in Naples, and he had gone straight to Rome. Pope Urban had favored and received him. Lately he had granted him a long audience. Campanella had told the Pope that he had been in touch with distinguished Germans whom he hoped to win back to the One True Church. He had no difficulty at first. The German nobles had shown themselves well disposed to the Faith, when by an accident their talk turned to Copernicus.

"I told them," Campanella informed the Pope, "that the Church rejects Copernicus' teaching, or accepts it only as a hypothesis. There's a Papal Bull about this matter. Whereupon the Germans became very angry. They refused to hear any more about our Faith."

"A pity," the Pope answered. "We think otherwise. Had it been Our responsibility, that Bull would never have been issued."

Others had heard this saying of the Pope. They reported the whole conversation to Galileo. He was overjoyed, and showed the letter to everybody he trusted. First he read it to Celeste. Then he went to the Prime Minister, who had always shown a certain reserve in the matter of Galileo's astronomical convictions, since his politics inclined him to the Church. The Roman letter made a great impression on him. Then Galileo took the letter to Nencio, making the most of his opportunity to play with his beloved little grandson.

"Everything's going splendidly, my son." His face was radiant. "There won't be any trouble about the book. I'm beginning to be sorry that I didn't proclaim my faith in Copernicus more openly."

"I'm very glad to hear it, father. But we should be even happier if this Spanish business turned out favorably."

"That will come soon. Our luck has changed, son, God is helping us."

His trust was boundless. He firmly hoped that soon he would become a very wealthy man. He himself, who had no head for bargaining, would never have troubled about the "Spanish business"; but his son cared for nothing except money-making. It had been Nencio who remembered from childhood how his father had submitted some nautical invention to the Spanish Government. Now, Sestilia had a sister who lived in Madrid. She was the oldest Bocchineri girl, Alessandra. Although still a young woman, she had buried two husbands, and was now married to a diplomat called Buonamici. Nencio started at once to reopen negotiations about the invention through his diplomat brother-in-law. Buonamici, who was very

proud of his new and celebrated relative, was willing and helpful. He
took the necessary steps with the Spanish Government, and managed to
arouse a certain interest in them. Galileo wrote a new pamphlet about
finding one's position at sea with the help of the satellites of Jupiter.
They sent the essay to Buonamici and awaited the answer. The younger
Galilei was strictly businesslike; the elder full of boundless hope. He
was blindly certain his luck would change—a change for the better. Every
time he went out for a walk, he would enter a church and pray gratefully,
thanking God for a happy old age after so much struggle and suffering,
and for granting at last the fulfillment of his highest dream, the triumph
of the Copernican system. One day he entered Santa Maria Novella. He
stopped under the pulpit, where sixteen years ago Father Caccini had
preached against his "evil theories." Turning into the Spanish Chapel he
looked at Orcagna's famous fresco, the glorification of the *ecclesia militans,*
which shows the Dominican Fathers as black-spotted white hounds,
turning into glory the spiteful pun, *Domini canes*—the dogs of God.
What did all his nightmare terrors of hidden Dominican enemies matter
now? Or his fears even of the Jesuits? They were not bent on his destruction. They cared nothing for him or his affairs. And Cavalieri, the
Jesuit genius whom he had helped to get the professorship at Bologna,
was his stanchest follower and friend.

Judging by all the news from Rome, he deemed it advisable to settle
matters himself with the censorship. Riccardi, the kind and amiable
Monster, was a very sound friend, but a little lazy, as all fat men are. The
Lynxes wrote that they despaired of ever prodding him into action, and
even considered it better if the author did it in person. And Galileo
longed for another sight of Pope Urban, who had spoken those important
words. He looked forward to seeing the kind Niccolinis again, after so
many years. Castelli had made very good friends with them. If he mentioned Caterina Niccolini in his letters, he called her *la regina della gen-
tilezza.*

Galileo petitioned the Grand Duke for an audience, but the young ruler
of Florence was so busy that he could not receive him. Galileo had to be
content with the Prime Minister, who was all the more gracious in his
welcome. He gave him a message from the Grand Duke. His friendship
with the Pope was considered so valuable that Florence would pay for
his journey to Rome. The Embassy would be at his disposal: he would

receive a litter, servants, and money. He could stay as long as he felt inclined.

The Niccolinis received him just as graciously as before. They lodged him in the same suite; flowers, his favorite books and favorite wine were waiting for him.

"How kind God is," he muttered, deeply touched. "Celeste is my daughter, little Galileo my grandson, and you my friends! It's good to live, even when one is old, and it was worth while being born . . . for this."

With the Niccolinis on either side of him, he came out on to the loggia of the Villa Medici, to look over Rome again. He pointed toward the Vatican.

"There I shall win! The Pope is already won! A new world is beginning for science."

"I've already spoken to Father Riccardi, a kinsman of mine," said Caterina, "and asked him here tonight to supper. It's easier to discuss official matters over a meal."

"And I've already informed His Holiness," the Ambassador added, "that you're coming. He was very glad and wanted to see you as soon as possible."

"Thank you with all my heart," answered Galileo, "though even that I've already heard. Do you know what my pupil, the secretary Ciampoli, wrote to me? 'They long for you at the Vatican, even more than men usually long for a woman.'"

"Well, you can be proud; there isn't another scientist in the world who can get the same treatment from the Vatican. Others are treated quite differently. Have you heard about Morandi?"

"I know Morandi, the astrologer. But what about him?"

"He's being grilled by the Inquisition. The fool had read the approaching death of His Holiness from the stars and let someone else see the horoscope. Now he's in trouble. He ought to be glad if it only means prison. One must be very careful nowadays, Messer Galileo."

Galileo shrugged. "Poor man! I'm sorry, but I hate horoscopes as much as the Holy Father. Why should we seek the future in the stars when we make mistakes even about the present? But now it will be different. Tonight the final battle begins."

The incredibly fat Father Riccardi arrived for supper, and greeted his old friend uproariously. He would have hugged him had his paunch allowed him to. A special chair was standing at the table for him. He weighed at least 280 pounds.

"I've read the book," he said at once. "I've read it through. Not as my official duty, but from personal interest and affection. I congratulate you. It's a masterpiece, a gigantic book. As far as I can see, it should be immortal."

"You like it?" Galileo encouraged him. "Then it isn't so bad."

"I haven't any words to do it justice. A pity that it has to be corrected a little."

"Corrected? Do you want to change it? I thought not a single letter . . ."

"Several letters, Messer Galilei. This book treats Copernicus as a reality, not a hypothesis. It's an open proclamation of your faith in him."

"It doesn't matter," Galileo said nonchalantly. "His Holiness will not oppose it. He told Campanella about the Bull."

"They told me about that conversation. But alas! I haven't received a written confirmation. In my official capacity I only know of the decree prohibiting the new theory *expressis verbis*. I'm not even sure that it's permitted to handle it as a hypothesis. I have only private information on that. Cardinal Bellarmin gave you the permission, and later His Holiness repeated it. But I haven't received it in writing. And this book goes far beyond hypothesis. Every third page is a demonstration of Copernicus. It won't do, I'm afraid—and yet this wonderful work will have to be published. We'll discuss it at length, going through it bit by bit. I've already marked the different places when I read it. But believe me, I'll do everything to help you. You can trust me."

Galileo smiled.

"I respect your caution, Father. Your responsibility is very great indeed. But I have an idea. Let's wait till I speak with His Holiness. I'll ask him to inform you of his view. Will that be all right?"

"Oh, if it could be done," the Monster Father sighed, "I'd be the happiest man in the world. You have no idea how much this lovely niece of mine, Signora Caterina, is torturing me on account of your book, although you really don't need any spokesman with me. I'm not interested in the scientific side of it; it's all the same to me whether Copernicus or Ptolemy is right. But the book is so interesting, amusing, and colorful, you expound such wonderful things about the real importance of science, that I'm simply enraptured. Though I may easily lose my job over it."

The big fat man was almost in tears, so that they had to console him. In the end they decided to wait for the result of the Papal audience. Next day his long round of calls began. First he visited Duke Cesi, who praised the book with real enthusiasm and at great length. The least he said was that nothing like it had been written since the time of the great Latin authors and the Church Fathers. But he shared Riccardi's anxiety. If they could get the permission of the censor by smoothing over the awkward passages, it would be worth the trouble. And the Lynxes would be happy and proud to publish it. Galileo repeated that a single word from the Pope would settle the problem of censorship. So the Duke was also waiting for the Papal audience.

Ciampoli received him with open arms when he went to the Vatican. His Holiness would receive him the day after tomorrow. He had canceled the appointments of three others, among them a foreign ambassador, because he wanted to have a long and undisturbed talk with the Florentine scientist. Galileo inquired at once how that important conversation with Campanella had gone. Had Pope Urban said what rumor repeated?

"Of course he said it," answered Ciampoli. "I heard it too. But you mustn't take it as a binding statement. His Holiness wanted to be polite to Campanella, that was all."

"But he did say it?"

"He did."

"Then everything is all right. He'll want to be polite to me too."

"Let's hope so. But I want to ask you something important. What connection have you with the astrologer Morandi?"

"Who's now being tried by the Inquisition? None. I think we exchanged some letters about thirty years ago. Since then I've heard little about him. Why do you ask, Monsignor?"

"I just wanted to know. Well, don't forget to be punctual. Half-past nine."

Galileo arrived at a quarter past. He talked to Ciampoli, telling him about his latest scientific results. Then the long-awaited bell rang, and the scientist was kneeling at the feet of the Pope. Urban helped him up gently and embraced him.

"Pardon my clumsy movements, Holy Father, but I'm still a cripple. I have turned sixty-six. I must be thankful that I was able to get to Rome, and I am so happy to see your face again."

"Time passes, my friend. We also are on the wrong side of sixty. But by God's mercy We can't complain. Well, tell Us about beautiful Florence. We heard that you have enriched Italy and human knowledge by a great work."

"Yes, Holy Father. I've written about the two systems of the universe— those of Ptolemy and Copernicus. And I was happier than ever to hear that Your Holiness didn't identify yourself with the Papal edict concerning this matter."

"What?" The Pope raised his voice suddenly. "Not identify Ourselves with a Papal edict? Whoever said such a foolish thing? Can We deny any command of Our holy predecessors? Are We known thus? Is it thus We have defended Papal authority? Who talks such rubbish?"

"I crave your pardon," Galileo stammered. "I heard that you were kind enough to tell Father Campanella that if it had been your doing, the Bull would have never been issued."

"Perhaps We said that. We don't recall it now. But the decree was doubtless issued. Issued by a Pope. There's no sense in thinking of the 'ifs' and 'would have beens.' Have you still not given up that foolishness? Is your last book on the same theme?"

"It is, Holy Father. Since Your Holiness said that it was permitted to treat the matter as hypothesis, I was bold enough to sum up the scientific results of forty years' work . . . my humble work is now at the censor's and since I only treated it as a . . . ."

The Pope angrily waved his jeweled hand with the Fisherman's Ring. Galileo fell silent. His throat was so dry he had to swallow hard several times.

"Our censors will examine it," said the Pope. "Riccardi understands his business. We don't mind if it isn't an outspoken confession of faith. But let's change the subject. How are things going with you?"

Cowed, in a low and toneless voice, Galileo began to talk of himself—of his family, his daughters, the birth of his grandson. Even the smiling interest of the Pope was not enough to give him back that joyful eagerness which had filled him as he entered the room.

"I must report," he said, "that I am not entitled any longer to the stipend

Your Holiness most graciously granted my family. My son is a doctor and a civil servant now."

"That doesn't matter. You'll receive the stipend. How much was it?"

"Sixty gold pieces."

"You'll get a hundred from now on. We want to show you Our affection. But tell Us now about your science. Not about astronomy; We are bored by that. About physics, interesting experiments, and such-like."

The audience lasted a long time, but Copernicus was not mentioned again. Galileo searched in his mind for ways of amusing the Pope. Suddenly he remembered something.

"A very amusing problem was presented to me by gay and disputatious company. Suppose a beautiful stallion is worth a hundred gold pieces. Now, who would make the bigger mistake: the man who valued it at ten or the other who valued it at a thousand gold pieces?"

The Pope's eyes lighted up. He repeated the question.

"Now I see that We must converse with such a scientist to hear interesting things. That's why We like your company. Well, let's see. The horse's real value is a hundred gold pieces . . ."

He started to think aloud. Galileo interrupted him. He had kept his presence of mind even under the heavy blow, and had led the Pope skillfully and imperceptibly toward the correct solution. The Pope was happy to formulate it himself; ten, one hundred, and one thousand formed a geometrical progression, and the man who maintained that the horse was worth ten times its actual value had committed an equal error with the arguer who said its worth was ten times less. Nobody could deny that Pope Urban had a clever and penetrating mind—not only in such small matters, but in great affairs.

"It's most regrettable," Galileo risked it now, "that Your Holiness has lost all interest in systems of cosmology. With such a mind, you could easily survey the teachings of all the scientists."

"We've already surveyed them. In this very room you tried to convince Us, but you could not! We're a hard nut to crack, old friend, whether it's foreign policy or the stars. *Ad vocem*: stars! What connection did you have with that foolish impostor Morandi?"

"None, Holy Father," Galileo answered surprised. "Monsignor Ciampoli has asked the same. Why did you ask?"

"No reason at all. The stars . . . and how long are you staying in Rome?"

That meant that the audience was over. Galileo had to give up all hope of assuring the triumph of Copernicus. He bade farewell with a heavy heart, though the Pope was very friendly and gay. He embraced Galileo again, patted his shoulder.

"In case We have no time to see you again, take home the assurance that you carry Our affection and apostolic blessing to the end of your life."

The Pope had shown few people such kindness. But Galileo was not content. He told Ciampoli everything. The secretary advised him to get the book passed quietly through the censor's hands, and everything would be all right. Duke Cesi, Castelli, and the Niccolinis shared this opinion. So Galileo went to call on Riccardi at once. He decided to be quite honest and tell him everything about the audience. It would have been easy to distort the Pope's words a little and influence the stout Riccardi. But Galileo was too honest. Riccardi nodded gently and patiently.

"You see, I knew all this beforehand. Let's continue now where I left off. The responsibility is mine; and, if you are willing to smooth out a few awkward passages, I'm willing to shoulder it. But we must shield ourselves against all possible danger. You must write a preface, and an afterword. I'm thinking of the kind of thing which the pupil of Copernicus put in his book when it was published."

"And in these I must deny the whole book? I've a statement from Bellarmin that nobody can force me to do that."

"You needn't deny it. All you need do is to say tactfully that you're expounding an unusual system of ideas. Anyhow, we've plenty of time to talk about that. In the first place, we must finish those small corrections. It's very easy, only a question of words. Where you say 'doubtless' we'll put 'presumably.' I know the man who can do it. Rafaello! Rafaello! Come in!"

A tall, gaunt priest with an alert face entered the room. Riccardi introduced him: Father Rafaello Visconti, a mathematician, and his kinsman. He had already read the manuscript and was willing to make the corrections. At once, if Messer Galileo wished it.

Galileo felt better. It would have been more satisfactory, of course, if he had got the unconditional imprimatur by a simple command of the Pope; but even this was not so bad. Even this was victory! He would write the preface and the afterword, not only to reassure Riccardi, but to keep himself within the law. Then the book could be published; and, since it would bear the Papal imprimatur, nobody could harm him. . . .

By now it was the end of May, and stifling heat descended upon Rome. The older he grew the less was he able to stand such heat. His head ached unbearably; he got palpitations of the heart. His old illness began to threaten him. But he forced himself to wait for publication. A week later the long-expected message came: Visconti had finished the corrections. Galileo had himself carried to Riccardi in a litter.

"We can discuss the preface now, Monsignor. I'll have it ready by tomorrow, then you can give me the imprimatur, and I leave the day after. This heat is dangerous for a man of my age. Sometimes I feel a stroke approaching. Can I have the manuscript now to take a look at the alterations?"

But Riccardi shook his head.

"I'm afraid it won't be as quick as that. I myself have to control the changes made."

"But why? Didn't you talk it over with Father Visconti? He's a reliable man."

"No doubt he is. But the responsibility will be mine. Believe me, my heart bleeds to see you so impatient and afraid for your health. But the manuscript is very long, and every letter can be important in it. It's my duty to check all the alterations and read the whole thing right through to judge of how it looks as a whole, now that it has been corrected. That's natural, I think. Don't you see?"

"What am I to do? I can't help seeing it. But you must also understand my impatience. I implore you, Monsignor, to finish it quickly, so that I can go home as soon as possible."

Riccardi promised to work day and night. He was kindness itself. And even Galileo could not deny that he had to take a serious responsibility, a grave personal risk. And this fat priest suffered almost as much from the heat as he did.

So a whole month passed with Galileo urging on the work. At first he kept going to see Riccardi, then he sent Signora Caterina, and even the Ambassador. Weeks passed, and still the work was not done. Galileo felt so ill in the terrible heat that he stayed in bed. They brought him ice to cool his head, but even so he lay gasping for air. Caterina spent long

hours at his bedside. Galileo confided in her as he had never done before
to anybody. He told her his whole life; his youth and sufferings. He
spoke of Marina, his mother, Michelagnolo, but especially about Celeste.
Caterina listened intently, and what this old man told her about his
daughter impressed her so that she made up her mind to write to the nun.
These talks eased the endless weeks of suspense. And yet the work was
not done. At the end of June, Riccardi informed the Ambassador that he
was sorry, but the larger part was still unfinished.

Galileo could not stand it any longer. He got up and went to Riccardi,
telling him a little sharply that he was tired of waiting. He would like to
discuss the preface and epilogue and then go home. Riccardi almost implored him for patience. He promised to do his best. As for the preface,
he wanted Galileo to mention the Papal Bull in it, emphasizing the hypothetical nature of his book. The epilogue was not absolutely necessary.
When they parted, Riccardi repeated again and again that the permission
was certain and ready in principle; it remained only a question of formalities. Galileo could go home safely; let him have a little more patience and
take care of the health so important for science.

"Monsignor, I have a last question. Give me your frank answer—we
are alone here. You have asked me, as others did, and even His Holiness,
what connections I had with Morandi. Tell me, why were they asking
this? I was unable to get a straight answer."

Riccardi frowned.

"Neither can I give you one, Messer Galileo. I can only say that in your
place I would draw one conclusion from these questions. Your enemies
tried to get you involved in the charges of the Inquisition against Morandi."

"I suspected as much. But, for God's sake, who are my invisible enemies?"

"I haven't the faintest idea."

He would not say more. Galileo took a warm farewell of the Niccolinis, Castelli, and his other friends; he settled with Duke Cesi the questions of type and proof-reading on his return in the autumn; then he set
off in the hellish heat for Florence. Nightmares tormented him again.
Again some vague and horrible fear possessed him, terror of—he could
not tell what. It was like his first fear of the Inquisition. But through
these fears he clung to the reality of two names. One was Duke Cesi, the

rich nobleman, president of the famous Lynxes Academy, whom he knew never would forsake him, who supported him with all the weight of a whole crowd of learned men. The other was the Pope himself, who might differ with him about Copernicus, but still loved him as a man.

He reached Florence very near collapse. It took some weeks before he had rested and gathered strength. But the imprimatur was still delayed.

Instead came a letter from Stelluti: Duke Cesi had contracted some mysterious fever and died in a few days. At the same time came news from Germany: Kepler was dead.

VI

Outside in the world, everything was in chaos. Trouble, sickness, war —one could hear of nothing else. For twelve years the great conflict had raged, becoming more and more universal. Gustavus Adolphus, King of Sweden and a Protestant ruler, had landed with a large army in Pomerania. He advanced steadily; the tide seemed to have turned. The Catholics had suffered one shattering defeat after the other. And, as if the angry heavens would chastise humanity for its blood-guilt, the plague broke out again in all its horror. When the first news came of mysterious deaths, the Italian cities set up commissions to trace back each death to its origin. These commissions reported that there was no likelihood of a general plague. But the deaths increased by leaps and bounds. Milan became horribly plague-stricken. People did not dare to stay in their houses, but roamed the streets. The bravest among them took straw whisks, lit them, and rubbed the walls with the flaming bundles, since it was said that this process would arrest the disease. A nervous madness took hold of men and women; and the general belief spread that the plague was caused by mysterious foreign spies who possessed some black powder, and if they sprinkled it on anybody, he would surely get the plague. It was even considered enough to powder the walls of a house to infect all those who lived within. One day the news came that such an *untore*, as the mysterious poisoners were called, had sprinkled the walls of the Cathedral. Mobs raged through the city. The authorities set a price upon the heads of the miscreants. And, since the populace paid no heed to precautionary measures, they ordered corpses dead of the plague to be carried openly through the town that all might see the horrible blue rash, and be warned. Processions were ordered, and Milan prayed for mercy. Huge crowds gathered, many of them already infected, to follow the glass coffin of St. Charles.

All this became known in Florence, and was told by smuggled letters or uncertain rumors, since the Tuscany frontier was defended by a merciless control against the plague. Fernando, the young Grand Duke, behaved very wisely. He created an institute of hygiene, with unrestricted powers, and was forever conferring with his experts. One decree followed the other. The roads were patrolled, gathering in the streets forbidden. Drummers were sent through the town proclaiming the first precautions to be taken in case of sickness. The sick were mercilessly isolated even from their own families. Convents and monasteries were ordered to be transformed into hospitals. None of the inmates could leave them, and laymen were forbidden to visit these places—only letters were allowed. Galileo could not see his daughters. Only Celeste's letters consoled him.

Excitement rose higher and higher. Everybody talked of the plague. People were well satisfied with the Duke's instructions and trusted them. Nobody knew whether there was any sickness in the town. Some denied it, others knew of several cases. But it was always the pestilence. . . . People told each other incredible stories. They said that the poisoners were working quite openly in Milan. A Milanese had confessed that he had met a coach with six horses near the Cathedral. The coach stopped and the men inside it forced him to enter. They took him over unknown roads to a wonderful palace where gold stood in barrels and chests. They told him that he could have as much as he liked, if he would sprinkle a small phial of the poison about the city. He refused; whereupon he was returned in a single moment to the Cathedral square. This story went from mouth to mouth in Florence, and people believed it. They stared at every stranger suspiciously—he might be a poisoner. . . .

Galileo did not leave his house; he was afraid. He loathed the thought of the plague spreading to Florence, and dreaded catching it. He had even given up seeing his son very often. And when after much hesitation he ventured as far as the Costa San Giorgio, he found Vincenzo very much excited.

"Do you know, sir, what's happened? The Pope has sent a severe reprimand to the Grand Duke, protesting against the powers of the health commission and demanding the withdrawal of all decrees which affect monasteries and clerical persons. The palace today was like Bedlam, there was such a confusion."

"And what has the Grand Duke done?"

"What can he do? The Jesuits are his masters. He has decided to withdraw all the decrees. Every member of the health commission must go to the Archbishop, ask for forgiveness, and do penance. Well, I can't just stay here and do nothing. Thanks to your beloved Pope, the plague will soon be in Florence. Sestilia is pregnant again . . . and the baby . . . I don't want to wait till it's too late."

"Well, where are you going?"

"I don't know yet. But I'd like to warn you not to show yourself in the streets. Some people say that the plague was brought on us by the new stars. Everybody knows your connection with them. Some excited man may attack you . . . in Milan the rumors all say that the poison of the plague is brewed secretly by the scientists, with a mixture of frog spawn, sea foam, and corpses."

Galileo heard all this in silence. It shocked him to think that the Church in such a terrible time should interfere in matters outside her scope, jealously asserting her authority and destroying the most necessary precautions. Pope Urban was an able man; all this could not have been his doing. And yet, when he considered more closely, it seemed not unlikely, since the Pope was proud and self-assertive, always suspicious of revolt. And the Grand Duke Fernando had been educated all his life to obey the Church. . . .

Galileo was horrified at the possibility of being attacked in the streets of Florence. But after all—everybody was wrought up almost to madness. The world had gone mad. So he kissed his little grandson and went home. Soon came a letter from his son. Nencio had got leave from the Chancery and had moved out to Montemurlo, a little village near Florence. There he shut himself up with his family. Galileo was left completely alone. He did not leave the house for weeks, nor even speak to anyone. Letters were his only link with the world. Soon he received two which moved him deeply.

One of them came from Munich. Michelagnolo was dying. He had asked a friend of his, an Italian, to write to Galileo: the dying man asked his brother's pardon for all he had done against him and commended his wife and children to his care. But the unknown writer had forgotten to give any address to which Galileo could have written, so that the fate of these survivors remained a mystery.

The other came from Rome, and had been written by Castelli. "For reasons which I prefer not to write," he advised the scientist to give up the idea of printing his *Dialogue* in Rome, and asked him to find a Florentine printer. Galileo knew about the "reasons." With the death of Duke

Cesi, the Academy of the Lynxes had collapsed. There was nobody to lead and guide them. The members quarreled among themselves. Galileo had lost the support of a rich and authoritative body. So he would have to resign himself to publishing the book in Florence, provided he could get the imprimatur, which he had still not received. He sent one letter after the other to Riccardi, Visconti, the Embassy; but all he got was promises and fresh excuses. For nights on end he could not sleep. He thought over the problem—what did the Papal censorship want? If they had intended to refuse their permission, they would surely have said so long ago. Why then keep on asking for a little more patience and still not sending it? Riccardi had had plenty of time to read the *Dialogue* three times over, weighing every letter.

Again he was invaded by blind terror of vague, mysterious, sinister powers. And the latest Roman news came like a blow in the dark. Father Scheiner, the Jesuit scientist of Ingolstadt, who had been silent for a long time, had joined the fray again. Their dispute had ended many years ago when the Mayor of Augsburg had been acting as their connecting link. They had respected each other, and in their controversy about the discovery of the sunspots they had treated each other with the courtesy of equal opponents. Now, after many years, Father Scheiner published a book entitled *Rosa Ursina*. It was a violent and insulting work, haughtily belittling Galileo, arrogantly claiming the distinction of first having discovered the spots on the sun. There had been no rumor of this book when he was in Rome. It had been written since his return to Florence, received the imprimatur with surprising speed, and was published already. . . .

What was this? It was as though an invisible hand had kept back his manuscript so that this other work could be published first. But was it possible that Riccardi, the jovial and kindly Monster, should debase himself to such hypocrisy, allow himself to be used as an instrument of an organized attack against his friend? Galileo found it impossible to believe. But, then, why no imprimatur? And who were the people who wanted to get him involved with this astrologer tried by the Inquisition? Who incited the University of Pisa to do its best to reduce his salary? Yet the Pope had embraced him, given him money and every encouragement. . . . The old man sat clutching his head—bemused with thoughts.

More news from Rome. Castelli had spoken to Riccardi. The Monster had answered with seeming innocence that he could not understand

Galileo's impatience. Had they not agreed that Galileo was to return to
Rome after the heat? He was waiting for him. But if he could not come,
that was different, of course. The manuscript would have to be sent. The
Monster would need another complete copy, since the whole thing would
have to be gone through again at the time the preface was revised. Galileo
wrote an angry reply: He had only one copy, which he needed for his own
work. There were certain things he wanted to add—for the benefit of
Father Scheiner. Anyhow, such a bulky package would never be passed
by the sanitary authorities. Another long wait for the reply. At last it
came: Let him send the preface; everything would be settled now.

At last the plague broke out in Florence. People died like flies. Galileo
did not leave his house. Every day brought news of some well-known
citizen dead of the pestilence.

The old man worked at his preface, keeping it along lines discussed
with Riccardi, weighing every word with malicious glee.

> Some years ago, a welcome edict was published in Rome directed
> against the false and dangerous teachings of the present, and espe-
> cially that theory of Pythagoras which refers to the movement of the
> earth. This was done to allay the perilous disquiet of our age. Some
> daringly maintained that this decree was issued after careful con-
> sideration, but was born of ill-instructed prejudice. Complaints were
> heard that counselors completely unversed in astronomical observa-
> tions were strong in fettering the wings of searching minds by such
> unlooked-for prohibition. Hearing these complaints, my diligence
> could not keep silence. I reflected that I must show myself to the
> world as the confessor of sincere truth, in full knowledge of this wise
> decree. At that time I had been in Rome and received not only the
> attention but the praise of the most distinguished Prelates. And this
> edict was not published without my full and detailed assistance and
> explanations. In my present work, therefore, I should like to show
> to foreign nations that we in Italy, and especially in Rome, know far
> more about this subject than they imagined beyond the mountains.
> Collecting my own thoughts about the system of Copernicus, I should
> like to explain to them that the Roman censor was even then familiar
> with all this, and that Rome not only issues dogmas for the good of
> souls but scientific thoughts for the delectation of the mind. That
> was my reason for taking sides with Copernicus in my humble book,
> treating his thoughts exclusively as hypothesis.

He delivered another short attack against the Peripatetics, then he
explained the system of his work. The preface took a long time to write,

but at last he sent it to Riccardi. If the censor insisted upon another general revision, he could entrust it to some clerical person in Florence. At last came a letter: Riccardi did not object to this method. He wanted to choose Father Clementi for it; but, if the author preferred someone else, let him make his proposal. This started a new long correspondence. Father Clementi was known as a stubborn Peripatetic. On the other hand, Father Jacinto Stephani, a close friend of Galileo's, Councilor of the Florentine branch of the Inquisition, was a learned, sensible, and well-meaning man. Riccardi accepted him, and Galileo braved the dangers of the plague by going into the city with his thick bundle of manuscript. The streets were deserted. He had to ring for almost an hour before someone came to let him in. Father Stephani had heard about the proposed task. He took the bundle of closely written sheets and promised to do his very best.

From there Galileo went to the printers. As he walked along the Bargello he heard a peal of bells. He hurried for shelter into a doorway, trying to hide his face with his hands, holding his nostrils and mouth. But his curiosity was stronger, and he watched the grim procession pass. There was a city watchman in a red doublet walking in front, clanging his bell. Three corpses were carried after him, two men staggering under each of them. Only the outlines of the dead showed under the blankets. When they had passed, Galileo still dared not leave the doorway. The horrible bells were still clanging in his ears. It took him a long time to risk continuing his way. He swore to himself that he would never leave his house again.

The printer was called Landini, an old acquaintance. It rejoiced them to meet. Whenever two friends came together nowadays, they were always glad to find each other still alive. They discussed the work, the type, the size, the number of copies. As for the price, Landini could not give an immediate answer. He promised to prepare an estimate, and send it on to the villa. He would start work as soon as he received the manuscript; his workmen were idle in these disorganized plague-stricken days. Galileo started on his long way home through the deserted streets, past bolted and shuttered windows. If anyone met him, both tried to keep the street between them. He glanced back from the bridge and saw that Florence was dead. Horrible bells again in the distance—he hurried on.

For weeks he did not leave his house. A letter told him that his second grandson was born, a fat, healthy baby whom they christened Carlo. Even later news came with the next: Father Stephani had finished reading his manuscript. His opinion was that the author of this book ought to have been requested to publish it, not hindered by continual obstacles.

The manuscript was sent on to Landini. The work began. Every moment they expected the imprimatur, which was still delayed. Galileo wrote an urgent letter demanding his preface. But days and weeks passed without an answer. He sent a long memorial to the Prime Minister, describing these incessant difficulties and requesting the Grand Duke to intervene. His request was granted. The Florentine Government sent an official letter to Niccolini, commanding him to visit Riccardi and urge the matter. Niccolini reported that this was done; everything would go smoothly now. Riccardi would grant the imprimatur with a special declaration to cover himself. Ten days later came Riccardi's answer, but not the permission. He had promised it, he wrote, but only on condition that Galileo come to Rome and carefully revise his manuscript with Ciampoli's help. Father Stephani did not know the Pope's mind, and might easily have missed something which would cause trouble.

Galileo almost tore his hair with rage. The preface had been sent months ago to Riccardi. Had he lost or forgotten about it? He wrote another long letter to the Prime Minister, asking for an audience of the Grand Duke, together with Father Stephani, Councilor of the Inquisition in Florence. His Highness would be informed about everything during this audience, and no doubt would be moved to personal intervention. He sent off the letter, but soon decided that this behavior was very childish. Grand Duke Fernando would scarcely be expected to meddle in matters which concerned the Inquisition. He might expose himself to a severe reprimand for interfering with Church business. And the Court rejected his request. The Grand Duke did not wish to grant such an audience. Niccolini would do his best in Rome.

And indeed the Ambassador really urged Riccardi tirelessly, till at last he got him to agree that the final decision should rest with Father Clemente Egidio, Chief Inquisitor of Florence. Father Egidio promised to read the manuscript quickly, and he kept his word. He had received instructions from Rome that the theory of Copernicus must be treated only as a hypothesis and, since Galileo had kept this form, he could raise no objections. He found the book an unmistakable defense of Copernicus, but to judge

of this was not his task. He had only been commanded to check the
hypothetical nature of the arguments. He would have granted the imprimatur, but the preface was still missing. Riccardi still kept it. Some of
the sheets were already set up, but still the permission had not arrived.
Galileo wrote to Riccardi, but got no answer. He wrote again. No answer!
At last he wrote a furious letter to Niccolini. The Ambassador went to
Riccardi's lodgings and told him that he would not budge until he received
the revised and approved text of the preface. Thus the preface came back
to Florence, the Chief Inquisitor approved it, and Galileo dared to risk
another visit to the city. He met many funerals; the number of dead had
risen to several thousands. He crouched in horror along the walls till he
reached the printing office. They had to insert separate pages for the
preface, since the beginning of the book was already in print. The type at
the little printer's was all used up, so the preface was set in different
lettering.

But it was set at last! And the first page bore the official imprimatur
of Holy Church.

Two years had passed since he had finished his manuscript. Riccardi
had said at first that it would be passed "in a few days." Eighteen months
was a little longer than those "few days." These eighteen months had used
up Galileo's strength. He was sixty-six when he finished the greatest work
of his life, but then he had felt no more than sixty. Now he was sixty-
eight, and he stood waiting in the anteroom of the Grand Duke to present
the first copy—he had dedicated his work to Fernando—feeling well over
eighty.

The audience lasted only two minutes. Fernando very graciously
offered his hand to kiss, expressed his princely gratification that the book
should be dedicated to him, and so "accepted" it, which meant that he
would pay for the printing. He also expressed his deep concern about the
terrible plague and the fatal victories of Gustavus Adolphus. Finally he
dismissed his scientist with a gracious smile. Galileo left the audience
chamber and asked for a litter. His legs seemed to be giving way under
him, his rupture threatened with new danger, and he was so terrified of the
plague that he felt he might burst into tears at any moment. The courtiers
nodded sympathetically and sent for a litter. The old man dragged himself laboriously down the stairs; all his strength seemed gone.

At the gates of the Palace he stopped to rest. At that moment came a splendid coach with four white horses in glittering harness. A priest got out of it and glanced at this old man, panting for breath:

"If it isn't the great Galileo! Don't you recognize me? I'm Ascanio Piccolomini, Archbishop of Siena."

"Of course I recognize you, Monsignor. But my sight is getting bad. My eyes are so old. . . ."

They began to talk; they were old acquaintances.

Galileo had always been a favorite with the members of that famous family. The young Archbishop, almost a boy, listened compassionately to the grumblings of this tired old man.

"You must take a long rest, Messer Galileo. Whenever you feel like it, you are always welcome at Siena. A good bed and a well-laid table will always be ready for you. And real rest."

"Thank you," Galileo sighed. "There's only one real rest for me. The last one. The great work of my life is published. I feel like Moses: my mission is ended."

VII

In the previous autumn Castelli had written enthusiastically that as soon as the *Dialogue* was published, he would read nothing else except his breviary. Now Galileo was eager to send him a copy. He had already prepared a long list of people to whom he wanted to send copies in a sumptuous binding. They were all ready but could not be sent to Rome. There was a strict sanitary cordon between the Papal State and Tuscany. Every packet and letter was disinfected with acids and strong vapors. A common letter would have stood such a process, but the leather-bound books would have been ruined.

Letters began to come in from parts of the world to which the book could travel freely. Cavalieri, the Jesuit of Bolgona, did not hesitate to call it remarkable. Fra Micanzio, who had been Fra Sarpi's secretary and bodyguard, reappeared; he sent congratulations from Venice and could scarcely find words for his admiration. Campanella also received a copy in some mysterious way; and he sent a long, appreciative letter. Messages of reverence and admiration followed each other, homage to the great scientist. Galileo was happy. Spring came, and now he managed to get permission for a visit to his daughters. For endless months they had only exchanged letters. Now at last they could all three embrace and rejoice that they were still alive. He took the letters of praise to the convent and displayed them to the nuns. He had great difficulty in reading them; his sight was getting worse and worse. Celeste read them aloud, and he could not have enough of her flattery.

"Nobody in the world could have done this, only I," he said proudly.

"Nobody could write such a book, that's true," Celeste sighed.

"Writing was the smallest part of it. But to succeed in publishing such a work!"

To spread Copernicus' fame all over Europe—through the official medium of the Church!

He always carried a copy about with him. He opened it now. The last page contained all the clerical authorities who had given their permission to publish it. The Chief of the Papal Censorship, Riccardi. All the officials of the Florentine Inquisition. Six different names and dates.

"Do you see? I had it printed here, so that my attackers should see what priests have sponsored the publication. Even so they'll attack me. Let them come. I'll settle them. The Pope's favor and affection are behind me."

"God bless His Holiness! I'll ask the others, too, to pray for him."

"What is the news up here? It's such a long time since I've seen your convent."

Celeste told him everything. Suor Silvia, the lovely nun whom they considered the most beautiful woman in Florence, was wasting away. She could not eat, and her lungs were in a bad state. Suor Achilla was diligently playing the organ. Suor Grazia, poor old soul, who had always been feverish, had died a short time ago. Suor Oretta was in bed with inflammation of the kidneys; she could not get better. Suor Maddalena was still a good cook—she had a great talent for making even the poorest materials delectable.

They were sitting in their usual place, which offered a wonderful view. Down in the distance Florence lay in the hazy spring sunshine; all around the wavy lines of the fresh green hills enchanted the eye. Near by the building of the Certosa stood on its own low hill. It was all beautiful, full of peace and sunshine, as though there had been no plague, no Peripatetics to spoil the world.

"I've thought," Galileo said, "that I'll change my quarters. The Bellosguardo villa is too big for a lonely old man. Then again, it's too far away from everything and yet in the city. I'm going to move."

"Where to?"

"Guess, Celeste! Quite close to you. I'd like to live at Arcetri. Perhaps I'll find some suitable house. There's peace and quiet here. It would be so nice to spend the rest of my life close to you. I could visit you every day. What do you say?"

Celeste wept at the mere thought of such happiness. She urged, encouraged, implored her father not to lose a single moment. He must ask someone today to visit every house in little Arcetri. Galileo promised. He had planned only tentatively; but, since Celeste was so happy about it, he would do something at once.

And, as though God wanted to favor their happiness, he found the house in a few days. The finest villa in Arcetri, three minutes from the convent. Galileo was enchanted by it. The owner wanted to move into Florence for family reasons. He wanted only three gold pieces a month for the villa and the garden. Galileo did not hesitate; they signed the contract, and he moved in. His belongings were packed on high wagons covered with tarpaulins which they had soaked in vinegar. The two valets, Giuseppe and Gepe, were happily excited by the move, delighted to leave the pestilential city for the quiet mountain.

The Pian de' Giullari, a long, winding road, led to Arcetri. Small cottages lined its sharp gradient and milder slopes; behind the stone walls of the little gardens the wedding pomp of flowering cherry trees laughed at the passers-by. In the midst of this row of houses rose the Jewel. This was the name of the villa: "Gioiello," and it deserved its name. A one-storied, pretty building, with a high stone wall toward the street, its gracious beauty turned to the long sloping garden. A tower with a single window was built at one corner, eminently suitable for the new master to watch the stars through the dreamy, silent nights. On the first floor the house had a covered veranda opening on the courtyard, a roomy and airy place, closed toward the street. Nobody could look in there. A variety of rooms, a pretty well in the courtyard, and somewhat farther on a gardener's cottage, a woodshed, and a barn for carriages. Even in his dreams Galileo could not have wished for more perfection. But the view from the windows opening on the valley gave added beauty. Farther toward the city the huge mass of the Pozzo Imperiale towered. Beyond that the city itself, the domes of the Cathedral and the Medici crypt, the delicately outlined watchtower of the Signoria, the gently glowing colors of Giotto's Campanile, the towers of Santa Maria Novella, and the other churches.

A happy, ordered life began in this Jewel-villa. Galileo bought a mule, since even short distances were too much for him. Every day he visited the convent. The mule soon learned that they had only one path to follow. His master had received permission for these daily visits. In a month he knew every house along the road, the white and yellow flowers in the cracks of the crumbling walls, the pinias, cypresses, olive trees, here and there a smiling rosebush; he knew the urchin playing in the doorway of the third house, and the brown dog excitedly barking in the next. He had a vineyard again in the garden of his own house. He put on a big blue apron, donned a large straw hat, and played around happily with his

pruning knife among the growing vines. He seldom visited the city.
Gepe walked down every second or third day to fetch the letters. And the
tired old man read happily in the solitude of his villa the repeated praises
of his *Dialogue*.

But when he heard that a distinguished acquaintance of his, Count
Magalotti, was going to Rome, he took the road down to Florence. Count
Magalotti was related to the Barberini family, therefore to the Pope himself. He could be sure of special treatment at the frontier. Galileo went
down to the city, although there were still ten or twenty deaths of the
plague every day. But his terror was less than his desire to send books to
Rome. The Count was ready to take them along; he was traveling with
plenty of luggage, and the box with the books did not make much difference. So ten copies of the *Dialogue* started on their way to Rome, while
the author hurried back to his quiet solitude, to have himself rubbed down
with vinegar from the top of his head to the soles of his feet.

Weeks passed, and at the beginning of summer Count Magalotti wrote
to him. He had sent the books to their various addresses. Although the
exciting news of the great war and the destruction of the plague interested
everybody more than scientific problems, this great and daring work had
not remained without its effect.

"Galileo will have plenty to do," the fat Father Riccardi had said. "The
Jesuits are sure to attack him."

That did not surprise Galileo. But it annoyed him a little that Riccardi
had spoken of the Jesuits. Why had he not said "Peripatetics"? That he
had named this powerful and secret Order again roused in Galileo the
nameless terror of being pursued by secret enemies. Then he heard that
Father Scheiner had come to Rome. What was this Jesuit doing there—
just now? The answer was easy: his attack on Galileo had been published
recently; he was in Rome to study its effect. A young physicist, called
Torricelli, Castelli's pupil, who had begun to correspond with Galileo, had
met Father Scheiner.

"Galilei has behaved very badly toward me," the Jesuit said. "That's
all I can tell you."

But whether he or someone else moved the secret levers, a slow hostility
had begun to ferment around the *Dialogue*.

Yet Galileo was waiting for public attacks, pamphlets, and books of controversy, struggles of opposing cosmologies. Instead there were quite different moves.

On the title page of the *Dialogue* was printed an ornament of three dolphins forming a circle. An anonymous denouncer complained against it, saying that it must mean something and certainly its meaning was sacrilegious. The denouncer gave an endless list of all the many different kinds of godless things which the three dolphins symbolized. Riccardi became scared, but was soon pacified when Galileo told him that the three dolphins were the usual imprint of the Landini printing works. They used it in every book they published.

"I was really amused," Galileo told Celeste, "to hear how frightened the fat priest was. And it was rather typical that my enemies found nothing else to attack in the *Dialogue*. I've triumphed, Celeste, no doubt of that! If poor Kepler could have lived to see this!"

Then a new charge was invented: why had the author used different lettering for his preface, and added special pages to divide it from the work itself and discredit its contents? But Riccardi himself replied that he had kept the preface back, when the book was already being printed. These pinpricks delighted Galileo. He was living happily in his villa, almost longing for a real attack on a scale to give him scope for new arguments based on the Papal imprimatur.

But one day he received tidings which at first he did not want to believe, they seemed so incredible. Landini sent a message that he had received a decree from the Vatican forbidding him to sell the book till further notice. It had been suspended. Of course, this could only be a mistake. All the same, he had his mule saddled and rode down into Florence. Landini showed him the decree. It seemed quite in order. Signature, seal, and stamp were all as usual.

His pulse began to beat more quickly. In an instant blind terror had flooded his mind and driven away the happiness of the last few months and the joy of congratulatory letters. He went home tormenting himself with questions which he could not answer. The night was spent in sleepless agony. Next morning he had high fever. He fancied he had caught the plague. He searched for its symptoms, questioning his servants about them all.

His son arrived. He had risked the trip to Florence. His first visit

was to the Chancery, and the news he heard there sent him scurrying up
the hill to his father.

Cioli had told him that an official inquiry had been started in Rome
against Galileo. It was not the Inquisition, but a specially appointed board.
Nobody knew what was the charge, the subject of the inquiry, only that
the investigation had been started, since Rome had sent official notification
to the Florentine Government. Cioli had written to Niccolini asking him
to visit Riccardi and find out the truth. The old man kept repeating:

"I can't understand it, I can't . . ."

"Don't worry, sir. The Pope can get you out of anything. And what
about that Spanish business? It would be nice to earn a little money by
the moons of Jupiter."

"Oh, it never came to anything. The Spanish Government didn't consider the time suitable for discussions. But why need you torture me with
the Spanish business? I'm going mad with this uncertainty. What can it
be?"

Nencio was not alarmed. He spoke of the children, looked around the
garden, and left. Galileo was waiting in a daze to hear from Niccolini.
He was quite beside himself. Even Celeste could not comfort him.

Not many days later he received a summons from the Prime Minister.
He must come at once; they had important news from Rome. He dressed
in nervous haste and shouted to the servants to saddle his mule. He felt
a sickening pain in the pit of his stomach.

Cioli's face showed that he had unpleasant news. He searched silently
on his desk and handed Galileo a letter. The old man tried to decipher
the tiny scrawl which his weak eyes could scarcely read, and the paper
began to shake between his fingers. It was from Niccolini to Cioli.

Yesterday I had no time to report to Your Excellency what had
happened to me in the business of Messer Galileo at the Vatican. It
so fell out that I could speak to His Holiness in person, although
without any result. I am beginning to agree with Your Excellency
that the world will collapse about our ears. When our talk turned on
the evil with which the Inquisition is forced to deal, His Holiness
was seized with sudden fury and turned upon me.

"Your Galilei is meddling with the gravest and most dangerous
things, which don't concern him in the least."

I replied that Galilei had never published anything without the permission of His Holiness; that I had myself received his preface and sent it back to Florence for printing. The Pope answered with mounting anger that Galilei and Ciampoli had tricked him. Ciampoli had told him that Galilei would do everything as commanded, and that all was in order. The Pope knew nothing further of the matter, never having read the book nor seen it. Ciampoli and Riccardi had behaved very knavishly, although Riccardi declared that he was also deceived; that they had induced him to give the imprimatur by means of all sorts of honeyed lies, wheedled the permission out of him to have this Dialogue published in Florence, neglected his conditions, and even printed his name in the book, although in his official capacity he had nothing to do with books published abroad.

I answered then that to my own knowledge His Holiness had appointed a commission; therefore I begged him in all humility to give Galilei a chance to clear himself.

"In such matters," His Holiness answered, "the Holy Office merely examines the work and commands the author to withdraw all forbidden passages."

"But doesn't Your Holiness agree," I replied, "that Galilei ought to be informed of the objections which the Holy Office takes to the book before they try him?"

"We've already told you," he answered violently, "that this is not the usual procedure. Such matters are never discussed beforehand; they are kept secret. Galilei knows very well what the objections are. We've discussed all these matters with him and told him Our views."

"And yet I beg Your Holiness," I urged him, "to consider that the author dedicated this book to our Prince, whose Court mathematician he is. I hope that Your Holiness will treat him leniently and instruct your men to do the same."

"We have already forbidden books," he said, "which contained Our Holy name in their dedication. In such matters, when religion is attacked with the most cunning weapons, His Highness has only one duty as a Christian Prince—and that duty is punishment. Tell His Highness not to meddle in this affair, or it will involve him more deeply than he supposes." "But I am quite sure," I said, "of receiving renewed commands from him, which will force me to trouble Your Holiness again. I hope that if a book which has once passed the censors should be forbidden, Your Holiness will not refuse to listen first to the author's defense."

"That would be the worst which could happen to Galilei. Let him take care that the Holy Office does not summon him. This commission consists of theologians and other persons well-versed in all sciences. They are all pious and learned men. They'll weigh every letter in the book, since this is a case of the worst blasphemy which the Holy See has ever encountered."

Then the Pope again began complaining that Galilei and Ciampoli had tricked him. He told me to communicate to His Highness his firm opinion: that this theory is in the greatest measure godless. His Highness should be careful not to endorse it in any way. . . . His Holiness added that he was treating Galilei far more honestly than Galilei had treated him, because he had been deceived by Galilei, while he—that is to say His Holiness—had not passed on the matter direct to the Holy Office but to a special commission—a very great favor.

On the whole I encountered hostility everywhere. As for the Pope, he could not have spoken more harshly of our poor Galilei. Your Excellency can imagine in what frame of mind I returned.

The letter went on to say that Niccolini had visited Riccardi. The fat Censor did not consider the matter so very grave. He thought it probable that the commission would object to a few passages, which would have to be altered. But this did not diminish the terrible shock which Galileo felt as he read the letter. When he had finished it he could only stare blankly at the paper. His mind was blank.

"By God, this is no small matter!" exclaimed Cioli.

He said much more, but Galileo did not hear. Cioli's words seemed to come from an immense distance, almost from another world. He was still staring at the paper. The Pope had turned on him! The Pope was angry! The Pope raged, saying that he had tricked his benefactor!

He was unable to discuss the situation. He rose unsteadily and began to take leave, interrupting Cioli in the midst of a sentence. He turned from the astonished Prime Minister and shuffled unsteadily to the door. Outside stood the mule. He climbed into the saddle. The whole world around him had changed. It was as though he had entered this palace from the earth but had come out into a strange new planet.

At home he went to bed at once. He had not even strength to visit Celeste. He lay rigid, staring into vacancy. They brought him food, which he could not touch. It began to grow dark; he did not light a lamp. All that night through he did not sleep, but he was scarcely thinking.

Next day a letter came from the Chancery. The Pope had appointed the learned Chiaramonti, with full powers, to head the commission which would deal with his case.

He sat rigid with horror. Chiaramonti—with whom he had nearly come to blows years ago at the Marchese Guidubaldo del Monte's table.

The man was his mortal enemy. Slowly his mind began to work. Even by day phantoms tormented him which once had only tortured his sleepless nights. This devilish organization had picked the most hostile "expert" in all Italy. The Pope had been drugged with some hellish brew. What else could have made him turn away from his friend?

At last he took his grief to Celeste. His daughter listened to the incredible story, amazed. But she kept her head. She began to reason. There must be some mistake! Surely it could be cleared up, and then everything would come right again. For a while he listened as though he were managing to believe and take comfort. Then suddenly he cried:

"They'll have me before the Inquisition! You'll see, Celeste; they'll have me before the Inquisition."

"Hush, father! Didn't you say that they had appointed a special commission for your sake—to avoid citing you? Don't lose your head, try to think calmly. . . ."

"No," he answered in stubborn fear. "The Inquisition . . . they want to torture me. . . ."

Celeste was unable to help him. He dragged himself home. His state was almost bordering on madness. He waited for the Holy Office to summon him. Sometimes he heard a knock on the door; they were coming! His diseased imagination worked so feverishly that his thoughts were like the gibberings of a lunatic, whose whole world is his fixed idea.

"They haven't come today," he told Celeste.

"They, father?"

"They didn't come. To take me away."

"But where, father? And who are they?"

"To the Inquisition. They. My enemies. I don't really know who they are."

This lasted three weeks.

And then "they" in reality came for him. He was not surprised. A summons came from the Chief Inquisitor of Florence: Galileo must come to the city at once, on important business. He set out obediently. The Inquisitor informed him that proceedings had been started against him, and that he would have to appear before the Holy Office in Rome.

"Yes," he said, almost with satisfaction. "I told them, but they wouldn't believe me."

"What did you say?"

"They said that a special commission had been appointed to look into my case. But I knew at once that it would really be the Inquisition."

"You were right. That is what the Vatican has decided. And now I must ask you to write a statement which I shall dictate. I must send it to my superiors in Rome."

Galileo sat down unprotestingly. The Chief Inquisitor dictated:

Florence, 1st October, 1632. I, Galileo Galilei, attest that today the Very Reverend Father Chief Inquisitor has summoned me at the command of the Holy Office in Rome, to remove myself within this month to Rome, and report to the said Holy Office and to the Father Commissarius, who will give me further instructions. I will follow this command obediently during the month of October. I have given this declaration with my own hand. I, Galileo Galilei, manu proprio.

He left the document, took polite farewell, and went home almost re-assured. Sickening and horrible uncertainty was at last changed into something definite. Events at Rome had caused the Pope to judge his case even more gravely, and so he was referred to the Holy Office.

But relief soon passed and terror came back to him. What would they do to him? By all the rules of common sense he would be questioned and then told that his book was partly or wholly banned. But had events up to now been according to common sense? The mystery of the Pope's change of mind was maddening. Nothing was impossible now. The prison of the Castel Sant' Angelo. To be burned or broken on the wheel. The horrible instruments of the torture chamber. Then they would chain him to the wood and light the pyre underneath his feet. The flames would catch his clothes, his beard . . . He screamed and flung out his arms to scatter this nightmare.

He visited Cioli and implored him to instruct Niccolini—he must try everything. He was prepared for any kind of penance, would blindly obey every command the Pope might lay on him—only let them spare him the Inquisition. Cioli promised to do his best. Niccolini wrote back saying that he had tried every method, but all in vain. Galileo sent a long and desperate latter to Cardinal Antonio Barberini, the Pope's nephew. He was careful to write to him as "Your Eminence," since Pope Urban had recently issued an edict by which the Cardinals had so to be addressed in order to enhance their authority. He sent off his letter on October 13th and awaited the answer. It never came. Niccolini wrote that this letter might do him more harm than good. He would try once more with the Pope himself.

His last effort failed completely. The Pope insisted that Galileo must come to Rome. At the same time he dismissed Ciampoli, sending him to a tiny provincial parish. This was no laughing matter. And the Chief Inquisitor of Florence again summoned the old man.

"Why have you broken your promise? October is past. Today is November 19th."

"I crave forgiveness, Very Reverend Father. I hoped that certain steps I had taken might bring some result."

"Well, you'd better rid your mind of such foolery. You must be in Rome within a month."

"Yes, Father."

He was humble and terrified. He glanced round the room searching for a hidden trap door, which might open and swallow him. But this was the usual arid clerical office. He hurried home like a fox going to earth. And wrote letters. To Cioli, Castelli, Niccolini, everybody. He implored them to get him at least a little respite. He dreaded the plague and was feeling very poorly indeed. And this was true. The emotional stress had made him ill. His rupture was becoming enlarged. His eyes were inflamed. He could not sleep for nights together, nor close his eyes during the day for more than a few minutes' uneasy sleep, from which nightmares roused him. He lay in bed and waited for letters. His daughters were not allowed to visit him. Porzia, the old housekeeper, fidgeted round him, crying silently.

The new date set for his departure had not passed, and yet, on December 18th, the vicar of the Chief Inquisitor came to his house. This was a harsh and savage man who shouted and bellowed at the invalid. Had he lost his reason? Was he trying to disobey the Inquisition?

Galileo was weeping bitterly. "I'd go—but I haven't the strength."

"Are you really so ill? That's easily said. Send us a proper medical certificate. It must be signed by at least three doctors, whom I shall name. Because you can't deceive us here. Rossi, Ronconi, and . . . let's say Cervieri."

"Yes, Father."

"I must warn you that whoever has tried to cheat the Inquisition has always rued it. *Laudetur.*"

The sick man sent for the three doctors. They arrived together. Obviously they had discussed the case. They examined him thoroughly, first with suspicion and distrust, but in the end they shook their heads.

"Certainly this is more than a joke. You can't possibly travel in this state; it would be too dangerous."

So Christmas passed. On January 1st he began to feel a little better. He could even drag himself to the fireplace. Cioli wrote to him in the name of Duke Fernando himself. The Grand Duke expressed his sincere sympathy, but begged him not to risk a severe penalty and to set out for Rome as soon as he could. At the same time the Chief Inquisitor sent a message. The Vatican commanded him to put Galileo in irons if he should prove stubborn, and send him as a prisoner to Rome. If he was ill a doctor could travel with him, together with a Clerk of the Inquisition, whose expenses he would have to pay.

But the old man did not wait for the irons. On January 20th he dressed, had his luggage made ready and himself carried down to the litter. But first he visited the convent and took his children in his arms. All three were crying. Then he set out.

On the frontier of the Papal State they put him into quarantine. He had to submit to medical examinations and an endless process of disinfection. It took him three weeks to reach Rome. When he saw the towers of the city on the horizon, his terror made him burst into tears.

The litter bore him to the Embassy, where the Niccolinis received him with even more than their usual kindness. He rested a little, and then they had supper together. During the meal Niccolini would not talk of the Inquisition; but, when the servants were out of the room, he put his hand on the old man's shoulder:

"You must be very careful. You're in great trouble."

"I know, I know. My secret enemies . . ."

"No, no," the Ambassador interrupted. "You mustn't imagine things. All this comes directly from the Pope. He's very angry with you."

"But why?" Galileo burst out. "Why, in God's name?"

"For two reasons. First, because he's convinced that these new teachings are very dangerous. He thinks that if ever it took foot this new system of cosmology would undermine all present authority founded on the system of Catholic teaching derived from Aristotle and the Fathers. It would shake the Church's power over souls! But this is only one of his reasons."

"And the other?"

"The other," the Ambassador glanced around him and lowered his voice, "is entirely personal. Some people have made him believe that the fool Simplicio in your book was meant for him."

"What? But why? How? My mind's a blank! This is pure nonsense. I'd have been a madman to do that! And why should I slander my benefactor? No, the Pope can't possibly believe . . ."

"But he does. What's more—he's even convinced of it. You know how suspicious he is of any revolt against his dignity or his personal pride. And you made your Simplicio use an argument which once you heard used by His Holiness. The Pope remembers it distinctly. You know, when Sagredo and Salviati are discussing ebb and flow to prove the earth's movement, Simplicio answers that such an argument is blasphemy, because it seems to cast a doubt on God's power to control the tides. The Pope has admitted that this really was his argument. And so he considers it past question that you have mocked him and shamed him in Simplicio, as a stupid and ignorant man."

Galileo could scarcely draw his breath. He had simply forgotten from whom he had heard this naïve argument. Now he remembered clearly that it was the Pope. . . . His enemies had found with satanic skill the real weapon against him. Every step of the Pope's was now understandable. . . .

He stretched out his hand for the glass to moisten his cracked lips with wine. But he upset the glass, and the red wine stained the tablecloth. No one tried to save it. He whispered dazedly:

"I'm lost."

VIII

After a sleepless night Galileo rose and dressed himself. According to his instructions he had to report to the Councilor of the Inquisition, Boccabella. The Ambassador told him that Boccabella was a gentle, soft-mannered, understanding priest, who had helped in many difficulties. It was very lucky that he should have been put in charge of the case.

Still dazed after a sleepless night, he set out for the Inquisition building. His throat was dry as he ordered two litter-bearers to carry him to the Santa Maria; and when they came within sight of the large building, which years ago he had left with his mind at peace and a light heart, his breath seemed to fail. It needed an effort to find the strength to sit up and get out of the litter. Yet even today the elegant building in the mild February sunshine did not look sinister in the least. It was almost impossible to imagine that men had left these doors to go to the scaffold. He dragged himself helplessly down the passages, asking his way till he found Monsignor Boccabella's room. And indeed this priest seemed the soothing incarnation of benevolence. Galileo was suddenly reassured. But his joy lasted only as far as the first sentence.

"While you were on your way," the friendly Boccabella told him, "there have been changes in our organization. I've received another appointment which I regret deeply, because perhaps I could have helped you. Now rest a little, and then I'll take you to my successor."

"But why were you given another appointment?" the old man asked in a querulous voice. "Why can't you help me, Monsignor?"

"Nobody is allowed to criticize the commands of the Holy Office. But even so I can give you some advice. That is, if you're willing to listen."

"I'll be most grateful."

"Then take my advice, and never contradict your accusers. Accept everything. Show docility. If anything can mollify His Holiness, it's complete penitence and good will. I say this because scientists are apt to cling stubbornly to their theories."

Galileo listened gratefully and obediently. He nodded with the willingness of a schoolboy. Boccabella tried to console and reassure him. His punishment would not be too severe. He must keep on hoping. Never lose hope! But this encouragement was worse in its effect than any threat, since the nervous old man kept telling himself that surely a great danger must be threatening him, if he needed so much reassurance. Then Boccabella ushered him into another room, introduced his successor, and took leave.

Father Firenzuola was a wholly different man, with an immobile face and a rigid bearing.

"Galileo Galilei. Yes. Well, at present I only have to tell you that the place and time of your detention for trial will soon be fixed. You'll be notified. Till then you're forbidden to leave your present lodging, the Florentine Embassy."

"Detention . . . for . . . trial."

"Yes. During the trial you have to remain in this building. . . ."

"But forgive me . . . a prisoner . . . they didn't tell me about this. . . ."

"It's quite useless to argue. You are here to take orders, and to obey. Now go home and wait till we send for you."

A curt nod to show that Galileo was dismissed.

On tottering feet Galileo found his way back to the litter. Back at the Embassy he wanted to see the Ambassador, but found only Signora Caterina.

"I implore you, Your Excellency, don't let them take me. They're going to torture me. I can't bear that. . . . I beg you to take pity and get me away from here. . . ."

He was put to bed, and she sat by his side and tried to comfort him. She had the greatest difficulty in calming him. When the Ambassador arrived and heard what had happened, he sent his secretary to Cardinal Barderini, the Pope's nephew, with an urgent request for an audience. The Cardinal replied that he would see him the next day.

"If only they don't come and fetch me today . . . not today. . . ."

"Don't be afraid, they won't. Even if they do, I'll find some excuse. I'll visit two more Cardinals whom I know well, Scaglia and Bentivoglio. Don't be afraid. . . ."

He was not left alone for a moment. At night a valet kept watch in his anteroom. He slept two hours, but when he awoke he felt a pain in his left wrist. That meant the beginning of his arthritis and fierce agony. It would be terrible if they took him in such a state to the prison of the Inquisition. But the Ambassador brought good news: Cardinal Barberini promised to intervene on his behalf. Strictly speaking, that was a breach of regulations; but perhaps the Holy Office would allow for the fact of his illness. But he must not receive visitors, leave the house, or talk to anyone except his hosts.

Therefore, when they announced a visitor next day, he sent a message that he could not see anyone. But the visitor insisted, saying that he was sent by the Holy Office. An old acquaintance entered, Monsignor Serristori, one of the readers of the *Dialogue*. Galileo had never suspected that he had anything to do with the Inquisition.

"I come as a private person," Serristori said. "My visit has nothing to do with this trial. My respect and pity have brought me to see Your Honor."

Galileo took all this as genuine. It did him good to unburden himself to this friend. The conversation turned to his case, and he answered every question freely. Serristori spent a long time with him and promised that he would come back soon. The sick man felt very grateful and told the Ambassador.

"Didn't you realize why he came?" the Ambassador asked.

"No. Why?"

"To examine you and get you to make admissions. That is their method. The Inquisitor finds out the opinion of the accused about the matter, the weak points of his defense and the strong arguments which may have to be overthrown. If Serristori comes again, be very careful what you say. I hope you didn't discuss Copernicus?"

"Oh, yes, we did," answered the trembling Galileo. "I told him that I really believed in Copernicus, but that, since I was not allowed to say so, I treated my belief as a hypothesis!"

"That was very foolish. Why must you be so stubborn about Copernicus?"

"But, Your Excellency, what am I to do? I can't deny him!"

"Of course you can. Whom are you harming by denying him? Copernicus and Kepler, who are both dead? I don't suggest that you should suddenly start abusing what up to now you have been proclaiming as the truth. That would make a bad impression. But why must you always keep insisting? Well, I've brought you good news. The Pope's nephew never attends the meetings of the Holy Office. He finds them dull. Now, at my request, he's promised to attend the next. I suspect that they'll discuss your case there. Of course, we can't find out anything. The terrible strength of the Holy Office is the deathly silence of every member. They can force even those who don't belong to them to hold their tongues."

"But how? And whom?"

"Well—me, for example. I've known for a long time that you'd be summoned by the Inquisition. The Pope himself told me. But he demanded my word of honor to tell nobody. I didn't even tell my wife. On the other hand, by order of the Pope, I reported it officially to Cioli. But he had to keep silent too. Did he tell you anything?"

"No! Did he know?"

"Of course he knew. But, had he talked, he might himself have been summoned by the Inquisition. Well, now the Pope's nephew and Cardinals Scaglia and Bentivoglio seem favorably disposed toward you. In my opinion these proceedings will be very lenient. Believe me, there's no danger of torture and irons. I give you my word of honor. I'm only waiting now for the Papal audience for which I've applied. I must officially report your arrival. I'll try to find out the Pope's intentions about you and whether he's still so angry. I want to give you one piece of advice. Show full submission. It's dangerous to defy Pope Urban. Especially for you."

The sick man promised everything. He endured his sufferings and waited. He could not see anybody, but he could dictate letters. He also received some. Celeste wrote almost every week and enclosed letters for Caterina. They had been corresponding for some time now, and, although they had never seen each other, a warm friendship existed between them.

Galileo had been in Rome a fortnight when the Ambassador was summoned by the Pope. It was a long audience, and when he came back he gave a close account of all that was said. He had reported officially that the accused had arrived and given himself up to the Inquisition. The Pope nodded stiffly. The Ambassador asked him to be merciful to this sick man. Whereupon Urban had burst out angrily:

"Merciful? Haven't I done enough for him already? He is even allowed to live in the city. Do you realize what a favor that is? The son of Fernando Gonzaga was brought in a litter to Rome, clapped into the Castel Sant' Angelo, and kept there during his whole trial. And he was a Gonzaga! We should have done the same with Galileo, but we wished to show our friendship for the Medicis, at whose Court he was a high official."

Niccolini had ventured to request that the trial might at least be as speedy as possible, since this was a very sickly old man.

"Unfortunately, as to that we can promise nothing," the Pope coldly replied. "The proceedings of the Holy Office always take time."

But the most important thing was his answer to the Ambassador's question as to the real nature of the charges against Galileo, who, after all, had published his book with the permission of the Papal Censorship. The Ambassador had hoped to be able to bring the discussion round to Simplicio, and so to clear up this tragic misunderstanding, at least partly. But Pope Urban refused to be led to this. And, indeed, it would have been too much to expect that he should ever directly broach a topic which seemed a deep and dangerous insult both to his authority and his pride. He had only answered:

"It was monstrous to publish this theory, especially in such a deceitful form. Galilei pretends to treat it as a hypothesis, but he does nothing but bring up proofs. He declares himself for Copernicus. Thereby he has directly infringed the official interdiction which Cardinal Bellarmin, in the name of the Holy Inquisition, laid on Copernicus in 1616. We have found the documents in the records of the Holy Office. Galilei acknowledged it. He must have remembered it. But he kept silent, didn't tell it to Riccardi, deceiving him just as he deceived us. He will be punished for this."

The Ambassador reported this interview word for word. He even tried to mimic the Pope's voice. Galileo listened to him in terror, though the pain in his joints made every movement agony as he sat in bed.

"Memorandum? What official memorandum?"

"I don't know. According to the Pope, you were warned officially in 1616 of some interdiction, and this procedure was taken down in a memorandum. This has been found now in the archives."

"Impossible. There were no proceedings against me. It was Copernicus and poor Foscarini. Lorini of Florence had denounced my so-called followers. I was only a witness in the whole affair. I still remember clearly that Cardinal Bellarmin asked me to visit him in his lodgings, and there he told me . . . what did he tell me? . . . it's more than seventeen years now. . . . I must try to remember. . . ."

"Try hard, because this is very important."

Galileo stared into the past, gathering all his wits.

"Wait a moment. First I had a long talk with Bellarmin. He told me all his reasons for considering that this new theory was very dangerous, capable of overthrowing the civil power of the Papacy. I listened very attentively and was deeply impressed by his clear wisdom, but he couldn't convince me. Then the Holy Office met and decreed that the sun moved around the earth. Foscarini was banned and Copernicus suspended, with the proviso of *donec corrigeretur*. After that the Papal decree was published. Before that Bellarmin sent for me unexpectedly. I remember our conversation clearly. Some Dominicans were also present; I didn't know them. He vaguely mentioned our former talks, in such a way that only I could understand what he was saying. And he warned me that it must only be treated as a hypothesis.

"Your Excellency, at the same time they had permitted Copernicus to be published! Changing only a few words! Even in Copernicus' dedication to Paul V, for instance, only one sentence was deleted. Where he asserts that his teaching in no way contradicts Holy Writ."

"But he didn't forbid it *expressis verbis* and generally?"

"They hadn't put him on the Index! They left his whole theory for Catholic readers as a hypothesis! Why should they have forbidden me something which they allowed to Copernicus? I remember it clearly, and I'm willing to swear an oath that there was no question of a complete and full interdiction."

"And yet the Pope said that there was such a memorandum in the archives of the Holy Office."

"But to what should this memorandum refer? There was no meeting or trial or questioning in which I took part."

"Messer Galileo, you should not be so ready to swallow all that people tell you. Serristori was here a while ago. He emphasized that he came as a private person. But do you think there are no records of his visit? I'm sure there are! In the same way a memorandum could have been made of your private conversation with Bellarmin. And now, when someone has succeeded in inciting the Pope against you, Urban doubtless commanded' the Holy Office to seek out any traps in which they could catch you. They found this old injunction and memorandum. It contained the interdiction. They reported it to the Pope. 'What's this?' the Pope may have said. 'I didn't know about this. So he was forbidden to speak about Copernicus, and yet he did. He told Riccardi nothing about the injunction, swindled the imprimatur out of him! He shall pay for that!' And so we get to the present stage of these proceedings."

"But, if they made some records without my knowledge, surely they must contain the statement that Bellarmin had no objection to a hypothesis. Later he gave me the written assurance that I need not deny any of my teachings. I have it still. I've brought it with me. Would you pull out that top drawer? It's there."

The Ambassador found and read the document; he shook his head.

"This is very cunningly drafted. It certainly contains the statement that you aren't forced to deny or retract anything. But there's no mention of any hypothesis in it. It's wiser not to mention this document at all. And you cannot know what is in that memorandum. They could have drawn it up in any way they pleased. It's highly probable that Bellarmin didn't include his permission to treat your theories as a hypothesis—if only so as to cover himself."

"But Pope Urban himself told me that it was different to treat this matter as a hypothesis, that it was permitted."

"Let's admit that. But who is to say just where a hypothesis begins and where it ends. Who judges whether you have advanced a hypothesis or tried to prove something? The Pope. And he is very angry with you just now. There's no appeal against his decision. I tell you, Messer Galileo, and I can't say it often enough, be thankful that you're still alive. Don't argue; accept all their assertions, even if they aren't true. If they should report to the Pope that Galilei is stubborn and disobedient, you would be in the gravest danger. But, if you are careful, you'll be acquitted. I implore you to accept my advice."

"But, for the love of God, how can they impute to me such an impossible intention? Why should I mock at the Pope, who was kind to me, wrote an ode in my honor, granted me a yearly stipend, showered favors upon me? Who could ever suppose me such a madman?"

"Messer Galileo, that is something you must convince the Pope of, and not me."

"Couldn't I speak to him? Suppose I were to throw myself at his feet . . . if only he could look into my eyes and see the truth in them. He used

to like me very much . . . and I still don't understand what it was that
made me such a fool as to put into Simplicio's mouth an argument which
I'd heard him using. I'll swear it on the Bible, before the altar, that nothing
could have been further from my mind than a crazy notion of mocking
the Pope. Do you think—oh, answer me, please—he'd consent to receive
me?"

"Out of the question. The Pope said: 'Let me not set eyes on this Galileo.'
If it were possible I'd keep you back by force. We all know Pope Urban.
The very sight of you would enrage him so that I scarcely dare to imagine
what might happen. You must stay here quietly, accept everything, and
show marked submissiveness. I'll do all I can. I've written to our Prince
and asked him to send personal letters to Cardinals Scaglia and Bentivoglio. Cioli doesn't like it, but . . ."

"Cioli? What has Cioli got against me?"

"Do you still not know Cioli's character? He's like a weathercock on a
tower, veering with every wind from Rome. While you were still the
Pope's favorite, he honored you. Now that the Pope has turned against
you, he speaks of you in quite a different way. I'll be frank, although I'm
speaking of my superior; he's working against you at home in the Court
of Florence. But, thank God, the Duke pays even more attention to me.
So you'll get those letters."

Niccolini was right: Grand Duke Fernando wrote very warm letters to
the Cardinals; he even wrote to the Pope himself, thanking His Holiness
for allowing his Court mathematician to stay at the Embassy and asking
him to hasten the proceedings. But there was no sign of this. The Pope's
anger had not cooled. When the Ambassador presented himself at the
Vatican again, to present Fernando's letter, there came a surprise: Urban
himself began speaking of the cause of his fury.

"We regret the necessity to inflict pain on Galilei, who was once Our
friend and a guest at Our table; but the interests of the Faith come before
everything."

"Holy Father," the Ambassador replied, "I'm sure that if Galilei is questioned he will have a satisfactory answer to everything."

"We can't believe that," the Pope interrupted. "There will be one question he never can answer. The supreme power of God is beyond all
doubt, but Galileo tries to prove everything by mere scientific arguments.

For instance, he dares to assert that the idea can only have one origin. That is to say, he maintains that God would have found it impossible to create things except in the way He did."

"No doubt," the Ambassador answered, "yet God chose just this way. Galilei only suggests that out of many thousand possibilities, all of which lay within His power, God selected this particular one."

This therefore was the fatal argument which Simplicio had been made to use in the *Dialogue*. It was this which confirmed the Pope's opinion that his enemies were right in their accusations; and he, the Pope, had stood for Simplicio. Urban had been deeply hurt by the daring and rebellious sneer. He betrayed his constant itch to avenge his dignity and intelligence. The Ambassador's words increased his rage. His face was fiery red; he roared with anger.

"But that isn't for Galilei to decide! God is all-powerful, and Galilei can't prescribe His course."

The charge which everyone in Rome was whispering, though nobody mentioned it openly, was of such a kind that it could not be mentioned. The Pope could not openly admit that someone had actually dared to jeer at him. So that nobody could face him and say: "It isn't true, that absurd Simplicio doesn't represent Your Holiness."

The Pope ordered proceedings against the unhappy Riccardi, who was suspended from office. Ciampoli had been sent away. There was no hope of mercy. The Pope was resolved to punish drastically. Castelli, who was still at his master's side and possessed considerable influence in the Vatican, had been sent unexpectedly on a holiday—on some transparent childish excuse. Boccabella had been replaced by a far less gentle and kindly man. Campanella had been working hard to get appointed to the College of the Holy Office, and he had certain hopes. Now he was told that he could never expect it. Everybody knew that he was a follower of Copernicus. The two most influential Cardinals, Scaglia and Bentivoglio, had received the Grand Duke's letters. Both of them visited the Ambassador to tell him that, though they were deeply conscious of the honor of this personal request, to their greatest regret they were quite unable to intervene, since the rules of the Inquisition prohibited any declaration, whether oral or in writing.

In the meantime, the sick man became worse and worse. His pain had reached the state where he groaned and writhed, screaming aloud and never sleeping. He had lost the ability to think and reason about his case. His nerve had failed. Signora Caterina called one doctor after the other, but they all shook their heads and could do nothing. And still, as though to break the prisoner's strength by a long torture of silence and suspense, the Holy Office gave no sign.

One morning, two months after his arrival in Rome, Niccolini entered his room. His face seemed to be changed.

"Something has happened?" cried out Galileo.

The Ambassador sat down at his bedside and took hold of his parchmentlike old hands.

"Listen, Messer Galileo, and be calm. I give you my word that you have nothing to fear. They won't hurt you."

"What is it?" he stammered in a whisper.

"You're to be questioned by the Holy Office."

"Oh, thank God! At last! At last I'll be allowed to speak! I shall have an answer to all these trumped-up accusations. This is great news!"

"Must we begin all that again? You want to argue and refute! Didn't you promise me to be blind, deaf, and dumb? To say yes to everything? Mark you, if you break your promise, I won't be able to help you. You must show complete obedience, do you understand? But that wasn't what I came to tell you. The rules of the Holy Office compel a prisoner to live in the official building throughout his trial. So now you'll have to leave the Embassy."

"No, no! I won't, I can't! I'm afraid! They're going to torture me! Hide me there in the vaults! They're going to tear me with hot fangs! I won't go!"

With his sound hand he clutched the bedside as though the torturers were surrounding him, ready to drag him away to be questioned, as though he would resist them as long as he could.

"Be sensible and pull yourself together! I've given you my solemn word that they don't mean to torture you, and I've arranged everything. You'll be properly lodged. They won't lock the door of your cell. You can take my man to nurse you. We'll send your meals from the Embassy. If you're able to get up, you may walk in the corridors by day. Calm yourself and believe me. I've tried to keep this news from you till the last moment, but now you had to be told. Get ready; you must go there today."

The sick man sobbed even louder and felt suddenly faint. He swooned, and when he came to himself, Signora Caterina was standing beside him, bathing his forehead with perfumed water.

"Be strong," she said gently. "If Francesco's word isn't enough for you, I also swear that you won't be hurt. Be strong and try to think of Celeste."

Two servants helped him into his clothes. Although they were extremely careful, his hand and leg made him scream with pain at the slightest touch. He asked for his papers. Now he no longer sobbed, but his teeth were chatering as if he were freezing. They carried him slowly down the stairs to the waiting litter. It took him nearly ten minutes to get inside. Signora Caterina kissed his forehead.

"I shall send you linen, medicines, paper, and quills today. God bless and keep you."

The Ambassador also entered the litter. It was a long way from the Trinità dei Monti to the Minerva. But his pain, as though sheer terror had numbed it, was a little easier. All the way Niccolini kept repeating his advice: to obey unhesitatingly, blindly. In the doorway they embraced. To descend from the litter was fresh agony. The gates closed behind him.

IX

It was April 12th when they led him into the Council Room of the Holy Office. Two men supported him, the servant of the Embassy and a Dominican friar. They set him down in the anteroom. He was in great pain again, clenching his teeth and groaning; with all his strength he tried to control himself. From inside the Council Chamber came many voices, but their words were inaudible.

"Are those my judges?" he asked the Dominican.

"I can tell you nothing," the monk replied.

He waited, touching with his right hand his helpless left arm to move it slowly and carefully. Then he fingered the bandage of his rupture. He swallowed hard, his heart was pounding. The door opened and a monk called his name. They helped him up and into the room, which was large and well lighted. In the middle a long table with a crucifix. And on the other side of the table three priests: Firenzuola and two others. The accused was led to the center of the long table, face to face with his judges. The President of the Court, who sat between the other two, glanced up.

"Is the accused ill?" he asked in Latin.

"I have sharp pains in my joints and ought really to be in bed."

"Then we permit you to be seated throughout the trial. But before you sit you must take an oath. I declare the proceedings opened."

The servant and the Dominican were still at his side, and he leaned on them. The clerk had soon taken his description: Galileo Galilei, Court mathematican, seventy years old, of Florence. Then Firenzuola rose with the other two judges. He announced the oath: "I swear to speak the whole truth . . ."

"So help me God, the Blessed Virgin, and all the Saints of God."

The judges sat down again; a chair was brought for the prisoner. He lowered himself slowly with many groans. Firenzuola signed to the Dominican and the servant, who bowed and withdrew. "Let the accused say whether he knows the reason why he is summoned here before the Holy Office."

"I have no official knowledge of it. But I think it is to answer for my recently published work."

"Is this the book?" asked the President, holding up the copy.

"It is."

"Entitled *Dialogue*, etc. To save time we shall simply refer to it as *Dialogue*, throughout this trial, and shall not use its full title. Well, then. Do you acknowledge that you have written every word in this book yourself?"

"I do."

"Very well. Now let us turn to the preliminaries. Beginning with the year of Our Lord sixteen hundred and sixteen. Did the accused visit Rome in that year?"

"Yes, I did."

"What was the reason of your visit?"

"I had heard that the doctrine of the immobility of the sun and the movement of the earth, as stated by Copernicus, had various opponents in the Church. A certain Father Caccini preached against it in Florence and against its followers. I therefore came to Rome to assure myself as to the official viewpoint of the Church. This happened, not in 1616 but in December, 1615, though I stayed in Rome till the beginning of the following April."

"Never mind that. Let us say that you were here in 1616. Did you come by your own decision?"

"I did."

"Didn't you receive any call or summons?"

"No."

"Think again. Weren't you commanded by the Holy Office at that time to appear in Rome?"

"Not at all," he answered with surprise. "I had nothing to do with the Holy Office. I'd heard that there had been some denunciation; but the man Lorini didn't denounce me, only what he called my disciples."

"Are you quite sure that you hadn't been summoned? Have you any witness that you came of your own free will?"

"I discussed the journey with my Prince, His Highness Cosimo of blessed memory. The Prime Minister of Florence, Picchena, also knew of my decision. And Guicciardini, who was the Ambassador for Florence."

"I see. And all these are dead, of course."

Galileo did not answer. He began to see the trend of these questions. They wanted to prove that he had already been tried by the Inquisition. And in that case his offense would be judged with double severity. The instinct of the hunted animal sharpened his wits again.

"So you insist," the President said, "that you hadn't received any official summons and came to Rome of your own free will?"

"Yes, I remember it clearly; there cannot be any doubt of it. And if I had received any summons there would be a record of it in the archives. But that record cannot be found, because I myself decided to take the journey."

"Very well, let's leave all that for now. Tell me, what clerical persons did you meet at that time in Rome?"

Galileo first mentioned Bellarmin. Then he named Father Grienberger, Count Querengo, Cardinal Del Monte, Orsini, the Dominican General Maraffi, Cardinal Gaetani. . . .

"Now tell us what you discussed with these men."

"Yes, Father. I'll leave Cardinal Bellarmin to the last, because with him I talked most and discussed the most important things. With Father Grienberger we talked mostly about my beloved late master, Father Clavius, but also about Copernicus. Count Querengo I had met in Padua. I discussed with him the essential meaning of the Copernican system and the possibility of influencing the Prelates of the Church in its favor. The same questions I discussed with Cardinal Del Monte and Cardinal Orsini, who enjoyed the special favor of Pope Paul. With Father Maraffi, I talked of the Dominicans who had attacked me. Cardinal Gaetani, an important official of the Holy Office, I asked to request Campenalla, at that time still imprisoned at Naples, to give an expert opinion, which he did. But mostly I argued with Cardinal Bellarmin. He thought . . ."

He stopped suddenly. He had been going to say that Bellarmin thought the doctrine of Copernicus would threaten the whole spiritual and temporal structure of the Church. But if he told these people that, he would give them arms to use against him.

"Well, why do you hesitate?"

"Forgive me, I was only collecting my thoughts. Cardinal Bellarmin thought that the doctrine of Copernicus contradicted the literal meaning of certain passages in the Bible. We talked often and at great length about this, but I was unable to convince him."

"What, generally speaking, was the source of these conversations?"

"The interest shown by higher clergy. At that time proceedings had been started against the works of Foscarini, Zuñiga, and Copernicus. The Prelates wished to be informed of the scientific essentials of the problem; therefore they consulted me, as an expert. But only in the capacity of an expert; I had no other status. I came freely to Rome; the proceedings of the Holy Office did not touch me personally. I was interested in them only as an astronomer. It was also important for me to know what the Holy Church said about this teaching in which I believed."

"Well, and what did the Church say?"

"The controversy on this teaching that the sun stands still and the earth moves was decided by the Holy Congregation of the Index as follows: To assert such an opinion directly is in contradiction to Holy Writ, and therefore forbidden; such an opinion must only be asserted in the way Copernicus asserted it, as a mathematical possibility."

"Was the accused informed of this? And if so, by whom?"

"I was informed. By Cardinal Bellarmin."

"Very well. Tell us exactly what His Eminence told you, whether he informed you of anything else, and what it was."

"His Eminence told me that it was permitted to maintain the doctrine of Copernicus as a hypothesis, just as Copernicus himself had done. His Eminence knew that I conceived the doctrine only as a hypothesis. This is proved by the letter which His Eminence sent to the Carmelite Provincial Foscarini, and of which I possess a duplicate."

He selected the letter from among his documents and laid it on the table.

"Dated April 12, 1615, a year before the decree of the Inquisition. I have underlined one sentence here. 'Your Reverence and Messer Galilei would do wisely, I think, if you would be content to treat this matter hypothetically, and make no positive assertions.'"

The letter caused surprise. One judge handed it to the other. Galileo had treasured it for seventeen years. The Lynxes had given him the duplicate. The President said a little sharply:

"There is no need to talk about 1615. We want to know what happened in February 1616."

"Yes, Father. In February, Cardinal Bellarmin informed me that the doctrine of Copernicus taken as reality was in contradiction to Holy Writ;

therefore it was forbidden either to maintain or to defend it, but permitted to conceive of it as a theory and write about it in that sense. To prove this I have a document given to me by His Eminence Bellarmin on May 26, 1616, in which he says that the doctrine of Copernicus must not be directly asserted nor defended. Allow me to present a copy of it."

He drew forth this paper. For a long time he had been uncertain whether he should use or withhold it. In the end he decided that it must be shown. The points against him he could not explain away. But the judges could see that Bellarmin did not force his scientific integrity.

"When you were informed of this, were you alone with Cardinal Bellarmin?"

"No. Some Dominican Fathers were also present. But I didn't know them and haven't seen them since."

"Were you told of any interdiction at that time? Think carefully."

"I want to tell you everything I know. His Eminence sent for me one morning. He reminded me of certain matters to which he felt I must first draw the attention of His Holiness before I talked to anyone else about them."

"What's that you're saying?"

All the judges stared in surprise at Galileo, who did not answer. The President shook his head. Firenzuola's face became still icier as he spoke:

"That must be put into the records. The accused can continue."

"Thereafter the Cardinal explained to me that I must neither uphold nor defend the Copernican doctrine. I must only treat it as a theory."

"Only as a hypothesis. I see. Did anybody hear him saying that?"

"Perhaps the Dominican Fathers . . ."

The President suddenly changed in tone. Up to now he had been asking his questions monotonously. Now he shouted at the accused.

"Perhaps. You say—perhaps! What talk is this? Were the Dominican Fathers present or not?"

The old man winced. Something told him that now it was beginning. Now he must show absolute obedience and not a trace of argument.

"I don't remember. Seventeen years are a long time."

"So perhaps they weren't present at all?" Firenzuola continued his attack.

"Perhaps they weren't."

"So perhaps nobody heard the Cardinal say it?"

"Maybe. I don't remember."

"But if your memory is so bad, perhaps you can't even remember exactly what words the Cardinal said."

"He may have said something which I can't remember any more."

"Suppose that I refresh your memory? Suppose I read you the records of that hearing? Even then would you still be as forgetful?"

"I hardly think so, Monsignor."

"Well, listen to this. I have the record here in front of me."

Friday the twenty-sixth. In the Palace inhabited by His Grace the Cardinal and specifically in his private apartments, after the aforesaid Galilei was summoned and appeared, the Cardinal adjured Galilei in the presence of Fra Michelangelo Segnitius de Lauda, Chief Inquisitor of the Holy Office, to give up his erroneous convictions; immediately afterward the aforesaid Chief Inquisitor in my presence, in the presence of these witnesses, and likewise of His Grace Cardinal Bellarmin, commanded and prescribed Galilei in the name of His Holiness the Pope and the Holy Office, to renounce completely the doctrine of the immobility of the Sun and the movement of the Earth, not to maintain it in any way, not to teach it, neither in writing nor orally, nor should he defend it, since otherwise the Holy Office would start proceedings against him. Galilei accepted this injunction and swore obedience. In witness whereof Nadino Nores etcetera, Augustino Mongard etcetera.

"What do you say now, accused?"

Galileo's temple throbbed. He remembered clearly that it had not happened in this way. Only Bellarmin spoke; the Dominicans had hovered around in silence. This record had either been drawn up falsely at that time, or someone had fabricated now a pseudo-memorandum containing the fatal expression "not to maintain it in any way, not to teach it . . . nor defend it." Not even in the form of a hypothesis! His first instinct was to cry out: "This document is a forgery!" But he could not. To accuse the Inquisition of forgery? His next step would be to the scaffold.

"Well, why don't you answer? Do you remember that it was thus?"

"I can't remember."

"You can't remember. But it might have been thus?"

Galileo was silent. He felt giddy. Firenzuola roared:

"Well? Might it have been thus? Or do you suggest that the records lie?"

The words came slowly, hoarsely, almost like groans from the tortured old man.

"It might have been thus."

"At last! So you received an unmistakable injunction?"

"I can't remember what was said."

"This protocol remembers better than you do, though, and you admit that it may have happened like this. Well, have you anything more to say?"

"I would humbly call the attention of Your Eminences to the fact that the document which His Eminence Bellarmin gave me does not contain the expressions 'neither to teach it orally nor in writing,' 'not to maintain it in any way.' "

"It doesn't contain them. But the records do. Well, who was it that issued the injunction?"

"His Eminence Cardinal Bellarmin."

"Haven't you heard with your own ears from the record that you were informed by the Chief Inquisitor of the Holy Office, in the name of His Holiness the Pope and the Inquisition?"

"I'd forgotten that. Nor do I seem to remember the presence of His Reverence the Chief Inquisitor."

"But he might have been present? Well? Speak! Speak!"

The accused had great difficulty in answering. He answered in a voice that could scarcely be heard:

"Yes . . . he might have been present."

"Good! So now we can sum up the following facts: The Holy Office ruled that this doctrine was blasphemous; the Chief Inquisitor officially forbade the accused in the name of His Holiness the Pope and the Holy Office to maintain such a theory in any way, or in any form. Now answer my question: Did you, after receiving this injunction, ever ask to be released from it to write your *Dialogue*?"

"No."

"And why did you not request such permission?"

"I didn't suppose that I had infringed an injunction by my book."

"You didn't suppose that you infringed an injunction which you had received? And in spite of which you wrote your book! Tell me, how did you get the imprimatur from the Reverend Father Chamberlain at the Vatican?"

Galileo related in detail his dealings with Riccardi.

"Did you tell the Father Chamberlain about the interdiction of 1616? No? Then why not?"

"Because my book does not directly teach Copernicus. I enumerate all the counter-arguments."

"And are they stronger? Well? Did you hear my question? According to the accused, which arguments are stronger in his book? Those for, or against, Copernicus?"

"Those . . . against . . . him . . ."

"And the arguments for him? Are they weak?"

Suddenly the accused broke into sobs. He was being asked to pronounce judgment against the work of fifty years.

"Yes, they are weak."

Angelus bells rang through the window. At once the judges were on their feet. The prisoner had to rise unaided, groaning and gasping for breath. The Inquisitors finished their silent prayer, and the President said:

"Before I close the proceedings, the accused must take another oath."

He had to swear to say nothing about this examination to anyone in word or writing. Two priests came to support him. He took the oath.

"So help me God and the Blessed Virgin and all God's Saints!"

And now the President gave his order.

X

Galileo thought that they were taking him to the torture chamber. He was still in tears as he limped away, leaning on two human crutches. Step by step they helped him down stairs and along passages. He was almost beside himself with fear. Instead they opened the door of a well-furnished suite—a suite of three rooms, all of them clean, light, and airy. He gazed around in timid amazement. This could not really be the truth. But at the same time came a knock at the door and the President of the Court himself entered.

"I hope that you'll find this suite to your liking."

"Are all the three rooms mine?"

"Yes, we've taken them temporarily from one of our Brothers, who has moved into another part of the building. You have the Florentine Embassy to thank for it. Her Excellency Signora Niccolini has already sent your luggage. Your servant is to sleep in the anteroom. As a special favor we are not going to lock your door, but you must not leave this part of the corridor. All this is an unheard-of concession."

The servant came to report that the prisoner's dinner had come from the Embassy.

"Very well, then I won't disturb him. If you need anything, your servant can always find me in the building. Now sign this protocol of today's session. I wish you a very good appetite. . . ."

First that horrible cross-examination—and now this! Galileo thought that he was dreaming. Firenzuola left, and he crept into bed, where he ate his meal. Signora Niccolini had sent him all his favorite dishes and a flagon of her best wine, which he gulped down greedily, and fell fast asleep. He slept for sixteen hours—the first real sleep he had known for weeks. When he woke next day, the sunlight was streaming through his window. His first thought was about the proceedings. He winced, remembering the mental torture; but his physical pain was less than before. The quiet rest and the huge physical relief that there were no torture chambers to be faced had done his health good. On the third day he was able to get out of bed and totter around in the three rooms, leaning on his servant or clinging to the furniture. On the fifth day he dressed and went out into the corridor. He was only allowed the use of a short section of the long passage in which to exercise. He must not go beyond the turn of the wall. Sometimes he glanced into the courtyard, where fresh flowers looked gay and friendly. It was difficult to think that these were the flowers of the Inquisition.

On the fifth day Firenzuola visited him, with official news that the Holy Office had asked three experts to decide how far the *Dialogue* transgressed the injunction which its author had received seventeen years ago. Melchiore Inkhofer and Agustino Oregio found that the author had certainly maintained and defended the forbidden doctrine in his work; the third expert, Zaccaria Pasqualiga, thought that he had also taught it.

"I tell you this," Firenzuola said, "because it proves you guilty beyond all question. Therefore you may soon expect your punishment. Try to reconcile yourself and be contrite."

"What will be my punishment?" he stammered.

"Even if I knew, I couldn't tell you. But you must know that your crime is a very serious one, and probably your punishment will be heavy. The only comfort which now remains to you is to seek for repentance within yourself and regret deeply what you have done."

"Forgive me, Monsignor; could I hope for a milder punishment if I do public penance?"

"Penance done for reward shows no real contrition. Of course the judges will decide whether your penitence is sincere or only the usual mumming of the accused."

With that he departed. But Galileo was left with the terrible thought, "a heavy punishment." That could only mean one thing—the stake. Pope Urban thought that he had held him up in the figure of Simplicio to the ridicule of the whole world. Therefore Pope Urban would burn him publicly. This was not such a wild idea. Pope Paul had had an unlucky man beheaded because he had compared Pope Gregory to Tiberius in a manuscript which had never even been published.

The physical improvement of the last few days was all spoiled by this visit. His pain returned, racking his body so that it was difficult not to scream. He dug his head into the pillows and moaned, panted, gnashed his teeth. Sometimes, when it was sheer impossibility any longer to bear this torture alone, he would send for his servant and grip his hand. "What will they do to me, Giovanni? Will they torture me? Will they burn me alive?" The servant could not bear the sight of such agony. He went to see the Inquisitor of his own accord. Firenzuola and Sincero, the attorney of the Inquisition, came into Galileo's room. They were astonished at his state. They questioned him about his ailment, even consoled him. Firenzuola promised to find something to ease his pain.

"I've brought you good news," he said next day. "The Holy Office is willing to permit your return to the villa of the Florentine Embassy. That is to say, when you can bear to move; for now you cannot."

"No, no—though I long to get back there."

"Well, well, come now! Take hold of yourself. We promise you that as soon as you can stand on your feet, you shall be taken back to the Embassy. But there is a condition attached."

"I'm willing to fulfil any condition."

"You must give some token of your full and complete repentance."

"Yes, Father. What token am I to give?"

"It will lose its meaning should I prescribe its nature. You must think of some way in which to show your deep contrition."

And so they left him with his pain, having set him a riddle. He himself must find what it was they wanted. Now he was prepared for everything, racked as he was from head to foot and in constant dread of being burned. His whole being longed for the Embassy, the consoling warmth of the Niccolinis.

He struggled for a whole week, sending for a copy of his book and reading certain passages with deep attention.

In a week the decision ripened in him; he would apologize humbly, asking only for his poor sickly life. He sent a message to Firenzuola.

"Monsignor, may I be received by the Holy Office? I want to make a declaration with full repentance."

"Very well. Repentance is always welcome to God, and we also can appreciate it. What is your state of health? Tomorrow, April 27th, we have a meeting. Can you appear then?"

"Yes. I'd even go there dying, because I can't stand this any longer. But, Monsignor, for God's sake, they won't send me to the stake if I show real penitence?"

"Are you setting conditions? What sort of a penitence is this? It displeases the Holy Office to hear such words."

"No, no, I have no stipulations. But look at me, Monsignor, I'm hardly alive. Even now, there's only a tiny spark of life left in me. I don't know what I'm saying. Be merciful to me. . . ."

"I told you that if you show real penitence we'll let you go back to the Embassy. Tomorrow you must appear before your judges and give a token of your remorse—but without stipulations."

All that day and night he thought of nothing but what he could say to his judges. Early next morning he was still repeating the humbling sentences. A strange instinct took hold of him: as if he had joined forces with his torturers and were helping them with savage lust to humiliate, torment the man who had been Galileo Galilei. "How I have sinned against myself," he thought suddenly in these moments of upheaval. Why did he punish himself so cruelly? He could find no answer.

In the early morning they led him before his judges. The three priests with crucifix in front of them sat waiting.

"We have been informed that the accused wishes to make a declaration."

"Yes, Monsignor," he answered softly, with bowed head, "if you will deign to hear me."

There was a pause. The well-prepared sentences would not come.

"Well? We are listening."

"Ever since my last examination," at last he began, "I have repeated your questions in my mind and striven to collect my memories. Especially I tried to recall the injunction of seventeen years ago, that I must not maintain, defend, or even teach the doctrine of the earth's movement 'in any form.' Then I remembered that I hadn't read the *Dialogue* for three years, and ought to go through it again now, to see whether, against my best intentions, something hadn't slipped out of my quill in consequence of . . . in consequence . . ."

"Well? Well?"

"Forgive me, I'm very excited and short of breath. Whether something hadn't slipped from my quill in consequence of which the reader and the Church authorities could accuse me not merely of general disobedience but of having encouraged, in certain passages, the opinion that I had set myself up against the teaching of Holy Church. By the great kindness of the

Holy Office I was able to send out my servant for a copy. I have read it very attentively, weighing every word. I hadn't read it for such a long time that it seemed to be a new book, written by a stranger. And I must acknowledge something most repentantly . . ."

"Speak."

"In several passages I perceived that a reader who did not know my method of thinking, might receive a false impression. Because, although I wanted to refute the false doctrine . . ."

He swallowed hard and stopped. He was now denying the whole scientific aim, faith, and conviction of his life. But nothing happened. Only something glinted for a moment in Firenzuola's eyes.

". . . the false doctrine," continued Galileo, "by accident I presented the arguments in such a way that the reader might have gathered the opposite impression."

He stopped again and collected his thoughts. Oh, yes, he wanted to mention the argument of the Pope and humiliate himself to the Jesuit Scheiner. If the Jesuits meant to send him to the stake, he must win their mercy.

"Especially I elaborated two arguments which might seem too extreme from one who was trying to prove the exact opposite. One was about the sunspots, the other about the problem of ebb and tide. I would like to explain how it happened. Since I wanted to disprove the false doctrine . . . the false doctrine, my method of composition required, especially in such a dialogue form, that I should expound these fallacies as fully as possible. Otherwise I couldn't have refuted them. But human vanity got the better of me. I delighted in the skill of my mind, in my power of finding clever and easy arguments, even for falsehood—in possessing a finer intellect than others. But though, like Cicero, *avidior sim gloria quam satis est,* if I had to write these passages now, I'd do them differently. I'd take the strength out of them in such a way as to make them seem not even plausible. Therefore I want to declare to my judges that I have been at fault, out of vain ambition, carelessness, and . . . ignorance. . . ."

Galileo Galilei had denied truth and lied. He had spurned the sacred birth of science. He looked eagerly at Firenzuola and the two other judges. He waited for their praise—or at least approval. Surely they must know what a terrible decision he had taken in these last weeks of infernal agony, how in two minutes he had renounced the thought of his whole life, was kneeling here in the dust to the Peripatetics. Firenzuola ought to be feeling jubilant. Galilei as a scientist was dead. But the Inquisitor showed no signs of satisfaction. He resumed in a monotonous voice:

"We take cognizance of this declaration and command the accused to repeat it in writing with his own signature. This document will be enclosed in the records. Now you can go."

No praise, not a word about the Embassy, no reward for this unheard-of betrayal. Galileo turned toward the door and began to cry.

"I want to go back," he said, sobbing, to the Dominican at the door. "Let me go back. I want to say something else."

He dragged himself back. The judges were still in their places.

"I want to add something," he said in a weak, tearful voice. "Something more. Even more than this."

"Yes?"

"I want to make it even plainer that I don't consider this . . . this accursed doctrine of the moving earth and stationary sun. That I never thought it was true. . . . I ask only for opportunity and time, Very Reverend Fathers. . . ."

"No tears! Collect yourself and speak."

"The three characters in my book had agreed to meet again in the future and discuss other questions of natural science. Therefore I have the possibility to continue my work. I promise to enumerate again the arguments of the false and accursed doctrine and disprove them as far as the merciful God enables me to do. I will prove that the earth is immobile and the sun moves around it . . . the sun . . ."

His sobs made his words incoherent. He staggered and had to clutch the edge of the table. He fell on his knees, weeping desperately.

"Mercy . . . don't burn me . . . don't . . . I implore you on my knees. . . ."

They did not answer, but waited till his fit passed. When he calmed down a little, Sincero helped him to his feet, while Firenzuola said:

"You can also put this new declaration into writing. Now I will ask the promised favor of His Holiness. Prepare to return today to the Embassy."

The old man began to sob again, but now with relief. Firenzuola declared the proceedings to be adjourned. Both he and the third judge came over to him, consoling, quieting Galileo.

"No more tears," Firenzuola insisted, "but listen, for I have something important to tell you. I am acting against the rules of the Sacred College, but I want to show you our special good will as reward for your penitence. There will be another hearing soon, when I shall command you to submit your defense within eight days to the Holy Office. Think it over. It must be very sincere, repentant, and especially very brief. And now return to your rooms and rest."

The same afternoon he moved back to the Embassy. It happened with surprising quickness: Firenzuola obtained this favor as soon as session rose. It was as though the Pope's permission had been all ready, waiting for the repentance of the accused. Niccolini had known nothing about it; the Holy Office kept its secrets. He received the old man with happy surprise, embraced him gently, and hastened to send a special courier to Florence with the glad news. Signora Niccolini wept for joy.

When Firenzuola gave him permission to depart, he warned him that he must tell the Ambassador nothing of the way in which his case had been tried. He was also forbidden to see visitors or leave the Medici villa. These last two stipulations meant nothing to him. If he was able to walk he could always sun himself in the beautiful garden of the villa. But it was very hard to keep silent about his case. He longed to go over it all with the Ambassador, ask his advice, find out about the probable punishment. But, humbled and terrified as he was, he dared not break the command.

He gave much thought to his written defense. A difficult business, since he would have to dart like a squirrel between falsehood and truth, and in such a way as not to wound the susceptibilities of the Holy Office. He could not question the full interdiction, acknowledgment of which had been forced out of him. He tore up several different versions before he hit on the final form. He made it short, as they had commanded. His line of thought was simple and clear. He had been informed of the injunction contained in that fatal memorandum. Yet at the same time Cardinal Bellarmin had given him a document which proved that he had never been commanded to deny officially any standpoint, and, though one sentence of this document mentioned interdiction of Copernicus, it did not use the expressions "in any way" or "not to teach." He had forgotten in these seventeen years the oral command, while he possessed the written directions of the Cardinal. Humanly it was quite understandable that he should forget the verbal information, while he clung to the document which did not forbid the form of hypothesis. He had written the *Dialogue* as a hypothesis, and if it caused any misunderstanding he was prepared to make every reparation: prepared to write a book refuting Copernicus.

Ten days passed without news of his case. But fate did not spare him other trials. Celeste sent alarming letters: the plague, already abating, had broken out more venomously. There were cases in the suburbs of Florence, and people were dying by scores in the city. Here at least was a subject of deep alarm he could discuss with the Niccolinis.

"Your Excellencies"—he showed them the letter—"fate has forced me into a horrible situation. Here I live in terror of the stake, while at home the plague threatens my family. I am full of fears. If my daughters die of the plague, my despair will kill me. Your Excellency, what is the sin for which God punishes me like this?"

"Wait a moment," said Signora Caterina. "I too have had a letter from Celeste. Let me read it to you—you'll feel calmer."

They read the letter together. It glowed with warm love and the certainty that her father was near the end of his troubles. Nobody else could offer such comfort, give such sweet peace. She was like the saints; her letter was like the pardoning hands which the blessed stretch out to souls in Purgatory.

On May 10th they summoned him again. Firenzuola in a dull official voice informed him that he had permission to compose and present within eight days his written defense. That ended the hearing. They permitted him to return to the Embassy.

Although up to now he had been almost mad with despair, now he fell into the opposite extreme. This denial of the greatest thought of his life seemed to him a monstrous sacrifice. Only life was worth more than that. He had paid the highest price for his bare existence, the most he could give, in exchange for his few remaining years; his judges must know what it had cost him. The Pope must hear how this victim of outraged vanity had gone to the last limits of self-abasement. If really he had secret organized enemies, they had won a full victory. What more could they want? Galileo felt like a man who had been taxed of everything save his life, and now as a pauper was meeting the bailiff. He had ceased to fear torture or burning alive. He knew that he would receive severe punishment, that he would have to add chapters to his *Dialogue* disproving Copernicus, that he himself would have to do penance. His scientific career was over, but the gentle joys of his old age remained.

He sent hopeful letters to all and sundry, avoiding carefully any reference to his case. But certain signs pointed to the fact that others were also spreading the news of a better turn in his affairs. Suddenly more letters began to arrive; many more congratulations, expressing joy at the results. One of them came from Ascanio Piccolomini, the young Archbishop of Siena. He sent warm greetings to the scientist, urging him to come to Siena and recuperate there from the strain and suffering. He promised him a litter and servants, an affectionate host who would do all he could. The pleasant tone of these letters gave him assurance. His health improved, his joints began to ache less, he could walk for a long time in the garden, and in general had begun to feel much better. All he wanted now was to hear his sentence soon.

But the Holy Office kept silence for many weeks. Niccolini tried to urge their decision, but the Inquisitors refused to discuss the matter—that would have been against the rules of the Holy Office. The Pope saw him once and gave him a noncommittal answer. The most he could do was to turn to Florence and ask the Grand Duke to intervene. But even this proved unexpectedly difficult. One night the servant who was putting Galileo to bed seemed to have something on his mind, but hesitated. Galileo noticed it and began to question him.

"Promise me, Your Honor, not to betray me."

"You can trust me, sirrah."

"I've heard something from their Excellencies' butler. He was listening one day when His Excellency and the Signora were talking about you. They were very angry with Lord Cioli of Florence. Because, if you don't mind my saying it, though I'm only a servant, Cioli is a bad man and is doing his best to spite Your Honor. He's written my master a letter saying that you ought not to be living here, and costing the Court a lot of money when you could lodge for nothing in the prison of the Holy Office. Their Excellencies were both very angry about it. The butler heard what His Excellency has written to Florence. He wrote to my Lord Cioli that you cost no more than fifteen scudi a month. So you could stay here for six months on a hundred scudi. And if the Government took objection to this, His Excellency would be glad to throw the money at their heads, out of his own pocket. But, for God's sake, Your Honor, don't tell on me, because we two servants would get into trouble . . ."

His host's kindness deeply touched Galileo. Although he could not betray his servant, he took the earliest opportunity to mention the cost of his stay to Niccolini. His host interrupted.

"Our Duke is no miser to haggle over a few gold pieces. Don't let that trouble you; you've trouble enough here. You can stay as long as you like; the rest is my business."

"I only mentioned it . . ."

"Don't waste your breath, old friend. I have more important news. I've received a summons for tomorrow morning from the Pope. I asked for an audience to plead your cause."

"Pleading is not enough, Your Excellency. Try to find out what my punishment is likely to be. Shall I be told to make a pilgrimage, or go for a certain time to a monastery? That is the sort of punishment the Holy Office inflicts if it is lenient, and perhaps you could ask what they mean to do with my book."

"I'll do my best. And as soon as I know I'll come back to tell you."

The Ambassador returned next day at noon and found Galileo in the garden.

"Your sentence is prepared, Messer, but I still can't find out what it is. It can't be very severe, but I'm afraid it won't be very mild either. I asked the Pope frankly. He told me that the sentence had been passed by the College of Cardinals in the Holy Office, according to the tribunal's report, but he didn't know it. Of course, that is impossible, since probably he has fixed it himself. But they always keep the verdicts of the Inquisition a strict secret till publication. When I insisted, he only said: 'We don't know in the least what will happen to him. He must be punished. The mildest sentence would be detention in a monastery for a certain time. After sentence has been passed, you must visit us again. Then we can discuss what we can do to spare him any really great sorrow.' This at least makes it clear that there's no danger of the stake or whatever else you were so afraid of. So let's hope for the best. We shall soon know now."

Three days later, on June 20th, the summons arrived: the accused was to be ready next morning at nine, at the Holy Office. He felt very much excited, but not terrified. He knew that they were going to let him live.

He felt rather curious to know what they meant to offer him in exchange for forswearing himself and his life's whole work.

Next morning, at nine sharp, he faced his judges. He could stand again. There were still only three of them to judge him, and he felt surprised that in such an important case sentence should be pronounced with so little solemnity. Why had the Peripatetics of the Church refrained from making this an occasion for public rejoicing, a feast of triumph?

"We will question the accused again," Firenzuola said. "Take the usual oath."

He repeated it and was amazed. A new questioning? Was the Pope mistaken about the sentence being ready? When they allowed him to sit down he was still surprised.

"Has the accused any new declaration to make?"

"No."

"Let him tell the Court how long ago he began to believe that the earth moves round the sun, and whether he believes it still."

"A long time ago. That is to say, before the Holy Congregation of the Index decided the matter by decree, and I was not informed of it. I was still uncertain what to think, and considered both systems of the universe, those of Ptolemy and Copernicus, as possible. But once the Congregation had decided the matter, I was convinced by the wisdom of my superiors. Then every uncertainty was dispelled from my mind, and I knew at once that Ptolemy's theory of the earth's immobility and the sun's movement is indisputable."

"Why, then, did you write a book so long afterward, dealing with the very certainty? Can you deny that this work gives the impression that the accused believed in Copernicus in his secret soul?"

Galileo had begun to answer, but Firenzuola's face was suddenly hard again. He almost shouted:

"You've taken an oath to tell the truth! Answer us therefore truthfully and plainly. Did you and do you uphold this Copernican heresy? We aren't interested in what you are prepared to declare to us! Tell us what you believe in your heart! The truth!"

The old man trembled. He could not turn back on the road he had taken. They were forcing him to lie—under oath.

"As for my *Dialogue,* it wasn't written because I believed Copernican heresy. All I did was to try to serve the community by setting forth the astronomical arguments for these two cosmologies. I wanted to show that neither Ptolemy nor Copernicus brings decisive proof, and that, therefore, if we seek for certainty, we can only find it in higher teaching, only in the decision of Holy Church—as is shown by many passages in my book. I declare upon my conscience and oath that, after the decision of the Church, I did not and do not uphold the accursed teaching."

"These are idle words. The accused uses his tongue very skillfully, but he cannot convince. His arguments for Copernicus were much better! Prisoner, I warn you to tell the truth, because we have other instruments."

But Galileo answered stubbornly: "No. Once they forbade this doctrine, I turned away from it. That's all I can tell you. Here I am in your hands, Very Reverend Judges. Do with me whatever you wish."

The three judges rose. Galileo stumbled to his feet. The President of the Inquisition pointed to him and cried in a solemn voice:

"In the name of the Holy Office, I warn you for the last time to speak plain truth, or we shall use the instruments of torture."

Galileo blenched, but his nerves were steady. His brain worked with lightning speed. What should he say? If he altered anything he would both admit that he was a perjurer and had written his book with deliberate malice. He looked straight in Firenzuola's eyes:

"I came here to obey," his voice was tremulous but distinct. "I repeat that after the Church had decided, I ceased to believe in Copernicus."

Firenzuola thought for an instant, and then glanced at his two companions. They understood his questioning look, which remained a mystery to the prisoner. Both of them nodded. The President shrugged.

"Now go to the anteroom and wait till we call you."

He shuffled away and sank onto a bench suddenly, feeling a strong desire to sleep. His knees trembled. He became aware that he was sweating profusely. "Horrible! Horrible!" he muttered. Steps came down the corridor, and the noise tortured him so that he cried with pain. It was an endless wait. How were they going to torture him? And where? Here in the dungeons? Or in the Castel Sant' Angelo? He would never get over it. He would die. . . . Celeste, Celeste, why aren't you here? . . .

The door opened and they summoned him.

"We shall now read the record of your last examination."

They did. It was precise and faithful.

"Sign it."

He obeyed silently.

"Very good. Sentence on your case will be passed tomorrow. The proceedings are ended."

"May I go home?" he cried out happily.

"Not now. Our rules forbid it. You must sleep here tonight. You will sleep in the same rooms as before. Well, have you any request? Why do you hesitate?"

"The Ambassador is my very good friend; he will be anxious about me. Would it be possible to notify him that I am kept here and have suffered no harm?"

"Any harm you might or might not have suffered is an official secret in these proceedings. But we will notify the Florentine Ambassador that you remain here. You are dismissed."

They led him to his former rooms. He heard one sentence over and over again, like the promise of salvation: "This ends the proceedings." Now they would not torture him. Now—that at least was certain. For some reason known only to themselves they had wanted to make him forswear Copernicus under threat of the rack—and with Copernicus all he had taught and written, or publicly maintained, for sixteen years. All his enemies were suddenly in the right. Father Grassi, Scheiner, Chiaromonti, everybody. Well, what did it matter? He would retire to the Jewel Villa, prune his vines, visit Celeste, sometimes play with his grandsons. Yes, but first he would have to do penance, as his judges prescribed. It did not matter. He wanted only a few years of peace in his hermitage at Arcetri.

In the afternoon came a servant with parcels from the Embassy, and a bunch of flowers from the Embassy garden. Long before sundown he was in bed, but could get no sleep, although he had ceased to be in pain. A strange thought tormented him: All men die once; he would die twice. Already he was dead as a scientist.

XI

Next morning he was early awake. He was so impatient to be up that he dressed without help and paced his room. It was almost noon before he was summoned, and then by no less a personage than Firenzuola, who gave him a document. Bells were ringing outside.

"Glance through this, and tell me at once whether you can read it fluently. Read a few lines aloud. . . ."

Galileo tried to focus his weak eyes on the parchment scroll.

"I, Galileo Galilei, son of the late Vincenzo Galilei, seventy years of age and a citizen of Florence, appear in person before the Court, and kneeling at the feet of Your Eminences . . ."

"That will do," Firenzuola interrupted. "Run through it quickly. When your sentence has been pronounced you have to read this aloud on your knees. Be careful not to mumble and stutter. Read it on your way into Court. I shall go on ahead of you."

Firenzuola hurried away. Two Dominicans with lighted candles stood on either side of the prisoner. He read the scroll, which contained nothing surprising: a solemn abjuration of all he had taught. The punishment concerned him far more.

To his great surprise they led him into a church. The choir stalls right and left of the altar were not occupied today by Dominican monks, saying their office, but by Cardinals in all the glory of their purple—all doubtless members of the College of the Holy Office, assembled to punish the accused. The judges formed a separate group of three. The other benches were packed with bishops, canons, and monks, crowded together. Carmelites, Jesuits, Dominicans, Minorites, Franciscans, Theatines, and many more in brown, in black, and in white. The two Dominicans led him to a table. Between two burning candles stood a crucifix and a parchment-bound Bible. When he came to his place, Firenzuola rose, and in Latin asked the College's permission to pass sentence on Galileo Galilei. The Cardinals nodded all together. Firenzuola took a sheaf of documents and

508

handed them to Cardinal Ginetti, the youngest among them, who began to read:

"We, Caspare Borgia, Cardinal of the Holy Cross of Jerusalem; Fra Felice Centino, Cardinal of Saint Anastasius; Guido Bentivoglio, Cardinal of Santa Maria del Popolo; Fra Desiderio Scaglia, Cardinal of Saint Charles; Fra Antonio Barberini, Cardinal of Saint Onufrius; Landivio Zacchia, Cardinal of Saint Peter; Berlingero, Cardinal of Saint Augustine; Fabricio Vereseppio, Cardinal of Saint Lawrence; Francesco Barberini, Cardinal of Saint Lawrence of Damascus; and Deacon Cardinal Marzio Ginetti, Cardinals of the Holy Roman Catholic Church by God's grace, Inquisitors against heresy appointed by Christ's mercy and the Holy and Apostolic See to purge all Christendom, declare as follows":

Galileo glanced at the men in red. He knew them all. Most of them had been his friends. Now they all stared at him. Probably he was being discussed. They were whispering in the back benches.

"Whereas you, Galilei," Ginetti continued, "son of Vincenzo Galilei, seventy years of age and a Florentine, were denounced in the year 1615, at this Holy Office . . ."

Denounced? So it was true? Those fears and nightmares had not been idle.

". . . for upholding certain false doctrines spread by many, namely, that the sun is the center of the universe and immobile, while the earth turns every day on its own axis; and, moreover, for corrupting pupils whom you instructed in this; furthermore, for spreading this heresy by letters which you wrote to certain mathematicians in Germany . . ."

Galileo was hardly listening. He heard only fragments:

" '. . . therefore the Holy Office . . . desiring to take steps against the confusion and damage caused to Our Holy Faith . . . contrary to Holy Writ . . . We were pleased to act leniently . . . on February 25, 1616, . . . a Congregation in the presence of His Holiness . . . requested His Eminence Cardinal Bellarmin . . . to enjoin you to give up the aforesaid heresy or, if you should prove obstinate and recalcitrant, the Inquisitor of the Holy Office was to call on you to abjure it, never to expound, defend, or instruct others in it. And should you not rest content in this command, you should be put into prison . . .

" 'In obedience to this decision, on the following day the aforesaid Cardinal Bellarmin reproved you mildly in his private apartments; the Inquisitor of the Holy Office at that time commanded you, in the presence of a public notary and witnesses, to give up completely the false doctrine, never to defend or teach it in the future in any form, verbally or in writing. To destroy the harmful theory completely and avoid its spreading further to the damage of Catholic truth, the Holy Congregation of the Index issued a decree prohibiting books defending it, while the doctrine itself was branded as false and contrary to Holy Writ.

" 'Now, last year a book was published in Florence. Its title page described you as the author. The Holy Office had taken cognizance of the fact, that as the result of this book, the false teaching of the moving earth and stationary sun had found more and more credit daily. Therefore we carefully examined the book and found in it an evident transgression of the interdiction of which you were informed, because you defended the already banned theory, although trying at the same time by all kinds of subterfuge to create the impression of not positively maintaining it, and only treating it as probable; this also being so, it was resolved at a sitting of our Holy Congregation, that His Eminence the Lord Cardinal Bellarmin should admonish you to renounce the aforesaid heresy . . . And should you refuse, the head of our Holy Office should strictly enjoin you to renounce it, neither to instruct others therein nor yourself defend it or expound it . . . and if then you should still prove recalcitrant to punish you with imprisonment.' "

All this has been forged, thought Galileo, seeing it all in a flash of memory; this record is forged. He had come to terms at once with Bellarmin; the Head of the Holy Office had been given no further say in the matter. The record was forged! Who could have forged it? Who could have given the Pope the satisfaction of finding the "original record?" He tried to keep his mind attentive to the droning voice. He listened, but his ears buzzed; he heard only fragments again:

"Therefore, at our command you have been summoned to the Holy Office, where under oath you acknowledge having written and published a book . . . acknowledge that in consequence of the book's composition, the arguments for the false doctrine could more easily lead the intellect astray than be refuted . . . when a date was set for preparing your defense, you presented a document written by His Eminence Cardinal Bellarmin personally . . . This document said that you had nothing to deny nor were you punished, but merely informed of the command not to maintain or defend the false doctrine. And, as this document did not contain the expressions of 'in any way' and 'not to teach,' according to you it is humanly possible that you had forgotten these expressions in so many years, and therefore did not mention them when asking for the permission of the Censorship. . . . But this document which you used for your defense was only an aggravation of your case, because it contained the statement that the doctrine was contrary to Holy Writ, and yet you dared to expound, defend, and maintain it. We considered that you did not confess everything sincerely in the matter of your intentions. Therefore we held a more strict examination, in the course of which you answered in a Catholic spirit . . . and so . . . weighing every circumstance . . . we have passed the following final sentence. . . ."

There was a slight movement in the benches. Galileo drew a deep sigh.

Ginetti continued:

"In the name of Our Lord Jesus Christ and His Glorious Mother, Mary Immaculate, we announce, proclaim, and expound by means of this our definite and final sentence, which we sitting here as judges . . ." Yet still the sentence was not spoken; there came a long list of jurists, each with his titles minutely described . . . Galileo's whole body was trembling. Would he ever hear what lay in store for him? . . .

"That you laid yourself open to grave suspicion of heresy; that is to say, you believed and stubbornly maintained . . ."

This led to a long exposition of Copernican theory. Tirades which for the tenth time repeated what was already said. And still no sentence . . . Ah! At last!

". . . thereby you have exposed yourself to all the penalties prescribed by canon law and other general and special constitutions. Yet we are willing to acquit you of these as soon as you have denied and damned with a sincere heart, not with dissembling words, the aforesaid errors, heresies, and all divergencies from Catholic and Apostolic teaching, according to the text prepared by us. But in order not to leave your grave and damnable error and disobedience without punishment, to give you a warning for the future, and to create a dread example for others, we decree that the book entitled *Dialogue of Galileo Galilei* be placed under the public interdict; while, as to you, we sentence your person to imprisonment in the charge of this Holy Office, for a term which we ourselves shall decide; and as a penance you are enjoined to repeat the seven penitential psalms every week for three years; we also reserve the right to change, lessen, suspend, and ameliorate, fully or in part, these penalties. . . ."

Galileo felt faint. His heart beat madly. The prison of the Inquisition for an indefinite period: this was the end. Death. He had not expected this. But he had not even time to be terrified. Firenzuola began to speak:

"Galileo Galilei, have you understood your sentence?"

"Yes."

"Are you willing to renounce your errors in the form prescribed by Their Eminences?"

"I am."

"Then place your left hand on the Holy Bible and repeat the text aloud. Kneel now."

Galileo put his hand on the Holy Book. Heavily he crouched down on his knees. He tried to read, but his eyes were too misty. He had to wait. At last he began:

"I, Galileo Galilei, son of the late Vincenzo Galilei, seventy years of age, and a citizen of Florence, appear in person in front of the Court and, kneeling to Your Eminences, the Most Serene Cardinals, Chief Inquisitors of heresy over all Christendom, looking with my eyes at Holy Writ, touching with my hands its parchment, do hereby swear that I always believed, believe, and with God's help shall believe, whatever the Holy Roman Catholic and Apostolic Church decides, maintains, and teaches. Yet, though the Holy Office commanded me by force of law to forswear completely my false belief in the sun as the center of the universe and immobile . . . whereas the earth is not its center and moves . . . furthermore, though I was forbidden to maintain this doctrine in any form whatsoever, whether verbally or in writing, to defend or teach it . . . nevertheless, I, though knowing that this doctrine contradicted Holy Writ, have written and published a book in which I expounded this already accursed teaching and defended it with strong arguments, although without drawing final conclusions, and so have been found most suspicious in heresy; for I maintained and proclaimed that the sun was the center of the universe and immobile, while the earth was not the center of the universe and was moving. Since I wish to dispel this grave and well-founded suspicion in the presence of Your Eminences and all Catholic Christians; therefore, with a sincere heart and without dissembling I deny, damn, and condemn the aforesaid errors and heresies and all such teachings inimical to Holy Church. I swear furthermore that I shall never do or say in writing or verbally anything which could raise this suspicion against me; should I meet a heretic or one to be suspected of heresy, I shall denounce him to the Holy Office or the local Inquisitor or Bishop. I swear to comply with all the penances prescribed now or in future by the Holy Office. If, God forbid, I should break any of these promises, denials, or oaths, I will accept whatever penance or punishment either canon law or the general and special constitutions impose on such criminals. So help me God and this Holy Bible which I touch with my hand."

Firenzuola motioned him to rise. The two Dominicans came back to stand on either side of him, with their burning candles. His old legs, grown numb in the long kneeling, almost gave way under him. They guided him through the side door of the church into the monastery, but not into the unknown terrible prisons—only to his comfortable rooms. Only now they turned the key in the lock. "For an indefinite period." Probably till death. Celeste, Angela, Nencio, and the two grandchildren were gone from him forever.

He stretched himself on the bed and began to cry softly; his sobs became louder.

"So this is what you've betrayed everything for! For this? You wretch, you miserable wretch. . . ."

He beat his forehead with his fists. He would have liked to spit in his own face. He abused and damned his own soul. The door opened. They brought him food. Not the servant of the Embassy: one of the Dominicans. He shook his head and would not touch it. He was alone again with his shameful thoughts, which plagued him all the rest of that day. Sometimes he grew weary of self-torture, then it started again. Nobody came to him, only the Dominican in the evening to take away the untouched food and bring his supper. He ate a little now, but began to weep again, undressed himself, lay down and wept the whole night. The dark was full of ghosts and terrors which almost maddened him, so that he raved. He choked with fear and remorse, struck himself in the face for a coward, a wretched weakling, as though he were enraged with another man. He did not sleep at all. In the morning he dressed and continued his terrible self-destruction: he rolled about on his bed and abused himself horribly, almost like a madman.

Next day at noon Firenzuola came to him and made him sign the oath he had read in the church. He could not stop crying.

"Hush! You ought to be thankful to get off with such a mild punishment."

"But I'm not thankful," he burst out wildly. "What use is such a life to me? Take me to the torture chamber, break my bones, beat me; I deserve no better. Terrible, terrible . . ."

Now he roared, losing all restraint. Firenzuola could not hide his anxiety. He was afraid that the prisoner would go mad. He endeavored to soothe him.

"Listen! There's still some hope that His Holiness will forgive you. Think of that and . . ."

But he saw that this weeping old madman could think of nothing, and left him alone. When the key turned in the lock and the steps receded, the prisoner straightened, and yelled across the empty rooms:

"His Holiness may forgive me if he likes. But I shall never forgive myself. Never! Never! Never!"

And he sobbed again. It was like a flood bursting its gates: the abased, violated mind took its revenge. He realized that for seventy years he had had good reason to be proud of himself; and now, at the bitter end of his life, he had lost self-respect. His fits became more and more insane. He lay with his face to the wall and would not turn his head to notice a visitor. Voices around him whispered helplessly; he did not care. There were moments when he thought he was going to die. This prison and his awful self-accusations seemed to be more than his tired, sickly body could bear.

Thus he suffered from Tuesday morning to Thursday evening.

Then he turned at the sound of Signora Niccolini's voice.

XII

Pope Urban had at once revoked the sentence of the Holy Office. He had intended it so; he would scare the guilty man with this threat of imprisonment, only to show then that he could be merciful—that his was the power. Galileo must remain a prisoner, but in the comfortable prison of the Embassy. Here his condition improved a little, but his mind was still bitter with self-reproach. But now at least he talked more coherently. The Ambassador gave almost his whole time to Galileo's affairs. He could see how grave his condition was, and became seriously afraid for his life. From morning to night he went the rounds of Cardinals, visited even the Inquisitors, who could discuss the matter now that it was made public. He was received by the Pope and besought him to allow this broken old man to be imprisoned in his villa outside Florence, where he could see his daughters. But this the Pope would not allow. The matter was too serious for that, he said. This guilty man must expiate his sin; as it was, he had received unusual favors. There was plenty of time for him to go home. Let him be content for the present with this permission to attend Mass from the Embassy. Then let him be imprisoned in Siena, the Ambassador urged, with Archbishop Piccolomini as his keeper. This pleased the Pope better, but he still hesitated.

The Ambassadress kept Galileo company. With endless patience and kindness she strove to soothe him. He told her all the things which weighed on his heart. He told her what a terribly humiliating thing it was to bear the knowledge of such a betrayal. That he had perjured himself over and over again in his fear of death. There was hardly a sentence in his long confession which had not been a lie. And the gravest perjury he had committed at the end, in the church, when he swore with his hand on the Bible that he renounced the doctrine with a sincere heart and without dissembling. It was a lie, because he still believed in what he had been proclaiming all his life. He had damned himself horribly in the church. "So help me God," he had said after all those lies. He had committed another mortal sin: confessed and taken the Holy Communion in the

515

house of the Holy Office without daring to confess his perjury. Therefore he had taken the body of the Lord unworthily. And, while for seventy years he had been a pious and faithful Christian, now the Inquisition had forced him into the gravest crimes. He could never atone for them. Because he did not dare to confess his perjuries. The Ambassadress reproved him gently. No priest would ever break the seal of confession.

"No, no," he cried out. "I don't dare to confess it. For if I did, they would really burn me. I'd have to confess that I still believe in my cosmology—which I abjured so cravenly and wretchedly. And yet I believe in it more than ever!"

"Don't deceive yourself," Signora Caterina said. "It was love of life which forced you into it. We are allowed to do many things in self-defense, both by human law and the law of God. Just think how terribly Celeste would have suffered if they had burned you."

"Oh, yes, Celeste. How can I ever speak to her again, look her in the eyes? When she hears how I lied to them at this trial, how I perjured myself on the Holy Scripture, she will know that I have committed the worst crime of which any Catholic can be guilty. She'll die of shame. I don't know how I shall face her."

Niccolini was still working on his behalf: in a fortnight he had achieved permission that the prisoner should be interned in Siena. On July 6th Galileo set out. Archbishop Piccolomini's litter had been waiting for him for several weeks; now at last he could take it. He said good-by to the Niccolinis, embracing them both with the deepest sorrow. They, too, could not hide their emotion.

"Till we meet again," Caterina said.

But he shook his head.

"Every farewell is the last for a sick old man. God bless you both for being so kind to me through the bitterest time of my life."

He drew the curtains of the litter as though to shield himself from the heat; in reality he wanted to shut out Rome, which had hurt him so terribly. When they came out into the country, he felt a little easier in his mind. But only a little. Because, though he had left the great mass of stone behind, with its Pope, its Cardinals, the overpowering strength of its organization, its Holy Office, and its intrigues, the world-wide power of this city dogged him, putting out invisible tentacles which would wrap him round for the rest of his life.

Ascanio Piccolomini, the young Archbishop, lived in a magnificent ancient palace, not far from the sloping square of the slim-towered City Hall, near the Loggia del Papa. It was a huge two-storied building, with the proud coat of arms of two Popes on its front. The Piccolominis had given two Popes to Christendom; Pius II and Pius III. The latter had reigned for only twenty-six days; but Pius II, world-famous humanist under the name of Æneas Sylvius, had been one of the greatest and most majestic of the heads of the Holy Catholic Church. The young scion of this great family, Archbishop Ascanio, who had known the scientist since his childhood, received him with affectionate friendship. He assigned to him a set of beautiful rooms where a whole host of servants cared for his needs. If this was a prison, it was a distinguished one.

First he showed the old man over the palace and explained the relics of his great family. As Pope Pius II, Æneas Sylvius had established a family archive, and the Archbishop gave an account of the traditions and living members. No less than eight Piccolominis had been canonized. There were many generals, cardinals, archbishops, bishops, and Papal pages. Guido Piccolomini had been a child when he died, and yet the Church had made him a saint. Giovanni Piccolomini was the famous "Moon Cardinal," because he had designed a new coat of arms: a cross with five half-moons. But every explanation led back to Pope Pius II, the pride of the family, who had taken special care of his kinsmen. He had even adopted some, made an Ammannati a cardinal and granted him his coat of arms.

"Ammannati," Galileo said. "My mother, God bless her memory, was an Ammannati girl."

"Really? That is interesting. Which branch of the Ammannatis?"

Soon they discovered that they were distantly related. The Archbishop was tact and kindness personified. He carefully avoided any mention of the great trial. On the first evening he invited a guest, an astronomer called Marsili, who lived at Siena and was an old acquaintance and correspondent of Galileo's. But, being astronomers, they could not help discussing the great discoveries of the Florentine scientist. They touched Copernicus often, but always the Archbishop interrupted them and managed to steer them off the delicate points. After supper they walked in the beautiful, well-kept garden where everything was rich and peaceful. But then night came; loneliness and the tortures of remorse. The attentive host saw next day that his guest had not slept.

"Messer Galileo, permit me to offer you some advice."

"I need only one counsel, Monsignor. Tell me how to win back my freedom."

"I can't do the impossible. But if you listen to me you'll find peace. I advise you to work."

"Work? I? Dare I write a single word?"

"A thousand if you wish. Last night I enjoyed your reasoning about heat and the center of gravity. I'd like to read it in a book. You have discovered a host of new things in physics. Why don't you put them into a book? You could teach the whole world your own physics. Here you have everything for your work: quiet, comfort, my fair-sized library. Marsili has many special books. Take my advice and work again."

"It would be difficult, Monsignor. My soul is so heavy and tired."

"I know. But I also know that sometimes work means rest. And if we give food to our mind, it can't devour itself."

Galileo was surprised that this young Archbishop should say such wise things. But all the Piccolominis were sharp-witted.

"Thank you for the advice, Monsignor, and I'll try it. And I thank you even more for your kindness which inspired the advice. But frankly—I don't think I can do it."

"Sit down before a sheet of paper. It will cry out for words. Promise me to give it a trial."

Galileo smiled weakly and gave his promise. He put down the paper hopelessly and took a quill. What could he write, after being silenced with such cruel severity? His whole life-work was so complete, every thesis formed part of a rounded whole; it was impossible to take out details without betraying his basic conviction. It was not the oath which held him back. A hundred or a hundred and one perjuries . . . what was the difference? But his fear. The science of the Church had attained its aim: succeeded in terrifying the greatest European fighter for new knowledge.

But, staring at the empty paper, he began to think of the fundamental difference between the old and new science. The ban on Copernicus was the lesser evil. The greater was the lack of coherent thought. The Copernican question was only one instance of this larger and more general defect. Scientific thought had reached a cul-de-sac; the Church had raised the Peripatetic doctrine to the level of religious dogma and thereby forced the human intellect, which knows no limitations, to sterility. Every branch of science would be affected by this decision—it would hamper medicine as much as physics.

A new system was needed. A new freedom of thought. A revaluation and fresh grouping of fossilized, ancient ideas, free of all metaphysical trammels. One ought to go back to the most elemental things: to matter, power, light. A new formulation ought to be given, free of every prejudice, dividing theology strictly from science, and rigorously determined to avoid bringing the concept "God" into the calculation of a pyramid's cubic contents. God had created the world and created it in such a wonderful way that a thousandth part of it dazzled the eye with the radiance of its laws. The really religious scientist had no business to inquire into the mystery of creation, which was infinite, and therefore not to be appreciated by the limited human mind. He had to examine the laws of nature and define the interrelationship of phenomena. The more he could discover without theology, the more he would be able to glimpse the blinding wisdom in all God's work, the more he would proclaim God's glory.

He had begun his career in the same way, although not quite consciously. His mind had fortunately been strong, so that the petrified and lifeless authorities were not able to fetter his thinking. He was a youth when he discovered the law of unhampered fall, determined the laws of the pendulum. Later he discovered the principles of specific gravity, of heat, of the conservation of energy. Then he had invented the telescope, and, thereby opening larger horizons, had become an astronomer. It was a tempting thought to return to fields he had left decades ago, and to form a system of all these thoughts. Return to the ancient idea, to matter. To scrutinize it and look into its particles. To divide it *ad infinitum*.

He put down his quill and no longer noticed the white paper. The mill which had been standing idle for many months began to work again.

"Well," his host asked in the evening, "did you manage to do anything?"

"I haven't written a single word," he answered, "but I think I shall be able to write a book."

"Good! I'm very glad! And the title?"

"I don't know yet. But one thing I do know. The expression 'New Science' will come into it."

Marsili came and was astonished to find the old scientist so changed in a single day. Now the conversation was lively and free.

"I have still one great scientific desire," Galileo said. "There's still one problem which I mean to solve before I die."

"Some invention perhaps?"

"Yes. I want to find a way to measure the velocity of light."

"I don't understand."

"I'd like to measure somehow the path of light from one place to the other. I see that Monsignor is amazed. And yet even the ancients suspected that not only sound takes time to spread, but even light. Let me explain it, although it will probably bore Signor Marsili. You have probably observed that if you look at a woodcutter from a fair distance, you see the glint of his axe but hear the impact only a little time afterward. Because the sound needs time to reach the listener from the place of its origin. In thunderstorms we know that we hear the thunder a considerable time after seeing the lightning, although they originate at the same time. That means that sound takes time to travel. You can even measure it with an hourglass. Well, I'm convinced that the same thing applies to light. Light is much quicker, yet it needs time. That is the time I want to measure."

"How curious," the Archbishop said, pointing at the horizon beyond the trees. "The sun is just setting. What about her last rays? Do they come like messengers?"

"Exactly. The last ray of the sun starts through space and arrives here in a certain time. By that time the real sun may have set. Therefore, if I look at the sun, I'm deceived. She isn't really there any longer. I only see her because she was there a certain time ago. But in the meantime the earth has turned away eastward. . . ."

He had said it. He quickly glanced at his two listeners.

"I mean," he added gently, "the sun was moving, not the earth."

He turned away, murmuring some apology, and left them. He was ashamed of his weak tears. Yet soon he was calm again. The Archbishop's help had given his mind a certain direction, a definite trend, and this was a full blessing for him. He still found it difficult to sleep, but he had shaken off the terror of evil dreams. For many years the infinitely great had been his province. Now the storm of fate turned him back and forced him to examine the infinitely small. There was really no difference. The infinite was always infinite.

Slowly he began to jot down the scheme for his book on New Science. He remembered a great many things which he had barely noted down five or twenty-five years ago, and put aside, because astronomy left no time for physics. These notes were still in his villa, in locked drawers. But . . . were they still there?

A friend of his, called Rondinelli, was living there now. He seldom wrote, but Celeste kept him informed. His servant and Porzia, his housekeeper, often came to see her at the convent. She kept the accounts, looked after the garden, and sent on his letters and kept things going.

Nencio's brother-in-law, Geri Bocchineri, was still proud of his famous relative and also wrote frequently. He wrote now that all Galileo's Florentine friends, especially those who were reputed followers of Copernicus, were being watched by the Inquisition. There was only one explanation of that: the Holy Office was really afraid of him. It might happen that one day the Inquisitors would invade the villa and search it and confiscate his scientific notes and the correspondence of fifty years. But Geri had no definite knowledge, and Celeste did not mention any such move. To write and ask her was impossible, since he did not know whether his letters were being censored.

This was a source of great anxiety. But it was even worse to feel himself a prisoner and an exile. He had no wish to go out into the streets of Siena, when all the world would point and stare at him, the victim of this famous trial; and yet the knowledge that he could not leave these gardens stung him to fury. At times he thought of imploring the Pope to imprison him in his own villa in Florence. He wrote petitioning the Ambassador and the Tuscan Court. Piccolomini intervened on his behalf. Once, when he was going into the country, he petitioned Rome for leave to take Galileo with him. But to every plea, to every inquiry, Rome had always the same unyielding no. The prisoner must rest content. It was too early to ask for mitigation of sentence.

It was as though fate itself had so arranged things that every circumstance intensified his longing to be with his children.

First he received bad news of Celeste's health. Suor Celeste had always been delicate. And now she was beginning to suffer from the strain of long months of anxiety for her father. And, worse still, the San Matteo convent had been turned into a hospital during the plague. Eight women were being nursed there even now. It was hard to tell whether they were really plague-stricken. In every letter which came from Florence, the old man suspected some hidden misfortune. He could never rid himself of the thought that his daughters might contract the plague. Perhaps they had sickened already, and he knew nothing of it!

A member of his family had died of it, although he only heard it later. The wife of his nephew, the Landucci boy, that pretty little Anna Diocianti, whose marriage he had arranged and whose dowry he had paid, died in a few days, leaving two small children. Galileo had generously signed a deed allowing her six gold pieces a month. Now the bereaved young husband demanded the money, even after the death of his wife. Celeste, who managed the family money matters provisionally, continued the payment on her own responsibility, but informed Landucci that he had no legal right. He answered sulkily that his children had a right to maintenance. It looked as though he would even sue his uncle.

Worse news reached Siena: Nencio was doing very badly at his post. He had been several times reprimanded. In the end they had transferred him to Poppi as an administrative clerk, but his legal knowledge had proved insufficient for the simplest cases, and he neglected his work. Geri, his brother-in-law, himself a clerk of the Chancery, wrote angry letters to Siena. Something would have to be done. Albizzi, the chief of Nencio's department, was openly threatening to dismiss Galileo's son. Cioli himself had intervened on his behalf several times, but that could not go on forever. Nencio would lose his post. The young man himself did not seem to care much. He still seemed to rely on his father's influence. His mind was full of other schemes. He had found out that the neighboring house on the Costa San Giorgio was for sale and wanted his father to help him buy it. It was months since Galileo had had a word from him, but now he wrote demanding a hundred and fifty gold pieces for the first instalment. He had somehow managed to win Celeste for his scheme, for the gentle nun implored her father's kindness and leniency. Galileo was in despair— what would happen to Nencio if he lost his post! In the terrible days just after the sentence he had been forced to pay Nencio's debts—two hundred and fifty gold pieces. And now the boy, who ought to have been hard at work in the country, was wasting his time in plague-ridden Florence to buy a new house!

All he could do was to keep writing desperate letters imploring his transfer to Florence. But the Pope had ceased to trouble about the prisoner—his chief concern was to blot out Copernican teaching once and for all. It was apparent that he had deeper motives, more than mere wounded pride and misunderstanding. The alleged slight was fully avenged. But those who made him believe that Simplicio was a caricature of the Pope had probably also made him fear that the new theory was undermining all spiritual authority, and must be rooted out. And Pope Urban was a clever man with a sharply developed sense of power. Guiducci, his friend and faithful disciple, wrote that the Vicar General had come to his house and, in the name of the Florentine Chief Inquisitor, summoned him to attend a conference without naming the subject to be discussed. Guiducci had obeyed the summons. He had been late in arriving at the conference and was surprised to find a numerous company, inquisitors, canons, monks, and many former friends of Galileo. The Chief Inquisitor had announced that, commanded by the Holy Office in Rome, he would read out the sentence passed on Galileo, and the oath by which he had abjured his heresy. Having read it, he closed the meeting. Guiducci asked why he had been summoned. Rome had instructed the Chief Inquisitor to collect all available scientists.

Galileo showed the letter to Piccolomini, who smiled uneasily.

"Didn't you realize that this would necessarily follow? They will do it in every city in Christendom which possesses an archbishop or an inquisitor. Even in America and Japan! So your name will be known all over the world."

"Even here in Siena?"

"Naturally. It was done a few days ago. I didn't want to upset you by letting you know. I myself received the instructions. The accompanying letter insisted that the sentence and your oath must be made known to every learned man all over the world as a warning."

Galileo had not thought that his shame would become world-wide. Never before had a man been so humbled. He thought of his oath being read everywhere. In Venice, where Micanzio would hear it, and all the priests and senators he had known. In Padua, where the professors of the Bo were listening. In Bologna, in front of the professors of the "dotta città." And in Pisa! To the delight of Count D'Elzi and his scheming colleagues. How happy Father Scheiner must have been when he heard it in Ingolstadt! And what did the pupils of poor Kepler say when it was read in Prague? Or Gassendi, follower of Copernicus, though a priest in France? And his thousands of pupils in every land, from Torricelli to Count Noailles?

It reopened the wound! He could think of nothing but his new shame. He tried to view it with Dante's eyes. Fate had loaded him with incredible honors; he of all mankind had been the first to discover new stars; he had discovered physical laws which began a new epoch—and then, at the zenith of glory, had been hurled down to the nadir of such a betrayal. Yet history and the verdict of all these scientists were as nothing compared to Celeste's thoughts when she should hear of this. At present she only knew that he had been sentenced. But when she heard of his shameful oath—what would she feel then about her father, whom she worshipped almost as a god?

The Archbishop did his best to pacify him. They had begun to trust each other sufficiently to talk quite freely about Copernicus. Piccolomini was even curious to hear more of this damnable theory. Galileo hesitated. Then, having prudently insisted that he did not believe in his own explanations, had even denounced them under oath, he went on to expound the Copernican theory and the arguments on which it was based.

Piccolomini did not seem very much startled: "All this sounds convincing enough to me. I think your sentence was unjust."

"Monsignor, have you no fear of the Pope?"

"No," said Ascanio indifferently. "He couldn't very well harm me. It would be inadvisable to touch the Piccolomini family—as he knows very well. I'm fairly safe here in Siena, since Siena is ours! If anything should happen to me, the Pope would have a rebellion on his hands. You must have seen for yourself that Siena is a different world. This isn't Florence. And I, as an ancient Etruscan, have every reason not to be too respectful to Rome."

"Why not, Monsignor?"

"You ask me that? I thought you were an enthusiastic patriot. Did you never hear what happened about Urbino?"

"Perhaps I did, but I never understand politics."

"Well, I understand them. The Duke of Urbino died, and, by all divine and human laws, Urbino should have belonged to Tuscany. But Pope

Urban laid hands on it. He simply announced that Urbino belonged to the Papal States. Do you realize how much territory and how many castles we lost? And what did they say in Florence? They sent in despair for Cioli. Cioli, the Prime Minister, resigned himself piously to the will of the Church. And His Highness Fernando, whom his tutors had taught to follow Rome, swallowed hard and said nothing. I only wonder that His Holiness did not ask for Siena; they'd have given it to him! But perhaps that might not have been so easy. Politics are very useful, Messer Galileo; there is much to be learned from them. My cousin Ottavio, whom you know well, has now taken the side of the Emperor in the great war. He writes to me often. I correspond with others and hear many things. I can tell you we live in an evil world. I envy you because you can escape to your science."

"Alas, I count for nothing in science now. I've lost it."

"Rubbish! Of course you count for something! Do you suppose that oath is taken seriously?"

"But, Monsignor, I took it on the Bible."

"Yes, yes. Everybody knows that you had to choose between the stake and your oath. Of course, it would have been more dignified to be a martyr. But it's easy to see that nobody wants to be burned alive. It was an oath under duress. Didn't you swear that you would denounce all followers of Copernicus whenever you found them?"

"Yes. I swore that."

"And do you really think that was taken seriously? Do you think even His Holiness believed you? Calm yourself, and work in such a way that the Inquisition can't lay hands on you. You can stay here as long as you please. I know how you long to be back in Florence, but remember that now you might be in prison, in the Castel Sant' Angelo or the dungeons of the Sopra Minerva. Here it's a little better and less monotonous. That reminds me: tomorrow we expect an interesting guest, a French poet, called Saint-Amant. He'll have plenty to tell us. And now sleep well and don't torture yourself."

The French poet arrived, a handsome man of forty who did not look like a poet at all. He belonged to the retinue of Crequi de Blanchefort, Ambassador of France to the Holy See; and, since Richelieu had transferred the Ambassador to Venice, he traveled ahead of him. Thus he came to Siena. He was most respectful to Galileo and expressed his joy at becoming acquainted with so famous a man! Galileo replied politely in Latin, but Saint-Amant laughed and stuck to Italian.

"I hardly know any Latin, Messer Galilei; I was a very bad scholar. I preferred modern languages; a soldier can always use them better."

"A soldier? But aren't you a poet?"

"Both. I'm a commissioner of French artillery. I also write poems, but, alas, only in French! I'm sure you'd enjoy them, because I heartily abuse Aristotle. It's his fault that literature can make no advance. Every spirit is equally oppressed by him."

"So even poets feel that?" Galileo was amazed and delighted.

"Yes, even poets."

He conceived a strong liking for the poet-soldier, who proved a very charming companion. He played the lute exquisitely, and when Marsili came after supper, they made music for a long time. He knew the events of the great war and the whole diplomacy of Europe. He explained that it was no longer a question of religion. France was persecuting the Huguenots at home, but allying herself with the Protestants on the battle-field. On the other hand, Protestant princes were fighting on the Catholic Imperial side. The whole thing was mixed up, had become the maze of a hundred different interests—whereas fifteen years ago it had started under the banners of the Faith.

"What about Munich?" Galileo asked.

"For the moment I don't know what's happening there, but it has been plundered several times."

"Did you hear anything about my cousin?" the Archbishop said.

"He is a very talented man. He will achieve what Wallenstein only aspires to, and become a Prince of the Empire. Wallenstein has lost all prestige. The candidates for his place are Ottavio Piccolomini and Gallas."

"Do you remember the little Ottavio, Messer Galileo?" the Archbishop inquired. "He was listening when you argued with my uncle about the trajectory of a cannon ball."

"Oh, yes. Since then I have found out the physical law which determines the trajectory of gun shot. Cannon balls follow a parabola. And a pupil of mine, Cavalieri of Bologna, later arrived at the same result, quite independently."

This aroused the interest of Saint-Amant. They started a long technical discussion, and the Frenchman listened to Galileo as one might to an oracle. He praised him ecstatically.

"You see?" Piccolomini smiled. "You still count for something as a scientist. Everybody respects you."

"Everybody!" said Galileo. "I should like to know what my daughter thinks of me."

Soon after this, a rather less distinguished guest came to the palace, but he brought the prisoner far more happiness. It was Gepe, the little servant from home. Celeste had found out that someone was going to Siena and had contrived to get Gepe a seat in the carriage. Galileo flung his arms round the boy. Gepe had brought a letter, a cake made by Celeste, Tuscan wine, and news. News of the mule, the smaller cherry tree, the iron rim of the well, the damage done by weasels, and the countless other events of the Jewel Villa.

"Have any priests been visiting the house?"

"No, master. Why?"

"Not even once?"

"Oh, no."

"Nobody has disturbed my papers?"

"Of course not. Messer Rondinelli cannot touch them. The keys are here, Maestro, and another set with Suor Celeste."

"Now tell me, what did you hear about me at home?"

"That Your Excellency would like to come home, but the priests won't let you. Nothing else."

Gepe spent three days in the Palazzo Piccolomini, and he had never had three more glorious days. The Archbishop gave him a new jacket. He ate so much in the kitchen that they feared for his health. Then, when his master had questioned him enough, he went back to Florence. Galileo felt terribly jealous.

Soon came a letter from Suor Celeste.

I wouldn't like to think you doubt me or fear that I cease for a moment to commend you to God's grace, because that is my chief task on earth, and I often fear for your spiritual and bodily well-being. To prove this I want to tell you that I have received a copy of your sentence with permission to read it. In some ways it has made me very sad, and yet I am happy to have seen it, since it furnished me with the opportunity to do you a service, no matter how small.

You must let me take on myself the duty of saying the Psalms for you once a week. I have already begun, and it fills me with happiness. First, because I think that a prayer accompanied by obedience to the Church will be accepted; second, because I am glad to take these thoughts off your mind. I wish I could take your place in other things! I should be happy in a much smaller prison than this cell, if that could free you.

He pressed this letter to his cheeks, and at night kept it under his pillow. Not that he had ever troubled to say these Psalms, not even once. He had quite forgotten about it, although he had sworn to perform this duty. This girl, who had taken no such oath, was incomparably better and purer than he. God could not spurn any man who had such an advocate.

XIII

And at last, on a December day, a letter came which gave him freedom. Niccolini wrote that, though he could not obtain a complete pardon, the Pope was willing to let him leave at once for Arcetri. There he must only leave his villa to go to the convent to visit his daughters. He would be allowed to see friends and relatives, but only a few at a time to avoid all suspicion that he was giving scientific lectures.

Galileo set out almost immediately. To the very last, the Archbishop kept urging him to work. But Galileo's mind was not on science; he longed for home and for his children. It had been winter when he left for Rome; it was winter again when he returned. His Calvary had lasted eleven months.

Here was the villa, as unchanged as though he had only left it yesterday. The big broom stood in the same corner of the courtyard. The same smell came from Porzia's kitchen; his mule stood as peaceably as ever in the same stall. Upstairs the friendly fire was burning. He opened his drawers, went through his precious papers, and hurried to the convent to see Celeste. They stood there hugging one another as though indeed they were one flesh. Angela, too, embraced her father with becoming joy; but then she vanished. They remained alone—these two who loved each other, each like a sun of warmth in the other's sky.

"But what's been happening to you?" he asked, holding her at arm's length.

"Why, father? Don't you think I look well?"

"You look about half the size. Have you been ill?"

"Yes, I've had a deal of suffering. But don't let's talk about me; it's all over now. Let's talk about you; or rather you must listen to me, and you mustn't tire yourself. *Dio mio,* where shall I begin, there are so many things! Vincenzo Landucci with those six gold pieces a month. . . . And Nencio's house . . . wait a moment, here are my notes, I've put down everything. . . ."

She talked and talked. They were sitting side by side in the brick-floored, white-washed parlor, shamelessly holding hands. But Galileo was only half listening. He watched his daughter and was frightened to see how ill she looked. Her small white face had once made her look like a child of fifteen, but now—although she was only thirty-three—she might have been fifty. Her rough habit seemed to be empty of a body.

She did not say a word about the trial, the sentence, or anything connected with it. And she did not allow her father to mention it.

"You shall tell me all about it another time, as soon as you're strong again. Now it would only excite you. Let's just talk about the vineyard. Do you know what I did? I sent for a telescope and watched Giuseppe through it, to make sure he was doing a thorough job. I could see the vineyard clearly; I could even count the grapes with your invention. How wonderful it was . . . to be proud of my father, such a great man. . . ."

Galileo squeezed his daughter's hand and felt very humble; how could he ever have feared that such perfect love would fail him, even for a minute! When evening came and he had to leave her, he said good-by to her till tomorrow; but he turned back stealthily from the gate and asked for the Mother Superior.

"Reverend Mother, what is the matter with my daughter? She has aged ten years in one. Has she been ill?"

"I can't tell you, Messer Galileo. She's been working very hard indeed. As a nurse she always set the example. She wouldn't even take enough sleep. It was a special grace of God which kept her from catching the plague. Suor Caterina, poor soul, died of it a short time ago, and Celeste was nursing her. But I think that none of all that did her so much harm as her grief and anxiety about you."

"How did she bear these months?"

"She prayed and hoped. We were all amazed at her. Even I sometimes got the feeling that her face was glowing in the dark as though it were surrounded with a halo."

"And did she never complain about me? Did she never say that she was afraid?"

"Never. On the contrary, she encouraged us whenever we were anxious on your account. I hope that now you have come home safely she will get back her health. We have less work because the plague is practically over. There's some good in every evil. You at least have been kept clear of the pestilence."

"Yes, but not Celeste. I'm still terrified at the thought that she may have caught it. And how has Angela behaved?"

The Reverend Mother shrugged her shoulders.

"She hasn't changed. She lives in her shell. She never talks more than she can help. She is very lax in our holy exercises. I have often to scold her. Sometimes she raves and gets very angry. But when she has scolded herself out, she grows silent again. She also has been unwell, but her constitution is much stronger. Calm yourself, Messer Galileo; everything will be much better now."

Galileo went home reassured. His luggage was already unpacked. He classified the notes he had made at Siena, among the rest, and saw that his work on the "New Science" would progress well. He decided to go on writing in dialogue. At the end of the *Dialogue* the characters had agreed to meet again. So Sagredo, Salviati, and Simplicio would gather afresh, not now to talk astronomy but to lay the foundations of a completely new system of physics. He thought that he would have them meet in the Venetian Arsenal. There were so many machines, cranes, pillars, levers, instruments there which they could use as a starting point for everything. The book would begin a new epoch in the history of natural science. And perhaps he would remedy the harm which his scientific integrity had sustained.

This knowledge, coupled with the quiet and comfort of his home and the close proximity of his daughters, healed him like a quick medicine. Now he only wanted to go into Florence. He had doctors to visit with his small ailments, family affairs to settle here and there. He had begun to wonder whether he dared ask Pope Urban to grant him this liberty, when one day Gepe came rushing into his room crying:

"The Grand Duke is here!"

Yes, Fernando II, His Serene Highness, Grand Duke of Tuscany, accompanied by Cioli, an aide-de-camp, and a Court priest, had come to pay a surprise visit. Perhaps his conscience was pricking him for not having said one single courageous word to the Pope during the whole trial on behalf of his famous subject. Galileo received them with humble courtesy and could not thank them enough for this great honor. Fernando was not yet twenty-four, a soft-voiced, almost timid, clumsily moving young man.

The visit lasted only a few minutes. The Grand Duke inquired after the health of his Court scientist, and then added that his inclination to him was unchanged. It was only important that he should show himself a penitent and faithful son of the Church. Finally he asked what favor he could grant him.

"Your Highness, I have a very great favor to ask. If you would be kind enough to get me permission to visit the city. No doctor would come out here in winter time, and I cannot afford to pay a carriage. If Your Highness would write to Cardinal Barberini, who can obtain much from the Pope, his uncle."

"We will do our best." The Grand Duke glanced at Cioli. "We should be very sorry if such a favorite subject of ours could not take part in our wedding feast."

He gave him a hand to kiss and departed. The old man accompanied them to the gate. He managed to put in a few words of excuse for his son. The two Court coaches rolled away, while the population of Arcetri stared open-mouthed. The Grand Duke had been engaged for a long time to the Princess of Urbino, Vittoria delle Rovere, who had just turned fourteen. She had been promised the whole of Urbino as her dowry, but the Pope had seized it. Princess Vittoria had only some family heirlooms left.

The old man still waited for further liberty. It would be really important since his nephew had taken action against him for the six gold pieces a month and he was prevented from appearing in court. He sent some friends to represent him, and he and Celeste discussed the case.

But he had to be careful not to tire her. She had altered strangely since her father came. Joy had not given her back her strength; on the contrary, she was wasting away at a frightening pace. It was as though all through the previous year she had clung to life by superhuman efforts; and now, when her tense anxiety relaxed, the reaction set in. She had no ailment which could be named, but she was shrinking as though the light in her eyes were burning up the oil of her body. Only her eyes remained, those beautiful, large, mysteriously deep eyes. Walking was tiring her out. She had to spend almost the whole day in bed now, getting up only in time for her father's visit. Her voice became a whisper, her parchment fingers had no strength in them to press Galileo's. Once every week they read the Psalms aloud, but with long pauses between each verse since she was always out of breath.

Yet her father was hopeful. After all, Celeste was only thirty-three and had no disease. She must be prevented from falling ill, and helped slowly but surely to get back her strength. He was always striving to keep her amused. But much of what he heard he withheld from her. The court had decided in the lawsuit in favor of young Landucci and against the defendant. News had come by word of mouth from Siena; news which had seemed too dangerous to write. Some anonymous scoundrel had denounced Ascanio Piccolomini at the Holy Office. According to the denunciation, the Archbishop had openly and repeatedly asserted that Galileo's sentence was unjust. He had also said that Galileo was a genius whose name would live in spite of the Holy Office. Although it was strictly forbidden to mention the proceedings of the Inquisition, the Archbishop sent word to Galileo assuring him that there was no cause for worry, since the Holy Office could do him no harm.

Such news as this he kept from Celeste, but the villa gave them a hundred things to discuss. She sat quietly listening to her father, answering him with gentle gaiety. But every day she looked more frail. And so it continued for three months. Then one day at the end of March Galileo was unable to see his daughter. Celeste was too ill to leave her cell. He was terrified, though Angela assured him that this was only a passing sickness. He wanted to see Celeste at any price. But he could not pass beyond the enclosure. No men could enter the convent but doctors and priests.

Next day came news: there was no change in her, nor any reason for anxiety. He would probably soon be seeing her. But the third and fourth days brought the same message. And this was too much. He implored the Mother Superior to let him in to see his daughter.

"Your Excellency, don't break my heart. You know it's impossible. Get permission from the Church authorities for this special case!"

"But I am forbidden to go into Florence, and you know how long a letter takes. For Jesus' sake, let me see my daughter! Suppose me a doctor or a priest. . . ."

"Very well, if she isn't any better tomorrow, I'll break our rule."

Next day, in the afternoon, they permitted him to go into her cell, when all the other nuns had been locked away. It was the first time Galileo had seen Celeste's home. It was the meanest, poorest little room, narrow as a prison cell. On the wall a crucifix, and below it a woodcut of her father which had been published in his treatise on the sunspots. Celeste lay there under the images of those whom she loved best. Now that she was not wearing her white coif, her head looked startlingly small on the rough linen. Angela was sitting beside her, on the one chair. But she gave up her place to her father.

Galileo knelt down beside the bed and took in his arms the wasted body of his daughter.

"My little sweet one, my only one . . . you must get better . . . I'm terribly worried . . . what is the matter?"

She touched his hair with her weak little hand, but she could not stroke it.

"Dysentery," she answered quietly, almost indifferently. "I'm in God's hands."

Then she closed her eyes and did not speak. She might have been resting or unconscious. After a long time she smiled.

"What is it, sweet?" the father asked.

"I dreamed just now, and I could see mother. She was as beautiful as she used to be long ago in Padua. And she loved me very much."

Then she asked, after some time with closed eyes:

"Father, what was Aristotle's teaching about God?"

"But, little one, you aren't well now . . . won't you be tired if I. . . ."

"No, no, tell me, I can listen."

"He said that God was immaterial; therefore not moving the world in a physical but a spiritual way. That he awakened the desire to love in every being. And that if we love Him, we find in ourselves all that is good, perfect, and eternal."

"How beautiful this is. Aristotle must have been a Christian. Why were you so cross with him, father?"

"My sweet, I promise I'll be more patient."

There was deep silence again. Almost an hour passed before she spoke.

"Father . . . I love you so; I cannot tell you how much. . . ."

A little later the Mother Superior came with the doctor. Galileo rose; they nodded silently. The doctor sent him out to wait in the corridor. Half an hour later he came out.

"She's unconscious," he said. "It's better to leave her now. You ought to go home. The Abbess was too shy to tell you."

"Yes, I'm going," he answered obediently. "I'll only look in just for a moment."

He went in again, bent over her and kissed her forehead. She did not move. Galileo turned to the Mother Superior.

"Did she want to confess?"

"She confessed and took Holy Communion this afternoon. And . . ."

"I know. The last sacraments. I'll go now . . . I'll . . ."

He stopped, forgetting what he was about to say. The Abbess gently led him out. The doctor took his arm and helped him along. Outside a cart with mules was waiting.

"Doctor, isn't there any hope?"

"I'm afraid not. She'll probably remain unconscious now till the end. I'm terribly sorry, Messer Galilei."

Galileo did not answer. The cart rattled away, while he walked alone through the dark silence. When he opened the door, Porzia met him.

"A priest is waiting for you. He's been waiting for almost two hours."

"What priest?"

"I don't know. He said he came from the Holy Office. The drawers are locked. Giuseppe took him to the study."

"Good. Go to the convent, Porzia. Suor Celeste is very ill. Stay there and bring me word if anything happens."

Porzia screamed and rushed out through the gate. Galileo went up the stairs. The priest was waiting and rose at his entrance.

"*Laudetur*. My name is Father Fanano, and I come to you from the Holy Office."

"God greet you. What is your business?"

"I bring you a command which has come from Rome. You are not to molest the Holy Office with repeated requests for mitigation; otherwise they may lose patience. If you cannot rest content, you will be summoned to enter the Sopra Minerva prison. Kindly sign this declaration that you received the command."

Galileo signed it obediently.

"Will you please inform the Chief Inquisitor that my rupture is so enlarged that only a doctor can bandage it? That's why I dared . . ."

"That is no excuse," interrupted the priest. "The city is near enough; doctors and drugs can get here easily. *Laudetur.*"

"*In aeternum,* amen."

Father Fanano departed and Galileo dismissed the matter. He sat down to wait. He did not touch his supper, but drew up his chair to the window from which he could see the convent. He sat and stared at the lighted cell. He waited thus till three in the morning. Then he heard the clang of the gate, and the desperate wailing voice of Porzia. Celeste was dead.

XIV

It took him months to get over this blow, and even when he could work again he knew that his intellect was impaired. His two remaining children did not care much for him. Her father's visits wearied Angela —she never knew quite what to say to him. He still visited the convent, but really he still came to see Celeste. He sat for hours in the tiny church whose walls and floor were the burying ground of the nuns. Celeste's gravestone was fresh in the wall.

Nor did Nencio give much thought to his father. He had lost his post and found another with great difficulty; he was appointed secretary to the Vicar of San Giovanni. As long as Galileo refused him the money to buy his house, he pestered his father every day. But, when he had found another post and when the house was bought and he had the two houses made into one, he hardly troubled about his father.

Yet the old man longed more than anything to be loved. He wanted at least a thousandth part of that deep love which he had lost through the death of Celeste. He felt so lonely that he humbled himself before Angela and Nencio, trying to get a little warmth in his arid life. Yet he could not fail to see that he was a burden to them. They wanted to live their own lives. They knew he was being well looked after and had no remorse about leaving him alone.

He could not do anything except work. He finished his book, and it became what he intended it to be: a new path hewn through the rocks for those who would follow him, a new and uniform conception of the physical world. He wrote it for scientists, not for the general public. He wrote it partly in Latin and partly in Italian, choosing the former for the technical passages, with their special scientific terms, while he kept the more general parts in Italian. And, while it was without unity in its outward form, it showed a concise and logical unity in its meaning. And all he said was being said for the first time in the world.

It began with Sagredo and Salviati discussing the material of machines in the Venetian Arsenal. Simplicio soon vanished. The Pope might

536

think he was still being mocked. But Sagredo and Salviati went on talking. First they tried to find out why smaller machines worked better than those built of the same material, by the same plans, but on a larger scale. This was a question which had never been raised by the engineers. But he did not spend much time over it; he had many other things to say. The discussion turned to the durability of matter. How durable was the pillar, the bar, the crossbar, the metal wire? And what made matter capable of resistance? Why did not the rope snap when lifting a block of marble? Probably its fibers were connected in such a way that even if some of them broke, the whole rope was held together. But how was this resistance to be explained in the case of stone and iron, which had no fibers? Aristotle—again and always Aristotle—said that things endured because the *"horror vacui,"* the terror of vacuum, the avoidance of every opening, hole, or crack, was a basic principle in nature. This explanation was false. You could not pump more than eighteen ells of water into an empty cylinder, because nature was sucking back the water to avoid a vacuum—this was acceptable. But you could put immense weight on a simple metal wire. Could the *"horror vacui"* be so great? No, the resistance of bodies had another reason. We have to break matter into the smallest particles, divide it to the last limit to find its secret. And suppose we divided these particles into others invisible to the eye, yet indivisible, then we could speak of the *"horror vacui"* but in a much deeper sense than Aristotle's. Among these tiny ancient cells there were such infinitely small and infinitely numerous vacuums which nature "wanted to fill out by any means," yet the tiny granules of matter were indivisible, could not be broken up any further; and this explained their invincible clinging. That was the reason why iron was hard, why an iron rod did not break if it carried a weight. "This thought is still raw, it must be digested." If he were given time, he would digest it. If not, the coming centuries would. The atoms had started on their way in natural science.

And how did matter change in its arrangement of millions of atoms? How did it melt, for instance? By an extremely quick movement of its own, the atoms invisible to the human eye!

Sagredo and Salviati discussed the velocity of light. Since Siena, Galileo had thought out a proof that light needs time to progress. The experiment was very simple. Let three men stand on a huge plain: let two hold lamps, let the third observe them. Let them agree that one shall put out his light, while the other follows his example as soon as he sees that the light is out. First let them stand a mile apart for this experiment. Then repeat it at a distance of five miles. The third time the distance would be increased to twenty miles. The third man would see that, the farther the two men were from each other, the longer the time between the putting out of the first and second light. The velocity of light could be measured—by a method invented by Galileo.

Then came sound. The immense field of acoustics. All new material.

And the unhampered fall. The behavior of objects floating on or submerged in water. Specific gravity. "What miraculous oceans do we reach slowly and imperceptibly among the vacuums?" The author himself cried out in his enraptured wonder at the thought of this ocean of new discoveries. His mind was as elastic, keen, and untrammeled as in his youth. His thought ate like an acid through the cracks of the problems raised, and crumbled the secrets.

The book was finished. He thought for a long time to whom he should dedicate it. He knew of nobody. But chance brought him the right man.

Two of his Padua pupils emerged from the past. One of them was a Provençal, Niccolò Peiresc. He was now middle-aged, a Councilor of the Provençal Parliament, a learned and influential statesman. Campanella had told him what the Holy Office had done against his world-famous master. He wrote to Arcetri, recalling himself to his professor and offering to use his political influence. He began to bombard Cardinal Barberini, brother of the Pope, with letters and sent copies to Galileo. Peiresc was Catholic, but a courageous and independent one. Yet, though his letters were almost insulting in their indignation, they did not bring any results.

His other pupil was Count Noailles, that gay young student who had sat on his right hand in the Paduan house. He had become Ambassador to the Vatican in the place of Blanchefort and now he wrote to his former professor. As French Ambassador, he had access to the Pope. He even dared to mention the matter of Simplicio to Pope Urban. He said quite bluntly that a rumor had spread through Rome that Simplicio was intended for His Holiness. It was an impossibility, he said. He proved to the Pope that is was nonsense to impute such an intention to an author who had no reason to mock the Pope, and every possible reason to court his favor. At the end of the audience, the Pope declared that he was convinced. He had always thought well of Galileo and respected him even now. But this new doctrine of the universe was a grave menace to the Church; it could not be allowed. Count Noailles did not give up his persistent siege. He found an ally in Niccolini, and proved himself such a fearless partisan that Galileo decided to dedicate his book to him. In his dedication he stressed one point: "If fills me with a sense of well-being to feel myself under the protection of a distinguished foreigner," giving bitter notice to the ruler of Tuscany that his subject could not expect much from *his* protection.

He had finished the book and only needed a publisher. Rome was ruled out in advance, since no publisher there would ever dare to take the risk of printing any book by Galileo, nor could he hope much of the Censorship. The present Censor could scarcely forget that the fat Riccardi had been dismissed by Pope Urban on account of Galileo. And the Florentine Censor had also been punished, so that nothing could be expected at home. His book was written; yet here he was, as helpless as any unknown beginner.

At about this time Archbishop Piccolomini came to Florence and visited him. He talked with all his usual freedom and self-assurance, saying things which Galileo had never considered.

"Your great mistake was not to have consulted some skillful advocate in canon law. Your sentence was plainly unjust. And the College of Cardinals had no right to sentence you at all."

"What do you mean, Monsignor?"

"Why were you sentenced? The Church had never proclaimed the doctrine of Copernicus as contrary to Holy Writ. No, don't interrupt! The College of Cardinals may have proclaimed it, but not the Church. Pope Paul had never signed any such decree, nor was it ever passed by a Council. Thus you have never defied the Church itself. Therefore, they had no right to sentence you. They might have tried you for defying the Holy Office—if you had not submitted your book to the Holy Office. But you had already received the imprimatur, and this shifted all responsibility on to the Censors, so that legally the Holy Office ought really to have condemned itself. The sentence is invalid; therefore, the oath it prescribed is null and void. So you need not be troubled with pangs of guilt. I explained this to some friends of mine at Siena and got denounced."

"And what happened? Didn't you have any trouble, Monsignor?"

"No, I simply denied it. It seemed the simplest thing to do. But, to continue—I can tell you something even stranger. This sentence is, moreover, invalid, because there are grave errors of form in it."

Galileo gaped at the Archbishop. He rose, went over to his desk, and took the text of the sentence from a drawer.

"Give it to me," the Archbishop said. "Here! See for yourself! I've examined it carefully. It begins by enumerating the judges. 'We, Caspare Borgia, and so on.' Ten Cardinals. Now let us turn to the end. Count the signatures. Seven. And look who was missing. The most important. Borgia, Zacchia, and the Pope's nephew, Francesco Barberini. I know them all. They are sensible and honest men, the strongest pillars of the Church. They probably felt that to sign would go against their consciences. They defied the Pope. Not to mention Francesco, the favorite nephew who could do anything. He never attended the meetings of the Inquisition; he found them wearisome. It was a great wonder that he consented to take part in your case. Borgia had nothing to fear, being the Viceroy of Naples, besides Cardinal. But Zacchia! Do you know what it means to refuse a signature demanded by Pope Urban? Well, to cut it short: this sentence was not signed by some of the judges. . . ."

"Then it isn't . . ."

"It isn't valid, I tell you. But what difference does that make! If you try to protest, you'll go to the stake, I can assure you. I'm only telling you this to appease your conscience, because in Siena I saw how bitterly you reproached yourself. Shall I finish my lecture on canon law? Copernicus is still unbanned by the Church. Pope Urban has neither condemned him *ex cathedra,* nor has any Church Council pronounced against him. Copernicus is only at odds with the Holy Office. It behooves you to keep silence, but only because you have been threatened. In the depths of your soul you can regard yourself as of the best of Catholics, even if you still maintain what you always believed. This is my conviction. But don't consult any other expert in canon law, or you'll find they'll denounce you."

But Galileo felt an unspeakable relief. In his innermost soul he knew himself a good Catholic and believer in God. The Archbishop had taken a heavy weight off his soul.

But now something deep in his Catholic mind began to protest. Something was the matter with the Church. It was wrong that the Church of Christ should send an army led by canons to seize Urbino. There was something wrong when religion forced the Florentine officials who were only obeying the Grand Duke's orders to do public penance because they had tried to fight the plague; it was surely wrong for the Church to organize a procession of the Madonna dell' Impruneta with a huge and easily contaminated crowd following the holy image. And it could not be right if in difficult scientific problems non-experts decreed what should or should not be believed in questions which had nothing to do with religion. At the time of Columbus they had asserted that the earth could not possibly be spherical, that it was impossible that people should live on the other side of this sphere, upside down. Now they knew that they were wrong. In a hundred years they would know they were wrong now. And, just as now nobody could accuse Columbus of heresy although Torquemada wanted to burn him, so too in a hundred years Galileo, who asserted that the earth moved, would be considered a good Catholic. And, if all this was true, then something must be the matter with the Papacy. The Pope's spiritual dominion could not be absolute.

"Have I become a Protestant?" Galileo asked himself anxiously, having thought all this. But, no, he told himself immediately. He believed all the dogmas which the Reformation had rejected. It filled him with joy every day at Mass to become aware of the mystical and beautiful transubstantiation. He would not have exchanged for anything the beauty and splendor of Catholic Churches, with their music, their incense-laden mystery, their stained glass, their tinkle of bells under vaulted arches; nor the relics of the saints, nor the vestments rich with cloth of gold, nor the gentle peace of Italian monasteries. Yet, against all this he maintained the system of Copernicus, and would never give it up as long as he lived. Since to teach it openly was impossible, he would have to maintain it by a subterfuge, while still proud in the knowledge that he was a Catholic. It would no doubt have been more dignified to die as a martyr, but this was the more useful way. His secret work would show that God's work was finer and greater than Ptolemy had ever conceived, that the wonderful wisdom of the Creator merited even deeper admiration. What was the function of science if not this? If he did his scientific duty he was more Catholic than a body of ignorant men using falsified records, proclaiming as science impossibilities, twisting the law to suit themselves, so that even the judges they had appointed would not all consent to sign their sentence.

He began to be frankly glad of his friendship with Diodati in Paris. Diodati was a Protestant and a Copernican. The accursed *Dialogue* had so delighted him that he had decided to make it known to the Protestant world. After long negotiation, he had succeeded in getting the Elzevirs to publish it, in a Latin translation made by Bernegger of Strasbourg. So now this hotly contested *Dialogue* had made its way into the world. The Holy Office could not reach to Leyden, and Pope Urban had no power over Protestant states, nor even all Catholic ones. He could not touch the French Protestants. The elderly prisoner in his Florentine villa, whose book had been confiscated and banned, had been muzzled too late. Coaches and ships took the copies of the Elzevir edition all over the world. Salviati, Sagredo, and Simplicio were read in London, Cracow, Breslau, and Lisbon. Everybody could get a copy —except the author. Had it been known that he had any part in preparing this Latin translation, they would have taken him instantly to Rome and burned him alive there. But he worked in secret, risking the wrath of the Inquisition. He was prepared to perjure himself again.

About this time his third grandchild was born—a boy. Since Galileo could not go to the christening, he had to be content with choosing the name. The child was named Cosimo. Almost three months passed before he could see it. Sestilia brought the baby up to Arcetri. He looked at this tiny boy and played with him and began to feel happy. But suddenly his sadness returned.

"Alas, I can't see him very well. My eyes are getting worse every day."

"Are they?" Sestilia asked indifferently.

"Yes, every day. Writing has become a torment. I sent Master Torto my own prescription to cut the lenses for my spectacles, but it's no use. Especially my right eye."

"Don't worry, father. You'll soon get better."

"I don't think so. I only hope my eyes will last my lifetime. Nencio couldn't come?"

"He's so busy. He sends you his best love."

Nencio seldom visited the Jewel. It took so long and was such a nuisance. He came only when he wanted something. His father knew that a visit meant that he needed money, or perhaps a letter of introduction. And when, shortly after Sestilia's visit, Nencio one day arrived at the villa, he began by saying that this time he had not come to take but give. He had brought something very important.

"Well, speak up. Only get your breath first."

"I've brought you something gigantic, father. Thirty thousand gold pieces."

"A tidy little sum," chuckled Galileo. "Put it down on the table."

"Don't joke, it's serious. The Dutch Government has offered thirty thousand gold pieces to the man who can invent a sure method for determining a ship's position at sea. I remember that you had some idea about this, discussed it with the Spaniards, and then gave it up."

There was a note of veiled complaint in his voice. He reproached his father for not trying to make money when he had so many people to support.

"Now, wait a moment. You mean the fixing of longitudes? How do you know about it?"

"A friend of mine told me. He's read the proclamation. If you like, I can get it for you to see; but I didn't want to do it openly."

"Why not?"

"Father, Holland is a Protestant state. And you've taken an oath that you wouldn't . . ."

"All right, all right. That was a long time ago. Well, copy out this proclamation of yours and don't talk to anyone. There is no need for the Inquisition to know about it."

"Leave that to me, sir. Do you really think it can be solved? That would be fine! I've always wanted to keep a coach so that the children could have plenty of fresh air. Thirty thousand gold pieces, *Dio mio!* Well, I won't disturb you any longer. We'll set to work on it at once."

Galileo obeyed. He worked out the formula for determining a ship's position on the open sea by means of the satellites of Jupiter. The whole essay was only a few pages long, but it was worth a hundred times the thirty thousand gold pieces to a nation of sailors. Nencio had brought him the proclamation. It was true: the Government of the Netherlands had organized a competition. The prize money had been collected by the owners of the Dutch merchant marine. Galileo sent his work secretly to Leghorn, and from there to Diodati in Paris. Soon he heard that it had reached Holland.

Now his thoughts were always beyond the frontiers, since he could not be a prophet in his own country. France, the German states, Holland, all aroused his interest. And he was proud to find that his fame was even greater in foreign lands. Whenever he wrote to a foreigner he received a very respectful answer. The Elzevirs had succeeded so well with the *Dialogue* that they begged him to send them another manuscript. He sent them a lengthy memorial addressed to the Dowager Grand Duchess, in which he maintained that Copernicus had taught nothing in contradiction to Holy Writ. At the same time came news that the accursed *Dialogue* had been translated into English. The interest of Europe was increasing. The old truth that to forbid a thing is to make it more desirable was proved again. The doctrine of Copernicus spread everywhere, while without the help of the Inquisition it would have passed unnoticed for many years.

He dreaded the fury of Rome. But Rome did nothing, though the authorities rigidly refused to consider the requests to restore his liberty, made by Peiresc, Count Noailles, and the Grand Duke. The culprit had been sentenced to imprisonment "for an indefinite period." But the Pope would not even say how long this "indefinite period" might last. Galileo himself could send no petitions, because this had been forbidden him on the evening before Celeste's death. Pope Urban already considered himself magnanimous because he had granted two requests which could not very well have been refused.

One was that he should leave Arcetri for one day when the Grand Duke had invited him to visit the Mezzomonte villa. In the morning the Court coach fetched him, bringing him back at sunset. It was the first time he had left Arcetri in three years. And, though that day was a day of freedom, he could not enjoy the sight of the world. His eyes had really begun to fail; he could not see three yards in front of him. The grand-ducal family received him with marked esteem. The Court had been living quietly in mourning for the Grand Duke's younger brother, one of the last victims of the plague. The Medici Court, which had once been brilliant, was scarcely recognizable now.

It was as though the wife of the late Cosimo had transplanted here that icy spirit of bigotry which recalled the Court of Philip of Spain.

Galileo was presented to the new Grand Duchess—a child of fifteen. His own eldest grandchild was not much younger, and yet Her Highness had now been married for a year—even if only nominally. The wedding had taken place, but the married couple still lived in separate apartments. It was very hard for the scientist and the Grand Duchess to find something to talk about. And Galileo was more or less monopolized during his brief visit by Cristina, the Duke's grandmother. Years ago he had seen her as a young woman, on that fatal day when Giovanni de' Medici had demonstrated his dredging machine at Pisa. Now she was old, and these two old people sat apart from the others in friendly talk. Mostly they talked about Cosimo with tears in their old eyes.

"I feel," she told him when they parted, "as though this was the last time we should meet. If so, take my blessing and affection. My son loved you dearly. Do you still sometimes look at the Medici stars?"

"I would, Your Highness, if I could see them. For these last months I haven't been able to use the telescope. My eyes are too bad."

He drove back to his prison. The Court coach, drawn by grays, trundled away in the dark. Galileo sat and thought of the Medici stars. This time he did not look for them in the sky, but only on paper. He tried hard to work out even more precisely his method of determining longitude, in the hope that the German sailors might also be interested. Money did not tempt him much; he had few financial cares. But the thought that here in his study at the Jewel he could change the whole system of navigation excited him.

The other favor which the Pope found it difficult to refuse was connected with Count Noailles, now recalled to Paris. He traveled through Leghorn, but had no time to go to Florence. Therefore, in the course of his farewell audience, he begged Pope Urban to allow his beloved master to meet him in a little village on the road between Rome and Leghorn. Pope Urban gave his permission reluctantly. Count Noailles hastened to notify Galileo. They were to meet on October 16th in Poggibonsi, where the Roman highroad from Florence turns toward Leghorn.

Galileo reached it first in a litter loaned him by the Court. He still felt a prisoner while he was waiting in front of the crossroads inn.

Someone stopped suddenly in front of him.

"Don't you know me, my beloved master?"

"Forgive me, my sight is very poor, but I thank God for letting me meet you here. . . ."

They embraced each other with fervent joy. The Count had reserved a room where they could talk in peace. They sat down, and Galileo called for strong wine.

The Count laughed:

"This is like old times. Do you remember how often we got drunk in your big house? I see you still relish good wine."

"I do, although I shouldn't. The doctors tell me it's bad for my joints, my kidneys, and my eyes. But I can't give it up. I had a daughter, a nun, who could manage to keep me off it a little. But now she is dead. How are you, my dear Count? I haven't even looked at you properly."

"You'd better not. I'm as old as you are—almost sixty. Once you were the famous professor and I the callow young student. Now we're simply two old men. But I mustn't forget; you spoke of something in your letter which I can't understand. That you were bringing me—?"

Galileo fumbled in his doublet and drew forth a sheaf of papers.

"The manuscript of my new book. Dedicated to you. I've had four copies made, to be sure of not losing it on the way. Will you please give it to Elia Diodati in Paris—I mean, if you aren't ashamed to deal with a heretic. He is a faithful friend of mine. He'll know where to send it. Your luggage won't be examined on the frontier."

"Why? Are you still writing heresies?"

"Not at all. But the Inquisition had better not know that Diodati is my Paris agent."

"I understand. And of course I'll take it. I shall be able to read it on my way. And now quick, I have much to tell you and time is short. First the Pope—that's the most important."

He gave detailed accounts of all his audiences. Nothing had really been achieved. The Pope would still not hear of a pardon. Even mitigation could not be expected for a long time.

"A long time!" Galileo sighed. "Where shall I be then! But what of our friends? I hear that Castelli has at last been allowed to return to Rome."

"Yes, they've given him back his professorship. I've spoken to him, and he sends you a very interesting message. He has been talking with . . . what's the fellow's name . . . a Jesuit in Tyrol . . ."

"Grienberger?"

"Yes, yes. Well, Castelli met him and they talked about you. This Grienberger, who seemed to like you, was full of sympathy. He said something strange which Castelli did not dare to put into writing, but he dictated it to me. Here it is. Listen. 'If Galilei could have won the good will of the Jesuit College at Rome, he would stand now in his full glory before the world. He could have written anything he liked, even affirmed the doctrine of Copernicus.' Isn't that interesting? So it seems that you have the Jesuits to thank for all your troubles."

Galileo shook his head.

"Yes, 'Jesuits' but not 'the Jesuits.' No, my dear Count. I know quite well who caused my ruin. I've ceased to think, as once I did, that a world organization hatched some mysterious plot against me. There's a Jesuit whom I love as my own son, Cavalieri. He's a genius and a professor at Bologna. A young man, but he has the gout so badly that he walks on crutches. He adores me; his Order knows about it, yet he has no trouble. No, my dear Count, I know where I have failed. I was conquered by the fact that those who possess religious power also demand civil authority. And I was trapped by those who guard this civil authority. Jesuits too. Perhaps mostly Jesuits. But not as an Order. It's unimportant, anyhow. The fight is over."

"Alas, it is. They've managed to crush you."

"Oh, no. I've really triumphed. The whole of Europe has heard my voice. Do you know what happened? I have used the sun as my torch to light the mind of the world. In Rome they're trying to put out the sun. They blow and rage at it, but its light only dazzles their eyes. I've won, my dear Count, not these people. Even if they continue to torture me, even if I have to die a prisoner."

"You're just the same as ever," said Count Noailles. "I feel like a student again when I listen to you. But my time's up. I must go. God bless you."

Count Noailles' coach went on to Livorno. Galileo's litter swung along the road back to his prison.

He soon heard from Diodati that the Dutch authorities had received his essay on navigation with great excitement, and had appointed a committee of four scientists to examine it carefully. It was progressing well and would probably succeed. The manuscript he had given to Count Noailles had also arrived; the Elzevirs themselves acknowledged receipt. They would be delighted to print this work—had already begun setting it up. But it was too long to be ready soon.

The prisoner trembled more for his frail life than ever before. He wanted to live long enough to see his work published. When the Grand Duchess Cristina died, he walked for hours in a terrified daze about his rooms. He prayed, and his prayer had always the same burden: "A little longer please, dear God." Even when his terror left him, the settled fear of death remained. He kept strict watch over himself. He was afraid of every cough, and forced himself to abstain from much wine or tobacco. He told himself that he must not die until these things had been accomplished: he would have to win the Dutch competition, see his book published, and get back his liberty. After that he would not mind dying. He acquired the habit of praying every night: "Please God, let me die as a free man."

His first two wishes did not seem impossible. The Elzevirs were working slowly, but his book was getting into print. The Dutch experts had examined the essay. One of them, Realius, sent him a letter saying that Holland accepted the idea in theory, and would probably buy it. But there was much to discuss about the practical applicability, since details had not been given in this short essay. Holland was taking it so seriously that one of her experts would come to Florence. Most of these things could be cleared up in a personal interview. Let the great scientist be assured that Holland was eternally grateful.

Galileo was unable to read this letter himself. There was no lens which could help him. His left eye saw objects dimly; the right could only guess at outlines. It was easy to recognize his servants, because he had got used to the difference in their steps. But men and women of the outside world he recognized only with great difficulty. Blindness was coming swiftly upon him.

In four months he had lost the sight of his right eye. At first he did not even know it. But when, one day, he walked in the garden his left eye began to smart: he rubbed it and the world became quite dark. He tried to open them both together and knew at once—he had lost his right eye.

He sent for his son. He had to send for him three times. Nencio very kindly agreed to spend two afternoons a week with his father— for a special payment. There were many letters he could not read himself and answers which he had to dictate. Nencio grumbled at all this work. But a secretary would have cost more money, so he undertook it. He pestered his father for news from Holland.

His indifference almost broke Galileo's heart. Angela behaved in the same way when he tried to win her. And he needed kinsmen whom he could love. Such happiness was his deepest need. Now he remembered Michelagnolo's children and his wife. What had become of that widow and all her children? Cencio, the eldest, who had behaved so badly in Rome, must now be thirty. Perhaps he was long married and had a family. And the youngest, Fulvia, must be ten. Perhaps they were in dire poverty, but dared not turn to him.

One day he talked of Michelagnolo's children to Nencio. He wanted to find out what had happened to them. He almost quarreled with his son. Nencio would not hear a word of them. If they did not write, that was their business. There was no sense in having eight or ten idle parasites in the house. But Galileo insisted. He also realized that this bad sight made him almost helpless, exposed him to everything. And if he lost his other eye, he would find himself at Nencio's mercy. His son would be able to write any letters he chose and keep back anything he liked.

He demanded to see a letter written to Father Micanzio. He had asked the monk to make inquiries in Munich. He kept this letter and sent it off by Giuseppe. Nencio grumbled, talked about good-for-nothing relations, and the astonishing character of his father who never seemed to learn by experience. But Galileo had his way. Micanzio's inquiries brought quick results. A letter came from Alberto in Munich—from the little Court page who had wept so bitterly when he had to leave Florence. Now he was a young man of twenty. He wrote that his mother and sisters were all dead, and only the three boys remained. They were trying to live on the Court pension of their father.

This was the Alberto whom Celeste had liked the best of her cousins. And, in spite of Nencio's strong protests, Galileo insisted upon inviting him. He scolded his son severely, and wrote to Father Micanzio. Finally, father and son quarreled bitterly. In their anger they both aired all their grievances. Afterward Nencio thought it wise to apologize, and the father hastened to kiss and embrace him. But he never could forget this quarrel. He had realized that his son did not love him.

He sent for his little servant to lead him over to the convent. There he did not even ask for Angela, but went straight into the church, sat down beside Celeste's grave, and complained to her of his wretched loneliness.

The Grand Duke had also heard that Galileo was going blind. His Highness came again to the Jewel. This time he brought his father-confessor, who tried to comfort the old man, and advised him to pray for consolation.

"It's all in vain, Your Highness." He shook his head. "I'll die blind. But I implore Your Highness to help me regain my freedom."

"That's very difficult," the Grand Duke sighed. "His Holiness doesn't like to consider this question. I think he's already a little angry with me, but I'll try to find some way. Niccolini can't mention it any more. His Holiness seems to be implacable. Perhaps I can think of something."

Then he left in the company of the silent priest. Nencio visited his father twice a week. They sat side by side like two strangers, master and secretary, without a single affectionate word.

One September day Alberto arrived. He was gay, young, and eager to please. Galileo could hardly see his face. But Porzia whispered to him that she had not seen such a handsome youth for a long time: he resembled his uncle miraculously. The young man made a place for himself in the Jewel and enchanted everybody with his perfect manners. His first visit was to Celeste's grave, taking some flowers. He waited hand and foot on his uncle, seeking his favor, and proved a very sensible boy. He treated Nencio with every sign of real affection, and from the very beginning kept reassuring him with tactful hints that he did not expect any financial help. But Nencio's distrust was stubborn. Alberto went down into Florence to see Sestilia and the children, and won their hearts. In a few days Nencio had begun to feel that really he had nothing to fear from his cousin.

"How marvelous," Porzia said. This handsome boy is like what you must have been in your youth."

The old man's vanity was tickled.

"Really? A very handsome boy, you say? I wish I could see him."

Now he could hardly see anything, even with his remaining eye. One December morning he awoke to complete blindness. Yesterday he had still been able to see dim outlines. And now he was quite blind. This new blow did not cause him any deep despair. During the last months he had slowly accustomed himself to the terrible thought. He found out that one could live even so.

On rainy winter days Nencio often missed his work. Alberto took his place, although Nencio always drew the pocket money his father had apportioned for his task. They lived like hermits on the hilltop: the nephew from Munich and the blind uncle. They talked for hours. Alberto read aloud, then Galileo took his lute. Since his blindness, he had returned to music. He played the old tunes of his childhood which he had learned from his father. When he tired of that he sat down comfortably in the armchair at the fire, smoothed the tight bandage of his rupture, stretched his legs, gazed with blind eyes into space, and began to dictate.

"Write very carefully, my boy. This is for Diodati, an important man. Well. 'In reply to your kind letter of November 20, 1637, in which you inquire about my health, I must tell you that my strength has been improved, but, oh, my esteemed sir, Galilei, your sincere friend and servant, is now completely and incurably blind.' Blind, have you got it?"

"Yes."

"Go on then. 'The sky, the earth, the universe which I have enlarged a hundred-, a thousand-fold beyond the known limits of the past centuries, by observation and clear deduction, has shrunk to such a narrowness that it does not surpass the confines of my own body. . . .' "

XV

But Alberto soon left again, although the old man urged him to stay. Nencio's poisoned hints were effective. His policy had been quite transparent. He expected the thirty thousand gold pieces to materialize, and was anxious not to let a near relation whom his father had grown to love remain beside him. So Alberto departed. Nencio took over his work and did all he could to have his father transferred to his city house.

"He wants the money in his house," thought the blind man. But he never said it, for secretly he longed to go with his grandchildren. His eyes were blind, and his soul fumbled blindly after warmth, begging for any scrap of love. So he allowed Nencio to petition the Holy Office.

His son wrote to Castelli, asking him to inquire about the possibility of a pardon. Or at least permission to move into Florence. Castelli sent a surprising reply: the Holy Office had informed him that there must be some misunderstanding. Galileo himself had not been barred from petitioning—he was only forbidden to send all sorts of influential persons to importune the Holy Office, the Cardinals, and the Pope. He could ask for anything he liked, and they would consider it.

Nencio proudly reported this.

"You see, father, I succeed in whatever I put my hand to."

"Certainly this seems an improvement. But I think they must have lied to Castelli. I remember every word Fanano said to me on the evening of Celeste's death. But the Holy Office says nothing without good reason. Probably the time of mitigation has arrived. Perhaps they are willing to pardon me and have started to pave the way for it. Well, see what you can manage."

Nencio did not need to be told. Castelli sent the text of the petition which he had agreed upon with the officials. It was quite short. According to the enclosed doctor's certificate, Galileo Galilei needed constant medical care; therefore he asked for permission to move into the town. There was no need to mention a pardon. Nencio copied the petition and sent it off in his father's name.

The weeks passed, but no reply came. Then, unexpectedly, Father Fanano visited the Jewel. He had brought with him a foreign doctor, not a Florentine, since the Holy Office put no faith in Florentine doctors' certificates. Fanano had now become Chief Inquisitor and conducted an almost official inquiry. He questioned the housekeeper and the two servants under oath, while the doctor carefully examined the master.

When Nencio heard of this unexpected visit, he was overjoyed.

"God is wise," he said. "He has turned your ailments to our advantage."

About three weeks later a letter arrived from the Florentine Inquisition. Fanano curtly notified the prisoner that his request was granted: he could move into the town but must first present himself at the building of the Inquisition and receive verbal instructions. Galileo gave orders to pack at once, and ordered a litter for next day. They took him straight to the Inquisition. His son helped him up the stairs. He tapped his way along a corridor, and heard the opening of a door. He felt on his face that he was in a sunny room. He was given a chair, and lowered himself carefully into it.

"Praise be to Jesus Christ," Fanano's voice said quite close by. "I have to inform you of a few very strict commands to which you must listen with an obedient and humble spirit. Do you hear me well?"

"Yes, Father."

"Well, I know that you are moving into your son's house on the Costa San Giorgio. I warn you that you must not leave the house, except at Easter when you can hear Mass at the nearest church. And what follows is even more important: You must not discuss the accursed doctrine of the earth's movement with anyone. Be careful not to receive visitors who could be suspected of such discussions. If you fail to obey these commands, you will be taken to a real prison and excommunicated. So take care in your own interest. Now go into the corridor and wait, because I must speak to your son."

They led him out. Nencio spent about fifteen minutes with the Chief Inquisitor. Then the door opened, the blind man felt his son's hand under his arm. But Nencio told him only at home, behind locked doors, what he had talked about with Fanano.

"Father Fanano has instructed me," Nencio began in pompous voice, "to see that you keep strictly to your instructions. Therefore, with all filial respect, I am now in a certain sense your supervisor. I must take special care not to let any visitor stay long. It is really rather amazing. The whole Holy Office is afraid that you may spread the doctrine. After all, you ought to be rather proud that the Church is so afraid of you."

"Too late," the blind man said. "The *Dialogue* is being read all over the world now. And soon *The New Science* will be ready.

"But there's nothing about Copernicus in it, father."

"You don't understand," the old man smiled. "It's an even more dangerous book than the other. *The New Science* teaches the world to think in a different way. I have started it. I, Galileo Galilei, have changed the world. Now send the children in. . . ."

The two boys rushed in uproariously. Little Cosimo was two, and began to talk. Young Galileo, his favorite, had turned eight. They demanded a story. *Orlando Furioso* was their favorite.

Nencio was content to leave the old man to play with the children and talk to Sestilia. He gave all his time to the Dutch business, the tempting dream of thirty thousand gold pieces. He had taken all sorts of complicated precautions so that nobody should know about his correspondence with the Dutch experts. And if his father had to dictate an answer he locked the doors and sent away everybody, even from the neighboring room. The letters were long and difficult. The Dutchmen explained their objections in wordy screeds. They were still at the starting point: in principle they accepted the system of the Florentine scientist, but found difficulties in its practical application. Every letter could have served for a scientific essay. The secret correspondence lasted a long time. The Dutchmen always said that they hoped much from a personal interview: one of their experts, Hortensius, had for long been meaning to come to Italy, but had had to postpone his journey again and again for various reasons.

Nencio became more and more excited. The thirty thousand gold pieces were getting more and more real. And one day the message came that Hortensius was leaving Holland. The young couple became all attention and affectionate care. They anticipated every wish of their father's. Sestilia asked him what she should cook. His grandchildren climbed into his lap and stroked his beard. One room was furnished as a guest room; perhaps the Dutchman would consent to be their guest. Nencio felt excited every morning at the thought that the guest might arrive that day. But all he got was another letter: Hortensius was in Germany and would come on to Italy from there.

Then suddenly the Chief Inquisitor appeared in the Costa San Giorgio. The astonished Nencio led him in to see his father, who was in bed, having felt too ill to get up that day.

The Inquisitor refused a seat. "I have only come to say a few words to you. We have been informed that this house is expecting a foreign guest."

"We don't expect anyone." Nencio's voice was tremulous with fear.

"I won't argue now about that. I have reported my information to Rome, and have received today the instructions of the Holy Office. It is my duty to transmit them personally. If you expect a Catholic guest from a Catholic country, then naturally you can receive him freely: but of course you are strictly forbidden to discuss the movement of the earth with him. But should he be a Protestant or a Catholic from a Protestant country, you are forbidden to let him enter the house. To break this command may entail the gravest consequences. *Laudetur.*"

The blind man listened to the steps of the departing priest and doors closing after him. Nencio came rushing back:

"Father," he cried in despair, "what was this? We're all ruined. How did they find out? . . . I've been so careful. . . ."

"My dear boy, you ought to have known that the Inquisition can see through walls. I'm not surprised."

"It's terrible. What are we to do?"

They argued a long time. Finally Galileo decided that Hortensius must be notified not to come. The discussions could be continued by correspondence.

There were two German merchants living in Florence, brothers called Ebers. They had settled in Florence long ago. Everybody considered them diligent, honest, and sober men. One day the two Ebers came to see him, saying they had received a letter and a gift from Germany for the scientist. Nencio led them into his father's room. Galileo was in great pain. The doctor had prescribed some medicine which had been wrongly made up by the apothecary, who had sent a draught which poisoned his intestines.

The Ebers brothers introduced themselves. They explained the purpose of their visit. A German business friend of theirs had asked them to deliver the gift and letter of a certain stranger to Galileo. Nencio opened the letter eagerly and read it aloud. Hortensius wrote without mentioning his proposed visit, but sending in the name of the Dutch Government the enclosed gift as a token of the serious nature of their discussions.

"What kind of a gift?" Nencio was very excited.

The blind man could hear a casket being opened; then the clink of gold.

"A chain," Nencio cried. "A thick gold chain! Oh, how beautiful. Take it, father, and lift it."

He fingered the massive gold links; his hand passed down the chain to a large medallion. He felt the work: it was finely chiseled. A princely gift. Nencio's excitement could be felt even through his silence. The sick man thought a little, then he said:

"My heartiest thanks for all your trouble. Will you do a kindness to a sick old man very near his end?"

The two Germans answered that they would do anything.

"Then forget the contents of this letter. Let it remain here. Take it, Nencio, and burn it at once. I ask you to write and tell your client that I am very ill and feel my end almost upon me, and therefore I can make no promises to conclude these negotiations acceptably. And so it would not be honest to take the chain. Will you please return it to your client."

"But, father!" Nencio was appalled.

"Send it back," the old man's voice commanded.

He held out the heavy chain. The two Germans took it from him and put it away. They courteously expressed their regret, their sympathy, and so departed.

"Father, what have you done?" cried Nencio furiously. "Do you know how much that chain was worth? A fortune! We could have asked the Germans to keep quiet about it. They're trusty men. Don't you ever think of the future of your grandchildren? I've never known such frivolous heartlessness."

"Enough!" the sick man shouted. "I've settled the matter. That ends the whole Dutch business."

"Do you mean you aren't going on with it?" his son said, aghast.

"Haven't you even noticed how ill I am? If Hortensius himself were to come here now, I'd say just the same to him. Now let me rest. I feel very faint."

Nencio left him alone, slamming the door, and from that day on showed a marked coolness to his father. He refused to let the children stay in the sick-room. Frigid indifference replaced the former attentive care. The sick old man was left alone to suffer. Now nobody ever had time to read to him; nobody cared about his whims.

Meanwhile his new book had been published, and at last by devious ways he received a copy. He fingered it for a long time to get a picture of its form. He opened it and stroked the printed page. He longed to read it. But Nencio was always out of the house, and Sestilia busy with the children.

A short time after the visit of the Ebers brothers, Fanano appeared again. Now he sat down at the bedside.

"I have been informed that you refused a gift sent by the government of a heretic country."

"Admirable!" the sick man smiled. "Who told you that?"

"Never mind. In any case I reported it to Rome, where it made a very good impression. His Holiness personally commands me to tell you how much he approves of your action. I bring you his message, and congratulate you on his approval."

"Many thanks, Father. And, since the Holy Office thinks so well of me, I have a request. Send me back to Arcetri. No doctors can help me now, and I want to die there."

"Very well. I'll write to Rome and let you know."

Fanano took leave. He must have written at once, since Rome soon answered: The prisoner could return to Arcetri. Nencio did not hide his immense relief.

"The children give us so much to do that we really can't look after you properly. Porzia can do all that much better. And don't worry about the letters. I'll come up twice a week as usual. When do you want to move?"

"This minute! As soon as you can find me a litter."

Next day he was in the Jewel again. The inflammation had passed, and he suffered less, but could not leave his bed. His brain was numb. Nothing seemed to matter; he lay in a kind of wakeful coma, unable to sleep. Nencio came to write his letters, but he had no strength for them.

"I want to make my will," he said. "Get a public notary and some witnesses. You can fix the date."

"Surely there's time enough for that. You aren't really as ill as you imagine. But, if you feel you must make your will, I'll do all that's necessary. Are you certain you need to?"

Nencio sounded really worried. Once this tone would have made his father reproach himself with accusing his son unjustly of indifference. But suffering and disappointment had made him suspicious. Nencio was worried, of course, because if he died there would be no pension, and his monthly stipend would also be lost.

"I feel very ill, but perhaps if I rest here in solitude my health may improve. I don't want to work now; you mustn't trouble to come again unless I send for you. But don't forget the public notary."

Solitude rested his tortured nerves, and one August day there came another guest. At first he thought that it was Fanano bringing bad news, but his visitor was a young foreigner. He had come all the way from London to Italy, and had asked to be received by the famous man.

"What does he look like?" he asked Porzia.

"Very handsome, about thirty. A gentle face, and his clothes are very fine. But I didn't understand his name."

"Well, bring him in. But first tell him that I am blind."

Porzia left, and returned with the stranger.

"I humbly crave your pardon," said a very soft and pleasant voice in Latin, "I didn't know that you were ill in bed. Although I'm afraid that even then I couldn't have conquered my longing to see you."

"Be seated, sir. May I ask for your name?"

"I am an English poet, and my name is still unknown, but one day it will be famous. I'm called Milton, John Milton. Why do you smile? Because I'm so sure of myself? Do you consider it a fault in any really talented man?"

"Not in the least. On the contrary, a good sign. When I was a young man in Pisa, I was considered too arrogant to be spoken to—I thought so well of myself."

The visitor laughed—a frank, pleasant laugh.

"In you I recognize myself. My professors wrote in my doctor's degree at Cambridge: 'A virtuous and sober person, yet not ignorant of his own parts.'"

"That's excellent," Galileo laughed. "And what kind of poetry do you write, Domine Milton?"

The young man opened the floodgates of his soul. He recited in Latin his poems: "On the death of a fair child" and "On the morning of Christ's nativity." He spoke of his play *Comus,* and told Galileo how it had been performed in Lord Bridgewater's castle. Then he recited an ode which had been printed in a folio edition of Shakespeare, the greatest dramatist of his country.

"A dramatist? What did you say his name was, Domine?"

"Shakespeare. William Shakespeare. William is English for Guglielmo."

"Sciexpiro," the old man repeated in the Italian way. "A strange name. Have you been traveling long, Domine?"

"I started at the end of April. My first halt was Paris. There I met many interesting people. For instance, Hugo Grotius. Perhaps you know about him."

"Of course I do. Did you meet a scientist there called Diodati?"

"Oh, yes. He talked about you. His nephew was my best friend at Cambridge. One of Diodati's brothers is a physician in London. His son was up at the university with me."

When they found common friends, their talk became more intimate. The young man spoke about his family, the strange customs of Cambridge university life where they had only just abolished the birch. He spoke of his travels, the blunders of his clumsy English valet. Time passed, but neither of them noticed.

"And what are your plans, *amico?* What are you going to do when you return? How are you going to make your name?"

"I don't know. But I feel I'm going to write something great—in the style of Dante. I want to write about God and the relation of God to Man. My mind is full of thoughts on that. The idea of God has always attracted me."

They talked of God, and Milton was soon talking enthusiastically. At last he said:

"As a boy I dreamed of becoming a priest. And now I've only become a writer."

"Just like me. I see that in our Catholicism we have much in common."

"Forgive me." The young man sounded rather confused. "I am a Protestant."

"Really? Of course, you're an Englishman. I didn't think of that. Yet you talk of God just like a Catholic . . . strange . . ."

"What is strange?"

"That real faith never divides men. Divisions are created by men themselves. They talk of dogmas—and then at once they talk of heretics. They watch each other, instead of watching God."

They talked on for a long time. This young Englishman had a generous heart and a fine intellect. At last he stood up regretfully.

"It's getting dark, and I must leave you."

"I'm sorry for that. You see, for me it's always the same darkness. God preserve you from going blind in your old age, my son."

"I don't think I shall ever go blind," laughed Milton. "I have eyes like an eagle. Bless me, Messer, now, before I go, so that I may feel I've been blessed by Homer."

Galileo laid a hand on the young man's head; he stroked his silken and well-kept hair. John Milton took his leave. Galileo had broken the command and received a heretic . . . and yet he blessed him and wished him fame—he whose fame was lost in darkness.

His will presented many difficulties. The public notary refused to act, because canon law deprived those who had been sentenced by the Holy Office of the right to dispose of their property. They had to get leave from the Inquisition. Nencio managed to get it from Father Fanano. At last the public notary came to the villa. Two neighbors were brought in to act as witnesses.

"Draw up my will in the usual form," said the blind man. "I leave everything to my son, except two special bequests. An annuity of twenty-five gold pieces for life to my daughter, Suor Angela, and to the three sons of my deceased brother Michelagnolo a thousand gold pieces in one sum."

"What?" Nencio cried as though something had bitten him.

"A thousand," insisted the old man. "Not a word from you!"

The will was drawn up, read, and attested. Galileo was given a quill, and its point set to the parchment. He signed it blindly. They all left him; not even Nencio troubled to stay. As he said good-by, his voice was cold with rage.

The old man still kept his bed. His son had ceased ever to visit him. But one fine day he received the Grand Duke. This time His Highness brought one priest, but left him waiting in the hall. This visit had a special reason. Having listened to Galileo's complaints and consoled him, the Grand Duke came to the point.

"Listen, my friend. We hear you have been negotiating with Holland about a certain device for navigation. Never mind how I know. That isn't important. But Prince Giovanni, whom I have appointed admiral of the Leghorn Fleet, has asked me to sound you on the matter."

Galileo told him the whole story. The Grand Duke was all attention.

"So you gave it all up and let them keep their thirty thousand gold pieces?"

"What else could I have done, Your Highness? The Inquisition would have dragged me off to prison in Rome. And what use is money to me now? Your Highness pays me a thousand gold pieces, which suffice my needs. I'd have liked to leave some property to my grand-children, but if I can't . . . well, that's all there is to is."

"And what are you doing with your invention?"

"Nothing."

"Listen. You must give it to us. Perhaps I may be more successful than my poor father. Prince Giovancarlo is willing to discuss the matter personally with the Spanish Government. The Holy Office can't object, because Spain is a Catholic country. But, unfortunately, Prince Giovancarlo doesn't understand astronomy, and neither do I. We should need someone to whom you could explain it all in detail, in case you—well, er . . . God forbid . . ."

"Don't hesitate to say it, Your Highness. I've been making my will. You'd need someone to explain it all if I'm dead. I know of only one such man. For years I have been trying to get permission to have him visit me, but in vain. And I'd like to see him. If Your Highness is interested in the matter, try to get His Holiness to give Castelli leave to come here on a long visit. Of course I shall bequeath my invention to Tuscany as soon as it can be applied. I offered it to His Highness Cosimo, of blessed memory, and that still holds good."

The Grand Duke spent two hours with the sick man and left him with the promise to do his best. Galileo sent for his son. He did not want to continue their quarrel. He thought that Nencio would be glad of the news that some money might be forthcoming from Spain instead of Holland. And Nencio was duly impressed.

"And, speaking of money, father, I'm bound to reproach you. What induced you to make such a will! I ask you: what have your poor little grandchildren done that you should rob them of a thousand gold pieces? When I told them about your will, Sestilia cried for three days, and little Galileo said: 'Grandfather doesn't love me.' I only wanted to tell you this. The will has been witnessed. But you ought to know what pain you caused my wife and your grandchildren."

Galileo answered very cautiously. He did not trust this talk of love. He praised Alberto. But Nencio had counter-arguments ready.

"You've debts everywhere, father. We shall have to pay out the thousand gold pieces in cash, and sell property. We would be certain to lose over it. And then there will be the funeral expenses . . . forgive me, that just slipped out of my mouth. Still—it's the truth! And what am I to tell my son when he says that his grandfather doesn't love him?"

"Very well," the old man said, "I'll think it over. At present I can think only of Castelli. Will they let him come or not? That ought to interest you, too, because it may mean a lot of money."

No need to tell Nencio that. He began to come back to the villa. His father's health improved a little, and there was a large amount of correspondence. Letters arrived from all parts of Europe, from the greatest scientists and laymen, congratulating the author of *The New Science*. They called it glorious, epoch-making, the work of a genius; and the blind old man frankly delighted in all this praise.

Castelli got permission to visit him. It seemed that whatever the Grand Duke of Tuscany really wanted could be achieved. The trial itself would have gone very differently had the Grand Duke cared to intervene. But the visit proved disappointing. Castelli was accompanied by a priest. The Holy Office had forbidden him to see Galileo alone. They could talk only fifteen minutes at a time, and always in the presence of a witness.

Nencio was sent hurrying to Court. The Grand Duke wrote an indignant letter to Niccolini. What was the use of such a permission? The interests of the Tuscan State demanded that the two scientists should discuss the matter of the Medici stars in detail and at length. Castelli himself wrote to the Holy Office, swearing that he had not the slightest intention of discussing the forbidden doctrine with the prisoner. But the Holy Office remained adamant. Count Castelli, the Catholic priest, could only be allowed to see Galileo for fifteen minutes and never alone. They discussed the problem of navigation, but a thousand personal matters could not be mentioned. The blind old man was full of bitterness. This was far worse than if Castelli had never visited him at all.

Loneliness tortured him more than ever. There was nothing for it but to buy his son's insincere affection. No matter under what conditions, he needed someone with whom to exchange a word. He sent for the notary and changed his will, cutting out Michelagnolo's son.

Next day, Sestilia brought the three children. The eldest clung round his grandfather's neck.

"I'm so glad that grandfather loves me! I love you too!"

It was easy to tell from his tiny little voice that he had been trained to say this like a parrot. But Galileo, the blind beggar for love, shut his ears to that. Whether they loved him or not, let them make a show of it at least! And he took the little boy happily in his arms.

XVI

Castelli was recalled to Rome. He had studied in Padua and been a pupil of Galileo. They did not trust him. The Grand Duke of Tuscany could really do nothing against Rome. Some new man had to be found with training and knowledge to understand the work on navigation and then apply it. At last they found a young Florentine scientist, Vincenzo Renieri. The Holy Office did not object to him, and the old man could see him alone. It eased his solitude. And one day he even increased his household. Someone with a frightened, hesitant young voice was standing before him.

"Your Excellency," the voice stammered. "Your Excellency . . ."

It could get no farther. But the old man encouraged it.

"Speak up, my son, I won't eat you. Who are you and what do you want? Tell me your name. I hope you haven't forgotten that."

"No, sir. It's Vincenzo Viviani."

"Very well. And what do you want?"

"I want to be your pupil."

"What?"

"Let me stay here, Your Excellency. I'd gladly sleep in the woodshed and eat very little. But I want to be your pupil. You are the only one whom I want for my teacher."

"How old are you?"

"Seventeen."

"Who is your father? Where did you study? Tell me everything."

The boy told that he came of a Florentine patrician family, but his father was poor. Up to now the Franciscan monk Pietrasanta had given him lessons in mathematics, but Pietrasanta could teach him nothing more, and advised him to go to Galileo. So Vincenzo implored the old man to take him. His parents had nothing against it, he could come at once; he had left his bundle in the kitchen. Galileo was touched by so much enthusiasm and began to examine him. He soon saw that Vincenzo was very sharp-witted, had a clear mind which could grasp things instantly. His chief strength lay in geometry, of which already he knew

564

more than the experts of the Holy Office. Galileo called Porzia and told her that he was going to take the boy to live with him. Let him sleep in the anteroom and eat whenever he was hungry. But Vincenzo was hungry only for knowledge. He wanted to start learning at once. So great and learned a man as Galileo must surely begin to teach at cock crow, and keep on lecturing all day till the sun set and he fell asleep.

But this great and learned man was preoccupied with other things. He could clearly feel the approach of death. He no longer hoped to die a free man. Yet he still longed for even the least mitigation in his last few months. He longed to go to Mass at the Cathedral. Or visit the graves of his parents in Santa Croce. Sestilia's family lived at Prato; he longed to spend a few days there in the hot summer weeks. His desires had all become as modest as that. So he decided to turn to the Pope himself. He did not mention their former friendship; only described his sorrowful old age, his blindness, his tormented body. He asked for mercy, a little freedom of movement, an easier prison. It was the last request he would ever make.

Although he expected to be refused, the harshness of the refusal surprised him. Fanano sent word that the Holy Office had had enough of his constant complaints. Not only would he receive no further facilities, but in future he would be kept in stricter confinement: from now on, he would be forbidden even to visit the church of the convent unless it was empty. If he intended to go there he must notify the Mother Superior, who would arrange that he might be alone.

Galileo bowed to this decree. He knew at last that hope had gone out of his life. He sought in vain for his son's sympathy. Nencio was no longer interested. Galileo shrugged:

"Piace così a Dio, deve così ancora a noi."

This became his favorite saying at the end of his life. "If it pleased God, it must please us also." He had often occasion to use it. His body was hurrying into death. Four or five ailments attacked him at the same time, and if one passed there came two fresh ones. But his head remained clear. It was almost as though fate had given his body to corruption before death, to keep intact the sharp purity of his mind. Even in his worst hours of suffering, he could feel, when he considered his own intellect, that his thoughts were as keen as they had been at twenty.

Nencio would not resign himself to the loss of the Dutch money. The Medici admiral had undertaken to discuss it with Spain. But things worked out exactly as they had in Cosimo's time. At first there was immense enthusiasm, then it petered out. Nencio kept nagging his father to write in secret to Diodati. The only question was how Hortensius would receive this new approach. Then came news of Hortensius' death. And the other experts were inclined to mistrust the whole conception on account of the practical objections which Hortensius had raised.

One of the difficulties was the lack of a precise instrument to reckon with. This thought was an inspiration to Galileo. While Nencio bewailed thirty thousand gold pieces, his father's mind was absorbed by the problem. An instrument must be found to replace the hourglass and the sundial and all contrivances of the kind. A new sort of clock. The old man strove to invent it. For days he thought of nothing else. At last he dictated a little essay to Nencio, proving that the construction of the new instrument must be based on the principle of the pendulum. Somebody would have to make a drawing, which he would describe. Here the real difficulties began, but young Viviani proved a valuable help. Between them they managed to finish the plans. Nencio was sent into Florence to order the parts of the new invention from a skilled mechanic. That was a long and weary task, since the mechanic had to manufacture the parts of an instrument he had never seen. But at last it was ready. Galileo fingered the screws and pieces and tried to put them together. For a long time he could not succeed, and had to keep beginning again. At last it was finished. A pendulum moved a little hammer which caught rhythmically in the cogs of a wheel. This wheel moved another, which carried the hands around the dial.

The blind inventor could not see his work. He set in motion the pendulum; the wheels moved for a certain time, then stopped. He started it again; the tick-tock began, then silence.

"All right," he said. "That's all I wanted."

"What do you mean?" Nencio asked. "This isn't enough to give the Dutch. What sort of a clock is this which has to be constantly started by someone?"

"I don't care about the Dutch. I wanted to formulate the principle of the pendulum clock. It needs only one detail to make it work; some constant power to drive the pendulum. Let someone else find that! I've done my work."

"But, father, if only you'd finish it, then we could send it to the Dutch! And get the thirty thousand gold pieces."

"No, I've had enough of the Dutch, my boy. I may live two months, or perhaps two weeks. But my time's too short to risk the punishment of the Holy Office."

Nothing would move him. He was too old. The problem had ceased to interest him. Something else took his attention. Someone had found a strange stone near Bologna, which glowed in the dark. The superstitious villagers were much excited by it. Several scientists had seen and written about the stone. Fortunio Liceti, a former pupil of Galileo, published a volume on the subject, full of all sorts of nonsense. In his fiftieth chapter he tried to refute an astronomical theory of his former master. Viviani read it to Galileo, who seemed indifferent. Then came a messenger with a message from the Court. Would it not be wise to defend the honor of Florentine learning? At the same time Nencio received a secret warning. Liceti was an especial favorite of the Holy Office. The Court message had been inspired by the priests of the Inquisition. They wanted to trap the old man into some indiscretion. Either he would defend Copernicus and so incur the direct penalties, or attack him, and then they would use it to his discredit.

Galileo thought the matter over, then he started to dictate—about a hundred pages. He felt like a fish in his own element; he knew that he could not have composed a better essay at the age of thirty. There was no mention of Copernicus, neither for nor against.

But, as though they wanted to compel him to shame himself or play into their hands, he received a letter. It was from the Tuscan Ambassador in Venice, a priest called Rinucci. It contained a frank question about Copernicus. Rinuccini informed the old man that a scientist had observed at different fixed stars a parallaxis of a few seconds, which proved the Copernican doctrine. What was the truth in this matter?

This letter amazed him. What did this priest really want? Didn't he know that Copernicus had been banned by the Church? But surely it could not be possible that a Tuscan Ambassador would set such an obvious trap. Someone might have deceived Rinuccini. Must they still torment an almost dying prisoner? He drew a last deep breath and answered with bitterest scorn, the most telling irony. Did they really insist on a declaration? Very well, then he would prove Copernicus for the last time in a way to which no objection was possible.

The falseness of the Copernican system must never be questioned. Especially by us Catholics, since the authority of Holy Writ as interpreted by our greatest theologians opposes it. Their unanimous explanation has made it clear that the earth stands at the center of the universe and that the sun moves round her. Anything which Copernicus or his followers may ever have alleged to the contrary, has crumbled before all-powerful Divinity. For Divinity achieves its objects in infinitely different ways from any which seem to us to furnish correct explanations. Therefore let us not seek to tie the creative hand of God by stubbornly maintaining our error. My answer is that, while I consider the conclusions of Copernicus inacceptable, I find the arguments of Ptolemy, Aristotle, and their followers even more erroneous and false, since they can easily be disproved even within the limits of human knowledge.

"Perhaps they'll give me peace now," he said, when he sent off the letter. And they did. He lived on peacefully with Viviani, whom he taught every day, teaching him to solve new problems and think empirically. The boy would become an important scientist, significant in the history of geometry.

And, to his great joy, Torricelli, the physicist, joined his household. He had been living in Rome with his master, Castelli. But now Castelli sent him instead of himself to amuse the old man, help him in his scientific correspondence, and rouse him from his brooding thoughts.

Torricelli had already a considerable reputation. He had turned thirty, did independent research, published books. For him it was great happiness to live at the side of the world's foremost natural scientist. He had a room furnished for him in the Jewel. The villa became a miniature academy: an astronomer of seventy-seven, a physicist of thirty-one, and a geometer of eighteen. Three branches of science, three generations. Galileo was refreshed and reassured. He could teach and discuss all day, exchanging thought with two brilliant minds. Young Viviani was occupied in getting back to the pure sources of Euclid in order to see geometry afresh, discarding all the geometrical systems evolved through many barren centuries. He was eighteen and had almost constructed a new geometry. Torricelli, the more mature physicist, was trying to calculate the weight of air. He had found the basic principles of a method which he often discussed with Galileo. The level of the water in the irrigation cisterns of the ducal gardens did not correspond with the power of water pressure. It was a little lower than it ought to have been. As though some contrary power were pressing it back. This could only be the weight of the air pressing on the surface of the water in the cistern. Therefore the weight of air in some tube being filled must be calculable.

"I can see you're going to discover it! You only lack the spark of an idea! And I envy you such a glorious task. No, no, don't worry. I won't attempt it. My inventing days are over."

More and more letters came to the villa. They read every letter aloud and eagerly discussed the news, often speaking of a Frenchman called Descartes, who was having a fight with Gassendi.

"An interesting philosopher. He has laid down a very fine axiom, *Cogito, ergo sum.*"

"That isn't his," the old man replied. "It comes from my friend Campanella, who died recently in exile. He put it this way: *Cognoscere est esse.*"

"All the same, he is a great man," Viviani interrupted, "because he can express geometry by algebra. He can formulate every curve with an equation. This is marvelous and invented by him. The time will come when everything can be expressed by equations. The most complicated things. Even life itself."

"Why not?" Galileo said. "I had an acquaintance, called Porta, a member of the Lynxes. He was always talking about the miracles mankind would invent. He said the time would come when two people would be able to talk to each other from a distance of a thousand miles and hear each other's voices. Because, if light can be directed by mirrors in most complicated ways, why couldn't a sound-mirror be invented? He wrote a book about it, called *Magis Naturalis.* Everybody laughed at him. I didn't. There is nothing impossible to the human mind."

They talked on thus from dawn to dark.

Torricelli had come to him in October, and the following month was one of the happiest in his life, even in spite of his blindness and ebbing strength. When he woke in the morning, he enjoyed the thought of the long day. And at night, when he went to bed, he was shielded against the tortures of insomnia by the thought of tomorrow's pleasant companionship.

But a month later, in November, he fell ill again. He was in high fever and gasped for breath. He knew that his time had almost come.

XVII

His illness lasted six weeks. All his ailments attacked him together, as though they would conquer this stubborn life by a joint attack. His arthritis returned; his feet and hands became swollen and agonized. His kidneys were ceasing to function. His heart missed beats again and again, and then beat wildly. The news that he was dying spread through Florence. The Court sent regular messages of inquiry. A few days later Fanano, the Chief Inquisitor, came to see him. Having asked how he did, he inquired whether he had any wish. The old man shook his head.

"I have no more wishes."

Fanano departed. Torricelli and Viviani were constantly with him. They sat up with him on alternate nights. His insomnia grew so bad that he scarcely slept an hour in these six weeks. His physician said that he had never seen such a case. As he got worse, Nencio began to appear more frequently. His father might die at any moment, but the spark of God clung tenaciously to its mortal shell.

His thought remained clear to the end. Since he could not sleep, his tense mind worked on incessantly.

Strange thoughts preoccupied him. He implored his two friends to tell him whether there was some embossed ornament under the bronze reliefs of the great iron gates of the Cathedral and what was the finish of the design. Nobody knew. Nencio had to go to the Cathedral.

"There are three angels there," he reported, "placed like vignettes under each biblical scene."

"Yes, yes," the blind man answered. "Now I can see it. That was the only detail missing."

Then one morning he made Viviani fetch the oldest of his papers, which had been kept in strict order ever since his youth. He had them read to him for hours. There were some poems he had written as a child. He liked and praised them. Then next day he tried to remember the name of a young man, a student from Transylvania, one of his pupils at Padua who had died. Torricelli went through all the Padua notes, but could find no trace of him. He had decided to write to the Bo and ask for an urgent reply, when the sick man suddenly remembered Giorgio Korniss. Then he wanted to see the draft of a play he had meant to write in his boyhood. They found it and read it to him. He nodded contentedly.

He began to brood and said very little. Sometimes he let fall a remark.

"How strange: the lamp of Pisa and this pendulum clock. I began and finished with the pendulum."

Once he said:

"The great war has been going on since '18. For twenty-four years. Can Christ be pleased about it?"

Or he remarked:

"I was born when Michelangelo died. I am seventy-eight. I wonder who will be born when I die?"

On January 8th the doctor advised him to send for a priest. Medicine could do no more. He nodded obediently. He told Viviani to go for a priest. Nencio sent Gepe for Sestilia. The Vicar of Arcetri arrived. They left him alone with Galileo to hear his confession. He told the priest that he had lived in sin for eight whole years, because, though he took Holy Communion, he had never confessed the transgression of his oath.

"I am deeply sorry to have lived thus in the sight of God."

The Vicar absolved him and gave him the Last Sacraments. The others came back, and the priest still lingered. This was at ten o'clock in the evening. A little later came Father Fanano, with another official of the Inquisition. Had the sick man received the Last Sacraments? When they told him yes, he came in to see the dying prisoner.

"Galileo Galilei, I have been commanded to bring you the apostolic blessing of His Holiness, Pope Urban VIII."

"Thank you," a whisper came from the bed.

The two priests of the Inquisition also remained. Soon Sestilia joined them. She knelt down and wept, kissing his hand. They calmed her and led her to a chair. Eleven o'clock.

"What day is it today?" he suddenly asked.

"Wednesday," their several voices answered.

"Go to Angela tomorrow. Tell her to pray for me."

He said something more, but in such a low voice that nobody heard him. They all waited for an hour in silence: Nencio, his wife, Torricelli, Viviani, the parish priest, and the two priests from the Inquisition. Porzia and the servants sat in the anteroom. The dying man opened his blind eyes, and struggled for breath. Save the creak of chairs, there was no other noise in the room. Thus it lasted till four o'clock in the morning.

Then his body trembled—his soul slipped out of it. Quicker than the movement of the spheres, he rushed away into the Infinite. He saw everything and knew everything. He knew that a part of his own infinity would descend far away in England on a farmhouse. In that farmhouse a widow was bearing her child. The father had died a short time previously. His name was Newton.

But this vision lasted only a moment, and was not important. The infinite opened to him. In a tiny spot the scarcely visible sun was sliding away with the diamond dust of her satellite planets.

Galileo Galilei became one with God.